During the writing of this second edition, my beloved 83-year-old mother passed away. She was always a strong, supportive, encouraging, and loving voice in my life, and my success in this world would not have been possible without her. This second edition is dedicated to her life.

SUBSTANCE USE DISORDER TREATMENT

REVISED SECOND EDITION

SUBSTANCE USE DISORDER TREATMENT

Practical Application of Counseling Theory

TODD F. LEWIS

cognella®

SAN DIEGO

Bassim Hamadeh, CEO and Publisher
Amy Smith, Senior Project Editor
Rachel Kahn, Production Editor
Jess Estrella, Senior Graphic Designer
Alexa Lucido, Licensing Manager
Ursina Kilburn, Interior Designer
Stephanie Adams, Senior Marketing Program Manager
Natalie Piccotti, Director of Marketing
Kassie Graves, Senior Vice President, Editorial

Cover image and interior image copyright © 2020 iStockphoto LP/franckreporter.

This book was previously published by Pearson Education, Inc.

Printed in the United States of America.

cognella® | ACADEMIC PUBLISHING
3970 Sorrento Valley Blvd., Ste. 500, San Diego, CA 92121

Brief Contents

Detailed Contents

PART III Theoretical Approaches With Less
Empirical Support 285

Preface

It has been several years since the first edition of *Substance Abuse and Addictions Counseling: Practical Application of Counseling Theory* was published. As with many academic disciplines, new research, trends, and perspectives emerge quickly, and this is no different in the substance use disorder treatment field. One fact has remained unchanged, however, and that is substance use issues and associated problems continue to pose an enormous problem in our society. From the opioid epidemic that has scourged rural America to the increased drug use during the COVID-19 pandemic, drug use exacts an immense toll on our economic, physical, psychological, and social well-being. Now more than ever we need prevention and treatment approaches to help clients and their families navigate a healthy road to recovery.

The original (and continued) premise of the book rests on what I felt was lacking from textbooks when I was in graduate school and as a teacher of substance use counseling courses. There were two main problems I observed in published texts on substance disorder treatment: First, some textbooks included so much information, sample forms, and data that one was left overwhelmed and confused on where to even begin. There were plenty of ideas and techniques, but no organizing principle or theory to tie everything together. The other issue was that some textbooks are so general in their discussion of strategies and techniques that readers are left with a bevy of information but not much in terms of how to work with those struggling with substance use disorders. For example, after faithfully reading my assignments as a graduate student, I was left asking, "So, what do I actually do in a session with a client struggling with a substance use disorder?" My quest became to write a textbook that answers this question, turning to counseling theory as a roadmap. What the field needed, I felt, was an organizing set of principles from which to work with clients struggling with substance use disorders, and I believe that counseling theories provides that organization. My intention in this book was to fulfill a practical gap: To keep many of the elements of a substance disorder counseling core text for undergraduate- and graduate-level counseling students and other helping professions *and* focus on the practical application of counseling theory in the treatment of substance-related issues. I wanted to write a book that would give students and clinicians concrete descriptions of what counseling would "look like" if a client struggling with substance use was to be counseled from various theoretical viewpoints.

More About Purpose

Many substance use counseling textbooks discuss "individual" and "group" counseling interventions, but do so from a generic lens, providing little in the way of theoretical direction and specific strategies. Although overviews of individual interventions are helpful, their atheoretical nature is frustrating for students who desire to learn specific, theoretically grounded principles in the common theories of counseling and psychotherapy. A range of substance use textbooks provide an impressive array of topics and are excellent resources for clinicians; however, the coverage of substance use interventions is often too broad. Students are thus provided with an overview of treatment considerations but left without much of the "how to."

Other authors might dedicate one chapter to "Treatment of Substance Use Problems" or "General Treatment Approaches." There may be some description of motivational interviewing and behavioral strategies, but again the depth of this coverage is usually not extensive, and space is dedicated to more general topics such as individual, group, and family counseling; support groups; education; and treatment settings. In essence, the focus of these texts are more broad-based discussions with limited direction for application of theoretical techniques when counseling those struggling with substance use.

It is my belief that the counseling theories that mental health professionals learn about in their training can make a significant contribution to the substance use counseling field. Substance use disorder counseling, in my opinion, has strayed too far from theoretically grounded approaches, the result leading to counselors and substance use professionals who sometimes feel "left in the woods without a compass." In this text, I place counseling theory, and its application, at the forefront of working with clients dealing with substance use problems. Students will gain knowledge of *how* to apply counseling theory with clients whose lives are negatively impacted because of substance use issues.

In addition to theoretical application, this book is designed to cover unique aspects of substance use counseling, such as classifications of substances, neuroscientific aspects of substance use (new chapter), assessment, models of addiction, ethical issues, and substance-related terms and concepts, and thus covers essential topics important for a core text in substance use disorder training programs. My intention was to provide a textbook for academic instructors who teach any course in which substance use disorder counseling interventions are taught. It could be useful for an introductory substance use disorder counseling course, or a more specific course that focuses exclusively on counseling interventions. It also may serve as a supplementary text that addresses some of the practical gaps from other textbooks, as previously noted. It is my hope that the theoretical grounding of the text will appeal to instructors, enabling them to share with students specific examples from the text of how to apply theoretically grounded techniques.

A unique aspect of the text is that I use a "running case study" approach throughout. The case study, introduced in Chapter 1, is incorporated throughout the book in each chapter. The case has been updated to include multicultural considerations and revised *Diagnostic and Statistical Manual of Mental Disorders* (5th edition; DSM-5) diagnoses. Thus, students can follow how the client is conceptualized and counseled through the different theories. This approach has been adopted in other theories texts (see Corey, 2017).

The organization of the book is divided into three major parts. The first part includes Chapters 1 through 5 and consists of general information related specifically to substance use and substance use disorder counseling. Chapter 1 provides a brief introduction to the text, highlighting the importance of theory, providing information on evidenced-based practices, and presenting the running case study to be used throughout the text. In Chapter 2, I cover important terms and concepts related to substance use, models of addiction, and key ethical issues that substance use clinicians need to aware. In Chapter 3, the neuroscience of substance use is given attention, including brain-based interventions that clinicians can consider when counseling those struggling with substance use problems. Chapter 4 explores the classifications of substances, physiological and psychological effects, and dangers. Chapter 5 consists of information on screening, assessment, evaluation, and diagnosis of substance-related problems.

The second part of the text consists of theoretically grounded approaches that have empirical support in the substance use and counseling literature. These approaches are considered "evidence based" in that, in general, they have greater support from scientific outcome research as to their effectiveness in treating substance use problems compared to approaches described in the third part of the text. This part may be particularly important for students or professionals whose primary agency or place of employment places a strong emphasis on evidence-based treatment approaches.

It is important to note that the counseling theories outlined in Part II are not equal in the amount of empirical evidence. For example, some approaches (e.g., motivational interviewing) have more scientific support than others (e.g., substance use group therapy). In writing this part, the order of theoretical applications is generally from most empirical support to least. Part II begins with Chapter 6 and a thorough review of the principles and practices of motivational interviewing, followed by cognitive behavioral therapy and its applications (Chapter 7), relapse prevention (Chapter 8), group therapy (Chapter 9), and family therapy (Chapter 10).

The final part of the book includes theoretically grounded approaches that are supported by an extensive conceptual literature base, although they do not have the empirical research support as compared to the approaches in Part II. Despite the limited outcome research, the approaches in this part provide the clinician with a comprehensive, theoretical roadmap for how to conceptualize substance use problems as well as a complete system for intervention, including strategies and techniques consistent with the theoretical model. These approaches should not be thought of as "inferior" to the approaches in Part II: The limited empirical outcome research does not render any approach ineffective. Numerous authors have noted the implementation of these approaches in their substance use agencies or private practices. Several also have commented on how theoretically based treatment has provided a "breath of fresh air" from using a mishmash of techniques that lack an organizing theoretical model. This section includes solution-focused therapy (Chapter 11), Adlerian therapy (Chapter 12), Gestalt therapy (Chapter 13), and existential therapy (Chapter 14). The book ends with a brief chapter (15) where several considerations are provided for clinicians working with those struggling with substance use problems. Theoretical integration is a highlight of this chapter.

Within each theoretical chapter, I begin with a brief introduction, followed by an overview of the major tenets of the theoretical approach. Admittedly, I struggled with finding a balance between covering the theory sufficiently to provide background and at the same time not turning the text into a book on theories! This was easier to accomplish for some theories compared to others. For example, the Adlerian theoretical overview is quite extensive; however, this theory is multifaceted and complex, and I thus felt a bit more at liberty to expand this section of the chapter. Other theoretical approaches are more straightforward and thus did not require as extensive an explanation. Following an overview of the major tenets, I discuss each theoretical approach as applied to substance use counseling, followed by a survey of techniques and strategies that one could employ consistent with each theory. Multicultural considerations and the application of each theory to diverse clientele who may struggle with substance use problems are given focus across all theoretical chapters. This is followed by an example of how the theory might apply to the "running case study," demonstrating what the theoretical approach might "look like" with the same client. Where appropriate, smaller, mini case studies that highlight specific points/techniques about a theory, how to deal with different use issues, and strategies with clients from diverse backgrounds are provided throughout the text. Each theoretical chapter concludes with a summary of strengths, limitations, and potential ethical issues.

New to the Second Edition

Overall, the second edition has gone through a major revision, including the addition of new chapters, updated sections of chapters, and completely updated references. Here are some highlights of key changes:

1. Every chapter has been completely updated with new literature and references. Parts of most chapters have been rewritten to aid in clarity.
2. The running case study has been updated to incorporate cultural variables and the DSM-5 diagnostic process.
3. The motivational interviewing chapter has been almost completely revised to reflect growing trends in that area.The assessment, evaluation, and diagnosis chapter has been updated to reflect the DSM-5 and more recent literature.
4. The assessment, evaluation, and diagnosis chapter has been updated to reflect the DSM-5 and more recent literature.
5. A new chapter on the neuroscience of substance use has been added to this edition.
6. Although most theory chapters remain from the first edition, new empirical findings are included to update research on these areas.
7. Some of the theories chapters include new or innovative techniques as methods for working with clients struggling with substance use issues.
8. A brief new chapter is provided at the end, offering a "checklist" of considerations when working with those struggling with substance use problems. Theoretical integration is also a feature of this chapter.

9. The title of the book has been revised to *Substance Use Disorder Treatment: Practical Application of Counseling Theory.* The reasons for this change are outlined below in "A Comment About Word Selection."

A Comment About Word Selection

In writing about substance use and substance use counseling, an author has many choices of words to consider. For example, do I say substance abuse, chemical dependency, addiction, substance addiction, substance dependence, those struggling with substance use, substance use, or some combination? I have been taught to avoid labels, like "alcoholic," yet many of my clients admit they are alcoholics and do not mind my use of the word (although I use it sparingly, more in a sense of asking what the term means to the client). After all, it is their language, and if this term fits for them and does not impede the change process, what is the big deal?

Yet, language *does* matter, and the way we communicate with our clients has a large impact on whether they show up for the next session and plays a key role in one of the most powerful common factors in therapy: the relationship. As such, I have been intentional about avoiding more derogatory, labeling-based terms such as *addict* and *substance abuser* and instead tried to use the more respectful *client struggling with substance use* (or *substance use problems*). This wording of client problems was suggested by the American Psychiatric Association in the DSM-5 (APA, 2013).

After considerable thought, and preliminary feedback from outside reviewers, I have settled on the terms *substance use disorder, substance-related disorders, substance use problems,* and *those struggling with substance use issues* to convey heavy substance use and associated problems. These terms reflect more respectful and clinically useful terminology for substance use clinicians. In addition, the terms *abuse* and *dependence* are no longer in the DSM, suggesting a clinical preference to diagnose someone with a substance "use" disorder that is then specified on a continuum of severity. As such, I have greatly limited the use of these terms in the book. According to the National Institute on Drug Abuse (2021), the word *addict* is stigmatizing, but *addiction* is generally acceptable. As such, throughout the text the word *addiction* is an additional term, used sparingly, to convey heavy substance use if it fits within the context of the models, theories, or topics under discussion.

A couple of other points on wording are worth mentioning. Throughout the text I use the word *clinician* to refer to any mental health or substance use counseling professional who works with clients struggling with substance disorders or problems. On occasion, however, I may use the terms *counselor* and *practitioner*, which can be interchanged with *clinician*. *Therapy, psychotherapy,* and *counseling* are used interchangeably. In most instances, I use the term *client* rather than *patient*, a clear influence of my clinical training. However, it is important to note that *patient* is typically used more in medical settings, and so there may be occasions when *patient* is used within a medical context or discussion in the text. There are many client examples in the book, and I took strides to provide a bevy of diverse client examples. Regarding wording and gender, instead of using the rather awkward *his or her* when discussing a single client example, I have used *they* as a generic third-person singular pronoun. However, in cases where the gender of the client or counselor is known, I use *his* or *her* within the sentence. With all these wording issues, I may not have succeeded in every instance, but the awareness and intention were there.

The reader should be aware that there are probably more acronyms in the substance use treatment field than any other professional field! Sometimes, the sheer number can be over-whelming and difficult to keep in order. At the same time, they do serve an important purpose: Acronyms provide an easy way to abbreviate the long name of an organization or treatment approach and are especially helpful if these names are used frequently throughout a chapter. In most cases, I spell out the organization or treatment approach first followed by the acronym. Subsequent mentioning of the organization or approach is used with the acronym.

As with any textbook, there are numerous citations and references within each chapter. Although the second edition has been updated with new references, I also kept several of the references from the first edition, especially within the theories chapters. All counseling theories have seminal publications that provide a foundation for each theory, and it was my intention to keep these as much as possible. In addition, some studies that were performed years, and in some cases decades ago, still hold relevance today. Thus, whereas the second edition has significant updates across the board, a foundation of theoretical knowledge remains intact.

Todd F. Lewis
Fargo, ND, USA
June 9, 2022

References

American Psychiatric Association. (2013). *The diagnostic and statistical manual of mental disorders*, (5th ed.). American Psychiatric Association.

Corey, G. (2017). *Theory and practice of counseling and psychotherapy* (10th ed.). Cengage.

National Institute on Drug Abuse. (2021). *Words matter—Terms to use and avoid when talking about addiction*. http://nida.nih.gov/research-topics/addiction-science/words-matter-preferred-language-talking-about-addiction

Acknowledgments

From the start, I envisioned being the sole author of the book, and making this a reality required many days and nights of solo writing. The second edition also required long days and nights, as every chapter needed revision. I would be remiss not to mention those who have been a tremendous help in putting this second edition together. I am grateful to my department and colleagues at North Dakota State University, who continuously inquired about the book and how it was coming along and provided encouragement along the way. I also am grateful to the numerous mental health, academic, and addiction professionals, many of whom are cited in this text, whose dedication, research, clinical work, and writing have influenced me greatly. I could not have written this book without their wisdom and compassion to help others struggling with substance use disorders.

A special thanks to Kassie Graves, vice president, editorial at Cognella. It was a chance encounter that we had over email, which eventually moved to conversations over Zoom, where I pitched the idea of a second edition. Kassie was immediately enthusiastic about the project, provided encouragement, and helped me gain confidence in the process. I appreciated her patience with extension requests and other inquiries about the project.

I also would like to thank my beautiful wife, Denise, and two adorable children, Evelyn and Alexander, who were 7 and 5, respectively, when I completed the first edition and are now teenagers in their own right! For a second round, they endured long hours of "Dad writing in his office again." Their unending support, encouragement, and love I will always cherish. As with the first edition, this project is as much a part of them as it is of me.

CHAPTER 1

Introduction

W hen I ask students in the substance use counseling class I teach how many of them know someone close who struggles with a substance use problem, year after year *at least* 75% raise their hand. As a follow-up question, I ask them how many family members or close friends have struggled or currently struggle with serious negative consequences because of substance use; again the majority raises their hands. As a professional counselor and counselor educator, I have become astonished at the pervasiveness of substance use problems in our society. Whereas going over statistics on the prevalence and scope of substance use and associated consequences in the United States provides students with hard quantitative data, that simple survey conducted at the beginning of class tells it all. By simply looking around the classroom, one is hard pressed not to run into someone who either struggles with substance problems themselves or knows someone close who does.

The pervasiveness of substance use disorders begs the question of what or how is the best way to address these problems clinically. That is, what is effective substance use treatment? And what does effective treatment look like? Scores of scientific research have shown that there are a variety of approaches that are effective in treating substance use disorders, many of which are covered in this book. Some approaches have amassed an impressive amount of outcome research support, whereas others are more conceptual in nature. A survey of the literature suggests that there is much more information related to the first question (What is effective substance use treatment?) and less information on the second (What does effective treatment look like?). In this book, I attempt to address both questions, with a strong emphasis on the gap related to the latter question—the "how to"—with counseling theory as the foundation. This book is indeed written with the practitioner in mind.

In this introductory chapter, I set the stage for the rest of the book by discussing the importance of counseling theory and how it can be incorporated with greater intentionality into substance use treatment. This is followed by a brief overview of each theory presented in the book. A roadmap as to when certain theories would be most useful in substance use treatment is provided, followed by clarification of what is meant by "evidence-based approaches" and associated research. The running case study for the text is provided, in full, in this chapter. The chapter concludes with some general comments regarding multicultural issues and substance use counseling.

The Importance of Theory

The concept of theory has traditionally held an important place in the psychological sciences. *Theories of Counseling and Psychotherapy* is one of the first courses students take in mental health training programs and is most certainly required before students begin their internship experiences and see bona fide clients with real-life problems for the first time. On a practical level, theories offer an organizing philosophy for how problems in living develop. They also provide grounding from which to develop and implement techniques within a counseling session. Theories provide a framework for organizing personality, helping us understand clients and their presenting problems and how to best help them, and providing interventions to help individuals, couples, and families live their best lives (Seligman & Reichenberg, 2014).

Traditional substance use treatment has generally consisted of loosely defined and organized approaches based on mental health techniques without a central, organized set of principles (Rawson et al., 1993). This has led to a somewhat random application of therapy techniques to address substance use problems (Rawson et al., 1993). Some clinical settings bear a resemblance to case management or crisis intervention (Rawson et al., 1993) rather than facilities designed to assess, treat, and monitor those on substances. The intentional application of psychological theory and associated techniques can provide this structure. The field of substance use counseling and treatment has moved too far astray from psychological theories, which can offer clinicians with a comprehensive way to conceptualize clients struggling with substance use disorders as well as offer a system of techniques and strategies that can help clients on the road to recovery. Put differently, the theories presented in this text can provide the clinician with a set of organizing principles from which to operate when counseling those struggling with substance use issues.

It is no longer adequate to treat substance use disorders in isolation of other problems. Indeed, many, if not most, clients who present with substance use issues also have other clinical problems in their lives. Theoretically grounded approaches can be helpful guides when addressing clients with co-occurring disorders (discussed in greater depth in Chapter 4). Psychological theories were created to address problems in living, whether these problems stem from depression, anxiety, substance use, thought disturbances, or some combination of all. The sheer richness of theories makes them ideal for complex issues that characterize co-occurring problems. As we will see in Chapter 4, the literature on effective treatment of co-occurring disorders calls for an integrative approach, one that draws from many different schools of thought, theories, and traditional substance use treatment ideas. Theories give us ideas, ways to think about a problem or problems, and strategies for how to intervene.

Overview of Theories

The selection of theories for this text was based on a combination of empirical support, conceptual literature, and my own clinical experience. The theories presented in Part II of the text generally have more empirical support compared to the theories presented in Part III.

However, all theories have a substantial literature base from which much of the information in this book was drawn. In selecting theories to include, I also relied on the successes and struggles of my own clinical experiences. I have implemented "evidence-based" practices such as relapse prevention strategies, as well as less evidence-based approaches such as Gestalt therapy. With less positive experiences, I have learned (and continue to learn) that it is okay to switch approaches and try something new if a theoretical application is not a good fit for a client. Let's now turn to a brief overview of the theoretical approaches to substance use counseling that are presented in this text.

Motivational Interviewing

Any textbook on substance use counseling strategies *must* have a chapter on motivational interviewing (MI). Not only was MI born out of the substance use field, but it has amassed an impressive array of empirical evidence in support of its effectiveness with substance use disorders. MI is an excellent strategy to use at the beginning of counseling, which is one of the reasons it is presented first (MI is not technically considered a theory; however, its concepts are derived from many theoretical approaches and can be used as a standalone strategy with clients). The National Survey of Substance Abuse Treatment Services (N-SSATS) published results on the frequency with which substance use treatment facilities used certain clinical approaches; 93% reported using MI "frequently" in 2019 (Substance Abuse and Mental Health Services Administration [SAMHSA], 2020).

Cognitive Behavioral Therapy

In most counseling theories textbooks, there are separate chapters on cognitive therapy and behavioral therapy, with some mention of how the two have been combined as cognitive behavioral therapy. In doing the research for this book, it became clear that in the application of substance use counseling, cognitive and behavioral methods were *almost always in conjunction in the empirical literature*. As such, attention is given both to cognitive and behavioral theories separately, followed with a focus on their use in combination. Current approaches that rely heavily on CBT principles, such as dialectical behavior therapy, also are presented as examples. CBT and its variations are well-known, effective, evidence-based models used in substance use counseling. The amount of literature/empirical evidence to support their inclusion is impressive. In the N-SSATS survey, 94% of substance use treatment facilities reported using CBT "frequently" in 2019 (SAMHSA, 2020).

Relapse Prevention

Much of substance use counseling is relapse prevention. Although this is not a traditional counseling theory, it leans heavily on cognitive behavioral, person-centered, and motivational interviewing principles. Its inclusion is supported because of the strong empirical research base showing its effectiveness as an intervention to manage and prevent a return to substance use. In the N-SSATS survey, 96% of substance use treatment facilities reported using relapse prevention "frequently" in 2019 (SAMHSA, 2020).

Group Therapy

Group theory and practice has a theoretical and empirical base of literature supporting this modality as a "best practice" in substance use treatment. In this chapter, I discuss general considerations in the formation and functioning of a substance use counseling group, keeping consistent with general group theory. Although different than traditional therapy groups, mutual help groups (i.e., AA) also are discussed. Twelve-step group facilitation was found to be used "frequently" by 68% of facilities that treat substance use issues (SAMHSA, 2020).

Family Therapy

The problem of substance use often impacts the entire family, making family therapy an important part of any book on substance use counseling treatment. In this chapter, I focus on family systems theory as well as other approaches and techniques clinicians can implement in their work with families struggling with substance use problems. The material from this chapter comes from many different sources: clinically generated concepts, the experiences of family therapists, the writings of family systems experts, and empirical studies on family-based models.

Solution-Focused Therapy

Solution-focused therapy (SFT) is a brief, behaviorally based intervention that is applicable to substance use issues. SFT compliments MI (as the two share similar philosophies) and can even serve as an extension of MI. In addition, there is a growing base of empirical support for counseling clients struggling with substance use through this approach.

Adlerian Therapy

The inclusion of Adlerian theory is based more on clinical wisdom and experience than empirical evidence, although some empirical support exits. Adlerian theory is a wide-ranging theory that is analytic, cognitive, behavioral, and systemic. It is a comprehensive theory that has a lot to offer substance use treatment. Adlerian theory assumes substance use is secondary to general psychological problems and provides an appropriate contrast to the "addiction as disease" concept.

Gestalt Therapy

Gestalt therapy can be an effective and powerful approach to those struggling with substance use disorders. There is a growing theoretical base of literature that supports this notion, although the empirical work is scant. However, the lack of empirical support is not because this approach is ineffective, but that the concepts and philosophy underlying Gestalt theory are not as amendable to empirical investigation. A Gestalt approach can help those struggling with substance use live with greater awareness, integration, and authenticity on their recovery journey.

Existential Therapy

Existential theory, like Gestalt, is difficult to study empirically; however, there is a foundation of literature and clinical experience that suggests substance use often manifests as crises in meaning and other "givens" of existence. The role that lack of meaning, existential isolation, and anxiety play in substance use has been well established. However, relatively little has been written as to what an existential exploration of substance use would look like with clients. As you will see in this chapter, I have found that clients, even younger, adolescent clients, often respond very well to discussions around existential topics and themes.

Each theory presented in this text, no matter the level of empirical support, can be effective if the "how to" is demonstrated. Of course, not all theories will be a fit for every client; some clients might respond better with an explorative existential approach compared to a structured CBT approach. In addition, clinicians may be more comfortable with some approaches versus others. In all chapters I cite empirical research (if available) and note that more research may be desirable for some theoretical approaches. However, no approach is discussed willy-nilly; that is, there is empirical support, conceptual support, clinical support, and/or all the above. It is my hope that students, clinicians, and researchers will, from this book, have a template or model to apply in their practice or research. From a research perspective, understanding the "how to" can help design treatment protocols for future research studies. In essence, that is how much outcome research is generated; theory is presented first, followed by empirical investigation to test effectiveness.

The N-SSATS report demonstrated that many substance use treatment facilities use approaches that are well established in the substance use field: MI, CBT, dialectical behavior therapy (DBT), relapse prevention, and 12-step facilitation. However, the report also cited that 98% of facilities engage in *substance use counseling* "frequently." Substance use counseling is generally defined as short-term treatment that included supportive techniques, expressive techniques, approaches to enhance interpersonal relationships, and strategies to increase self-understanding. Long-term care assists clients in building and following through on a recovery plan. All the theories presented in this book promote one or more of these general counseling strategies, offer a conceptual framework, and provide techniques to assist in accomplishing short-term and long-term therapeutic goals. Furthermore, the National Institute on Drug Abuse (NIDA), based on decades of research, included "counseling and other behavioral therapies" as part of their 13 *Principles of Drug Addiction Treatment.* NIDA (1999) specifically noted that counseling and behavioral therapies are "critical components of effective treatment for substance addiction." Activities such as building motivation, building drug resistance and refusal skills, improving problem solving, improving interpersonal relationships, and replacing drug using activities with rewarding nondrug activities were mentioned as key benefits of substance use counseling.[1]

A Possible Roadmap to Theory Utilization

It is fair at this point to be wondering where in the recovery process should each theory be utilized (active use, transition [abstinence], early recovery, or ongoing recovery; Brown, 1995, 1997) or which theory best matches inpatient versus outpatient settings. Unfortunately, there

---

1   For a complete listing of the 13 principles of drug addiction treatment, visit www.nida.gov.

are no firm guidelines in terms of specific theoretical application for specific recovery stages or settings, although some suggestions can be inferred from the literature.

Brown (1995, 1997) outlined four stages in the recovery process. (Brown's developmental model of alcoholism and recovery was intended to understand alcoholism but can reasonably be applied to other substance use problems.) The first stage is active *drinking or use*, where denial is the main defensive structure as clients believe they have control over their use (when they clearly do not) and thus minimize subsequent problems. The second stage is *transition*, where clients develop little interest outside of substance use, and drugs have become the central organizing principle of their lives. Negative consequences begin to pile up. When clients come to see that (a) they have a substance use disorder and (b) they have lost control, they transition into the end of using and the beginning of abstinence. This is a critical and vulnerable spot for clients, as depression, anxiety, eating problems, and other addictions rise to the surface to fill in the void (Brown, 1997). According to Brown (1995, 1997), fundamental building blocks of recovery need to be in place for clients to move toward recovery. Relapse is a constant possibility. The third stage is *early recovery*, where the client begins to gain some momentum in the recovery process, experiences a decline in impulses, and is committed to attending a 12-step mutual support group in addition to regular counseling. Those in early recovery begin the shift from external support to internal support. Their world begins to open as they catch their impulses and make alternative choices to using. The fourth stage is *ongoing recovery*, where the client is firmly in recovery and has expanded their life interests and pursuits. Clients generally engage in deeper levels of self-exploration in this stage (Brown, 1995, 1997). Twelve-step attendance is still an important component, but at a maintenance level. It may take several years for a client to reach ongoing recovery (Brown, 1997). Notice how abstinence is in the middle of the model, as the client transitions away from using/drinking. According to Brown (1997), many have wrongly assumed that once a client is abstinent from substances, then treatment stops. As one can see, abstinence is really the *start* of treatment, rather than the end.

Brown's model clarifies the recovery process and provides insights into where certain theoretical approaches might be most useful. In general, the earlier in the model the client is (active use, transition, beginning of early recovery), the more one should rely on theoretical approaches discussed in Part II of this book: MI, CBT, relapse prevention, group therapy, and family therapy, in addition to assessment and evaluation procedures. As a client progresses from early recovery to ongoing recovery, approaches such as Gestalt therapy, existential explorations, and Adlerian interventions become more appropriate. These latter approaches may invoke greater emotion and generally involve deeper, more philosophical explorations that the client may not be ready to experience during active use or early recovery.

Indeed, Brown (1997) noted that for much of active use, transition, and even early recovery, clients are not ready to deal with deep psychological explorations or therapies that may have potential to dig up old emotional wounds. MI can be quite effective when a client is actively using or has reached abstinence but may be less effective and even unproductive when the client is solidly in recovery and is motivated to stay there. In the early stages of Brown's model, clients benefit more from practical considerations related to motivation (MI), negative thinking processes that maintain substance use (CBT), relapse concerns (relapse prevention), staying in therapy (both group and individual), and 12-step mutual help group attendance. As they build their recovery and are ready to delve into topics such as personal choice, emotional processing, and exploration, meaning, and awareness, Gestalt, existential, and Adlerian therapies become more relevant and useful as a way to strengthen one's life free from substance use.

These guidelines can generally be applied to inpatient versus outpatient treatment. For clients in inpatient treatment, who are most likely actively using, in transition, or in very early recovery, the theories in Part II of the book would be a good fit. For outpatient, where clients may be more firmly established in recovery, additional theoretical approaches would be appropriate. There is risk, however, is in oversimplifying the matching of theory to stage of recovery or location of treatment. For example, I work primarily in an outpatient facility and have used MI, relapse prevention, and CBT with my clients. In addition, I also have used Adlerian, SFT, and Gestalt in relatively early stages of the recovery process. Perhaps the more critical piece to consider when determining which theories to use are what would be the best fit for the client, good clinical judgment and intuition, familiarity with the theory, client motivation, client input, resources, and the cultivation of the therapeutic relationship. Buchbinder (1986) added that one's choice of a theoretical approach depends on many variables, including individual personality, professional training, peer and academic influence, and supervisory consultation. By and large, there are no firm "this is the only way to work" mandates in substance use treatment. Table 1.1 outlines one possible set of guidelines for what theoretical approaches fit best with what stage of recovery the client is experiencing.

TABLE 1.1   Brown's (1995, 1997) Developmental Model and Possible Approaches That Fit Best With Each Phase

Phase	Approach	Description
Active drinking or use	MI, CBT, group therapy, 12-step group attendance, family therapy (if family's goal is to help member stop using)	Treatment is usually focused on stopping or seriously limiting use rather than psychological explorations; client motivation and consciousness raising are important considerations.
Transition (to abstinence)	MI, CBT, relapse prevention, group therapy, family therapy, 12-step group attendance	Client is in emotionally vulnerable position; assessing motivation, relapse potential, and providing support via group and family care become important.

(continued)

TABLE 1.1   Brown's (1995, 1997) Developmental Model and Possible Approaches That Fit Best With Each Phase (*Continued*)

Phase	Approach	Description
Early recovery (1–3 years)	Relapse prevention, group therapy, family therapy, 12-step group attendance, solution-focused therapy; existential, Gestalt, Adlerian as client is ready and with caution	Treatment begins to move away from motivation issues (although these could still come back) and more toward preventing relapse and putting together a solid plan for recovery. Support continues to be important; slowly introduce other approaches with caution.
Ongoing Recovery (3–5 years)	Existential, Gestalt, Adlerian	Client solidly in recovery and more amenable to deeper psychological explorations.

Note: This chart is only one possible way to approach substance use counseling using theoretical approaches. For example, MI may be important to come back to even in later stages of recovery. For some clients, Adlerian or existential therapy might fit earlier in the process, depending on client motivation, pattern of use, emotional vulnerability, and so forth.

A Word About "Evidence Based"

It seems like a common buzzword in today's mental health practice is "evidence-based treatments" (EBTs) or "evidence-based practice." Many managed care and insurance companies mandate that clinicians use only "evidence-based" approaches lest they not get reimbursed for their services. Clinician training programs and agencies espouse the critical importance that treatment approaches are tied to the outcome literature. Traditionally, EBTs have referred to psychotherapeutic approaches, often grounded in theory, that have been supported as effective in clinical trials.

In the landmark book, *The Heart and Soul of Change*, Duncan et al. (2010) presented a cogent argument that scores of research have shown psychotherapy to be effective, yet little evidence suggests that any particular theory is superior to any other. Further, the authors argue, the clinician–client relationship, among other common factors, is one of the most important ingredients in successful client outcome, based on hundreds of empirical studies (Addis et al., 2006). Duncan et al.'s (2010) analysis suggests that there has been an overemphasis on EBTs, to the exclusion of the common factors and other treatment variables that have a much greater contribution to successful client outcome. According to this research, clinicians who incorporate an exclusive focus on "manualized" treatment protocols or other EBT-based interventions are "missing the boat." In addition, too much emphasis on EBTs has led clinicians to ignore other effective theoretical approaches that may not be as amenable to traditional scientific research. Lack of empirical evidence does not render an approach ineffective.

Does this mean that EBTs have no place in counseling and psychotherapy practice? Not at all. EBTs and theoretical approaches do provide a bevy of options for the clinician to consider (Mee-Lee et al., 2010). EBTs and theoretical approaches provide a comprehensive roadmap for how to conceptualize client problems and contain a plethora of interventions that *may* help a client on the road to recovery. The critical factor, however, is client feedback (Mee-Lee et al., 2010). That is, does this EBT or theoretical approach appear to be a good fit for the client? Is the client improving? Emerging empirical evidence suggests that EBTs and theoretical approaches should be utilized based on direct client feedback to better inform practice (Mee-Lee et al., 2010). I couldn't agree more.

The work of Duncan et al. (2010) has led, in part, to the reconsideration of what, exactly, EBT means. For example, the American Psychological Association (APA, 2006) created a task force to examine the meaning of evidence-based practice and settled on this definition: "Evidence-based practice in psychology is the integration of the best available research with clinical expertise in the context of patient characteristics, culture, and preferences" (p. 273). Clearly, this definition suggests that psychological treatment is a collaborative process, with clinical decisions based on client characteristics, values, and needs. The concept of EBT seems to be moving away from a one-size-fits-all approach to one that is unique to client circumstances. Research may still inform practice; however, it is integrated with a strong consideration of contextual factors.

EBTs, and the theoretical approaches upon which many are based, are best conceptualized as possibilities, strategies, recommendations, and approaches rather than the "end all, be all" to clinical treatment. If imposed as the final word, without flexibility and client input, therapeutic success is on a slippery slope. One approach is not going to fit every client, which is why client feedback and input is so important. Mee-Lee et al. (2010) noted that a current trajectory in the substance use treatment field is a more "consumer-driven, outcome-informed treatment system" (p. 396)." As such, a blending of EBTs (and other theoretical approaches), the therapeutic alliance, and client factors would appear to be a worthwhile goal in the therapeutic endeavor.

This book is *not* about comparing the effectiveness of different psychotherapy approaches for substance use counseling. Rather, the purpose is to show how theoretical application can enrich substance use counseling by offering a multitude of ways to better conceptualize client problems, explanations for how substance use begins and is maintained, and treatment/intervention strategies that align with theory. In its essence, this book addresses the "how to" of substance use counseling, with theory as the foundation. However, it is important to note that the therapeutic alliance and what the client brings to therapy must never be lost in one's application of any theory to substance use problems. Use of theoretical approaches without considering the alliance, client factors, and client feedback is barking up the wrong tree.

So, where does that leave us, and how should we make meaning of EBTs? The arguments posed by Duncan et al. (2010) cannot be overlooked. Perhaps the good news is that that psychotherapy is effective, although no one approach really appears to be any better than any other. Regardless, no matter what theory is implemented, clinicians need to have a strong grounding for the interventions they use lest they fall into the trap of using a hodgepodge of strategies without any roadmap, direction, or underlying philosophy. Of course, based on client feedback, this roadmap may need to be tweaked or adjusted along the way. If the therapeutic alliance is of critical importance, competent, skillful, and *flexible* use of theory can enhance this alliance!

For readers who have a strong allegiance to EBT approaches, the chapters in Part II of the book might be of most interest. However, as Duncan et al.'s (2010) work suggests, this does not mean that the theories in Part III are any less effective or important to implement.

CASE STUDY

The Case of Michael

Throughout the text, a "running case study" is used to illustrate the theoretical approaches described herein. As such, the case study is presented here, and each chapter includes how the client would be counseled using each theory. The case is based on a composite of my own clinical experiences; it does not represent a unique individual, but composite characteristics and real clinical issues drawn from several clients over several years. Although some may argue that composite case studies obscure or distort actual clinical events and the course of therapy for a particular client, there are several advantages to their use (Sperry & Pies, 2010).

Composite case studies may have more pedagogical worth than "real-life" case studies (Sperry & Pies, 2010). They allow for writers to better illustrate a theory or approach that a single case may be insufficiently broad enough to do. Composite cases represent more than one individual, often several clients, and therefore no identifying information can be recognized; the use of composite clients has support in the literature because it has been suggested that this approach balances the need to protect client privacy and provide a case example of sound pedagogical value (Sperry & Pies, 2010). Composite clients can be effective if they are based on real-world experiences and likely problems and situations clients face. Every attempt has been made to make the case as "real life" and authentic as possible, drawing from many clinical examples instead of just one. The "running case study" approach has been used in popular counseling theories texts (Corey, 2017).

In the following case study, I describe the background information of Michael L., who is coming to counseling due to increasing substance use and several associated problems. In each theory-based chapter, the reader will see an example of how the clinician operates from different theoretical perspectives to help Michael with his substance use problems, emphasizing select strategies and techniques used from that particular theory.

The client, Michael L., is a 32-year-old African American male who recently became verbally and physically disruptive at home. Michael worked at a local mill ever since he graduated from high school and was able to move up to supervising manager within a few years. Although Michael enjoyed his job, he became more edgy with his supervisees, prompting his manager to encourage him to seek help. Although his manager wasn't sure, he suspected alcohol played a role in Michael's recent poor performance and behavior. Michael was arrested 1 year ago for public intoxication after a local sporting event but has never had a DUI. Michael's wife, Anita, has grown increasingly frustrated with his recent behavior and said he is just not the same man when he drinks, describing him as "ugly and angry." She has threatened to leave him and take their two children, Monique (age 10) and Anthony (age 12). According to Michael, Anita is at the "end of her rope" with him, and his recent struggles at work have made her question his love and commitment to his family. Michael admitted that he likes to drink and have a good time, and that he can have one too many now and then. However, he somewhat minimized the extent or problems caused by his alcohol use. Michael said that he began alcohol use in his 20s. He reported that his father heavily consumed alcohol.

Although alcohol was the presenting substance related concern, upon further inquiry Michael reported using cocaine to help him cope with the stress he was under at work and at home. He noted that he struggled with boredom and loneliness and that his bar buddies introduced him to cocaine about 2 years ago. He has been using it ever since. Asked what he gets out of using cocaine, Michael stated that he feels "alive" and "energized" and that it allows him to temporarily forget about life. It takes away the anxiety, boredom, and daily grind of having a difficult job and raising a family. Michael admitted that Anita does not know about cocaine use. This, he reported, makes him feel even more guilty about where his life is heading.

Michael stated he feels like "half the person [he] I used to be." Complaining of fatigue and feeling down and angry, he struggles to find meaning in his life. He cares deeply for his family but can't seem to connect with them in the genuine, loving way he did in the past. If Michael had a bad day at work, he would often displace these angry feelings on his wife and children. Anita confirmed in subsequent sessions that Michael just seemed like a different person, yelled at the kids for no reason, and seemed "down in the dumps." Michael noted that he has always struggled with low feelings, but recently they had intensified. He did not see any connection between his substance use and low feelings.

Michael's background seems to go a long way in explaining many of his current struggles. He grew up as the older of two children. He and his younger sister, Anisha, lived with their mother and father until Michael was 16 years old, at which time their father left the family. His father drank excessively, and Michael called him an "alcoholic." As a result, the relationship between his mother and father was tumultuous to say the least, where alcohol seemed to play a large role. Michael denied any physical abuse in the household, but noted that his father's verbal abuse was rampant, especially toward his mother. When asked to give one word to describe his household growing up, Michael replied "chaotic." He cannot remember a time when his parents were not fighting with each other. At times, the incessant fighting and screaming became so unbearable that Michael would retreat to his room and cry himself to sleep at night. Michael vividly recalls going on trips to the local store with his mother, looking over at her, and seeing tears run down her face. He recalls several times in which he heard his father's car coming up the driveway at 3:00 a.m. and his keys jingling outside the door. His father would stumble into the house, intoxicated, with a very worried and upset spouse waiting for him.

Michael, to this day, loves his sister and stated they have always gotten along. They were close, especially during the years when their father was drinking at his heaviest. Because his father left when he was 12, he was forced to take care of his mother and sister, as if fulfilling the husband and fatherly roles before he was ready.

Based on Michael's description of the presenting issues, the clinician proceeded to complete a DSM-5 (American Psychiatric Association, 2022) diagnosis:

F10.20 Alcohol Use Disorder, Severe

F14.10 Cocaine Use Disorder, Mild

F33.1 Major Depressive Disorder, Recurrent, Moderate, Provisional

Z63.0 Relationship Distress With Spouse or Intimate Partner

Z56.9 Other Problem Related to Employment

World Health Organization Disability Assessment Schedule 2.0 (WHODAS 2.0)—overall scale average—3.5 (moderate to severe)

Other clinical observations:

Prominent use of displacement and denial

Pre-diabetic

Michael clearly met criteria for an alcohol problem, and this most likely made his other problems worse. He met criteria for alcohol use disorder, severe, as he reported six or greater symptoms related to excessive alcohol use. The clinician also believed that Michael was struggling with mild cocaine use disorder and depression. However, at this time the depression diagnosis is provisional as more information is needed to confirm.

The clinician noted key environmental stressors that likely exacerbate Michael's substance use. Specifically, the clinician noted two Z-codes (other conditions that may be a focus of clinical attention), relationship distress with spouse or intimate partner, and problems related to employment (American Psychiatric Association, 2022). The WHODAS 2.0 assessment, provided to give a snapshot of a client's overall level of functioning, suggests that Michael is experiencing moderate to severe difficulty in his life (American Psychiatric Association, 2022). Additional diagnostic information, although not part of the formal diagnosis was noted: After receiving a recent physical for work, Michael's physician stated he was prediabetic and that he needed to watch his weight and diet. In addition, Michael tends to rely on prominent use of the defense mechanisms of displacement and denial.

Overall, the clinician noted that Michael was struggling with issues of substance use and depression, was in danger of developing diabetes, and was functioning suboptimally. His struggles were especially salient in the marital and occupational domains.

Additional information became evident in the initial assessment. Alcohol seemed to be the key organizing theme in the household when Michael was a child. It was everywhere—in the refrigerator, his father's stocked bar, the cabinets, and in the basement. Alcohol was always served at family gatherings. Michael's father grew more and more emotionally distant as alcohol slowly consumed his life. The angry emotional tone frightened Michael and Anisha as they were never sure which father would come home after work. Michael reported that the sadness he saw in his mother was especially difficult. His father's departure left the house in further chaos, without any structure. Although Michael was secretly glad to see his father leave, he admitted that he still loved him because of that father–son connection and because "not all times were bad." Michael subsequently took on more responsibility at home, taking care of his sister and mother. Michael felt he had to "grow up" quickly during that time but harbors resentment because he could not take part in typical teenage activities.

Family History

Michael grew up in an African American, middle-class family. Both mother (Candice) and father (Ed) described their family of origin as lower middle class, with a breadwinner father and homemaker mother. Both also acknowledged having to work very hard to move up the economic ladder, especially given societal barriers and challenges of a Black family growing up in the South. Candice and Ed met in high school and married quickly after graduation and had Michael 2 years later. Ed described his father as a "steady" drinker, who was frequently verbally abusive. In retrospect, Ed believes his father drank heavily throughout his childhood and adolescence, although he believes his mother protected him and his older brother from much of their father's chaotic behavior. Candice reported that there was considerable conflict between her parents, who divorced when she was 14 years old. She rarely saw her father after the divorce. She reports no substance use by her parents. Other family members live close by, including Michael's aunt and uncle from her mother's side and an uncle from her father's side. He noted positive influences from her aunts and uncles and has two older cousins who he really looked up to during high school.

The preceding case study provides the background for the (long) case demonstrations in each theory-based chapter, usually at the end. Unless otherwise stated, the reader should assume that Michael is in the transition-abstinent early recovery stages related to the theories presented in Part II of the book (MI, CBT, etc.) and the early recovery-ongoing recovery stages related to the theories presented in Part III (Adlerian, Gestalt, etc.). Other parameters of the case may be provided in each theoretical chapter. Additional smaller vignettes are used throughout the text to illustrate key points or techniques; in all cases, names and identifying information have been disguised.

Multicultural Issues in Substance Use Counseling

Just as clinicians must understand one's cultural background to better conceptualize, say, depressed feelings, the same holds true for substance use problems. When formulating tentative hypotheses about substance use, a thorough understanding of diversity issues greatly increases the chances for an accurate assessment and competent treatment. Given that today's minority population will make up approximately one third of the U.S. population in the next 2 decades (Fisher & Harrison, 2018), the need for sensitivity, awareness, and knowledge of diversity issues in substance use counseling is needed now more than ever.

According to Miller (2021), the term *multicultural* refers to working with differences. Working with differences, of course, is not limited to ethnicity or race, but can include working with someone who is a different gender, who is disabled, or who is from a lower socioeconomic class. Miller provided general suggestions for substance use clinicians who wish to be sensitive and effective with individuals from other cultures. Among them were (a) clinicians must be aware of their own cultures and how these impact their lives, (b) clinicians should be aware of the sociohistorical-environmental aspects of some groups and how they have traditionally been treated in the United States, and (c) clinicians need to work at developing a "dialogue-friendly" milieu to help communication across cultural lines.

An example may make these guidelines more concrete. Assume a Caucasian clinician is working with an African American client struggling with a heroin use disorder. A multiculturally competent clinician would be sensitive to the social struggles African Americans have endured throughout U.S. history, from slavery to continued racism and oppression. A disproportionate number of African Americans are living in poverty in our cities due to institutional racism and inadequately funded social services. Keeping this history and background in mind, it also is important for the clinician to create a dialogue-friendly atmosphere: being genuinely interested, appreciating cultural differences, and getting the client's perspective on their current substance use problem rather than assuming it is the same as with any other client. This counseling stance builds rapport and encourages an atmosphere of respect and collaboration.

Substance use disorder treatment is unique in that there may be some universals in the experiences of all clients struggling with substance use issues (Matthews & Lorah, 2005). However, substance use disorders are an "equal opportunity problem" and don't discriminate in that people come together across gender, culture, ethnicity, and religion in their suffering and triumph. Yet, substance use and recovery may have *different meanings and interpretations* depending on one's gender, culture, ethnicity, or religion. For example, the 12-step mutual help group process of "giving yourself" to a higher power and "admitting that one is powerless" may offend many women who have had to endure a long history of societal oppression, limited rights, and feelings of powerlessness. Women for Sobriety, discussed in Chapter 9, was created to address this gender bias in traditional venues of substance recovery by emphasizing encouragement and empowerment for women who struggle with substance use disorders. Multicultural considerations are critical to successful substance use counseling and are infused throughout the book, with each theory-based chapter focusing on the multicultural implications of using that particular theory. For a good overview of multicultural issues in counseling, see Fisher and Harrison (2018) and Miller (2021).

Summary

In this introductory chapter, I presented a general outline of each theory in the text, with an emphasis on the importance of theories and how their application can enhance substance use counseling. A proposed roadmap as to implementation of different theoretical models was offered. Clarification of evidence-based treatments was provided; clinicians must always honor what the client brings to therapy and the therapeutic alliance in addition to theory application. The running case study will serve as the main vehicle from which each theory in the text is demonstrated. Finally, multicultural considerations in substance use counseling are of paramount importance, and thus are given focus in each theory-based chapter.

References

Addis, M. E., Cardemil, E. V., Duncan, B., & Miller, S. (2006). Does manualization improve therapy outcomes. In J. C. Norcross, L. E. Beutler & R. F. Levant (Eds.), *Evidence-based practices in mental health: Debate and dialogue on the fundamental questions* (pp. 131–160). American Psychological Association.

American Psychiatric Association. (2022). *Diagnostic and statistical manual of mental disorders* (5th ed., text revision). American Psychiatric Association.

American Psychological Association. (2006). Evidenced-based practice in psychology. *American Psychologist, 61,* 271–285.

Brown, S. (1995). A developmental model of alcoholism and recovery. In I. D. Yalom (Ed.), *Treating alcoholism* (pp. 27–53). Jossey-Bass.

Brown, S. (1997). *Treating alcoholism with Stephanie Brown, Ph.D.: Volume 2: The developmental model in theory: A live workshop* [Video]. Jaylen Productions.

Buchbinder, J. (1986). Gestalt therapy and its application to alcoholism treatment. *Alcoholism Treatment Quarterly, 3,* 49–67.

Corey, G. (2017). *Theory and practice of counseling and psychotherapy* (10th ed.). Cengage.

Duncan, B. L., Miller, S. D., Wampold, B. E., & Hubble, M. A. (2010). *The heart and soul of change: Delivering what works in therapy,* (2nd ed.). American Psychological Association.

Fisher, G. L., & Harrison, T. C. (2018). *Substance abuse: Information for school counselors, social workers, therapists, and counselors* (6th ed.). Pearson.

Matthews, C. R., & Lorah, P. (2005). An examination of addiction treatment completion by gender and ethnicity. *Journal of Addictions and Offender Counseling, 25,* 114–125.

Mee-Lee, D. A., McLellan, A., & Miller, S. D. (2010). What works in substance abuse and dependence treatment. In B. L. Duncan, S. D. Miller, B. E. Wampold, M. A. Hubble (Eds.), *The heart and soul of change: Delivering what works in therapy* (pp. 393–417). American Psychological Association.

Miller, G. (2021). *Learning the language of addiction counseling* (5th ed.). Wiley.

National Institute on Drug Abuse. (1999). *Principles of drug addiction treatment: A research-based guide.* National Institutes of Health.

Rawson, R. A., Obert, J. L., McCann, M. J., & Marinelli-Casey, P. (1993). Relapse prevention strategies in outpatient substance abuse treatment. *Psychology of Addictive Behaviors, 7,* 85–95.

Seligman, L., & Reicheberg, L. W. (2014). *Theories of counseling and psychotherapy: Systems, strategies, and skills* (4th ed.). Pearson.

Sperry, L., & Pies, R. (2010). Writing about clients: Ethical considerations and options. *Counseling and Values, 54*(2), 88–102.

Substance Abuse and Mental Health Services Administration. (2020). *National Survey of Substance Abuse Treatment Services (N-SSATS): 2019.* Author.

PART I

Basic Concepts of Substance Use Disorders Counseling

In Part I, I address several common terms, concepts, models, and issues related to substance use and addiction counseling. Much of the information in this section is unique to the substance use field. For those who are new to the language of substance use addiction, the material may need additional attention to fully understand the terms and concepts. In Chapter 2, terms, models, and ethical issues commonly found in substance use counseling are reviewed. Chapter 3, a new chapter in this revised edition, focuses on the brain, central nervous system, the exciting advances in the neuroscience of addiction, common routes of drug administration, and mechanisms of action. I attempted to provide a basic overview of these concepts to avoid complex jargon and medical language that is best left for texts that focus exclusively on these issues. In Chapter 4, all the major drugs of abuse are reviewed, including typical effects, effects of overdose, and dangers of use. Chapter 5 provides a thorough review of the substance use evaluation and diagnostic process, including formulations of treatment plans. It is my hope that the reader finds this chapter particularly relevant for their day-to-day practice counseling those with substance use problems.

CHAPTER 2

Terms, Models, and Ethical Issues in Substance Use Disorders

Substance use disorders have become enormous problems in our society, exacting a financial, personal, and societal toll that is staggering. As a counselor-educator and clinical counselor, I am astonished at how substance use problems ravage the lives of my clients. Well-meaning individuals, these clients have lost their way in search of a better life by turning to drugs and alcohol. Drug and alcohol use often are at the center of family and relationship problems, as I have observed spouses pleading with their significant others, or parents with their teenage children, to stop using. Popular media shows, such as A&E's *Intervention*, Netflix's numerous documentaries exploring the production, distribution, use of drugs, and government organizations such as the NIDA have shone a huge spotlight on the problem of substance use in American society. The opiate crisis continues to ravage rural America, and the COVID-19 pandemic has only exacerbated an already serious issue. It seems like a day does not go by in which we learn of the latest celebrity or sports casualty directly caused by over-consumption of substances.

In my experience as a clinical counselor, clients are often at a loss for where to turn or what to do when in the throes of substance using behavior. There is ambivalence about whether they have a serious problem, despite the cascade of negative consequences that envelope their lives. When clients do acknowledge a problem with substance use, they struggle with confidence in their abilities to cut down or abstain. Because important relationships have been damaged, repairing these takes trust, skill, and time without substances. Overwhelmed, clients struggle with self-efficacy and how to live a substance-free life.

Given the prevalence of substance use today, clinicians across a broad spectrum of disciplines (e.g., counselors, psychologists, social workers) will inevitably be confronted with the issue of problematic substance use in their various clinical settings, even if they are not substance use counseling specialists. No matter what the setting, clinicians will most likely see firsthand the plight of clients struggling with substance use issues in their day-to-day practice. Sometimes, these issues are not the presenting concern, but emerge after time in therapy. As I tell students in my graduate substance use counseling class, knowing the language of addiction is important, even if they will not have a professional identity as a "substance use counselor." The generalist as well as the specialist should be familiar with the unique vernacular of the substance use treatment field.

The purpose of this chapter is to familiarize readers with some of this language, first by introducing some general statistics on the scope of the substance use problem in the United States. Next, I discuss basic terms and concepts related to substance use and addiction. These terms and concepts will be used throughout the text, and many will be referred to across several, if not most, chapters. I also cover the important models of addiction, each of which can inform a clinician's philosophical approach to substance use interventions. Substance use clinicians must be familiar with the various ethical and legal issues that often crop up with clients, and the chapter concludes with this topic.

The Scope of Substance Use Disorders

Illicit substance use does not seem to be diminishing, at least in the United States. According to the National Survey on Drug Use and Health (Center for Behavioral Health Statistics and Quality, 2021), in 2020 59.1 million Americans aged 12 and older used illicit drugs at the time of the survey, a finding that has increased substantially since 2002. Related to alcohol, 138.5 million people (aged 12 and older) reported alcohol use in the past month, and an astonishing 61.6 million people (44.4%) were classified as *heavy, episodic drinkers*. Heavy, episodic drinking (i.e., binge drinking) is typically defined as five or more drinks in one sitting within the previous 2 weeks for men, four or more drinks for women. Among college students, estimates of heavy episodic drinking have ranged from 33% (NIAA, n.d.) to 44% (Wechsler et al., 2002), with some estimates at 50%. Wechsler et al. also found that 23% of college students engaged in *frequent* heavy episodic drinking (binge drinking several times within a 2-week period). Whereas alcohol continues to be the drug of choice among college students, other forms of problematic substance use (e.g., abuse of Adderall) continue to be on the rise.

It is remarkable that, despite the so-called "war on drugs," greater media, government, and community attention, and the colossal volumes of substance use research that fills numerous academic journals, the problem of drug use and addiction remains extraordinarily difficult to understand and treat. According to Doweiko and Evans (2019), substance use disorders have many unsuspected influences on society that show up in the home, workplace, primary care, and psychiatric/counseling facilities. It has become an ingrained feature of life in the United States, as it impacts many aspects of life (Doweiko, 2009). The toll of recreational drug use on lost productivity, health care, psychological, and relational health is shocking. Consider the following statistics:

- Excessive alcohol use accounts for $249 billion in costs to society (Center for Disease Control and Prevention, 2022), including lost productivity at work, legal expenses, medical expenses, and health care costs from alcohol-related accidents.
- Illegal drug use accounts for $193 billion in estimated costs to society, including $11 billion in direct health care costs (National Drug Intelligence Center, 2011).

- The National Drug Intelligence Center (NDIC) estimates that the annual cost of drug-related crime in the United States is $61 billion, with crack cocaine and methamphetamine most often contributing these crimes (NDIC, 2011).
- In 2018, 20.5 million people aged 16 or older drove after drinking alcohol in the past year, and 12.6 million drove after consuming illegal drugs (Center for Behavioral Health Statistics and Quality, 2019, as cited in NIDA, 2019).
- Substance misuse and substance use disorders can trigger or aggravate over 70 health conditions (CASA, 2015, as cited in Doweiko & Evans, 2019).

This list is by no means exhaustive, and there are many other problematic associations with substance use, such as interpersonal violence and anger, broken relationships, physical and/or medical problems, and suicide. Aside from these alarming statistics, *overall* substance use exacts an immense financial and personal burden on our society; it has been estimated that the annual cost of the excessive use of alcohol, illegal drugs, and tobacco combined in the United States is over $700 *billion* (Town of Rock Hall, 2015).

Undoubtedly, the extent of substance use and associated consequences are causes for concern and underscores the importance of working to understand the mechanisms, theories, treatment, and prevention of substance use disorders (Miller, 2021). Government agencies such as NIDA and the National Institute of Alcohol Abuse and Alcoholism (NIAAA) publish free information (much of it on the internet: www.nida.nih.gov or www.niaaa.gov) on the latest research and treatment approaches related to substance use disorders. In addition, the importance of substance use counseling and addiction training has been given increased recognition in recent years. This is evident in the professional counseling field: the 2016 Council for Accreditation of Counseling and Related Educational Programs (CACREP) standards require that addiction concepts be infused throughout training curriculums for accredited counseling and counselor education programs. Greater emphasis on training means better prepared practitioners in the field to help those struggling with substance use and its consequences. Now that we have a brief overview of the scope of the substance use, let's turn to some basic terminology that substance use clinicians should know.

Some Basic Terminology

To better understand substance use and addiction, it is important to have a general grasp of the *language* of addiction (Miller, 2021). Many common terms from the substance use addiction field are listed, along with a brief definition. Many are used throughout this text.

- **Substance misuse.** Substance misuse refers to using a prescription substance in a manner inconsistent with how the doctor intended it to be used. For example, an individual might take too many pain pills and for reasons other than managing pain. Substance misuse also refers to experiencing negative consequences because of using any substance excessively.

- **Substance abuse.** Substance abuse refers to the continual use of substances despite negative consequences and problems. A person may drink heavily on weekends and on one weekend receive a DUI. The next weekend, he is out drinking heavily again, placing himself and others at risk. It is important to note that the term *substance abuse* is no longer used in the DSM-5; the preferred diagnosis is now *substance use disorder*. (A more detailed explanation for this shift in language is presented in Chapter 4.) Although the clinical terminology has changed, the word *abuse* may still be used in substance use settings and among the lay public. However, I have attempted to use language more consistent with the DSM and NIDA (2021) guidelines throughout this book.

- **Substance dependence.** Substance dependence is the *compulsive, persistent* use of substances despite negative consequences. Other features of substance dependence refer to seeking out behavior to get the drug, unsuccessful attempts at quitting, and major interferences with one's personal and work life. Tolerance and withdrawal, discussed later, often are components of substance dependence. As with *substance abuse*, the term *substance dependence* is no longer used in the DSM-5.

- **Tolerance.** Tolerance is the body's adaptation to drug use such that over a time a person needs more and more of the drug to produce the desired effect. The "classical" conception of tolerance is physiological; the body physically adapts to consistent drug use so that the effect of the original dose no longer occurs. Tolerance also can be behavioral in that individuals learn how to hide the effects of intoxication from others (e.g., loved ones, the police). For example, a person may muster all their will to show a police officer that they are not drunk during a sobriety test, even though they clearly had one too many. If they do not get arrested, their behavior is reinforced, and behavioral tolerance is strengthened.

- **Withdrawal.** Withdrawal is one of the telltale signs that dependence has emerged. It refers to the physiological and psychological symptoms *when a person stops after an extended, compulsive period of drug use*. A general observation is that the withdrawal syndrome includes the opposite symptoms of those usually induced by a substance. For example, a common withdrawal symptom related to central nervous system depressants (e.g., barbiturates) is anxiety, the opposite of the drugs' drowsy effect.

- **Addiction.** Addiction refers to a compulsive need for and use of a habit-forming substance characterized by tolerance and withdrawal. The primary difference between dependence and addiction, however, may be in how the terms are perceived by others. *Dependence* was the formal clinical term used in the DSM-IV-TR, whereas addiction is a more generic term that often is associated with those who have hit "rock bottom" related to their chemical use. In my opinion, the two terms are essentially the same as both refer to compulsive, long-term problematic substance use despite negative consequences.

There are many other terms associated with substance use and addiction that will be defined throughout this text. It is important for substance use clinicians to be familiar with this language, if for no other reason to be able to connect and "speak the language" with clients who struggle with these problems. Sometimes, however, the clinician may need to learn terminology from their clients! That is, many clients are on the "front lines" of the current substance use and addiction scene and thus may have inside knowledge of the latest or most popular street drug, its effects, and its level of risk. Clinicians should not feel uneasy about learning from their clients. As you will see throughout this book, I encourage an egalitarian stance with clients, no matter what theoretical approach I am utilizing. I have found it respectful and helpful to ask clients what they know to help me better help them.

At other times, clients may not know the difference, for example, between misuse and addiction. Educating clients on the differences can help them get a better grasp of the extent and seriousness of their use. Such information may help clients realize that what they thought was casual use may indeed meet criteria for a more serious problem. Knowing the language of substance use addiction also facilitates communication among mental health, medical, and substance use treatment specialists.

Models of Addiction

There are several models of addiction that help practitioners conceptualize the likely causes of substance using behavior, thus greatly informing treatment and interventions. The range of causes is from entirely biological explanations to sociological factors. However, substance use behavior is most likely the result of multiple factors and influences. Practitioners often implement their interventions based on what model they believe best explains a client's substance use. This is not to say that they ignore other, relevant interventions (although that can sometimes be the case); rather, other approaches are simply not given as much emphasis. A review of the models of addiction is presented next.

Proponents of the *disease model* suggest that addiction is a progressive, deteriorating, chronic, long-term condition that cannot be cured but can be managed (Thombs & Osborn, 2019). The disease model is based on the belief that addiction is a disease of the brain and thus is primary. In other words, addictive behaviors are not thought to be the result of some underlying psychological or sociological disturbance, or the result of some moral flaw in the personality.

Thombs and Osborn made the point that there are actually disease model*s* (emphasis on the plural) rather than one overarching disease model. Peele (1996, as cited in Thombs & Osborn, 2019) noted two primary disease model "camps." The first, called the *susceptibility camp*, suggests that addiction is primarily a genetic/biological condition. A person is born with susceptibility toward addictive behavior and this susceptibility is the primary cause of addiction. The second camp, perhaps more common today with advances in neuroscience and addiction, is the *exposure camp*. The exposure camp suggests that a diseased brain is the result of exposure to toxic chemicals such as illicit substances. Indeed, MRI and PET scans of brains of individuals struggling with addiction do show substantial damage and limited blood flow to various parts of the brain, suggesting a "diseased brain" (Hoffman & Froemke, 2007). Likely, substance use is partly the result of both susceptibility and exposure, and, according to Thombs and Osborn (2019), they are not necessarily in conflict with each other but rather emphasize different aspects of addiction. According to the disease model, the only viable treatment goal is abstinence, primarily because the ingestion of drugs, even small amounts, leads to a loss of control.

The classic disease model of addiction is controversial from both philosophical and scientific perspectives. Although concerns vary, there are two major issues that are of significance. First is the disease model claim that addiction is a progressive disease in which the person deteriorates until death if not treated, analogous to other progressive physical diseases if left untreated such as cancer or heart disease. This assumption falls in the face of epidemiological findings that suggest many individuals with substance use disorders improve on their own and thus do not show an inevitable pattern of deterioration (Heyman, 2009). Another example in which the progressive disease argument does not hold is the phenomenon of "maturing out" (Peele, 1985). The observation of maturing out has been related to individuals with heroin use disorder stopping abusive behavior as life responsibilities mount and they entered their 30s. Heyman (2009) has made similar observations. If the progressive nature of addiction were taken literally, we would not see maturing out.

The second concern with the classic disease model is the notion of "loss of control." Loss of control is the foundation for how organizations like Alcoholics Anonymous (AA) define alcohol addiction. When an person with an alcohol use disorder takes a drink, for example, he cannot control himself; physiological mechanisms take over as his drinking spirals out of control. Loss of control, then, is believed to be a result of some abnormal mechanism or defect within the individual (Thombs & Osborn, 2019).

Although many individuals with substance use disorders experience, in their own analysis, loss of control, leading addiction researchers have rejected the loss of control argument (Heyman, 2009; Pattison et al., 1997). Fingarette (1988) has argued that the loss of control idea does not hold up to logical analysis. Taken literally, loss of control must happen after substances enter the body. That is, once a person takes a sip or hit, they would, in theory, not be able to control use and thus "fall off the wagon." If this were true, then cravings and urges would not be present when drugs *were out of* the person's system. Clearly, individuals experience cravings and urges, sometimes after years of being substance free, when drugs are not in their system. Tiffany (1990) proposed a model of cravings where cognitive processes are at the heart of urges to use and uncontrolled use rather than underlying, somatic responses, suggesting that psychological mechanisms may contribute to uncontrolled use rather than some physiological abnormality.

The central position of the *moral model* is that addiction is primarily a matter of making poor choices. Proponents reject the notion that the "disease made me do it" and place the responsibility for using squarely on the person's moral ineptitude. According to Fisher and Harrison (2018), the choice to use substances emanates from a flawed character or moral weakness. Do not let the simplicity of the moral model fool you; it has served as the foundation for our penal system and many treatment programs for decades. The idea that one has a moral flaw or defect can be so ingrained that many individuals struggling with substance use disorders harbor great guilt and shame.

Another element of the moral model is religious in nature; addiction is seen as sinful and the person is in need of religious and/or spiritual intervention. Instead of seeking a higher power for fulfillment, the individual uses drugs to fill a spiritual void. Proponents of the moral model suggest that individuals must pay a societal price for making poor choices. Interventions from this model include helping clients assess and make better choices, helping them strengthen their spiritual lives, and punitive measures such as jail or prison.

The *psychological model* holds that addiction emanates from a psychological disturbance and is thus secondary to this disturbance. Substance addiction is viewed essentially as a coping mechanism for negative mood states and other psychological problems. Proponents of the psychological model argue that an "addictive personality" may exist. Evidence for this lies in the observation that many clients who resolve their drug and alcohol problem go on to develop non-drug problems (or so-called "process addictions") with gambling, internet, sex, and so forth (Fisher & Harrison, 2018). However, it appears that the personalities of those struggling with addiction are many and varied and attempts to find an addictive personality have largely been unsuccessful (Fisher & Harrison, 2018; Ray & Ksir, 1990). The assumption that psychological problems lead to substance use problems has been proposed in the literature for several years. Zimberg (1978) argued that psychopathology was the "hidden problem" in substance addiction and that more attention was needed to understand these underlying issues in treatment.

The disease, moral, and psychological models all suggest that addiction is an individual problem. Proponents of the *sociocultural model* suggest that factors outside the individual are primarily or, at the very least, partially responsible for the development of substance use problems (Thombs, 2006). Thus, influences such as family, peers, culture, and socioeconomic class are instrumental in the development of addiction. This idea was advanced by Peele (1989), who was a vocal critic of the disease model of alcoholism first proposed by E. M. Jellinek (1960). According to Peele (1989), cultural beliefs and values related to drinking can have a profound effect on the intensity of drinking among its members. Peele uses the examples of Chinese, Jewish, Irish, and Native American populations to point out that people conduct themselves according to customs within their cultural milieu. For example, Chinese populations have low rates of alcoholism because drunkenness is seen as shameful, and members are expected to show high standards of restraint (Peele, 1989). Among those of Irish (Thombs, 2006) and Native American descent, acceptance of heavy drinking may occur to bond and cope with years hardship and persecution. Of course, there are exceptions to these generalizations; however, cultural interpretations can and do play a significant role in how its members carry out their behavior.

Thombs (1996) outlined four primary sociological functions of substance use: facilitation of social interactions, serving as a "time out" from social obligations, promoting group solidarity, and repudiation of middle-class values. Indeed, substance use may be a way for many people to let off steam, connect with others, or thumb their noses at the establishment. From an intervention standpoint, it is important for clinicians to assess the sociological reasons one might use substances. For example, if alcohol is used to connect with others, the client might be interested in finding ways to build relationships without alcohol or at least with less amounts of alcohol.

As one may suspect, the *biopsychosocial model* is based on the idea that multiple biological, psychological, and sociological elements combine to influence or cause addiction. From this perspective, addiction is not the sole consequence of one variable (e.g., an underlying psychological disorder) but a combination of variables that initiate and sustain substance use. The biopsychosocial model is not without its critics, however (Tavakoli, 2009, as cited in Doweiko & Evans, 2019). According to Doweiko and Evans (2019), although many professionals support genetic/biological, psychological, and sociocultural components in the onset of addiction, a grand, unifying theory has yet to emerge.

The biopsychosocial model is like another perspective on addiction called the *final common pathway* (FCP). The FCP suggests that substance addiction is the result, or final common result, of a multitude of factors that increase risk for substance use (Doweiko, 2009). However, whereas the biopsychosocial model suggests that genetic predisposition plays some role in addiction, proponents of FCP would argue that even those without a genetic predisposition may be vulnerable to substance use if they are in an environment that promotes this behavior. In essence, the FCP theory suggests that *any* combination of factors can lead to substance use and addiction.

Closely aligned with the biopsychosocial model is the *public health model* outlined by Miller et al. (2019). Proponents of the public health model note that three key components need to be taken into consideration in explaining addiction: the drug, the person, and the environment. Clearly, drugs influence the brain and body, with some producing more intense experiences than others. For example, for most people heroin will produce a more intense high than a hit of marijuana (a full exploration of the classification of drugs and their effects are presented in Chapter 4), giving heroin a stronger potential to become habit forming. Drugs are mind-altering substances. It would be silly to discount the role that the actual drug plays in substance use disorders (although it doesn't explain all the behavior). The individual person also plays a key role. Personality, history of use, motivation to use, past experiences, expectations of the drug's effects, and genetic susceptibility all interact with the drug to influence whether someone uses. Finally, one's environment may influence substance use. For example, working under extremely stressful conditions; experiencing chronic stressors such as unemployment, racism, discrimination, and/or poverty; living in a neighborhood where drug use is rampant; or simply belonging to a social environment that encourages heavy substance use may all impact one's decision to use. As one can see, biological, psychological, and social elements are contained within the public health model.

The models of addiction play an important role in substance use counseling. What model a clinician "subscribes" to influences how they will relate to their clients, what strategies will be used, and what the goals of treatment will be. For example, a clinician who believes strongly in the disease model will most likely encourage 12-step group attendance, ensure adequate social supports are in place, and establish abstinence as the only goal. A clinician who believes in the psychological model also might encourage 12-step group attendance. However, they will emphasize the underlying role of psychopathology in the onset and maintenance of addiction and implement strategies to address these issues (including many of the theoretical techniques in this book). In addition, they will work to coconstruct goals with the client that may include abstinence, a gradual lessening of substance use, or harm-reduction strategies, such as controlled drinking.

It also is possible to combine elements of different models when counseling clients struggling with substance use disorders. For example, a clinician might promote the goal of abstinence (believing that the client's addiction is a disease) and at the same time implement solution-focused strategies to address the client's depression and to achieve the abstinence goal (psychological model). The assumptions, strengths, and limitations of each model discussed are listed in Table 2.1.

TABLE 2.1   Assumptions, Advantages and Disadvantages of Each Model of Addiction

Model	Assumptions	Advantages	Disadvantages
Disease or medical	Addiction is a progressive, deteriorating disease that goes through a series of stages. Addiction is a chronic and long-term condition. Addiction can be treated but not cured. Addiction is a primary disease. Abstinence is only viable treatment option. Ingesting of drugs leads to loss of control.	Removes societal and moral stigma. Individuals are more likely to get help or treatment (because shame/guilt are removed). Treatment is more likely to be covered by insurance. A clear treatment goal (abstinence); straightforward. Increased funding for research. Language allows for commonality and communication among clients and clinicians.	Excludes those who do not fit in the disease model concept. Absolves individuals of personal responsibility. Makes excuses for deviant behavior. Ignores psychological variables. All-or-nothing approach. Lack of empirical evidence of disease concept. Treatment may seem too simplistic. Where do we draw the line in terms of disease concept (shoplifting, gambling, etc.)?
Moral	Addiction is the person's choice.	Promotes personal responsibility.	Judgment based.

TABLE 2.1   Assumptions, Advantages and Disadvantages of Each Model of Addiction (*Continued*)

Model	Assumptions	Advantages	Disadvantages
	Poor choices come from flawed character or moral weakness.	Empowers people to make good choices to change behaviors.	Contributed to the stigma associated with addiction.
	Addiction is seen as sinful and religious/ spiritual interventions are necessary.	Appeals to those whose worldview is based on concepts of right and wrong.	Can foster a sense of shame, guilt, and blame.
	Addiction is the culmination of a bankrupt spiritual life.	Brings a spiritual component to counseling.	Tendency to minimize the complexity of addiction.
	Drug represents a search for a higher power.		May promote stigma of addiction.
	Addiction is a black-and-white issue.		Individuals may not seek treatment out of guilt and shame.
	Moral model serves as the underpinning of our legal system.		
	Individuals must pay for making poor choices.		
Psychological	Addiction is driven by psychological stress.	Takes away the guilt, shame, and stigma associated with substance use.	Risk of labeling (using DSM-5 terminology).
	Addiction is used as a coping mechanism.	Addresses underlying reasons for turning to substance use.	Use of behavioral therapy (may not be effective for some individuals).
	Psychological problems are the primary condition, with addiction being the secondary one.	Clinicians can create and more accurately define treatment protocols and coping mechanisms.	May allow for external blame instead of encouraging personal responsibility.
	An "addictive personality" exists.	May be less chance/ risk of relapse because underlying psychological issues have been addressed.	Not a holistic model, thus may be seen as too narrow a focus.
	Social learning models can be helpful in explaining addiction.	May give hope for full recovery.	Encourages individuals to adopt a never-ending cycle in finding reasons to self-medicate (i.e., creating new psychological problems).

(*continued*)

TABLE 2.1   Assumptions, Advantages and Disadvantages of Each Model of Addiction (*Continued*)

Model	Assumptions	Advantages	Disadvantages
Sociocultural	Familial, peer, and cultural influences play a large and primary role in substance use. One must examine the individual in relation to their surrounding environment.	Encourages and promotes responsibility for certain societal norms. Systemic approach. Prevention is a key factor in mitigating problematic substance use. Educative in terms of learning about other cultural norms. Helps to identify at-risk populations in which prevention is needed.	Counseling becomes more complex with more people involved. Blame may be displaced on the culture instead of the individual. May promote/encourage stereotypes about different cultures.
Biopsychosocial	Many factors, including biological, psychological, and sociological, combine to influence or cause addiction. A myriad of causes all leading to a common pathway of addiction.	Model "captures everything." Promotes a team approach to treatment. Individualized, holistic, and flexible treatment plans for those using substances.	Treatment can be too complex; where does one start? Can create confusion and information overload.
Public health	Three components explain addiction: the drug, the person, and the environment. All three components interact with each other in a reciprocal fashion to produce addiction.	Intuitive model that incorporates biological, psychological, and social elements. Three components (person, drug, environment) serve as starting point for substance use assessment.	Broad model but lacks specific strategies for intervention.

Many of the theoretical perspectives discussed in this text are based on the moral, psychological, and sociological models. Their emphasis is on helping clients struggling with substance use to think more clearly and rationally, get in touch with their emotions, make better choices, and build healthier relationships. This is not to say that the disease model is ignored when using other models or theoretical approaches. Indeed, several clients struggling with substance use disorders strive for abstinence and attend 12-step group meetings. However, addressing the psychological, spiritual, and environmental components of substance use allows for a well-rounded and comprehensive approach to treating their struggles.

Ethical and Legal Issues Related to Substance Use Disorders

Ethical codes have been created by professional organizations (e.g., American Counseling Association, American Psychological Association, and the National Association of Social Workers) whose members may be involved in the direct care of helping someone struggling with substance use problems. Ethical codes are designed to provide guidance for clinicians so that they can act in the best interests of clients while at the same time operate with greater integrity and morality within their respective professions. Unfortunately, ethical codes of conduct cannot provide guidance on all ethical issues that arise; however, a profession's ethical codes can serve to inform professionals about appropriate ethical behavior (Crockett, 2017). Ethical codes may outline minimal standards of ethical practice, but not necessarily the optimal standards of practice. Across the helping professions, four key moral principles guide ethical practice and undergird the codes of ethics: autonomy (no one can choose for the client), nonmalfeasance (not perpetrating harm), beneficence (acting for and promoting the good of others), and justice (fair and equitable treatment to all clients; Crockett, 2017).

Every mental health clinician receives training in ethical and legal issues related to the helping professions. Unfortunately, codes, laws, and mandates change with the times, proving difficult to keep pace. As Smith (2001) noted, each ethical incident is taken on a case-by-case basis; setting precedent for ethical issues takes time, leading the clinician to make decisions based on personal experiences, doing no harm, and best judgment. Ethical concerns in substance use treatment are often complex and composed of many interrelated parts. In general, many ethical issues in substance use treatment revolve around problems and complexities with confidentiality.

In the substance use and addiction field, codes of federal regulations (CFR) place specific mandates on client confidentiality. These regulations, called *42 CFR*, were created in 1975 (and amended in 1987) and were established to guarantee confidentiality for individuals who were skittish about seeking help for substance use problems (Fisher & Harrison, 2018). Consider the resistance a client struggling with cocaine, an illegal substance, might experience when calling a treatment facility to schedule an appointment. Aside from anxieties about the treatment process, they also are essentially admitting they broke the law (Fisher & Harrison, 2018).

According to Fisher and Harrison (2018), 42 CFR addresses disclosure of records and other information on substance use clients. The authors' interpretation of this legislation and advice to practicing substance use clinicians is to avoid disclosing to anybody if possible! In essence, any mental health professional who works for a program that receives *federal assistance of any kind **and** provides any substance use counseling or treatment services* must comply with 42 CFR. Fisher and Harrison noted that even school counselors who work for a school district that receives financial aid for free/reduced lunch programs and provides referrals to local mental health agencies fall under the auspices of 42 CFR. Practitioners are prohibited from providing *any* identifying information regarding clients who receive *any* services from programs as defined in the regulation.

With minor clients, parental (or guardian) signed consent is required for disclosure of records only in those states that require parental consent for treatment. In addition, both parental and minor consent are needed. In states that do not require parental consent for treatment, the clinician (or program) would be in violation of confidentiality laws if they disclosed information, even to parents, unless the director of the program thought the child was at risk of harming themself or lacked appropriate judgment (Fisher & Harrison, 2018).

Although federal regulations, codes, and laws can make practitioners nervous, the strictness behind 42 CFR is necessary given the nature of substance use and its perception in society. It is a code that can help reluctant clients seek the help they need, because they can be assured that their confidentiality is protected. However, as with any confidentiality law, there are a few exceptions to 42 CFR in which the substance use clinician would not be held liable for disclosure. These include client written consent, communication among staff within an organization, medical emergencies, and committing a crime by the client on agency property or against an agency staff member (Miller, 2021).

Forty-two CFR is a major law that mental health clinicians, *even if they do not counsel clients who struggle with substance use but work for an agency that does include these services*, need to be cognizant of. Miller (2005) also suggested that substance use clinicians should contact their professional organizations and relevant licensing boards for direction on ethical guidelines. A rule of thumb I use is that, when in doubt, seek supervision and/or consultation. Although trained in counseling and counselor education, I do not claim to be an expert in all ethical and legal issues. Staying connected with other clinicians who have more experience and those outside the helping professions who study ethical and legal cases daily can provide perspective, support, and a wealth of knowledge around ethical decision-making. And the clinician gets to learn something in the process—a win-win situation! There also is a plethora of information on the internet that can help clinicians sort through key provisions of 42 CFR. For example, SAMHSA (2022) copublished a helpful FAQ guide, "Applying the Substance Abuse Confidentiality Regulations to Health Information Exchange."

It is important to stress that clinicians become familiar with state laws that compliment or extend 42 CFR. For example, some states have mandatory reporting laws for family violence, which is often associated with excessive drug and alcohol use. In addition, some state laws consider witnessing heavy alcohol use or illicit drug use as fitting within the definition of child abuse and represent a limit to confidentiality. Thus, although similar statutes exist across many states, it is incumbent on the clinician to understand the specific laws impacting their practice.

Other Ethical and Legal Issues

The previous section suggests that substance use clinicians need to be especially cognizant of confidentiality issues related to substance use treatment. However, all ethical codes need to be honored within one's practice. Following are some other ethical issues that may arise more frequently within substance use treatment.

Informed Consent

Ethical practice mandates that the client needs to be provided information that is critical to making an informed decision about treatment. Usually, informed consent includes information related to clinician specialties, training, certificates, education, licenses, cancellation policies, philosophy of counseling, theoretical approaches, and fee structure (Brooks & McHenry, 2015). Thus, securing informed consent is an ethical and legal imperative in today's mental health and addictions counseling practice.

All clients who enter a mental health facility need to be informed of the various treatment approaches available. Related to substance use treatment, the clinician should be able to explain differences among treatment modalities and make educated statements about efficacy. Clearly, this implies that clinicians be up to speed on evidence-based approaches to substance use treatment (many of the approaches discussed in this book have scientific support). In some cases, clinicians might not have much "wiggle room" for what approach they want to implement because insurance/managed care guidelines mandate approaches that have been shown to be efficacious. However, if clinicians have more flexibility in their practice, they may wish to apply approaches that may have limited empirical support but are conceptually sound and provide a good fit for the client's personality, severity of substance use, level of insight, and motivation. Whatever a clinician decides, it is incumbent on them to inform the client of benefits, risks, and potential effectiveness of any treatment approach.

The use of medication as a component of substance use treatment (e.g., buprenorphine, disulfiram) is common practice, and informing clients of these medical options probably falls under most informed consent guidelines. Some (e.g., Littrell & Ashford, 1995) have raised the possibility that nonmedical specialists who discuss medication with clients may cross professional boundaries. However, Littrell and Ashford (1995) noted that clinicians who keep to the facts, use reputable information sources, and do not advise clients on stopping or taking medication are probably not crossing boundaries. In addition, knowledge of common medications can help build rapport with prescribing physicians. Ponterotto (1985) suggested that communication and rapport are enhanced when clinicians can discuss medication effects, side effects, and compliance issues with psychiatrists. In my experience, many clients struggling with substance use issues often are surprised to learn of medications that may help them in their recovery. An honest discussion about possible medication options, followed by appropriate referral to a medical specialist, seems to fall within an appropriate informed consent discussion. Of course, whether the client follows through is up to them (honoring their autonomy).

Dual Relationships

A common ethical concern in the helping professions is dual relationships. "Dual relationship" refers to when a clinician enters a secondary relationship with the client that jeopardizes the primary therapeutic relationship (clinician–client). An obvious example is when a clinician enters a romantic relationship with their client. As Miller (2021) pointed out, however, many dual relationships are not so obvious. For example, in substance use treatment, some clinicians are in recovery themselves and may attend local AA or Narcotics Anonymous (NA) meetings. If their client also attends these meetings, anonymity and confidentiality may be compromised. This awkward situation makes it embarrassing for the clinician and potentially damaging for the client. Miller (2021) suggested nine questions substance use clinicians should ask themselves about dual relationships:

1. What are the different roles I have with this client?
2. Are these roles conflictual with one another or potentially confusing or damaging for my client?
3. What is the least number of roles I can feasibly have with this client?
4. What is the most important role I can have with my client?
5. Are there personal needs of my own that I am trying to have met with my client?
6. Is there anyone else in the recovering community who can meet these needs with my client?
7. Is a referral to another substance use counselor necessary to clarify my role and responsibility to my client?
8. Should I consult with another professional about these roles I carry with my client?
9. Am I trying to treat someone with whom I have a strong personal relationship (or with one of their family members) (p. 447)?

Clinician Self-Care

Across the mental health professions, clinician self-care is a critical aspect to practicing ethically. Brooks and McHenry (2009) called counselor self-care an ethical mandate in the counseling profession. Clinicians who are overly stressed, struggling with their own mental health issues, impaired by alcohol or drug use, overwhelmed, and/or disconnected are more likely to suffer a significant breach of their therapeutic duties (Brooks & McHenry, 2009). There are many concerns with clinicians who do not care for themselves, not the least of which could be a "boundary slippage" in which they inch closer to questionable practices with their clients (e.g., entering a dual relationship). Self-care can be anything from eating right and exercising to getting the appropriate supervision and following through on professional feedback.

My clinical experience has confirmed the common sentiment that substance use treatment can be very rewarding *and* stressful. Substance use clinicians need to be prepared for slow progress or multiple relapses. Third-party entanglements and unnecessarily long hours doing paperwork can add extra burden and stress to a substance use clinician's day. Self-care for the substance use professional is essential to mitigate these negative stressors. With greater self-care comes more competent practice. The good news is that, with patience, the negative is very often outweighed by the rewarding experiences of seeing clients give up their substance use and reclaiming their lives.

The NAADAC Code of Ethics

In 1974, the National Association of Alcoholism and Drug Abuse Counselors (NAADAC) formed as an organization dedicated to clinicians in the substance use and addiction treatment field (Brooks & McHenry, 2015). NAADAC indeed functions as a professional organization, sponsoring annual conferences, offering training and continuing education to its members (and nonmembers), and creating a set of ethical guidelines for substance use professionals to follow. Much information on NAADAC can be gleaned from their website (www.naadac.org).

The NAADAC code of ethics includes 10 broad ethical "principles." The NAADAC codes complement codes of ethics in other professions; thus, a substance use clinician would probably find little conflict with their professions' codes and those of NAADAC. The 10 ethical principles sponsored by NAADAC are listed in Table 2.2.

TABLE 2.2   NAADAC Code of Ethics (NAADAC, 2012)

Code number and title	Brief description
1. The Counseling Relationship	A relationship of equals is encouraged; great respect for building and nurturing the therapeutic relationship.
2. Evaluation, Assessment, and Interpretation of Client Data	Use well-established assessment instruments; makes appropriate referrals and decisions based on sound assessment.
3. Confidentiality/Privileged Communication and Privacy	Uphold confidentiality and explain limitations; adhere to confidentiality laws.
4. Professional Responsibility	Maintain objectivity and integrity and the highest standards in services and professional conduct.
5. Working in a Culturally Diverse World	Understand role that ethnicity and culture play in shaping one's worldview; assess for hidden factors that may impact treatment, such as disabilities that are not visible.
6. Workplace Standards	Professional addictions counseling is founded on national standards of competency.

(continued)

TABLE 2.2   NAADAC Code of Ethics (NAADAC, 2012) (*Continued*)

Code number and title	Brief description
7. Supervision and Consultation	Supervision of addictions professionals is carried out with ethical integrity and designed to help the supervisee grow as a professional.
8. Resolving Ethical Issues	Behavior should be consistent with legal, moral, and ethical guidelines; resolve problems with open and honest communication with all parties involved.
9. Communication and Published Works	Addictions professionals who publish works and communication pieces abide by copyright laws; conjectures or hypotheses that are not yet tested are stated as having less scientific validation.
10. Policy and Political Involvement	The addictions professional is encouraged to actively engage in the legislative process, influence public policy for the betterment of society, and strive for equal access opportunity and care to all human beings.

Note: National Association for Alcoholism and Drug Abuse Counselors, "NAADAC Code of Ethics."
Copyright © 2021 by National Association for Alcoholism and Drug Abuse Counselors (NAADAC).

Summary

Substance use and addiction can exact an enormous price on society, accounting for billions in lost annual worker productivity in the United States and an untold number of personal, financial, and relationship consequences. Substance use clinicians should be familiar with the common vernacular in substance use treatment. In this chapter, basic terms were covered such as *misuse* and *tolerance*, and additional terms and concepts will be introduced and defined throughout the text. Having a common language with clients and treatment staff builds community, precludes misunderstanding, and aids in treatment planning. Several models of addiction help to conceptualize substance use behavior and provide a philosophical grounding for clinical intervention. The disease model continues to be the most prominent in our society and is the undergirding of many substance use treatment programs in the United States. However, many authors have challenged the "addiction as disease" concept and argued that psychological, sociological, and choice also play powerful roles in addiction. Substance use clinicians also should have knowledge of ethical and legal codes related to their respective professions, the state in which they practice, and federal regulations. The most pertinent federal code that impacts substance use clinicians is 42 CFR.

In the next chapter, we'll turn our attention to the classification of drugs, the various mechanisms of action of drugs in the brain and body, and additional terms and concepts that are essential for the substance use clinician to understand.

References

Brooks, F., & McHenry, B. (2009). *A contemporary approach to substance abuse and addiction counseling.* American Counseling Association.

Brooks, F., & McHenry, B. (2015). *A contemporary approach to substance abuse and addiction counseling* (2nd ed.). American Counseling Association.

Center for Behavioral Health Statistics and Quality. (2021). *2020 national survey on drug use and health (NSDUH).* Substance Abuse and Mental Health Services Administration. https://www.samhsa.gov/data

Center for Disease Control. (2022). *Excessive drinking is draining the U.S. economy.* https://www.cdc.gov/alcohol/features/excessive-drinking.html#:~:text=Total%20costs,drinks%20per%20occasion%20for%20men

Crockett, J. (2017). Legal and ethical issues. In J. S. Young & C. S. Cashwell (Eds.), *Clinical mental health counseling: Elements of effective treatment* (pp. 31–52). Sage.

Doweiko, H. E. (2009). *Concepts of chemical dependency.* Brooks/Cole.

Doweiko, H. E., & Evans, A. L. (2019). *Concepts of chemical dependency.* Cengage.

Fingarette, H. (1988). *Heavy drinking: The myth of alcoholism as a disease.* University of California Press.

Fisher, G. L., & Harrison, T. C. (2018). *Substance abuse: Information for school counselors, social workers, therapists, and counselors* (6th ed.). Pearson.

Heyman, G. M. (2009). *Addiction: A disorder of choice.* Harvard University Press.

Hoffman, J., & Froemke, S. (2007). *Addiction: Why can't they just stop? New knowledge. new treatments. New hope.* Rodale Press.

Jellinek, E. M. (1960). *The disease concept of alcoholism.* Hillhouse Press.

Littrell, J., & Ashford, J. B. (1995). Is it proper for psychologists to discuss medication with clients? *Professional Psychology: Research and Practice, 26,* 238–244.

Miller, G. (2005). *Learning the language of addiction counseling* (2nd ed.). Wiley

Miller, G. (2021). *Learning the language of addiction counseling* (5th ed.). Wiley.

Miller, W. R., Forcehimes, A. A., & Zweben, A. (2019). *Treating addiction: A guide for professionals* (2nd ed.). Guilford.

National Drug Intelligence Center. (2011). *The economic impact of illicit drug use on American society.* U.S. Department of Justice.

National Institute of Alcoholism and Drug Abuse Counselors. (2012). *NAADAC ethical codes.* www.naadac.org/membership/code-of-ethics

National Institute on Alcohol Abuse and Alcoholism. (n.d.). *College drinking: Changing the culture—prevalence.* https://www.collegedrinkingprevention.gov/statistics/prevalence.aspx

National Institute on Drug Abuse. (2008). *Drug abuse costs the United States economy hundreds of billions of dollars in increased health care costs, crime, and lost productivity.* http://tinyurl.com/9z3ggfs

National Institute on Drug Abuse. (2019). *Drugged driving, drug facts.* https://www.drugabuse.gov/publications/drugfacts/drugged-driving

National Institute on Drug Abuse. (2021). *Words matter—Terms to use and avoid when talking about addiction.* http://nida.nih.gov/research-topics/addiction-science/words-matter-preferred-language-talking-about-addiction

Pattison, E. M., Sobell, M. B., & Sobell, L. C. (1977). *Emerging concepts of alcohol dependence.* Springer.

Peele, S. (1985). *The meaning of addiction: Compulsive experience and its interpretation.* D. C. Heath.

Peele, S. (1989). *Diseasing of America: Addiction treatment out of control.* Lexington Books.

Ponterotto, J. G. (1985). A counselor's guide to psychopharmacology. *Journal of Counseling & Development, 64,* 109–115.

Ray O., & Ksir, C. (1990). *Drug, society, and human behavior* (5th ed.). McGraw-Hill.

Smith, R. L. (2001). Research and contemporary issues. In P. Stevens & R. L. Smith (Eds.), *Substance abuse counseling: Theory and practice* (2nd ed.). Prentice Hall.

Substance Abuse and Mental Health Services Administration. (2022). *Substance abuse confidentiality regulations: Frequently asked questions (FAQs) and fact sheets regarding substance abuse confidentiality regulations.* https://www.samhsa.gov/about-us/who-we-are/laws-regulations/confidentiality-regulations-faqs

Thombs, D. L. (2006). *Introduction to addictive behaviors* (3rd ed.). Guilford.

Thombs, D. L., & Osborn, C. J. (2019). *Introduction to addictive behaviors* (5th ed.). Guilford.

Tiffany, S. T. (1990). A cognitive model of drug urges and drug use behavior: Role of automatic and nonautomatic processes. *Psychological Review, 97,* 147–168.

Town of Rock Hall. (2015). *What are the costs of drug abuse to society?* https://www.rockhallmd.com/rhad/faq/what-are-costs-drug-abuse-society.

Wechsler, H., Lee, J. E., Kuo, M., Seibring, M., Nelson, T. F., & Lee, H. (2002). Trends in college binge drinking during a period of increased prevention efforts. *Journal of American College Health, 50,* 203–217.

Zimberg, S. (1978). Principles of alcoholism psychotherapy. In S. Zimberg, J. Wallace, & S.B. Blume (Eds.), *Practical approaches to alcoholism psychotherapy.* Plenum Press.

CHAPTER 3

Brain Basics and the Neuroscience of Substance Use Disorders

Introduction

When I teach my substance use counseling courses to graduate students, I usually start the semester talking about the physiological and neurological aspects of addiction, including basic brain physiology, the function of neurons, and key neurotransmitters implicated when one uses substances. At first, I admittedly struggled with this section of the course and was relieved when we moved on to other issues such as models of addiction or strategies to help those struggling with substance use. Over time, however, I have grown to appreciate the vast amount of research and information on the physiology, pharmacology, and neuroscience of addiction. Although not a medical expert, I find that having a basic, yet sound gasp of the biological bases of substance use and addiction is an important adjunct to what I do as a counselor and counselor educator. The more I knew about the neuroscience of addiction, the more students, and clients, paid attention. Indeed, I have revised, expanded, and updated this section of the course over the years to reflect my growing appreciation.

Brooks and McHenry (2015) proposed that substance use clinicians should have a basic understanding of the physiological aspects of addiction as well as the drug effects on the body and brain. Having this knowledge can help clinicians in several ways, including aiding in treatment planning, helping clients understand physiological concepts such as potentiation and cross tolerance (discussed later), and assisting clients in comprehending and managing cravings and relapse.

In Chapter 2, several terms and concepts were introduced that are common parlance in the substance use counseling field. It was noted that knowledge of these terms assists clinicians in connecting with their clients and communicating with other professionals. Some additional terms are presented in this chapter. Although these terms and concepts are a bit more technical, they help give us a better understanding of the how drugs impact the brain and body.

In this chapter, I examine substance use and addiction from a neuroscientific lens, understanding very well that such an undertaking could be an entire book in and of itself! As such, my intention is to not to make you an expert in the neuroscience of addiction, but, as noted, have a grounding in the concepts to better inform your practice. Through my experiences as an educator and clinician, I intend to share with you some fundamental concepts related to the brain and addiction, reflect on how this information has been helpful in my work with clients, and suggest ways it can be helpful to your practice, too. Keep in mind that neuroscience has helped us gain a clearer picture of the underlying biological mechanisms of addiction, but many questions remain; despite enormous advances in neuroscience within the past couple decades, we still do not have a complete understanding of how the brain functions (Kuhn et al., 2019). Surprisingly, the influences of some drugs and how they exert their effects on the brain have yet to be discovered.

Neuroscience and Physiological Aspects Related to Substance Use Disorders

Although a complete review of the anatomy and physiology of the brain and central nervous system is outside the scope of this chapter and text, the reader is reminded of the importance of counselors having a *basic* understanding of the brain, its structures, and functions. Doing so can assist counselors in conceptualizing the addictive process through a neuroscientific lens or using psychoeducation to share with clients (DePue & Smith, 2018; Ekhtiari et al., 2017). Ekhtiari et al. (2017) noted that psychoeducation can not only help clients understand the negative consequences of drug use on the brain, but also strengthen motivation and remove the stigmatization of substance addiction.

Much of the information in the following sections comes from neuroscience and related research. Neuroscience is the branch of biology that studies all aspects of the nervous system, including the brain and how drugs impact its structure and functions (Campbell, 2010, as cited in DePue & Smith, 2018). In the sections that follow, I will begin with a review of the basic regions and structures of the brain, followed by an overview of the importance of neurotransmitters, especially those implicated in substance use behavior. This will be followed by biologically based theories of addiction based on stimulation of the mesolimbic dopamine pathway (i.e., the brain's reward center; Thombs & Osborn, 2019). The chapter will conclude with additional concepts such as key routes of administration, mechanisms of action, and terminology.

Brain Structure

Luke (2020) provided a useful heuristic to explain the structure and function of the brain. The heuristic counts 1–5, including one brain, two hemispheres, three structures of the brain, four lobes, and five systems for integration.

Brain

The brain is extraordinarily complex with thousands of different sites in which drugs could potentially exert their influence. It lives with a delicate balance of excitatory and inhibitory influences running through it (Kuhn et al., 2019). The average human brain is about 3 pounds of tofu-like matter made up of 1 trillion cells, 100 billion of which are neurons (Hanson, 2011). Neurons have been found to fire at about 5 to 50 times a second, with messages and signals crossing the brain in a tenth of a second (Hanson, 2011). The typical neuron is quite busy, making up to 5,000 connections with other neurons (Hanson, 2011)! Although there are many other cells in the brain, neurons are where most of the action takes place—storing information, sensing feelings, and initiating behaviors (Kuhn et al., 2019). The impact of drugs on the brain is complex; as drugs enter the body, they impact numerous bodily systems and functions, but most significantly the brain.

Hemispheres

The brain has two hemispheres that each have remarkably different roles. The right hemisphere is responsible for hearing and visual processing, creative capabilities, and awareness of space and time (Luke, 2020). The left hemisphere is responsible for processing facts, reasoning, speech, linear thinking, and analysis (Luke, 2020). To simplify, the left hemisphere is involved in logic and reasoning processes, and the right hemisphere is involved in creativity, imagination, and insight.

Structures

There are three overarching structures in the brain, following the line of human evolution: The lower brain (i.e., hindbrain or reptilian brain), the midbrain (limbic system), and the cerebral cortex (Luke, 2020). The lower brain includes structures such as the medulla, cerebellum, hypothalamus, and thalamus and is primarily responsible for regulating physiological functions such as heart rate, blood pressure, and breathing. The midbrain includes key structures including the amygdala and hippocampus. This region plays a role in emotion, memory, and reward (Miller & Beeson, 2021). Finally, the cerebral cortex includes the four lobes of the brain: frontal, temporal, parietal, and occipital (these will be briefly discussed in the next section). There are many additional structures within these structures that all play a role in human cognition, emotional expression, social skills, and behavior (Luke, 2020).

Lobes

The frontal lobe is a large region located in the front of the brain. Its primary functions include reasoning, solving problems, judgment, and decision-making (Luke, 2020). As you will see later in the chapter, repeated drug and alcohol use have a significant negative impact on the frontal regions of the brain. The temporal lobes are located on both cerebral hemispheres of the human brain (Luke, 2020). The temporal lobes are associated with learning, emotion, recall, and communication (Guy-Evans, 2021). The inner part of the temporal lobes is essentially the limbic system, including the hippocampus and amygdala (Guy-Evans, 2021). The parietal lobe is behind the frontal lobe and navigates the sensation of touch, such as pain or temperature (Luke, 2020). It also helps us gather our bearings when we are in space (Luke, 2020). The occipital lobe plays a critical part in vision, visual processing, and recognition of objects/people in the environment. It is in the back, lower portion of the brain.

Systems

There are five major nervous systems (Luke, 2020). The *central nervous system* (CNS) includes the brain and spinal cord. The *peripheral nervous system* includes nerves that extend out into the periphery of the body and assist with muscle coordination (Luke, 2020). The *autonomic nervous system* (ANS) is responsible for more "automatic" functions like breathing, heart rate, and blood pressure. The ANS is divided into two subcomponents: The *sympathetic nervous system* and the *parasympathetic nervous system*. The sympathetic nervous system is associated with the fight-or-flight response to environmental, interpersonal, or intrapersonal stressors or threats. When this system kicks in, the stress hormone cortisol is released and heart rate and blood pressure increase, preparing the individual to fight or, if needed, flee to avoid the situation. It is a protective mechanism that evolved to protect early humans from predators and threats. *The parasympathetic nervous system* is the exact opposite of the sympathetic nervous system as it is implicated in relaxation, calm, and balance.

A common clinical example is where a client has too much "sympathetic tone," meaning their sympathetic nervous system is constantly triggered with real and/or imagined threats and stressors, and the constant flood of stress hormones and chemicals starts to damage the organs and delicate systems of the body. The role of stress in substance use behavior has been well established (McCauley, 2020), and many clients cite stress as a significant reason for using or returning to use. Indeed, coping with stress is a major part of relapse prevention, discussed in Chapter 8. Part of my work with clients is to help them find a balance between sympathetic and parasympathetic expression. Usually, this entails teaching the client activities to trigger parasympathetic activity, such as deep breathing, meditation, journaling, and yoga/stretching. Clients learn that there are times that is it normal to feel heightened and on alert (sympathetic dominance), but also times for calm, balance, and relaxation (parasympathetic). Being in a naturally balanced state takes pressure off the client where they are less likely to act out compulsively.

Why Is This Important to Know?

Sometimes I get the question, "Why is it important to know about the brain? Can't we just know the effects of drugs?" In my experience, understanding the systems, structures, and regions of the brain can help clinicians create an alternative narrative for clients struggling with substance use problems. This narrative focuses on the structure and function of the brain and how drugs negatively impact these delicate systems. Clients usually appreciate this narrative, which provides them with insight, knowledge, and motivation from which to act. Another important consideration is that it is tempting to assume that all the structures in the brain operate in separate silos, each having its function but not influencing other parts. However, the brain is an incredibly intricate system where all the components work together; impact in one system, structure, or region of the brain can impact others. Drugs can target specific regions of the brain, but often their effects are more complex and widespread. Having a holistic picture of the brain and its interrelated functions can help clinicians better conceptualize the impact that drug use has on the brains of their clients.

Neurotransmitters

A primary way that neurons communicate with each other is via chemical messengers called neurotransmitters. When a releasing neuron is stimulated, it fires neurotransmitters through the presynaptic terminal (Kuhn et al., 2019, also called the "terminal button") into the synaptic region (or synapse), the small space between the releasing neuron and the receiving neuron. The postsynaptic membrane of the receiving neuron then absorbs most, but usually not all, of the neurotransmitter to complete the communication process. Leftover neurotransmitter in the synaptic region dissipates and is removed by general circulation, is broken down by other chemicals in the brain, or is reabsorbed back into the presynaptic terminal of the releasing neuron (Kuhn et al., 2019). It is during this process of communication between neurons that drugs have their most damaging effect (Brooks & McHenry, 2015). Figure 3.1 shows an up-close visual of this communication process between releasing and receiving neurons.

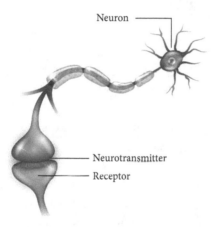

Neuron

Neurotransmitter

Receptor

FIGURE 3.1 Communication process between releasing and receiving neurons.

Neurotransmitters are key players in the brain and are significantly impacted by the use of drugs. There are over 200 variations of neurotransmitters in the brain (Brooks & McHenry, 2015), and their delicate interplay and impact on mood, behavior, and feelings can be seriously disrupted by the use of drugs. Following is a list of the most common neurotransmitters implicated in substance use and addiction:

- **Serotonin.** Serotonin regulates sleep, mood, and appetite (Brown, 2010). Certain forms of hallucinogens and stimulants are thought to impact serotonin levels in the brain and body.

- **Glutamate.** One of the most common neurotransmitters in the brain (Brown-Rice & Moro, 2018), glutamate is excitatory and is associated with learning and memory. Over the past couple decades, researchers have been increasingly interested in the implications of glutamate in substance addiction. For example, evidence suggests that glutamate meditates the reward effects of several drugs including alcohol, nicotine, cocaine, and heroin (D'Souza, 2015).

- **Gamma-aminobutyric acid (GABA).** Another one of the most common neurotransmitters in the brain, GABA has inhibitory action and is implicated in promoting relaxation. Valium, a benzodiazepine, mimics GABA in the brain (Hyman, 2009). Alcohol also increases the inhibitory activity of GABA (Kuhn et al., 2019).

- **Catecholamines.** Catecholamines refer to the neurotransmitters such as norepinephrine and dopamine. Dopamine is implicated in motivation and craving, whereas norepinephrine is implicated in the fight-or-flight response and sympathetic nervous activity (Brown, 2010). Many drugs increase the release of these neurotransmitters, so much so that their natural production becomes depleted over time, leading to feelings of depression (Volkow, 2007). Table 3.1 includes a list of common substances and neurotransmitters impacted.

TABLE 3.1   Common Substance of Abuse and Neurotransmitters Impacted

Substance	Impacted Neurotransmitters
Alcohol	GABA, dopamine, serotonin
Barbiturates	Acetylcholine, GABA (Cote & Wilson, 1980)
Benzodiazepines	Dopamine, GABA (drugrehab.org)
Amphetamines/cocaine	Epinephrine, norepinephrine, serotonin, dopamine, acetylcholine (DePue & Smith, 2019)
Methamphetamine	Dopamine, serotonin, noradrenalin, glutamate (Nordahl et al., 2003)
Heroin	Dopamine, enkephalin, endorphin (DePue & Smith, 2019)
LSD	Acetylcholine (DePue & Smith, 2019)
Marijuana	Acetylcholine (DePue & Smith, 2019)
Nicotine	Dopamine, serotonin, glutamate, adrenaline, endorphin, acetylcholine (DeCaria, 2021)

Mechanisms of Action

There is a risk of oversimplifying all the mechanisms of action that drugs have on neurotransmitters and neurons. There are probably hundreds, if not thousands, of *specific* actions that drugs can take in the body, and one person may respond differently even to the same drug and dose (Kuhn et al., 2019). However, there are four key mechanisms of drug action that I have found useful for didactic purposes and client education. When one looks closely at the different drugs and their impact on neurotransmitters and neurons, effects can essentially be boiled down to one of these four mechanisms of action (Plotnik, 1996):

- **Drugs increase the release of neurotransmitters.** An example might be how stimulant drugs release norepinephrine (Plotnik, 1996) or how amphetamines cause an intense release of dopamine (Smith, 2013).

- **Mimicry.** Some drugs mimic the action of neurotransmitters. An example is how morphine mimics the actions of endorphins by producing feelings of well-being (Plotnik, 1996). Opiates, in general, appear to act in the brain in a similar manner as naturally occurring opiate-like substances (Smith, 2013).

- **Drugs block receptor sites.** When a neurotransmitter is released by a releasing neuron, it travels across the synaptic region to be absorbed by the receiving neuron. Some drugs act in such a way as to block the receptor site so that the neurotransmitter cannot make the connection. The net result is usually more neurotransmitter in the synapse. Lysergic acid, a hallucinogen, is an example of a drug that blocks receptor sites (Plotnik, 1996).

- **Drugs block the reuptake process.** Reuptake occurs when the releasing neuron reabsorbs excess neurotransmitter back into its synaptic vesicles. Some drugs block this process, again leaving excess neurotransmitter in the synaptic region. Cocaine is a classic example of blocking reuptake. Cocaine is known to block the reuptake of dopamine (Johnson, 2003), leaving more of it in the synapse. This partially leads to cocaine's powerful effects of heightened awareness and motivation, euphoria, and increased energy.

The Reward Center and the Hijacking of the Brain

One fact about drug use that has almost universal agreement is that drugs, at least initially, are rewarding to the individual. Depending on the dose, type of drug, typical effects, and the person taking it, rewards can manifest in several ways, including feelings of profound well-being, euphoria, vast increases in energy and perceived strength, increases in self-confidence, feeling like problems are melting away, numbing of pain, and decreases or a numbing of negative emotions. In addition, researchers have learned that this rewarding experience is housed in the mesolimbic dopamine pathway (MDP) of the brain (i.e., the brain's "reward center"; Thombs & Osborn, 2019), which is comprised of a collection of neurons that respond to dopamine, a key neurotransmitter implicated in substance use and addiction.

The brain's reward system begins in the ventral tegmental area (VTA). The VTA is in the center of the brain and is a key regulator in dopamine release when something the person does is pleasurable (Brown-Rice & Moro, 2018). Dopamine then floods other neuronal structures, such as the nucleus accumbens, which is involved in the anticipation and searching of rewards (e.g., getting high from drugs; Thombs & Osborn, 2019). Direct stimulation of the nucleus accumbens is *highly* pleasurable, to the point where animal studies suggest that they will self-stimulate over and over if given the opportunity (Polk, 2015). The excessive dopamine release continues to the prefrontal cortex, which supports one's ability to make decisions and modulate behavior (Brown-Rice & Moro). From the dopamine release, the prefrontal cortex receives the message that a behavior was pleasurable and to do it again (Brown-Rice & Moro). Finally, the amygdala (along with the hippocampus) responds to pleasure and pain and plays a role in learning by associating pleasurable experiences with environmental cues, thus helping individuals remember the behavior that led to the pleasurable experience (Thombs & Osborn, 2019). Most drugs directly or indirectly alter the brain's reward system by flooding it with dopamine (Brown-Rice & Moro; Volkow, 2007).

The enormous influx of dopamine within the reward center produces such an intense euphoric effect that the behavior becomes powerfully reinforcing. This leads to an addiction cycle where drugs are initiated, an intense high is produced, the high reinforces drug-seeking behavior, which leads to more ingestion of drugs, and so on. According to Brow-Rice and Moro (2018), the positive reinforcement of drugs can be 2 to 10 times more powerful in the brain compared to "natural" rewards such as socializing, sex, or dining out. Many scientists believe that the rewarding nature of drug use is a major reason why people develop an addiction (Polk, 2015).

It is important to note that the repeated and prolonged exposure to drugs overstimulates the brain's MDP in such a way that specific changes in the brain occur (Polk, 2015). This supports the exposure hypothesis of the disease model, namely that the disease of addiction primarily sets in *because of* exposure to drugs and the corresponding changes to the brain. Let's briefly review some key brain changes that contribute to addiction, as outlined by several authors and researchers.

Key Brain Changes

The first brain change that contributes to addiction is the numbing of the pleasure center of the brain, primarily the nucleus accumbens (Polk, 2015). Through indirect stimulation of the nucleus accumbens, nonaddicted individuals can experience pleasure by engaging in daily activities such as reading or watching an entertaining show (Polk, 2015). However, drugs stimulate this region of the MDS to a much, much greater degree than everyday pleasures. The constant overstimulation of the nucleus accumbens from repeated drug use sets in motion homeostatic mechanisms where, over time, it will downregulate the pleasure response. Of course, this is the exact definition of tolerance. The person will need more and more of the substance to stimulate this reward center (specifically the nucleus accumbens), leading to increasing intensities of drug use to produce the same, original high. The other problem, however, is not just the development of tolerance to the drug, but the nucleus accumbens becoming less sensitive to *all* stimuli, including healthy, common pleasures (Polk, 2015). This finding has manifested in my counseling experience; clients engaging in heavy drug use could not experience any of the normal pleasures of life one would expect. Unfortunately, for these clients it was drugs, even with a downregulated pleasure response, that became the only way they could feel normal.

We have established that the initial feelings of pleasure one gets from drugs encourages their continued use through positive reinforcement. However, when one transitions to addiction (i.e., beyond occasional use), the pleasurable experience from drugs seems to lose its luster (Robinson & Berridge, 2008). If those struggling with addiction grow to like drugs less and less, gradually experiencing less pleasure, it seems paradoxical that they continue to use despite negative, sometimes devastating, consequences. Why is this the case? Why do those struggling with addiction seem to risk it all and continue to take drugs even though they do not receive the same pleasure from them? Well, it turns out that dopamine, once thought to be the "pleasure molecule" (Polk, 2015), is now thought to *not* be implicated in hedonistic responses to reward (i.e., pleasure; Berridge, 2006; Berridge & Kringelbach, 2008). Instead, evidence seems to suggest that dopamine is chiefly involved of the "wanting" of rewards rather than the "liking" of rewards, something Kent Berridge (2006) calls *incentive salience*. Of course, we are not talking about everyday wants that all of us have—wanting an education, wanting to become fit, wanting new clothes—but a deep, physiological, primal wanting or craving (Polk, 2015).

This places those struggling with drug use in a difficult predicament, namely that the liking (or pleasure) from a drug becomes blunted, but the wanting/craving for the drug becomes very strong because of the immense release of dopamine. This also points to a critical aspect of addiction: *Liking and wanting are not the same thing*. Clinicians who work with those struggling with drug use should understand that, over time, many clients do not consume drugs because they like them but rather because of the intense cravings driven by highly sensitive dopamine system. Indeed, an aspect of relapse prevention (a topic we turn to in Chapter 8), a critical piece to recovery, is helping clients better manage cravings for drugs, even after years of abstinence.

The *increased* sensitivity of the dopamine systems in the brain appears to be a consequence of addiction, leading to ever higher releases of dopamine, which corresponds to more intense cravings for the drug. This phenomenon, called *incentive sensitization* (Robinson & Berridge, 2008), says that recurrent substance use sensitizes the brain systems implicated in motivational processes (wanting), but not neural systems implicated in the experience of pleasure from drugs (liking). As Robinson and Berridge noted, with the continued use of drugs, an imbalance occurs in which the extent in which drugs are wanted is disproportionally higher than the degree that they are liked. Unfortunately, this process increases progressively as addiction develops in the individual.

Another major way that drugs impact the brain through associated learning (Polk, 2015). Dopamine has another function in the brain, and that is its relation to learning. When dopamine is released, it signals to the individual that whatever happened is important and much better than expected, motivating us to move toward it (McCauley, 2020). It forces us to pay attention so that we'll be able to guess when the reward might appear again (Polk, 2015). Simply put, the release of dopamine signals that something important has happened, which is then easily encoded in our memory. Because drugs release higher levels of dopamine, learning that takes place via addiction is especially strong (Polk, 2015).

The release of dopamine creates strong associations with not only the ingestion of drugs, but all the environmental cues that surround individuals when they use (Polk, 2015)—using buddies, bars, music, houses, paraphernalia. As time passes, environmental cues themselves trigger the release of dopamine, which, as explained, is implicated in craving/wanting. Stated differently, pairing environmental cues with substance use leads to conditioned learning that triggers cravings (Holt, 2021).

Think of someone who has a substance use disorder who is getting ready to travel to a house where his typical use will occur. Even though he has not ingested any drugs, his brain will start to release dopamine as he gets in his car, drives by an old using neighborhood, walks up to the front door, sees his using friends, smells the making of drugs, and sees all the paraphernalia laying around the table. By now, his craving/wanting of drugs is quite high, because of the dopamine release in anticipation of the reward of drugs. As such, there appears to be a process in which dopamine release "backs up" from ingestion of drugs all the way to the cues associated with it (Polk, 2015). This process explains why some clients who have been substance free for years may experience spontaneous craving when seeing something in the environment that they associate with using, such as an advertisement.

A third type of brain change happens because of addiction: the weakening of the prefrontal cortex (Polk, 2015). If you recall, the prefrontal cortex (PFC) is involved in judgment, planning, focus, decision-making, foresight, and attention span (Brown, 2010; Holt, 2021). It also is involved in self-control and inhibiting problematic behavior (Polk, 2015). If we think of the reward center for the brain as pushing an individual to want something now (even if it is not the best for them), the PFC is an intricate system that brings rational thought to the table. It helps people evaluate consequences of behavior to determine if it is a good idea. The continual use of drugs, however, weakens the functioning of the PFC, so that it has a difficult time overcoming the intense urges from the reward center (Holt, 2021). Neuroimaging studies have supported the role that a dysfunctional prefrontal cortex plays in addiction, leading to increased drug use, poorer task performance, and increased risk of relapse (Goldstein & Volkow, 2011).

A big reason that the PFC slowly loses its function is that repeated substance use reduces gray matter in that region of the brain. For example, Parvaz et al. (2016) found that, compared to healthy controls, individuals with cocaine use disorders who were abstinent and "treatment seeking" had increased gray matter volume in several regions of the PFC after a 6-month follow-up period of significantly reduced or no substance use. The treatment group also significantly improved in decision-making and cognitive flexibility, two mental functions critical in recovery. Similar increases in frontal white matter volume among alcohol-dependent individuals after 1 month of abstinence were noted by Gazdzinski et al. (2010). These studies not only demonstrated how reduced gray/white matter volume in the PFC is a consequence of drug use, but also the hope that one can recover that volume with a significant reduction in or abstinence from drug and alcohol use.

Injury, damage, and dysfunction to the PFC typically manifests as problems with planning, socializing, language, making decisions, and prolonged attention (Pirau & Lui, 2021). Interestingly, those who struggle with substance use also seem to show these same cognitive deficits (Polk, 2015). Indeed, a dysfunctional PFC presents an enormous challenge, as it can't navigate the strong craving signals from the reward center due to impaired response inhibition and attention, processes that underlie urges, substance use, and diminished self-awareness (Goldstein & Volkow, 2011). A person with an alcohol or cocaine use disorder may know very well that drinking or snorting is not in their best interests, but with a weakened prefrontal cortex, their ability to control their impulses or decide not to use is impaired. This impaired decision-making process spirals even more out of control as one's addiction progresses (Polk, 2015).

From the previous discussion, we can see the special role that dopamine seems to play in substance using behavior (Kuhn et al., 2019). However, dopamine may not tell the entire story of addiction (McCauley, 2020). There are other neurotransmitters, brain chemicals, and structures involved. For example, the neurotransmitter glutamate has been implicated in mediating feelings of pleasure (McCauley, 2020; White et al., 2018). Several drugs, including alcohol, nicotine, cocaine, amphetamines, and heroin, increase glutamatergic transmission in the brain, particularly in the VTA (D'Souza, 2015). Researchers have also found that part of the brain's reward system not only responds to dopamine, but also glutamate (Birgner et al., 2009). White et al. (2018), for example, found that amphetamines increased glutamate release and that it had a substantive role in increasing drug liking, the experience of feeling high from drugs, and positive feelings in healthy adults.

Once thought rare, numerous studies demonstrate that within the central nervous system the co-release of neurotransmitters is widespread (Lapish et al., 2006), although the specific corelease of dopamine and glutamine remains controversial (Lapish et al., 2006). Birgner et al. (2009), however, found neuron receptors in the reward center that not only respond to dopamine, but also glutamine. Through animal research, the researchers found that after the removal of glutamate signaling in the reward center, the reward system is blunted. These findings suggest that two key neurotransmitters are implicated in addiction: It seems that dopamine provides the motivation to seek, whereas glutamate provides the pleasure. And, when glutamate neurotransmission is removed, the experience of reward is compromised. As one can see, addiction may be more complicated than the "one neuron–one transmitter" concept (Dale's principle; Birgner et al., 2009).

Neuroplasticity

We have already seen from Parvaz et al.'s (2017) and Gazdzinski et al.'s (2010) studies that frontal regions of the brain can recover gray/white matter volume from damaged caused by heavy substance use. The process of the brain's natural ability to grow neurons, make connections, and change wiring patterns related to life experiences is called neuroplasticity (Psychology Today, 2022). Advances in neuroscience have found the brain to be adaptive and largely shaped by its environment (Galván, 2010). Experience can influence the development of neuronal patterns and structures, as well as restructure these patterns (Miller & Beeson, 2021). Brain plasticity refers to several actions including making new neurons, pruning neurons, making connections with other neurons, changing molecular structure, and altering gene expression (Miller & Beeson, 2021).

Neuroplasticity presents both good news and bad news for those struggling with substance use disorders. The good news is that if clients significantly cut out or stop drug use, focus on building positive habits, and engage in treatment, healing and growth in the brain is possible (McCauley, 2020). The bad news, of course, is that just as good habits and healthier ways of living can be wired into the brain, the act of taking drugs and being overwhelmed in an addiction comes with negative brain changes that can settle in and continue to reinforce bad habits. As substance use disorders express themselves, changes in neuronal systems point to ever-increasing dysfunction of underlying thoughts, emotions, and behaviors (Cramer et al., 2011).

Current thinking about neuroplasticity is that several environmental factors can have a positive influence on the brain, including therapy (Miller & Beeson, 2021). According to Miller and Beeson, all our behaviors impact brain structures and functions to some extent. For counselors, this means that we can help our clients form positive, long-standing habits, knowing that this will have a positive impact on brain development. Cramer et al. (2011) offered several strategies to promote neuroplasticity, including stimulating the brain, neuropharmacology, exercise, and cognitive training, including CBT. In addition, what seem to be common themes in promoting neuroplasticity include experience dependence, time sensitivity, and strengthening motivation and attention (Cramer et al., 2011). I hope readers can see the clear implications for mental health and substance use clinicians in promoting neuroplasticity. We may not be able to stimulate the brain or prescribe medication (although these options may be available for some clients by referral), but we can help clients develop healthier ways of living, encourage positive lifestyle habits (e.g., exercise), and strengthen client motivation and attention (e.g., MI) that can go a long way in healing one's brain and supporting recovery.

Routes of Administration

Drug users have many options in terms of how to get a drug into their system. Some methods are directly linked to an immediate experience of the drug's effect, whereas other methods take longer for the individual to experience the peak high. The four major methods, which encompass about 99% of drug misuse, include ingestion, injection, inhalation, and insufflation (intranasal; Miller et al., 2019). *Oral administration* (ingestion) takes about 15 minutes to produce drug effects, depending on what is in the stomach and other personal sensitivities and reactions (Johnson, 2003). In general, oral administration produces a longer duration of effect than other methods (Johnson, 2003).

The second route of administration is *intravenous injection*. This route produces a rapid onset of effects—from 30 to 120 seconds—with peak highs and relatively short overall durations (Johnson, 2003). Drugs can be injected in the vein, muscle, or underneath the skin (Miller et al., 2019). *Inhalation* is the fastest route of administration. Like injection, those who inhale via smoking crack cocaine or methamphetamine experience an almost immediate high—within seconds. The reason is because of the connection between the lungs and the brain; when drug chemicals are inhaled, they have a direct route to the brain along with oxygen-rich blood. The result is a relatively intense, immediate high. The duration of effect from inhalation, however, is short-lived (Johnson, 2003). The final route of administration is called *insufflation*. Insufflation involves vigorously inhaling drug powder through the nose (i.e., snorting), which comes into contact with the blood-rich nasal passages. This route can produce a relatively rapid absorption, but the *rate* of absorption tends to be lower compared to injection (Doweiko, 2019). Keeping in mind what route of administration the client prefers can give the clinician clues as to the intensity of use, the likely effect of the drug, and potential relapse triggers.

Additional Terminology

The following terms and concepts represent additional language that is often encountered when working with clients:

- **Cross-tolerance.** Cross tolerance occurs when an individual develops a tolerance to drug A. They then begin taking drug B, which is in the same classification as drug A, and notice that drug B does not have much of an effect. This is most likely because their tolerance to drug A has crossed over to drug B. For example, let's say a patient visits a physician for complaints about anxiety. They have already developed a tolerance to alcohol but did not share this with the doctor. The doctor prescribes Valium, a benzodiazepine that is in that same drug classification as alcohol (i.e., central nervous system depressant). When this patient takes Valium to manage their anxiety, they will notice that it does not have much of an effect. Thinking the prescribed amount is not enough, they will take more Valium until they feel an effect. Because the patient was already tolerant to alcohol, they also experienced some tolerance to Valium.

- **Potentiate.** Potentiate means that drug A increases the activity and effect of drug B. Keeping with our example, depressant drugs are known to potentiate the actions of other sedatives, placing the individual at substantial risk. So, taking Valium may increase the effect of alcohol in our patient and vice versa. It is interesting to note how many clients are unaware of the concept of potentiation, making it a worthwhile discussion in counseling. I have found discussing potentiation especially useful with adolescent clients, many of whom consume both alcohol and marijuana. As a point of information, I like to stress that alcohol further degrades driving performance for someone who is high on marijuana (O'Kane et al., 2002). Potentiation is why mixing drugs is highly dangerous: The client may not be prepared for how one drug effects the other.

- **Effective dose (ED).** The ED refers to the percentage of the population who would respond to a given dose of a drug (Doweiko, 2019). For example, the ED_{50} is the dosage level where 50% of the population would experience an effect of the drug.

- **Lethal dose (LD).** The LD is the percentage of the population that, in theory, would die from a certain dose of the chemical. The LD_{50} refers to the dosage level where, in theory, 50% of the population would die at that given dose of drug (Doweiko, 2019).

- **Therapeutic index (TI).** The TI (also called the therapeutic window) is an index to determine the relative safety of a drug. It is where the effective dose and lethal dose are compared (Doweiko, 2019). Put differently, the TI is the ratio between the effectiveness of the drug and the potential for toxic effects (Doweiko, 2019). If a chemical has a small TI (or narrow therapeutic window), there is a small margin between the minimum effective dose and the lethal dose. If a chemical has a large TI (or wide therapeutic window), there is a large margin between the effective and lethal dose. Thus, drugs with small TIs tend to be more dangerous because there is a fine line between what is effective and what is lethal; one "slip up" by the client in which more of a drug is taken can be extremely dangerous. Drugs with a larger TI are safer because the potential for toxicity or death from overdose is not as strong.

Doweiko (2009, 2019) provided a useful and relevant example of the importance of the therapeutic index. Barbiturates, powerful sedative drugs, have a very small TI, with a ratio of 1 to 3. Thus, taking two doses of some barbiturates beyond the therapeutic dose places the patient at serious risk. Benzodiazepines, another group of sedative drugs, have a much larger TI of 1 to 200. Thus, toxicity or fatality due to benzodiazepine overdose is much less common because of the high TI. It is no wonder that these drugs have largely replaced barbiturates for treatment of anxiety and insomnia. Unfortunately, most drugs have a small TI, and so taking them at high doses increases the risk of toxic reactions up to and including death (Doweiko, 2019).

- **Drug half-life.** Half-life is an important concept in pharmacology as it relates to the period drug is in the body. Biological half-life is defined as the period required for the individual to get rid of 50% of an ingested dose (Liska, 1997). It generally takes five half-life periods for the body to eliminate all of one dose of a drug (Doweiko, 2019). The breakdown is as follows:

Half-life period:

0 = 100% of drug in system

1 = 50% of drug is system

2 = 25% of drug in system

3 = 12.5% of drug in system

4 = ~ 6% of drug in system

5 = ~ 3% of drug in system (Doweiko, 2019)

Although I do not share these terms with my clients daily, I do find that having a basic understanding is helpful when educating or explaining substance use to clients is warranted. For example, it is helpful for me to know the TI of a particular drug, as this information can be valuable feedback for the client. If a client is combining drugs that have a known potentiation effect, again this information would be important to convey.

Brain-Based Interventions for Addressing Substance Use Disorders

The explosion of neuroscience research has led to advances in our understanding of addiction, the addictive cycle, and the impact that drugs have on the brain, brain structures, and neurotransmitters. The next logical step is to assess how we might, as mental health and substance use counselors, use this information to empower and better help our clients overcome substance use disorders. In this section, I propose four ways that we can use neuroscientific findings in substance use counseling to help our clients move forward. These strategies can be incorporated into any theoretical approach.

- **Psychoeducation.** Perhaps the most straightforward way in which clinicians can use neuroscientific understanding of the brain and addiction is to educate clients on the impact of drugs on the brain. For example, educating clients on how overstimulation of the brain's reward center leads to addiction, or the mechanisms for how drugs highjack the brain, give clients a biological perspective that explains their symptoms and substance use behavior. These descriptions can lessen the shame and guilt clients feel because they come to understand addiction as a disease process. Indeed, McCauley (2020) stated that neuroscience can help clients understand reasons for their substance using behavior, provide a narrative of what is happening and, ultimately, is therapeutic for clients. Clients may also respond to exploring consequences of use from a biological point of view, for example helping them see how prolonged drug use weakens the prefrontal cortex, impairing decision-making and judgment. This exploration may enhance understanding and increase motivation to make behavior changes. Exploring the topic of neuroplasticity (i.e., neurons can make healthier connections, even into adulthood) may help clients retain hope that they can improve with cessation of use and a proper recovery plan.

- **Cognitive therapy to strengthen executive control.** Clients who are in the throes of addiction often feel deeply stuck in intrenched patterns of behavior. That is because the connections neurons make with repetitive behavior, such as addiction, become stronger and stronger over time. The foundation of this principle is Hebb's rule, or the common refrain of *neurons that fire together wire together* (Calbet, 2018). However, because of neuroplasticity, neurons can rewire themselves in response to biological, experiential, and environmental changes to our thinking and behavioral patterns (Luke, 2020). Enter CBT as a method to help clients change negative thought and behavior patterns, which can turn addiction patterns to habits more aligned with recovery, growth, and healing. Many of the techniques discussed in Chapters 7 (CBT) and 8 (relapse prevention) would be useful for this purpose.[1]

- **Mindfulness practice to address craving.** I will discuss craving in greater detail in Chapter 8, but for now let's just say it presents a significant issue in recovery. The ability to manage cravings can go a long way in helping people stay free from alcohol and drugs. Mindfulness-based meditation has shown promise as a method to teach clients to better navigate drug cravings (Holt, 2021). From a neuroscientific perspective, a mindfulness practice can help clients bypass their typical habitual, substance using patterns by taming the emotional centers of the brain, strengthening

---

1   Although CBT is highlighted here, any therapeutic approach could potentially help clients shift perspective, adopt new patterns, think more logically, and feel better, thus also having an impact on neuroplasticity.

their prefrontal cortex (and thus increasing inhibitory responses), and reducing the intensity of cravings (Holt, 2021).

There are several excellent mindfulness practices through books, videos, websites, and so forth. The usual practice is having the client sit or lie down comfortably and being as fully relaxed as possible. They are then instructed to become fully aware of their experience without judgment (thoughts, feelings, sensations, cravings; Holt, 2021). If they experience an urge or craving for drugs, they are instructed to observe the craving and "sit with" the experience. Soon after they learn the transitory nature of urges as they will pass with time. In Chapter 8, I discuss the technique of "urge surfing," which likens drug cravings to waves in the ocean, rising, crashing into the shore, and then receding into the background. Holt (2021) offered the PASS acronym to assist clients in the process: *P*ause when one experiences a craving; *a*llow the experience to happen, using the breath as a foundation; *s*it with the experience as it changes in form and intensity; and *s*elect how to respond based on values and recovery goals.

- **Expressive arts activities.** I am a big fan of using art or creative activities in both my counseling and teaching work. Tapping into one's creativity in addition to counseling can enhance self-exploration, strengthen memory, encourage new coping skills, and enhance self-awareness (Emmanuel & Bentley, 2021). Creative activities also can help clients, especially nonverbal clients, find expression of thoughts and emotions. Emmanuel and Bentley described an activity where clients are asked to explore how drugs have impacted their brains. Called the *What's Wrong With My Brain* exercise, clinicians first provide psychoeducation on the neuroscience of addiction. This is followed by the prompt:

Based on what you took from the information I just shared, create something that represents what you think is happening in your brain as a result of substance use. You can use colors, shapes/drawings, and/or words to illustrate your brain. There is no right or wrong way to complete this activity. (p. 122)

Several prompts are used to process this experience, such as "Tell me about your artwork?" "How do you feel about your work?" and "What does this image show you?" (Emmanuel & Bentley, 2021). The psychoeducation piece does not need to be elaborate or overly complex. There are several excellent resources online that clinicians can use to provide a basic overview of how drugs impact the brain. One resource that I often share with my students is from NIDA. This government agency provides up-to-date information on all aspects of substance use disorders, including treatment and the latest from neuroscience. Their publication, *Drugs, Brains, and Behavior: The Science of Addiction* (NIDA, 2020) is an easy-to-follow guide on the neuroscience of addiction and is something that can be shared with clients. Emmanuel and Bentley (2021) offer a nice script example for what to share with clients based on this NIDA publication.

Summary

The neurobiology of addiction helps us understand how drugs impact the brain, leading to experiences such as reward, craving, and relapse. The substance use clinician must have a basic, yet sound, understanding of explanatory and treatment models supported by science and research, which includes the physiology and neurobiology of addiction (Holt, 2021). In this chapter, a basic outline of the reward system in the brain was presented, followed by the importance of neuroplasticity in the recovery from addiction. Brain-based strategies for clinical use were presented. Mechanisms of drug action and common routes of administration were described. In the next chapter, we turn to drug classifications, effects, and associated dangers.

References

Berridge, K. (2006). The debate over dopamine's role in reward: The case for incentive salience. *Psychopharmacology, 191*, 391–431. https://doi.org/10.1007/s00213-006-0578-x

Berridge, K. C., & Kringelbach, M. L. (2008). Affective neuroscience of pleasure: Reward in humans and animals. *Psychopharmacology, 199*, 457–480.

Birgner, C., Nordenankar, K., Lundblad, M., Mendez, J. A., Smith, C., Greves, M. L., Galter, D., Olson, L., Frederiksson, A., Trudeau, L. E., Kullander, K., & Wallen-Mackenzie, A. (2009). VGLUT2 in dopamine neurons is required for psychostimulant-induced behavioral activation. *Proceedings of the National Academy of Sciences, 107*, 389–394. https://doi.org/10.1073/pnas.0910986107

Brooks, F., & McHenry, B. (2015). *A contemporary approach to substance use disorders and addiction counseling* (2nd ed.). American Counseling Association.

Brown, S. (2010). Brain-based treatment strategies for children and adolescents. PESI Seminars.

Brown-Rice, K., & Moro, R. R. (2018). Biological theory: Genetics and brain chemistry. In P. S. Lassiter & J. R. Culbreth (Eds.), *Theory and practice of addiction counseling* (pp. 47–75). SAGE.

Calbet, J. (2018, March 14). Hebb's rule with an analogy: Psychology and neuroscience. *Neuroquotient.* https://tinyurl.com/y3s2fsum

Cote, I. L., & Wilson, W. A. (1980). Effects of barbiturates on inhibitory and excitatory responses to applied neurotransmitters in Aplysia. *Journal of Pharmacology and Experimental Therapeutics, 214* (1), 161–165.

Cramer, S. C., Sur, M., Dobkin, B. H., O'Brien, C., Sanger, T. D., Trojanowski, J. Q., Rumsey, J. M., Ramona, H., Cameron, J., Chen, D., Chen, W. G., Cohen, L. G., DeCharms, C., Duffy, C. J., Guinevere, E. F., Fetz, E. E., Filart, R., Freund, M., Grant, S. J., Haber, S., Kalivas, P. W. ... & Vinogradov, S (2011). Harnessing neuroplasticity for clinical applications. *Brain, 134*(6), 1591–1609.

DeCaria, S. (2021, December 21). What neurotransmitters does nicotine effect and how does nicotine effect dopamine? ePain Assist. https://www.epainassist.com/addiction-and-rehab/what-neurotransmitters-does-nicotine-affect

DePue, K. M., & Smith, R. L. (2018). The major substances of the use and their effect on the brain and body. In P. Stevens & R. L. Smith (Eds.), *Substance abuse counseling: Theory and practice* (6th ed., pp. 49–90). Pearson.

Doweiko, H. E. (2009). *Concepts of chemical dependency* (7th ed.). Brooks/Cole.

Doweiko, H. E. (2019). *Concepts of chemical dependency* (10th ed.). Cengage.

D'Souza, M. S. (2015). Glutamatergic transmission in drug reward: Implications for drug addiction. *Frontiers in Neuroscience, 9*, 404. https://doi.org/10.3389/fnins.2015.00404

Ekhtiari, H., Rezapour, T., Aupperle, R. L., & Paulus, M. P. (2017). Neuroscience-informed psychoeducation for addiction medicine: A neurocognitive perspective. *Progress in Brain Research, 235*, 239–264. https://doi.org/10.1016/bs.pbr.2017.08.013

Emmanuel, D., & Bentley, O. (2021). What's happening in my brain? Addressing the impact of problematic substance use on the brain through psychoeducation and expressive arts. In R. Miller & E. T. Beeson (Eds.), *The neuroeducation toolbox: Practical translations of neuroscience in counseling and psychotherapy* (pp. 120–124). Cognella.

Galván, A. (2010). Neural plasticity of development and learning. *Human Brain Mapping, 31*, 879–890. https://doi.org/10.1002/hbm.21029

Gazdzinski, S., Durazzo, T. C., Mon, A., Ping-Hong, Y., & Meyerhoff, D. J. (2010). Cerebral white matter recovery in abstinent alcoholics—a multimodality magnetic resonance study. *Brain, 133*, 1043–1053.

Goldstein, R. Z., & Volkow, N. D. (2011). Dysfunction of the prefrontal cortex in addiction: Neuroimaging findings and clinical implications. *Nature Reviews Neuroscience, 12*, 652–669.

Guy-Evans, O. (2021, April 13). Temporal lobe: Definition, functions, and location. *Simply Psychology.* https://www.simplypsychology.org/temporal-lobe.html

Hanson, R. (2011). *Buddha's brain: The practical neuroscience of happiness, love, and wisdom.* PESI Seminars.

Holt, R. W. (2021). A vehicle to pass through substance use craving and navigate the addiction recovery cycle. In R. Miller & E. T. Beeson (Eds.), *Neuroeducation toolbox: Practical translations of neuroscience in counseling and psychotherapy* (pp. 125–131). Cognella.

Hyman, M. (2009). *The ultramind solution.* Scribner.

Johnson, S. L. (2003). *Therapists guide to substance abuse intervention.* Academic Press.

Kuhn, C., Swartzwelder, S., & Wilson, W. (2008). *Buzzed: The straight facts about the most used and abused drugs from Alcohol to Ecstasy* (3rd ed.). Norton.

Kuhn, C., Swartzwelder, S., & Wilson, W. (2019). *Buzzed: The straight facts about the most used and abused drugs from alcohol to ecstasy* (5th ed.). Norton.

Lapish, C., Seamans, J. K., & Chandler, J. L. (2006). Glutamate-dopamine cotransmission and reward processing in addiction. *Alcoholism: Clinical and Experimental Research, 30*, 1451–1465.

Liska, K. (1997). *Drugs and the human body: With implications for society.* Prentice Hall.

Luke, C. (2020). *Neuroscience for counselors and therapists: Integrating the sciences of the mind and brain* (2nd ed.). Cognella.

McCauley, K. T. (2020). *Addiction & recovery update 2020: The latest clinical takeaways from neuroscience research.* Trauma & Addiction Online Conference. PESI Trainings. https://catalog.pesi.com/item/addiction-recovery-update-2020-latest-clinical-takeaways-neuroscience-research-67066

Miller, R., & Beeson, E. T. (Eds.). (2021). *The neuroeducation toolbox: Practical translations of neuroscience in counseling and psychotherapy.* Cognella.

Miller, W. R., Forcehimes, A. A., & Zweben, A. (2019). *Treating addiction: A guide for professionals* (2nd ed.). Guilford.

National Institute on Drug Abuse. (2020). *Drugs, brain, and behavior: The science of addiction.* https://nida.nih.gov/publications/drugs-brains-behavior-science-addiction/preface

Nordahl, T. E., Salo, R., & Leamon, M. (2003). Neuropsychological effects of chronic methamphetamine use on neurotransmitters and cognition: A review. *Journal of Neuropsychiatry and Clinical Neurosciences, 15,* 317–325.

O'Kane, C. J., Tutt, D. C., & Bauer, L. A. (2002). Cannabis and driving: a new perspective. *Emergency Medicine, 14,* 296–303.

Parvaz, M. A., Moeller, S. J., d'Oleire Uquillas, F., Pflumm, A., Maloney, T., Alia-Klein, N., & Goldstein, R. Z. (2016). Prefrontal gray matter volume recovery in treatment-seeking cocaine-addicted individuals: A longitudinal study. *Addiction Biology, 22,* 1391–1401.

Pirau, L., & Lui, F. (2021). *Frontal lobe syndrome.* StatPearls.

Plotnik, R. (1996). *Introduction to psychology* (4th ed.). Cengage.

Polk, T. A. (2015). *The addictive brain.* The Teaching Company.

Psychology Today. (2022). Addiction and the brain. https://www.psychologytoday.com/us/basics/addiction/addiction-and-the-brain

Robinson, T. E., & Berridge, K. C. (2008). The incentive sensitization theory of addiction: Some current issues. *Philosophical Transactions of the Royal Society B: Biological Sciences, 363,* 3137–3146. https://doi.org/10.1098/rstb.2008.0093

Smith, R. L. (2013). Major substances of abuse and the body. In P. Stevens & R. L. Smith (Eds.), *Substance abuse counseling: Theory and practice* (5th ed., pp. 51–97). Pearson.

Thombs, D. L., & Osborn, C. J. (2019). *Introduction to addictive behaviors* (5th ed.). Guilford.

Volkow, N. (2007). The addicted brain: Beyond willpower. In J. Hoffman & S. Froemke (Eds.), *Addiction: New knowledge, new treatments, new hope* (p. 56). Rodale.

White, T. L., Monnig, M. A., Walsh, E. G., Nitenson, A. Z., Harris, A. D., Cohen, R. A., Porges, E. C., Woods, A. J., Lamb, D. G., Boyd, C. A., & Fekir, S. (2018). Psychostimulant drug effects on glutamate, Glx, and creatine in the anterior cingulate cortex and subjective response in healthy humans. *Neuropsychopharmacology, 43,* 1498–1509.

Figure Credits

Fig. 3.1: Source: Adapted from https://nida.nih.gov/publications/drugs-brains-behavior-science-addiction/drugs-brain.

Fig. 3.1a: Copyright © 2016 Depositphotos/megija.

CHAPTER 4

Substance Classifications, Effects, and Associated Dangers

As with brain physiology and the neuroscience of addiction, substance use clinicians should have a basic understanding of the various classes of drugs, their typical effects, and associated dangers. Understanding a drug's effect can clarify drug taking motivations; for example, a person experiencing feelings of depression may consume central nervous system stimulants to serve as a "pick me up" and a way to overcome their low energy. Although reasons for consuming drugs can be complex, exploring their motivations and sharing the effects and dangers can address misinformation and fill in gaps in understanding. In this chapter, I cover numerous substance classifications and individual drugs, their physiological and behavioral effects, and outline the associated dangers when these substances are consumed.

Substance Classifications, Effects, and Dangers

As Brooks and McHenry (2015) asserted, clients do not plan to develop substance use disorders. They do not ingest drugs with the hopes of becoming dependent on them. Rather, individuals start using drugs out of curiosity, to experience pleasure, or to cope with some painful experience. There are several different categories and classifications of substances with different effects and dangers. Most drugs, however, also have associated "street names," with several names often referring to one drug. Hundreds of street names exist (Miller et al., 2019), and new names emerge on a frequent basis. Table 4.1 lists the street names for the most common drugs.

This chapter is not meant to be an exhaustive review of all drugs and all drug effects; individuals are constantly creating alternative substances in which chemicals are combined to experiment with the next best high (Perkinson, 2012). However, the major drugs that people consume—alcohol, cocaine, opiates, marijuana, hallucinogens, and methamphetamine—have been constant and are probably the most common drugs clinicians will see in their counseling offices. These, as well as other common drugs, will be the focus of this chapter.

TABLE 4.1 Street Names of Common Drugs

Drug of Abuse	Common Street Names
Alcohol	Booze, liquid courage, juice
Barbiturates	Downers, reds, red birds, yellowjackets, goofballs
Amphetamines	Bennies, black beauties, copilots, crank, ice, crystal, cross tops, glass, hearts, pep pills, speed, uppers
Methamphetamine	Crank, crystal meth, speed, ice, chalk, trash
Cocaine	Coke, snow, toot, candy, C, heaven, nose candy
Heroin	Smack, horse, junk, brown sugar, shit, mud
LSD	Acid, bartman, paper mushrooms, sugar, microdots
PCP	Angel dust, hog, elephant, killer joints
Marijuana	Pot, grass, herb, weed, ganja
Inhalants	Zombie juice, poppers, purple haze, ozone, climax, bullets, bolt

Central Nervous System Depressants

Central nervous system depressants (i.e., CNS depressants, sedatives, or sedative-hypnotics), work on the brain and body by slowing down nervous tissue throughout all aspects of the nervous system (Perkinson, 2012). General effects include slurred speech, disorientation, "drunken" behavior, and relaxed inhibitions. Overdose from CNS depressants can be dangerous and includes symptoms such as shallow respiration, impaired coordination, hypothermia, rapid pulse, coma, and possible death (Doweiko, 2019). The withdrawal syndrome from most CNS depressants includes signs and symptoms that are the opposite of the drug's effect: anxiety, insomnia, tremors, delirium, convulsions, and possibly death. Common CNS depressants include alcohol, barbiturates, and benzodiazepines. Let's look at these general drugs next, with a little more emphasis on alcohol given its ever-present nature in society.

Alcohol

The type of alcohol that humans drink includes *ethyl alcohol* or *ethanol*. There is no reliable record as to when alcohol was first produced, although given how it is formed in nature it probably happened by chance (Perkinson, 2012; for an interesting history in the development of alcohol, also see Doweiko, 2019). Naturally occurring yeast cells in the air feast on the sugars of fruits, vegetables, grains, and cactus plants, making carbon dioxide and alcohol as waste. As this process of *fermentation* continues, the content and level of alcohol rises, eventually killing the yeast that produced it (Perkinson, 2012). This goes to show that alcohol is truly a poison, especially at high levels.

The concentration of alcohol is measured in *proof*, or a value that is two times the pure alcohol content. For example, if a beverage is "100% alcohol," then it would be 200 proof. A glass of "24-proof" wine equals about 12% alcohol. A drink of 40% alcohol would equal 80 proof. One "standard drink" contains about .60 oz. of pure alcohol—typical for a 12-ounce can of beer, 5-ounce glass of wine, or a drink made of 1.5 ounces of 80-proof liquor. Interestingly, clients often miscalculate how much they drink because they think that one "drink," for example, includes a 40 oz bottle of beer. A 40 oz bottle would be slightly over three drinks. When assessing intensity of drinking with clients, it is important to clarify what one drink constitutes. We will take a closer look at alcohol and substance use assessment in Chapter 5. Clients may inadvertently believe that they have a "couple of drinks" a night when they are drinking much more.

Having this basic knowledge related to alcohol helps to understand the extent of one's drinking and to offer education and feedback. For example, if a client talks about having "151" at a recent party, I know that most likely they mean "151 proof," which translates to 75.5% alcohol content (compared to the average alcoholic beverage at 35%–40% alcohol)! I am aware, then, that this client possibly has no idea how much alcohol they were drinking and how they were putting themself and possibly others at risk. Providing education on the content of alcohol in drinks (e.g., what "proof" means) and feedback on how much is consumed may be an important first step in increasing awareness and motivation to look at one's drinking.

Effects and Dangers

Alcohol slows down general physiological functioning. However, this effect is often not the first effect perceived by others. That is, when one first consumes alcohol, the initial effect is the disinhibition effect (where alcohol *inhibits* inhibitory synapses in the brain; Doweiko, 2019). This partially explains why some individuals who consume alcohol start off appearing giddy, silly, and engaging in behaviors that they might not otherwise engage in. However, over time, the behavioral effects catch up with the physiological effects where all synapses become depressed, and the person begins to show visible signs of slowing down and intoxication.

The speed at which alcohol is absorbed depends on many factors, including the presence or absence of food, the preparation of alcohol (mixed drink or "straight"), and the size and gender of the person. Thus, a male who has no food in his stomach, who drinks straight liquor, and who is physically small will experience the speed and intensity of alcohol's effects differently than a female who has food in her stomach, who drinks mixed drinks, and is normal weight.

Alcohol is metabolized primarily by the liver. The enzyme *alcohol dehydrogenase* breaks down alcohol to *acetaldehyde*, which is broken down further to *acetate*. Acetate is then broken down to *carbon dioxide, water, and carbohydrates*, which are then excreted through the body (Liska, 1997). In general, individuals can metabolize about two thirds of an ounce of whiskey or eight ounces of beer in 1 hour (Liska, 2007). Indeed, a common suggestion to help clients control their drinking is to suggest no more than one drink per hour, not to exceed four drinks per "sitting." This slower rate of drinking allows the alcohol to be metabolized so as not to build up in the brain and body.

The amount of alcohol measured in the body at one time is indicated by the well-known *blood alcohol content* (or blood alcohol level), or BAC (BAL) value, which is generally measured in milligrams of alcohol per 100 liters of blood (mg/mL; Doweiko, 2019). A BAC of 0 to .08% corresponds behaviorally to giddiness and talkativeness, with some impairment in reaction time (Brooks & McHenry, 2015). A BAC of .08% is the legal limit set for operating a motor vehicle in all states. At levels between .1% and .3%, coordination and reflexes become compromised and the person experiences nausea, vomiting, and is visibly and outwardly drunk. At levels .3% and above, the person's movement is compromised, and they are most likely passed out and at risk of dying. BAC levels ranging from .4% to .6% results in coma, whereas .6% and higher usually leads to severe cardiovascular and respiratory depression, resulting in death (Brooks & McHenry, 2015).

Prolonged alcohol use can lead to several chronic physical problems and medical complications. First and foremost, excessive alcohol use taxes the kidneys, leading to kidney damage. However, it is the liver that takes the brunt of the toxic impact of alcohol, resulting in fatty liver, alcoholic hepatitis (swollen liver cells), and, if drinking has occurred long enough, cirrhosis of the liver (scarring of tissue within the liver, rendering it unable to function).

Alcohol impairs the quality of sleep such that precious REM deep sleep is compromised. Thus, an individual who is drunk may immediately fall asleep only to wake up a short time later without feeling rested. One can only imagine the sleep deprivation that occurs among those who consume alcohol on a nightly basis for months, even years. I am astonished that some clients often fail to see the connection between their fatigue, mood, lack of sleep, and alcohol consumption. If clients were to get a good night's sleep, their mood, energy, and concentration would most likely improve, and they would have greater psychological strength to manage alcohol cravings.

As if messing with sleep patterns is not enough, too much alcohol also impacts sexual functioning, and not in a good way. Of course, this universal truth about alcohol has been denied by alcohol producers who would have us believe that sexual abilities will only be enhanced if their product is consumed. It is true that alcohol may make one feel less inhibited and sexier (Kuhn et al., 2019). However, the effect of alcohol is on sexual *functioning*, not attraction. Chronic drinking, especially in men, can lead to reduced sexual drive, erectile dysfunction, lower testosterone, lower semen count, and, in some cases, smaller testicles (Kuhn et al., 2019; as the authors pointed out, this little tidbit is conveniently left out of television commercials). These consequences are more problematic with chronic, everyday drinkers, although sexual side effects have been shown among those who drink less intensely (Kuhn et al., 2019).

Two serious consequences of heavy, prolonged alcohol use are Wernicke's syndrome and Korsakoff's syndrome. Wernicke's syndrome is characterized by excessive inflammation of the brain (encephalopathy) and is manifested as confusion, poor memory, and disorientation (Perkinson, 2012). Korsakoff's syndrome is characterized by living in the eternal present; the person has trouble transferring experiences from short-term to long-term memory (Perkinson, 2012). Thus, the person cannot remember what happened a few minutes ago. The two syndromes often go together as "Wernicke's-Korsakoff's" syndrome in which the person has an unsteady gait, cannot answer questions, and may seem listless and indifferent to their environment (Perkinson, 2012). According to Perkinson (2012), Wernicke's-Korsakoff's syndrome is a neurological emergency that is treated by muscular injection of thiamine. The syndrome can thus result from years of dietary neglect (among other factors) that may characterize those with severe alcohol use disorder.

Barbiturates

Barbiturates are powerful sedatives that were originally used as an aid to anxiety and sleep (Doweiko, 2019). Today, they are used for these same purposes, as well as the control of seizures. Barbiturates were originally thought to produce minimal risk for dependence; however, clinical experience has shown that not to be the case (Ivanov et al., 2006, as cited in Doweiko, 2019). Barbiturates can be administered orally or intravenously (Brooks & McHenry, 2015). Common types of barbiturates include phenobarbital, pentobarbital, secobarbital, and amobarbital (Kuhn et al., 2019).

Effects and Dangers

Unfortunately, the effectiveness of barbiturates in slowing the body down is offset by their extreme dangerousness. They have a small TI, and so there is a fine line between the lethal dose and therapeutic dose (Doweiko, 2019). Excessive doses of barbiturates can be extremely dangerous because of the inhibition of the respiratory centers in the brain. Thus, excessive barbiturate use could slow down physiological functioning too much, leading to a cessation of breathing. This is one of many reasons physicians today rarely prescribe these drugs.

Barbiturates are short-acting substances that produce intoxication characteristics like alcohol (at least initially): disinhibition, elevated mood, and increases in self-esteem, energy and confidence. The person who is intoxicated on barbiturates may stumble around, slur their speech, and exercise poor judgment. However, the short-acting nature of barbiturates often leads to sudden shifts of sadness and depression (Erikson, 2001). With the introduction of benzodiazepines in the 1960s, barbiturate use has diminished in both its "street" and medicinal use. However, among some populations, the misuse of barbiturates continues to be a problem (Erikson, 2001).

Benzodiazepines

Benzodiazepines, or "benzos," are the most widely prescribed drugs for sleep problems, acute stress reactions, convulsions, and anxiety (Erikson, 2001). Introduced in the 1960s, benzodiazepines are considered mild tranquilizers that reduce anxiety, but without the same degree of sedation as that produced by barbiturates. Benzodiazepines have traditionally been considered safer sedatives than barbiturates, mainly because the TI is much higher (Doweiko, 2019). Indeed, death and serious illness rarely result from benzodiazepine overdose alone (Newton & Gomez, 2021). However, the combination of benzodiazepines with other CNS depressants, such as alcohol, can be quite dangerous (Newton & Gomez, 2021). Interestingly, approximately 2,000 different benzodiazepines have been produced, but only about 15 have FDA clearance in the United States (Newton & Gomez, 2021).

Effects and Dangers

Like all CNS depressants, benzodiazepines act on the central nervous system, leading to sedation, muscle relaxation, and lowered anxiety. Concerns with benzodiazepines often occur when they are taken with other drugs, which is quite common (Newton & Gomez, 2021). Potentiation and cross-tolerance with other CNS depressants may lead to inappropriate or excessive use of these drugs. Another concern is the potential to develop physiological dependence. Initially thought to be much less addicting than barbiturates, clinical experience has shown that misuse of benzodiazepines places one at enhanced risk for substance addiction. In general, the risk of addiction is minimal for those taking normal doses over a short period of time (Newton & Gomez, 2011). However, if benzodiazepines are taken as prescribed beyond a few months, the risk of neuroadaptation increases (Doweiko, 2019).

Central Nervous System Stimulants

CNS stimulants have the opposite effect on the brain and body as CNS depressants. General effects include elevation of mood, increased feelings of well-being, and increased energy and alertness (NIDA, 2011). Physiological effects include dilated pupils, increased pulse, increased respiration, increased blood pressure, increased heart rate, insomnia, and loss of appetite. Overdose from CNS stimulants include agitation, increases in body temperature, hallucinations, irregular heartbeat, and possibly death (Hoffman & Froemke, 2007).

The withdrawal syndrome from most CNS stimulants includes signs and symptoms that are the opposite of the drug's effect: apathy, long periods of sleep, irritability, depression, and disorientation. Common CNS stimulants include amphetamines, methamphetamines, cocaine, "ecstasy," and prescription medications such as Ritalin and Adderall. In this section, I cover the more traditional stimulant drugs: amphetamines, methamphetamine, and cocaine.

Amphetamines

Amphetamines have an interesting history in the United States, reflecting our somewhat ambivalent attitude toward them. They were used for medicinal purposes and as effective energy enhancers during long combat missions during World War II. However, by the mid- to late 1970s, medical specialists began to realize the dangers of amphetamine use and that, even medicinally, they were not as effective as once thought (Doweiko, 2009). It became clear, for example, that these drugs could not be used without risk of addiction, and thus their safety and usefulness were called into question. Today, many amphetamines, such as Adderall, come in pill form and are sometimes prescribed by doctors for medical issues to treat disorders such as attention deficit hyperactivity disorder (ADHD). Unfortunately, amphetamines can be easily abused (NIDA, 2011). Amphetamines can be taken in pill form, intravenously, smoked, or crushed and snorted (Brooks & McHenry, 2015).

Effects and Dangers

Amphetamines produce feelings of euphoria, provide relief from fatigue, increase mental alertness, and enhance mood, making those who use them particularly at risk for addiction. They also can produce short-term effects such as insomnia, irregular heartbeat, and mild paranoia

(Hoffman & Froemke, 2007). The most serious dangers associated with amphetamine use are cardiovascular effects such as high blood pressure, irregular heartbeat, and possibly stroke. Extreme excitation of the CNS can put an enormous strain on the heart and blood vessels, engendering considerable risk. As with other drugs that can be administered intravenously, those who use amphetamines can share needles, thus increasing their risk of contracting HIV, hepatitis B, and hepatitis C (Hoffman & Froemke, 2007). The withdrawal syndrome from amphetamines includes depression, "the shakes," tiredness, and unusual fatigue (Hoffman & Froemke, 2007).

Methamphetamine

Methamphetamine, a derivative of amphetamine, is a powerful stimulant. It comes in clear crystals (as "ice" or crystal meth) or powder and can easily dissolve in water or alcohol. Crystal meth is odorless and colorless, which makes it a nightmare for law enforcement officials to track down. Most methamphetamine produced and used in the United States comes from so-called "super labs"; however, in recent years, methamphetamine has garnered the national spotlight due to its production in small laboratories across the United States using inexpensive over-the-counter and often toxic ingredients (e.g., drain cleaner, battery acid, and antifreeze; NIDA, 2011).

Effects and Dangers

Methamphetamines have the general effect of increasing activity and feelings of euphoria. However, concomitant with these "good" side effects are increases in anxiety, hyperactivity, (Brooks & McHenry, 2015; Hoffman & Froemke, 2007), and aggression. To counteract the increases in anxiety, many of those who use methamphetamine will turn to benzodiazepines, alcohol, and marijuana (Brooks & McHenry, 2015).

Methamphetamine is an extraordinarily dangerous drug and has a high addiction potential (Brooks & McHenry, 2015). Long-term negative effects include psychotic behavior, hallucinations, respiratory problems, cardiovascular problems, and extreme weight loss/anorexia (Hoffman & Froemke, 2007). Other associated dangers include the risk of infectious diseases (from sharing needles), depression, intense cravings, anxiety, fatigue, aggression, and the development of "meth mouth."

Meth mouth is a condition in which the individual develops advanced tooth decay resulting from heavy methamphetamine use (Schep et al., 2010). Methamphetamine is known to induce bruxism (teeth grinding), trismus (difficulty opening the jaw), and dry mouth, and users tend to neglect oral hygiene in general (American Dental Association, 2022). Individuals who heavily use methamphetamine also are known to develop deep sores around their face and other areas of their bodies. These open sores are the result of a multitude of factors, including poor hygiene, the toxic effects of the drug, obsessive picking at the face and arms, lack of healthy blood flow to the arms (to preclude healing), and a compromised immune system (Meth Project, n.d.). As with amphetamines, one of the greatest potential risks from taking methamphetamines is cardiovascular problems. Withdrawal symptoms are like those associated with amphetamines.

Cocaine

Cocaine has had a varied and interesting history in the United States, characterized by peaks and valleys related to misuse. In the most recent uptick, cocaine use reached epidemic proportions in the 1980s, with a peak in 1986. However, there has been a steady decline in cocaine misuse since (Doweiko, 2019). In general, cocaine comes in two forms. Powdered cocaine is the most commonly available form and is a hydrochloride salt, made from the leaf of the coca plant. Crack is a form of cocaine that is processed with ammonia or baking soda and water, and then heated to remove the hydrochloride (NIDA, 2011). The resulting crystals or rocks are then smoked. Crack cocaine is a purer form of cocaine than powdered cocaine and has been considered the "fast-food" variety of cocaine—inexpensive, simple to hide, and hard to detect (Inciardi, 1992).

Effects and Dangers

Those who use cocaine often report numerous positive, subjective effects, including profound feelings of well-being, enhanced alertness, intense energy/strength, decreases in anxiety, increases in self-confidence, heightened sexual drive, and increases in mastery and power. As one can observe, it is no wonder cocaine can be so addicting. After all, who wouldn't want to feel more confident, sexy, and energetic? However, cocaine offers a false hope. The dangers of cocaine use and addiction rival that of amphetamines and include severe cardiovascular problems, irritability, nervousness, and agitation. Cocaine has a particularly strong effect on dopamine and dopamine receptors in the brain (Doweiko, 2019; Hoffman & Froemke, 2007). In general, cocaine is known to block reuptake of dopamine, or the reabsorption of dopamine back into releasing neurons. Thus, neurons eventually release all their dopamine stores without being replenished. The excess dopamine causes brain cells to limit the number of dopamine receptors, which alters the brain's ability to create pleasure (Hoffman & Froemke, 2007). The net result is, over time, a dopamine deficiency, leading to feelings of diminished motivation and depression (Doweiko, 2009). This may explain the general observation of the connection between cocaine use disorder and depression.

Short-term dangers of cocaine use include, but are not limited to, heart rhythm disturbances, increased respiratory function, increases in blood pressure/heart rate, decreased appetite, and simulation of manic symptoms. Long-term effects include reduction in number of dopamine receptors, nasal cavity irritation, loss of sense of smell and nosebleeds (from snorting cocaine), problems swallowing, and lung damage (Doweiko, 2019; Hoffman & Froemke, 2007). Cocaine misuse and cocaine use disorder can negatively impact almost every system in the body (Doweiko, 2019), resulting in a host of short-term and long-term complications.

It cannot be emphasized enough the dangers associated with cocaine use and addiction. It is not a gateway drug like alcohol or marijuana, so other drug use in addition to cocaine is probably likely, raising the risk for potentially fatal drug interactions. In addition, cocaine is often associated with criminal activity, increases the risk of infection, and has unpredictable consequences. Fisher and Harrison (2019) noted that, in the process of making cocaine, it often is adulterated with toxins, such as arsenic, as well as talc, sugar, lidocaine, or meth.

Adulteration is a method to increase the pharmacological effect. Indeed, the purity of "street" cocaine is uncertain. The withdrawal from cocaine includes cravings, fatigue, lack of pleasure, and sleepiness (Hoffman & Froemke, 2007).

Opiates

Opiates, also referred to as *narcotics*, are common drugs in which a person experiences a rush of pleasure followed by a dreamy, pleasant state in which their problems seem to disappear (Kuhn et al., 2019). Their primary effect is to kill pain (analgesics), although they do have similar effects as CNS depressants (Johnson, 2003). Other effects include slowed breathing, flushed skin, drowsiness, a sense of tranquility, and pinpoint pupils (Hoffman & Froemke, 2007; Kuhn et al., 2019). Although these pleasurable experiences are nearly universal, some individuals do develop nausea, vomiting, and constipation (Kuhn et al., 2008). Overdose from opiate drugs include slow and shallow breathing, clammy skin, convulsions, coma, and possibly death (Johnson, 2003). Withdrawal symptoms from opiates are extremely unpleasant and include experiences such as dilated pupils, vasodilation, rapid heartbeat, elevated blood pressure, vomiting, diarrhea, goose bumps, tremors, chills, nausea, cramps, and loss of appetite (Johnson, 2003). It is no wonder that many of my clients with opiate use disorder have stated that opiate withdrawal is one of the worst experiences that they have had to endure. Common opiate substances include opium, heroin, morphine, codeine, and prescription pain killers such as oxycodone (Percodan) and hydrocodone (Vicodin; Kuhn et al., 2019). For purposes of this chapter, only heroin and prescription pain medications are covered.

Heroin

Heroin is one of the most commonly used opioids that can quickly lead to addiction. Morphine, a naturally occurring substance extracted from the seed of the opium poppy plant, is chemically altered to make heroin. Heroin often looks like a white or brown powder or as having a black, tacky quality known as "black tar heroin" (NIDA, 2021). Heroin can be injected, snorted, or smoked, with injection and smoking being the fastest routes of delivery to the brain. Indeed, one of the reasons that heroin can be so addicting is the relatively rapid experience of a "rush" or "flash" of pleasure, a highly reinforcing experience.

Effects and Dangers

Short-term effects of heroin include the surge of euphoria upon initial use, followed by a dream-like state of drowsiness. Mental functioning typically becomes clouded, followed by heaviness in the extremities, increases in self-esteem, and decreased concern with problems and stressors in one's life (Kuhn et al., 2019; NIDA, 2021).

There are many associated dangers with heroin use. HIV and hepatitis infections remain a real threat for those who share needles. As with "street" cocaine, street heroin often is adulterated with toxic chemicals and almost never pure. Such additives can clog blood vessels, leading to severe heart, lung, kidney, liver, or brain damage. Long-term associated dangers of heroin use include collapsed veins, heart valve and lining infections, and liver and/or kidney disease (NIDA, 2021). Heroin overdose has a depressing effect on respiration that may result in pulmonary complications, such as pneumonia, or hypoxia, a condition where less oxygen reaches the brain, in some cases leading to lasting brain damage (NIDA, 2021).

The addiction potential to heroin is very strong. The initial rush has a high reward potential in the brain, and the individual may search their entire life to recapture the initial rush. Sadly, for some individuals there is a small to nonexistent window from use to addiction when using heroin. That is, people can become addicted to heroin after the first "hit." It is estimated that 23% of those who use heroin become dependent on it (Alcohol & Drug Services, 2016). The withdrawal syndrome from heroin, and opiates in general, is exceedingly unpleasant but often not fatal (Kuhn et al., 2019). Symptoms include restlessness, muscle pain, sleep problems, diarrhea, flu-like symptoms/vomiting, cold flashes, and involuntary leg movements (Hoffman & Froemke, 2007).

Prescription Pain Medication

Pain, as Doweiko (2019) noted, comes from the Latin word *poena*, translating to punishment, penalty, or penance. Indeed, the avoidance of pain is a basic motivation of life. Chronic pain impacts 100 million Americans and is a main reason a person goes on disability (NIDA, n.d.). Prescription pain medications include substances prescribed by a doctor for pain symptoms such as oxycodone-acetaminophen (Percocet), oxycodone-aspirin (Percodan), and hydrocodone-acetaminophen (Vicodin). These are powerful pain relievers, and over the last several years the misuse of prescription medication has been of particular concern of the U.S. Drug Enforcement Agency. Typically, these medications are taken orally, but in misuse situations they also can be snorted or injected (Hoffman & Froemke, 2007). All opiate medications bind to opiate receptors with differing levels of intensity (Kuhn et al., 2008). For example, morphine, hydromorphone, and fentanyl are highly effective pain-killing agents. Hydrocodone and oxycodone are moderately effective, whereas codeine is an example of a low-efficacy opiate medication (Kuhn et al., 2008). Thus, physicians must know the extent and intensity of pain as this helps them make decisions about the most appropriate medication. Unfortunately, clients can sometimes fake the amount of pain they are experiencing to get a stronger medication.

The understanding, management, and treatment of pain is a complicated issue, involving physical, psychological, and environmental components. I recall counseling a client who experienced severe pain every day, emanating from an accident (fall) at work. The client had been on pain medication for years and even by his physician's admission had a substance use disorder. His pain was debilitating, as evidenced by his need for assistance to simply get up from a chair and walk to my counseling office. I think it is important for counselors to understand the misery clients experience while in severe pain. It is not simply a matter of weaning off the meds and practicing some relaxation techniques. My strategy was to help the client find nonmedical methods to ease painful symptoms, in conjunction with his medical treatments. Many clients may find that, with practice, nonmedical methods may reduce the need for medication but may not be enough to completely stop medication. I learned there are no easy answers these difficult issues.

Effects and Dangers

Prescription pain medications produce similar effects to that of heroin and other opiates, without the initial rush. Effects also are relatively short-lived, ranging from 3–6 hours (Johnson, 2003). Common effects include drowsiness, constipation, nausea, and depressed breathing, especially when high doses have been consumed (Hoffman & Froemke, 2007). Other acute effects include euphoria, lack of motivation, and analgesic effects. Chronic use often leads to loss of energy, tolerance, physical dependence, and lack of ambition and drive (Johnson, 2003).

Long-term, chronic use of pain medications can lead to physical addiction and withdrawal symptoms that rival heroin addiction: nasty, but usually not lethal. However, overdose of these medications, or any opiate for that matter, can be deadly. In my experience, many of the clients in my clinical practice struggled with prescription pain medications. Like most individuals struggling with addiction, they did not start out thinking that they would misuse medications. However, if one pill is effective, then two will be even more effective, or so went their thinking. When I interview clients about their reasons for taking too many pain pills, typical responses include the following:

> "I felt back to normal."

> "My problems went away."

> "They took away my stress I was feeling."

> "They just made me forget about problems and feel good."

Clearly, prescription pain medication misuse represents a continued challenge within the medical, treatment, and societal communities at large. These drugs, while very effective at blocking or minimizing pain, have a strong addictive potential. A point to stress here is that prescription pain medications seem to not only take away physical pain, but also emotional pain. Indeed, this was a major reason for their continued misuse among my clients.

The Opioid Epidemic

For the past several years, the United States has experienced an "opioid epidemic" involving both illicit (e.g., heroin), prescription pain (e.g., Vicodin), and synthetic opioid (e.g., fentanyl) drugs. From 1999–2019, almost 500,000 people died from any opioid use (Centers for Disease Control and Prevention [CDC], 2020). One-hundred and thirty-six people die daily from opioid overdose, including both prescription and illicit drugs (CDC, 2021). This epidemic has roots extending back to the 1990s (the first "wave"), with increases in prescription opioids to address pain (CDC, 2011). The second wave began in 2010, with increases in opioid deaths related to heroin (Rudd et al., 2014). The third wave began in 2013, where the country experienced significant overdose deaths due to synthetic opioids, especially fentanyl (Gladden et al., 2016). Opioid-involved deaths often include other drugs as well, including cocaine, meth, and CNS depressants (Gladden et al., 2019).

Synthetic opioids, quite frankly, pose a nightmare for law enforcement and society. They are generally more potent, and thus more dangerous, than other opioids. For example, fentanyl is considered 50 times more potent than heroin. In addition, it is usually combined with heroin or other chemicals for a more intense high and effect. The increased potency is likely to cause overdose, leading to a doubling of yearly overdose deaths since fentanyl use began to take off in the United States (Lopez, 2022a). According to a *New York Times* report, fentanyl caused more overdose deaths in 2021 than any other drug (Lopez, 2022b).

Another concern with synthetic opioids is that they can be made in a lab, and thus do not require vast amounts of land and workforce to produce (such as opium poppy fields; Lopez, 2022b). This process increases the rate of production, lowers costs, and makes tracking for law enforcement extremely difficult. Indeed, law enforcement efforts have struggled to keep up with synthetic drugs because new ones consistently enter the scene. According to Lopez (2022b), many substance users prefer synthetics because they are cheaper and produce a more powerful high. The danger, however, is that synthetic opioids can be *too* powerful and are often laced with other drugs or chemicals (of which the combination of effects is unknown). The result is a likely overdose and increased risk of death.

Although methods to combat the opioid crisis are beyond the scope of this text, expanding treatment and focusing on harm reduction rather than limiting drug supplies seems to be the most immediate response (Lopez, 2022b). Mental health and substance use clinicians are encouraged to keep abreast of the latest developments in the synthetic drug development. For an excellent resource on keeping up to date, visit NIDA's National Drug Early Warning System (NDEWS; https://ndews.org/).

Hallucinogens

Hallucinogens are a class of drugs that produce visual and/or auditory perceptual distortions. The most commonly used hallucinogens include lysergic acid (LSD) or "acid," MDMA ("ecstasy"), and phencyclidine (PCP or "angel dust"). In general, hallucinogens vary widely in their effects; the same person might have completely different experiences using the same drugs at the same time of day (Kuhn et al., 2019). General effects include feelings of detachment, emotional ups and downs, and altered sensations. Hallucinations (seeing things that do not exist), pseudo-hallucinations (experiences that are not real but the user knows they are not real), and illusions (distortions of reality) are all common experiences (Kuhn et al., 2019). Also common among many hallucinogens is the sensation of being separate from one's body (Kuhn et al., 2019). Physical dependence is generally not produced with hallucinogens, although tolerance can and does develop with LSD (Kuhn et al., 2019). Psychological addiction may occur depending on the hallucinogen, individual, and environmental circumstances. Two hallucinogens, LSD and PCP, are explored next.

LSD

LSD is one of the most potent hallucinogens known (Doweiko, 2019; Kuhn et al., 2019). It is absorbed rapidly, and the first 4 hours are known as the "trip," with a gradual return to reality within 7–12 hours (Doweiko, 2019; Julien, 2008, as cited in Kuhn et al., 2019). Today's levels of LSD use are enough to produce potent hallucinations. LSD is typically taken in tablet, capsule, or liquid form (Hoffman & Froemke, 2007). Although mostly chewed or swallowed, Kuhn et al. (2019) noted that small amounts of LSD blotted on absorbent paper can be enough to produce a drug effect (yes, it is that potent!).

Effects and Dangers

When first ingesting LSD, the person might experience unusual sensations such as numbness, weakness, trembling, elevated heart rate and blood pressure, and dilated pupils. Nausea and jitteriness also might set in (Kuhn et al., 2008). The "trip" generally begins after the first 60 minutes to the 4th hour, in which the person experiences enhanced visual effects, wave-like motions, feelings of euphoria, distorted space perceptions, and a slowing of time (Julien, 2008, as cited in Kuhn et al., 2019). From hours 4 to 12, the effects of the trip dissipate, and the person slowly returns to a normal state (O'Brien, 2006, as cited in Doweiko, 2019). Other trip-like experiences may include the loss of boundaries, enhanced insight, heightened sensory data, and feelings of contentment.

Short-term dangers include increased heart rate and blood pressure, sleeplessness, dry mouth, and tremors. Long-term complications include flashbacks, which can occur within a few days to after a year of use. LSD users also may harbor chronic psychopathology such as schizophrenia or depression (Hoffman & Froemke, 2007). Related dangers of LSD use include impairment of judgment and reality. Understanding of common risks and dangers is severely compromised, making users at risk for accidents and injury (Hoffman & Froemke, 2007).

PCP

PCP or "angel dust" was first used medically as an anesthetic; however, it was soon discovered that patients would develop drug-induced manic-like symptoms that would last for 4 days (Johnson, 2003). PCP can be smoked, snorted, or ingested, but is usually smoked or snorted and mixed with alcohol and/or tobacco. The drug has a relatively long half-life, with subjective effects typically lasting up to 8 hours (Liska, 1997).

Effects and Dangers

According to Kuhn et al. (2019), PCP is a nasty drug that has a bad (and well-deserved) reputation. It produces effects like alcohol, amphetamines, and hallucinogens combined. It is generally taken for the stimulant-like feelings of well-being. However, when a person is strung out on PCP they can act, quite frankly, crazy (a complication of use technically called a "PCP-induced psychosis"; Doweiko, 2019). They do not attend to the environment and are belligerent and agitated. At very high doses, coma, seizures, and respiratory depression can result (Kuhn et al., 2019). Other complications include body dysmorphic effects, depersonalization, and seizures (Doweiko, 2019).

PCP users experience acute effects, including increases in heart rate and blood pressure, dizziness, nausea, and blurred vision. They have almost no awareness of pain or risk. Users also report panic-like symptoms, hallucinations, and aggression (Johnson, 2003). In terms of associated problems, PCP users are often in trouble with the legal system (Kuhn et al., 2008). They may become extremely aggressive and suicidal. Overdose can cause a host of physical problems in addition to coma and death.

Marijuana

Marijuana is the most frequently used illicit substance in the United States (Perkinson, 2012). It is a mixture of the India hemp plant's leaves, seeds, stems, and flower tops (Perkinson, 2012). The main psychoactive ingredient in marijuana is *tetrahydrocannabinol* (THC). Marijuana is typically smoked, but it also can be baked into foods. Individuals experience marijuana in a variety of ways depending on the potency of the THC, the individual's personality, and the surrounding environment. Marijuana takes a considerable amount of time to be eliminated from the body, affecting cognitive functioning for up to a day or more after initial ingestion (Kuhn et al., 2019).

Effects and Dangers

There are general effects of marijuana on mood, memory, coordination, cognitive ability, and sense perception (Perkinson, 2012). It is difficult to classify marijuana properly given its range of effects on humans. At low doses, the person might experience mild euphoria. At moderate doses, perceptual and time distortions may set in along with low motivation, and at high doses hallucinations and distortions of body image can occur. So, is it a stimulant, depressant, or hallucinogen? Well, technically marijuana does not fit neatly into any class of drugs; however, it is legally considered a Schedule I narcotic in the United States (Kuhn et al., 2019). Thus, according to the U.S. government, marijuana has high abuse potential and no accepted medicinal value. Clearly, marijuana is not in the same class as heroin (also a Schedule I substance), and the arguments about its medicinal potential are being waged in several states. According to the site DISA (n.d.), 18 states have "fully legalized" the use of marijuana, meaning it is used medicinally and is decriminalized in the state. Many states appear ambivalent when it comes to legalizing marijuana, allowing it in some contexts but not others. Only four states are listed where marijuana is "fully illegal." It will be interesting to see future developments in how the status of marijuana as a recreational and medicinal agent evolves across all 50 states.

Compared to other substances, the dangers associated with marijuana use are perceived to be relatively mild. However, that does not mean that THC is completely safe. THC does appear to interfere with short-term memory (Liska, 1997), but there is no conclusive evidence of disruptions in long-term memory. Smoking marijuana increases the risk of respiratory problems, including lung cancer (Doweiko, 2019). This is because marijuana smoke may contain from 50%–100% more carcinogens than cigarette smoke (Liska, 1997). In fact, three to four joints a day can do about as much damage as about 20 cigarettes (Liska, 1997). THC impairs judgment, making it a dangerous drug to consume while operating a motor vehicle (Kuhn et al., 2019). Marijuana and alcohol may potentiate each other, making the combination of these two drugs especially concerning. At high doses, marijuana can be toxic, but lethal overdose is virtually impossible (Kuhn et al., 2008).

There has been reported concern about marijuana's effects on adolescent users and their developing brains. Preliminary evidence suggests that marijuana may negatively impact learning and memory and, among chronic users during adolescence, produce negative effects on psychological functioning later in life (Kuhn et al., 2019).

For decades, conventional wisdom suggested that marijuana did not produce the addiction potential as other drugs. Indeed, despite documented withdrawal symptoms reported by those who chronically use marijuana, the intensity may not be at the level of other substances (Doweiko, 2019). However, tolerance, another hallmark of physical dependency, does develop to marijuana (Doweiko, 2019). As such, the presence of both withdrawal and tolerance places marijuana squarely among substance with addictive potential.

Inhalants

Inhalants refer to a group of substances made up of assorted chemical structures that, when inhaled, produce a state of intoxication (Perkinson, 2012). Examples include different types of glues, aerosols, gasoline, spray paints, fingernail polish, household cleaning products, hair sprays, nitrous oxide, and lighter fluid. The active ingredient in most of these products is hydrocarbons, which may depress areas in the brain; other chemical ingredients may stimulate heart function and have other effects (Kuhn et al., 2019; Liska, 1997). Inhalants do not fit neatly into any drug class; the chemicals that make up the range of inhalant substances have differing chemical structures, pharmacology, and toxic effects; the only commonality is that they are inhaled (Kuhn et al., 2019).

Effects and Dangers

When a person inhales something like spray paint, they are essentially replacing oxygen in the breath with hydrocarbon and other chemicals, leading to the altered state (Liska, 1997). Liska (1997) described these substances as brain depressants and deliriants; often young people sniff these substances with a desire to put themselves in a delirious altered state of awareness. The longer one inhales these substances, the more likely they are to experience restlessness, confusion, and disorientation. Extreme amounts may lead to coma or death (Liska, 1997). Fortunately, the risk of lethality from an overdose of inhaled nitrites is relatively small; however, chemicals in the solvent category (gases, glues, paints, etc.) can be extremely dangerous (Kuhn et al., 2019). Kuhn et al. drives this point home and takes the position that "these are the most toxic substances used for drug recreation, and [] believe they should never be used by anyone under any circumstances" (2019, p. 164).

Because most inhalants act as a depressant in the brain, combining inhalants with alcohol use will add the effect (potentiation; Liska, 1997). Other drugs that have a sedating effect, such as opiates, barbiturates, benzodiazepines, and cold medications, also can produce dangerous levels of impairment when combined with inhalants (Kuhn et al., 2019). Perhaps the most disturbing aspect of inhalant use is that it tends to be popular among our youth. Part of the reason for this popularity is that regular household chemicals are kept in garages and cabinets for easy access. According to the Center for Behavioral Health and Statistics Quality (2016), inhalant use was more common among adolescents between the ages of 12 and 17 compared to people in other age groups. However, that trend may be declining, at least among younger adolescents (Kuhn et al., 2019). Given the risk of inhalant toxicity, substance use clinicians need to be vigilant and concerned for clients who are engaging in this dangerous form of substance use.

Federal Drug Administration Schedule of Substances

In 1970, the U.S. Congress enacted the Controlled Substances Act, which categorized all drugs into five "schedules" based on (a) abuse potential and (b) medicinal value. This legislation was created due to the growing problem of drug use and addiction in American society. Drugs were now categorized to help with law enforcement, prevention, and treatment and rehabilitation. The schedule is arranged such that the lowest level (Schedule I) drugs are the most dangerous, have no medicinal value, and have a high abuse potential. Not surprisingly, most of these drugs are illegal. The five schedules and examples of drugs in each respective schedule are provided in Table 4.2.

TABLE 4.2   Federal Drug Administration Schedule of Drugs

Schedule	Definition	Examples
Schedule I	Substances with no accepted medical use; high abuse potential	LSD, heroin, marijuana
Schedule II	Substances with accepted medical use but with severe abuse potential	Morphine, cocaine, amphetamines, some barbiturates
Schedule III	Substances with accepted medical use but with moderate abuse potential	Opium, Tylenol w/codeine, most barbiturates, some stimulants
Schedule IV	Substances with accepted medical use but with mild abuse potential	Benzodiazepines
Schedule V	Substances with accepted medical use but with low abuse potential	Mixtures having small amounts of codeine or opium (e.g., Robitussin)

Summary

There are several classifications of drugs to assist in sorting out the myriad effects, dangers, and associated risks inherent when one overconsumes substances. The challenge for substance use clinicians is to utilize this knowledge in a way that empowers their clients. The substance use clinician must have a basic, yet sound, understanding of the effects and dangers of drugs and associated risks from taking drugs. Doing so enables the clinician to better understand their client's struggles, aids in treatment planning, and promotes best practices in the field.

References

Alcohol & Drug Services. (2016). *Heroin.* https://adsyes.org/heroin/

American Dental Association. (2022). *Methamphetamine.* https://www.ada.org/resources/research/science-and-research-institute/oral-health-topics/methamphetamine

Brooks, F., & McHenry, B. (2015). *A contemporary approach to substance abuse and addiction counseling: A counselor's guide to application and understanding* (2nd ed.). American Counseling Association.

Brown, S. (2010). Brain-based treatment strategies for children and adolescents. PESI Seminars.

Center for Behavioral Health Statistics and Quality. (2016). *Key substance use and mental health indicators in the United States: Results from the 2015 National Survey on Drug Use and Health* (HHS Publication No. SMA 16-4984, NSDUH Series H-51). Retrieved from http://www.samhsa.gov/data/

Centers for Disease Control and Prevention. (2011). Vital signs: Overdoses of prescription opioid pain relievers-United States, 1999–2008. *MMWR, 60,* 1487–1492.

Centers for Disease Control and Prevention. (2020). Wide-ranging online data for epidemiologic research (WONDER). http://wonder.cdc.gov

Centers for Disease Control and Prevention. (2021). Understanding the opioid overdose epidemic. National Center for Injury Prevention and Control. https://www.cdc.gov/opioids/basics/epidemic.html

DISA. (n.d.). Map of marijuana illegality by state. https://disa.com/map-of-marijuana-legality-by-state

Doweiko, H. E. (2009). *Concepts of chemical dependency* (7th ed.). Brooks/Cole.

Doweiko, H. E. (2019). *Concepts of chemical dependency* (10th ed.). Cengage.

Dudek, J., Eichler, B. A., Fernandes, J. C., & Fondario, A. (2014). Increases in heroin overdose deaths—28 states, 2010 to 2012. *MMWR, 63,* 849.

Erikson, S. (2001). The major substances of abuse and the body. In P. Stevens & R. L. Smith (Eds.), *Substance abuse counseling: Theory and practice* (2nd ed., pp. 33–76). Person.

Fisher, G. L., & Harrison, T. C. (2018). *Substance abuse: Information for school counselors, social workers, therapists, and counselors* (6th ed.) Pearson.

Gladden, R. M., Martinez, P., & Seth, P. (2016). Fentanyl law enforcement submissions and increases in synthetic opioid-involved overdose deaths—27 states, 2013–2014. *MMWR, 65,* 837–843.

Gladden, M., O'Donnell, J., Mattson, C., & Seth, P. (2019). Changes in opioid-involved overdose deaths by opioid type and presence of benzodiazepines, cocaine, and methamphetamine—25 states, July–December 2017 to January–June 2018. *MMWR, 68,* 737–744.

Hanson, R. (2011). *Buddha's brain: The practical neuroscience of happiness, love, and wisdom.* PESI Seminars.

Hoffman, J., & Froemke, S. (2007). *Why can't they just stop? Addiction: New knowledge, new treatments, new hope.* Rodale.

Hyman, M. (2009). *The ultramind solution.* Scribner.

Inciardi, J. A. (1992). The editor's introduction: The crack epidemic revisited. *Journal of Psychoactive Drugs, 24,* 305–306.

Johnson, S. L. (2003). *Therapists' guide to substance abuse intervention.* Academic Press.

Kuhn, C., Swartzwelder, S., & Wilson, W. (2008). *Buzzed: The straight facts about the most used and abused drugs from alcohol to ecstasy* (2nd ed.). Norton.

Kuhn, C., Swartzwelder, S., & Wilson, W. (2019). *Buzzed: The straight facts about the most used and abused drugs from alcohol to ecstasy* (3rd ed.). Norton.

Liska, K. (1997). *Drugs and the human body: With implications for society.* Prentice Hall.

Lopez, G. (2022a, February). Good morning. Overdoses are increasing at a troubling rate. *The New York Times: The Morning.* https://tinyurl.com/5axph979

Lopez, G. (2022b, May). Good morning. Drugs made in labs now cause most U.S. overdose deaths. *The New York Times: The Morning.* https://tinyurl.com/3e9drmjv

Meth Project. (n.d.). Deconstructing the damage. www.methproject.org/answers/

Miller, W. R., Forcehimes, A. A., & Zweben, A. (2019). *Treating addiction: A guide for professionals* (2nd ed.). Guilford.

National Institute on Drug Abuse. (2011). *Stimulants.* http://teens.drugabuse.gov/facts/facts_stim1.php

National Institute on Drug Abuse. (2021). *Heroin drugfacts.* https://nida.nih.gov/publications/drugfacts/heroin

National Institute on Drug Abuse. (n.d.). *Pain.* https://www.drugabuse.gov/drug-topics/pain

Newton, C., & Gomez, H. (2021, September 16). *Benzodiazepine abuse.* emedicinehealth. http://www.emedicinehealth.com/benzodiazepine_abuse/article_em.htm

O'Kane, C. J., Tutt, D. C., & Bauer, L. A. (2002). Cannabis and driving: A new perspective. *Emergency Medicine, 14,* 296–303.

Perkinson, R. R. (2012). *Chemical dependency counseling: A practical guide* (4th ed.). SAGE.

Rudd, R. A., Paulozzi, L. J., Bauer, M. J., Burleson, R. W., Carlson, R. E., Dao, D., Davis, J. W., Dudek, J., Eichler, B. A., Fernandes, J. C., & Fondario, A. (2014). Increases in heroin overdose deaths—28 states, 2010 to 2012. *MMWR, 63*(39), p. 849.

Schep, L. J., Slaughter, R. J., & Beasley, D.M. (2010). The clinical toxicology of metamfetamine. *Clinical Toxicology, 48,* 675–694.

Smith, R. L. (2013). The major substances of abuse and the body. In R. L. Smith & P. Stevens (Eds.), *Substance abuse counseling: Theory and practice* (5th ed., pp. 51–92). Pearson.

CHAPTER 5

Assessment, Diagnosis, and Treatment Planning

When I was in graduate school, I recall my Advanced Clinical Assessment professor stating throughout the semester, "You can never go wrong with a good, thorough assessment." I have found this wisdom to be true in my own clinical work, especially related to the evaluation, assessment, and diagnosis of problems related to the ingestion of drugs. A proper and thorough assessment helps the clinician determine the degree of substance use and associated features, the extent of substance use, how much it is interfering with the client's life, and the extent of consequences related to use. A thorough evaluation and assessment also provides insight into what historical, social, cultural, familial, or contextual factors play a role in problematic use.

As a rule, inquiry into substance use patterns should be made by every mental health practitioner with every client they counsel, even if the presenting problem is something other than problematic substance use. Indeed, most clinicians who conduct intake interviews or diagnostic assessments include some sort of questioning about the client's substance use history. Unfortunately, these inquiries are often brief, without sufficient follow-up, leading some clinicians to gloss over or miss the extent of problematic substance use or develop treatment plans that do not sufficiently address substance use issues. Clinicians may discover late in the treatment process that substance use is a significant problem and may be at the root of the client's psychological struggles.

In this chapter, I focus on the key elements related to the proper evaluation of clients struggling with substance use, including screening, assessment, and diagnosis. My intent is to provide practical screening and assessment guidelines for clinicians who work in general mental health agencies as well as those who specialize in treatment of substance use. I then review the DSM-5 criteria for substance use disorders and make the connection between a substance use assessment and diagnosis. Finally, I explore treatment planning considerations for substance use disorders, with an emphasis on Seligman's DO A CLIENT MAP model (Reichenberg & Seligman, 2016). Following this chapter, the reader should have a clear picture of the evaluative process that takes place when clients enter counseling struggling with substance use issues.

Evaluation and Diagnosis of Substance Use Disorders

Today's managed care system mandates that counseling and therapy be effective, efficient, and cost contained. To this end, the evaluative and diagnostic process plays a critical role in the rehabilitation of those struggling with substance use problems. Evaluation and assessment provide the undergirding of substance use treatment, not only as a place to begin treatment but also as an ongoing process throughout recovery. In addition, evaluation is an effective way to help clinicians determine if one needs professional help because their substance use has gotten out of control (Juhnke, 2002).

A high-quality, thorough evaluation procedure not only aids in case conceptualization and treatment, but also meets the ever-increasing demands of managed care. Consistent with good counseling practice, substance use evaluation should be a part of every mental health evaluation. The evaluation process is useful only to the extent that it is value added in professional practice (Miller et al., 2019). I agree with Miller et al. (2019) in that it is a mistake to conceptualize evaluation as what clinicians do at the start of treatment before the "real" counseling begins. It is rarely that clear-cut. Rather, evaluation is an *ongoing* process, where the clinician is consistently vigilant of what they need to know *right now* to better inform practice. In general, a complete evaluation of the client encompasses three main components: screening, assessment, and diagnosis (Doweiko, 2019).

Screening for Substance Use Problems

Screening refers to methods and procedures, often of a brief nature, designed to rule out the possibility of substance use problems. Screening is not the same thing as providing a diagnosis (determining if one meets criteria as established in a diagnostic manual) or assessment (a more thorough analysis of substance use problems, often as a follow-up to an indication of possible substance use issues via screening). Screening procedures are designed to "cast a wide net" or detect the possible presence of a substance use issue and the need for further care (Miller et al., 2019). In general, screening methods can be informal and observational, or more formal with the use of brief screening instruments.

Red Flags

Every client who enters counseling is screened by the clinician to provide a baseline and determine if additional assessment is warranted. Screening typically occurs via a diagnostic or intake interview; if the client reports problems in a specific area, the clinician has the option to focus in by asking more specific questions related to the substance problem. Screening also occurs through observation of the client's immediate signs and symptoms as well as their behavior outside of the counseling setting, including past history. Part of screening is addressing and exploring the "red flags" that provide clues as to what role, if any, alcohol or drug use plays in the client's life. These red flags become even more important when the client is not forthcoming about their substance use at the beginning of counseling.

In general, observational red flags fall into three categories: physiological, psychological, and behavioral.

Physiological

A brief inquiry into typical physiological issues or general medical conditions can sometimes point to the extent of possible substance use problems. Liver problems, hypertension, ulcers, tremors, or injection track marks are indications of severe use. For clients who use substances problematically and yet are not forthcoming with this information, these and other physiological symptoms can tip off the clinician to the possibility of problematic substance use and a need for further exploration.

An additional area of exploration, although not directly about current physiological symptoms, is the client's potential genetic predisposition. Inquiry about family history of substance use provides additional insights to help clarify the assessment and diagnostic picture. For example, a client who suggests that he has a drink "now and then," but insists his drinking is not a problem, may report that addiction runs in his family and that his mother and father drank alcohol heavily. In this case, the possible genetic link to alcohol use would warrant further and more targeted substance use assessment, especially if the client reports some negative consequences because of his drinking.

Psychological

Many clients report symptoms of depression, anxiety, or other emotional problems and use substances to self-medicate or cope. Indeed, psychological symptoms, such as depression and anxiety, often are associated with problematic substance use. Also associated with use are negative or difficult emotions such as guilt, shame, anger, or boredom (Thombs & Osborn, 2019). At minimum, practitioners should check in with clients who report negative emotions related to their substance use history, current behavior, and typical methods of coping.

Behavioral

There are many behavioral signs of substance use disorders, some of which are obvious (e.g., evidence of intoxication), and some of which are indirectly related (e.g., work problems). Perhaps the most important area of inquiry is if there has been any past treatment for substance-related problems. In my experience, clients who affirm previous attempts at treatment to address substance-related problems often currently struggle with those same problems. Additional behavioral problems often associated with substance use include legal issues, poor work history, financial problems, extreme talkativeness, poor judgment, erratic behavior, frequent falls, increase in risk taking, and frequent hospitalizations. From a screening standpoint, one or more of these behavioral issues should alert the clinician to the possibility of significant substance use.

Of course, just because clients report work-related issues, or that they are struggling with depression, does not mean there is a definite substance use issue operating behind the scenes. The red flags simply serve as data that the clinician can use in the overall evaluation process.

Numerous red flags, however, should alert the clinician that a substance use problem is possible, and further inquiry warranted.

Screening Instruments and Tools

There are many screening tools available, many of which are in the public domain (and thus free to the public) and accessed on the internet. Which screening tool to use can depend on several factors, including demonstrated validity and reliability, reading level, clinician familiarity, time commitment, and clinical utility/validity (i.e., will the screening device provide information that I don't already know?).

A common screening tool that is used for alcohol problems is the CAGE questionnaire (Ewing, 1984). The CAGE is a series of four questions:

1. Have you ever felt that you needed to Cut down on your drinking?
2. Have you ever been Annoyed by others who have commented that you drink too much?
3. Have you ever felt bad or Guilty about your drinking?
4. Have you ever had a drink first thing in the morning to steady your nerves and get rid of a hangover (Eye-opener)?

A yes response to any one of these questions indicates a need for further alcohol use assessment. A yes to two or more items suggests the client is alcohol dependent. Unfortunately, the CAGE, due to its obvious content, lends itself to deceptive responding (Fisher & Harrison, 2018) and would consider someone who is not currently using, but with a history of alcohol use, as a problematic drinker (i.e., it does not separate history from current functioning; Cooney et al., 2005, as cited in Doweiko, 2019). In addition, the CAGE may perform better among African American men but not as well among women and Hispanic men (Cherpitel, 1999). Brown et al. (1998) modified the CAGE by creating the CAGE-AID and adding drug use in addition to alcohol use within the four original CAGE questions (e.g., Have you ever felt that you needed to cut down on your drinking *or drug use*?).

Another useful screening device is the Substance Abuse Subtle Screening Inventory (SASSI; Miller, 1985), currently in its fourth edition, and its version for adolescents, the SASSI-A3. The SASSI instruments have become widely accepted as screening and assessment tools for substance use problems. The SASSI is designed to gauge both quantity and frequency of alcohol and other drug use, as well as subtler characteristics that often are associated with problematic substance use. The overall goal of the measure is determining the probability of someone having a substance use disorder. The SASSI has built-in measures to determine the degree of defensiveness clients have about reporting the extent of their substance use. It generally takes about 10 minutes to complete.

Other good screening tools include the Drug Abuse Screening Inventory (DAST; Skinner, 1982), the Michigan Alcoholism Screening Test (MAST; Selzer, 1971), and the Alcohol Use Disorders Identification Test (AUDIT; Barbor et al., 1992). There is a modified version of the AUDIT called the AUDIT-ID in which "other drugs" is added to each question, thus screening for both alcohol and drug use (Campbell et al., 2003, as cited in Miller et al., 2019). Each of these instruments asks several questions about alcohol and/or drug use and usually takes less than 10 minutes to complete.

The screening process does not need to include formal instruments to be effective. For example, Brown et al. (1997) formulated a straightforward, two-question process to detect potential problems related to substance use: (a) "In the last year, have you ever drunk or used drugs more than you meant to?" and (b) "Have you felt you wanted or needed to cut down on your drinking or drug use in the last year?" According to Brown et al., a yes to one of these items discriminated between those who have a substance use disorder (SUD) and those who do not with 81% sensitivity (i.e., proportion of those with SUDs who are correctly identified as such) and specificity (i.e., proportion of those without an SUD who are correctly identified). The NIAAA (2007) recommends a single question for alcohol-related problems: For men: "How many times in the past year have you had five or more drinks in a day?" For women: "How many times in the past year have you had four or more drinks in a day?" A standard drink generally refers to one 12-oz bottle or can of beer, one 4-oz glass of wine, one 12-oz bottle or can of wine cooler, or one 1-oz "shot" of liquor, either straight or in a mixed drink. The NIAAA (2007) guidelines suggest that if clients indicate that they have engaged in this pattern of drinking one or more times within the past year, further assessment is warranted.

Biological Screens

An effective adjunct to self-report screening instruments is biological lab tests designed to detect the presence of substances within one's physiology. Typically, biological drug screens occur by sampling via urinalysis or hair analysis. These tests may be most useful to corroborate self-report data, especially when there is high suspicion that one is not being honest about their substance use (Miller et al., 2019). Some agencies or substance use programs require random screens, particularly when medication is used as part of the substance use treatment. In my previous experience as a substance use clinician, clients who were enrolled in the Suboxone (a medication used to treat opiate addiction) program were randomly tested for the presence of other substances. The medical director of the program established a "three strikes and you're out" policy related to positive drug screens. Clinicians, however, may not have the ability to screen for recent drug use within their agency. Thus, creating a referral list of medical specialists who are trained to perform biologically based substance use screening tests can be quite handy.

It is important to know that biologically based screens are not a substitute for self-report data (Miller et al., 2011). Biological screening tests tend to have low sensitivity (thus producing a high false positive rate) and are impacted by one's age, gender, smoking status, metabolism, how the drug was taken, how long ago the drug was ingested, and the drug's potency (Miller et al., 2011). They are best used as one piece of the screening process and in conjunction with self-report data. If possible, the clinician should tap into all their available resources in the screening process: well-established screening instruments, biological measures, observational data (i.e., red flags), intake interviews, and collateral reports.

Assessment

If a client shows signs of problematic use through a screening process, a more through inquiry is warranted via assessment. Assessment for substance use problems is probably most effectively accomplished through an unstructured clinical interview (Doweiko, 2019). From the clinical interview, the counselor can make a formal diagnosis and develop the treatment plan. In some cases, clinicians may wish to infuse screening procedures, such as the CAGE questions, as part of the clinical interview. Thus, screening and assessment sometimes happen concurrently as the clinician sorts through the myriad of client data.

A thorough clinical interview addresses numerous components of the client's life, some directly related to substance use and others indirectly. Through open-ended and closed questions, the counselor seeks to understand: (a) What does the substance mean to the individual? (b) What do they get out of it (what is the benefit)? and (c) Does current use create any negative consequences or problems? The key components of a clinical interview are structured as follows:

- **Referral source.** It is important to know who is referring the client for counseling services and what, if any, expectations they hold. A referral from a physician may require access to medical notes or a phone call to discuss the client case and how counseling fits with medical management of the client's substance use problem. A self-referral prompts the clinician to inquire what led the client to seek help. Knowing the referral source and reasons for the referral provides the clinician with additional insights to help the client.

- **History of substance use.** In this section of the clinical interview, the clinician addresses previous use of substances, usually beginning with alcohol and preceding down a list of additional drugs (marijuana, cocaine, heroin, etc.). In many cases, the client will report struggling with only one or two drugs of choice, with possible experimentation with other substances. For example, I recently counseled a 44-year-old client whose drugs of choice were opiates (pain medication) and alcohol. He also reported marijuana use in high school but mentioned this as an "experimentation phase" in his life. This did not need additional clinical focus. Throughout the rest of the interview, our attention was centered on opiates and alcohol use.

  Another important element is the age of onset for the current substance of choice. Research has indicated that, at least for alcohol, the earlier the onset of use, the greater the relationship to heavy use in adulthood (Lewis & Watts, 2004). Knowing how early one started using a substance can give clues as to how significant the use might be currently.

  Any history of substance use should include questions about quantity of use, frequency of use, method of use, the last time the client used, and the effects of substance use on symptomology and functioning. This information provides the clinician with an overview of the extent of substance use and if the client has tried to stop before but failed.

- **Prior treatment history.** This includes information on previous medical care for substance use problems, previous counseling, past or present 12-step group attendance and attitude toward these adjunct services, how long abstinence was maintained in the past (or, if currently abstinent, how long the current period has been), and factors contributing to relapses. Prior treatment information helps illuminate what has been tried in the past, what was successful, what did not work as well, and reasons for unsuccessful attempts at quitting. I often ask my clients what they think has worked for them in how they approached recovery, whether using their own self-help activities, or formal medical and/or counseling interventions. I also ask what aspects of previous care were not a fit for them in order to avoid as much as possible previous roadblocks to recovery.

- **Current life functioning.** Although not directly related to substance use, questions about problems in current living often reflect underlying substance use issues. Sometimes a simple question or two can suffice: How are things going now? Or, tell me about your life and what you would like different if anything.

- **Family history of substance use.** Although genetics do not tell the whole story when it comes to substance use disorders, they do play significant role in combination with environmental factors (Thombs & Osborn, 2019). Confirming that family members have struggled with substance use suggests the client may have a similar tendency and can provide greater confidence in formulating a diagnostic and treatment approach.

- **Religious or spiritual beliefs.** Again, this is not directly related to substance use; however, experts have long noted that many with substance use problems struggle with a spiritual crisis or in some ways have lost their grounding in life. I have found that assessment of spiritual and existential issues usually brings up important discussions about meaning and purpose and how substance use may serve as a cover for existential crises.

- **General personal history.** This component includes areas such as work history, legal history, relationship history, and emotional functioning. Some of these elements may come about in previous components of the interview, so the counselor may simply need to cover what has not been discussed up to this point. Work and legal history can provide a powerful lens to help understand the extent and intensity of one's substance use. For example, a client who has repeatedly missed work, been fired several times, and who has repeated DUIs has a serious problem with alcohol, and treatment should commence accordingly. On the other hand, a client who has maintained a steady job for 25 years and has had no legal trouble but nonetheless wants to cut down on night-time drinking would have a much different treatment plan.

As Juhnke (2002) noted, the clinical interview humanizes the assessment process. In doing so, it allows a basic level of rapport, which may allow clients to open up and share more information than they would responding to other, more formal assessment formats. In addition, the counselor can be more intentional in looking for nonverbal information, such as obvious discomfort with a question, which can provide "grist for the therapeutic mill."

Dimensions of Substance Addiction

Miller et al. (2019) outlined seven dimensions of substance addiction that are interconnected but also operate independently. Each dimension is thought to be on a continuum from less severe/low risk to more severe/high risk. Knowledge of where a client falls on each continuum can provide useful clinical information and strengthen the assessment process. The seven dimensions are as follows:

- **Use.** Substance use is characterized by type of drugs used, quantity, frequency, and pattern of use (Miller et al., 2019). Quantity refers to how much one drinks or uses on a "typical occasion," frequency refers to how often one drinks or uses on a typical occasion, and pattern addresses the style of using (from periodic to steady).

- **Consequences.** Clients often do not come to counseling because they are drinking and/or using, but rather because their using behavior has gotten them into trouble. Exploring the consequences of substance use can lead to enhanced motivation and is a key part of motivational interviewing (Chapter 6). The consequences of substance use range from none to many within a typical day.

- **Physical adaptation.** Another dimension of addiction is the presence or absence of physical dependence. The presence of tolerance and/or withdrawal is usually the hallmark of physical dependence.

- **Behavioral dependence.** Instead of being physically dependent on a substance, clients may be psychologically dependent in which they develop a mental need for the drug to get through the day or cope with stress. They believe they cannot do this without the substance. Often, but not always, addiction entails both physical adaptation and psychological dependence.

- **Cognitive impairment.** The use of drugs alters brain chemistry. Even relatively brief stints with substance use can have noticeable negative cognitive effects. With long-term use of some chemicals, such as alcohol, permanent damage to memory, motor skills, and attention can result.

- **Medical harm.** Substance use also impacts physical health. We know today that smoking marijuana is especially dangerous due to high levels of carcinogens that enter the bloodstream. Cocaine and other stimulant drugs can have deleterious effects on cardiovascular functioning. Excessive, long-term alcohol use can damage almost every organ system in the body.

- **Motivation for change.** Lack of client motivation can make treatment planning and movement toward goals a difficult process. Knowing how important making a change in substance use is to the client can help clinicians gauge what strategies might be most helpful. There are many techniques that can assist in enhancing motivation to change (see Chapter 6).

Clinicians can use the seven dimensions of addiction as a starting point when assessing their clients. This can be useful in determining the extent or severity of one's substance use. For example, a client might self-report moderate use but be extremely high on consequences, behavioral dependence, and medical harm. Subsequent treatment could focus on these "higher" dimensions with an eye on reducing or eliminating use. Assessing the dimensions could be accomplished as part of a clinical interview. A more structured method includes drawing seven columns on a piece of paper, ranging from low to high, representing each dimension. The clinician could place an "X" that best fits the client's situation on each dimension (column). Once completed, the clinician has a snapshot of the client's substance use pattern, which can inform placement and treatment planning decisions. For more formal methods of assessment, there are several instruments (discussed next) that correspond with each of these seven dimensions. An example of the seven columns method is provided in Figure 5.1.

Heavy use	Many consequences	Physically adapted	Highly behaviorally dependent	Severely cognitively impaired	Severe medical issues	No motivation to change
	X					
X						
		X				
			X			
				X	X	X
Nonuse	No consequences	No physical adaptation	No behavioral dependence	No cognitive impairment	No medical harm from use	Highly motivated to change
Use	**Consequences**	**Physical Adaptation**	**Behavioral Dependence**	**Cognitive Impairment**	**Medical Harm**	**Motivation For Change**

Michael has indicated relatively heavy use and noticeable negative consequences as part of his use. Some physical adaptation is evident. There appears to be lower concerns for cognitive impairment or medical harm, but with continued use these may increase. The encouraging picture for Michael is that motivation for change is relatively high. This exercise could be used at additional points in the treatment/recovery process to gauge progress in counseling.

FIGURE 5.1   Example of the "Seven Columns" exercise used with Michael to assess the seven dimensions of substance use (based on Miller et al., 2019).

Assessment Instruments

There are a bevy of substance use assessment instruments the clinician can use to assist in determining the extent of problematic substance use. Objective assessments can add additional insights, as clients often do not reveal all aspects about themselves, either intentionally or unintentionally, throughout an interview. In addition to providing an indication of the extent of use (mild, moderate, or severe), objective assessments allow clinicians (and clients) to uncover or identify aspects about one's substance use that may be out of awareness. For example, I administered an MMPI-2 to a client who struggled with chronic marijuana use. The MMPI-2 is not an assessment specific to substance use, but it does include several scales that assess potential use as well as characteristics that might underlie use. When discussing feedback of his results, he was surprised to learn about his elevation on the Over-Controlled Hostility subscale and appeared to harness a lot of anger that manifested as physical symptoms. The ensuing discussion led to the insight that he used marijuana primarily to help him mellow out and cope with deep-seated angry feelings. This awareness provided greater direction in our counseling.

To review all substance use assessment instruments in depth is beyond the scope of this chapter. However, Table 5.1 provides a quick overview of the more common substance use screening and assessment instruments. Clinicians are encouraged to research objective measurements to determine psychometric integrity and usefulness for the populations they serve. Instruments have been designed for specific drugs and drug classes (e.g., cocaine) as well as for general substance use. An excellent resource for clinicians and researchers is the *Substance Use Screening and Assessment Instruments Database*, created by the Alcohol and Drug Abuse Institute (ADAI) Library (2020) at the University of Washington (http://lib.adai.washington.edu/instruments/). The database logs instruments in the public domain as well as those in which the author(s) hold a copyright. It also includes a "recommended" search function that provides information on the most well-established substance use assessment instruments to date. Search results lead to the authors of the instrument, description, psychometrics, related articles, links, and how to find the instrument, among other features.

TABLE 5.1   A Brief Review of Key Substance Use Assessment Instruments

Instrument/Type/Location	Description
Michigan Alcoholism Screening Test (MAST; Selzer, 1971) Type: Screening https://www.outcometracker.org/library/MAST.pdf	• 25-item, yes/no questionnaire • Most researched alcoholism instrument • Used as screening test only • Best at detection of those with severe alcohol problems • Addresses only alcoholism • Doesn't identify individual patterns of drinking • Can be used with virtually any population • Free and open to public

(continued)

TABLE 5.1   A Brief Review of Key Substance Use Assessment Instruments (*Continued*)

Instrument/Type/Location	Description
Substance Abuse Subtle Screening Inventory (SASSI; Miller, 1985) Type: Screening www.sassi.com/	• Alternative screening device to other measures in which items are easy to fake • Brief, easy to administer—less than 15 minutes to take • Adolescent version available • Robust validity/reliability
CAGE Questionnaire (Ewing, 1984) Description: Screening https://americanaddictioncenters.org/alcoholism-treatment/cage-questionnaire-assessment	• Four simple yes/no questions • Simple screening measure for alcohol abuse and dependence • Effectively discriminates those who have an alcohol use disorder from those who do not at or above 90% • Administered verbally
The Drug Abuse Screening Test (DAST-20; Skinner, 1982) Type: Screening https://www.mandarincounseling.com/sites/default/files/dast20.pdf	• 20-item self-report inventory • Assesses drug behavior, not including alcohol • Designed for adult drug users, male or female • Effective at differentiating several categories of drug users
The Alcohol Use Disorders Identification Test (AUDIT; Barbor et al., 1992) Type: Screening https://auditscreen.org/check-your-drinking/	• Quick, easy administration • Ten-item screening questionnaire • Decision process leads to brief interventions or referral for more serious problems • Appropriate across a number of populations, including college students, criminals, Armed Forces personnel, and psychiatric patients
The Alcohol Use Inventory (AUI; Horn et al., 1986) Type: Full Assessment http://tinyurl.com/74z8l43	• Two hundred–plus multiple-choice item instrument • Based on a multisyndrome model, where multiple manifestations of alcohol are assessed • Helps to provide a more thorough diagnostic picture • Easy to administer and score
The Addiction Severity Index (ASI; McLellan et al., 1980) Type: Semi-structured Interview https://tinyurl.com/yc8mfnfh	• Comprehensive; administered as a structured interview • Easy-to-follow manual • Assesses numerous areas of client's life including substance use, legal issues, relationships, and psychiatric problems • Utility with dual-diagnosis populations • Aids in treatment planning

Substance Use Screening and Assessment Protocol: An Example

The following are two proposed assessment protocols for mental health and substance use clinicians. These protocols are based on my clinical experiences and represent how I approach substance use screening and assessment; some clinicians may proceed with other protocols, use different instruments, or simply take a different approach. There is no one "right" protocol. Over my years of training, experience, and research, I have found the following sequences to be helpful in clarifying the diagnostic and treatment planning picture for my clients. I outline a protocol for alcohol and a protocol for other drugs. Clients who use both alcohol and other drugs could be assessed with a combination of protocols.

Alcohol

For alcohol, I first gather information about drinking from a *general diagnostic interview*. The diagnostic interview follows the format as outlined previously and is a good place to start. If it is clear (or even suspected) during the interview that the client has an alcohol problem, I then administer the CAGE and/or AUDIT assessments (see description in Table 5.1). The CAGE is a four-question assessment that can be asked after the diagnostic interview or infused as part of it. The AUDIT is a brief, alcohol-based questionnaire that is easy to administer and score. Like the CAGE, it can help identify those at risk for alcohol dependence.

If the client shows signs of an alcohol use disorder (through the CAGE and AUDIT), I usually administer the more extensive Alcohol Use Inventory (AUI; Horn et al., 1986). AUI results allow clinicians to compare the client's drinking behaviors to a normative sample of inpatient clients who struggle with severe alcohol use disorders. The AUI provides a strong basis for client feedback on drinking behavior, and thus lends itself nicely to techniques such as motivational interviewing. The AUI provides information that can be helpful for treatment planning purposes, such as clarifying the benefits, styles, and consequences of drinking and concerns/acknowledgments that the client holds related to drinking.

Optional assessments for alcohol use problems include the Substance Abuse Subtle Screening Inventory-4 (SASSI-4) and the Addiction Severity Index (ASI). According to the SASSI-4 website (www.sassi.com), the SASSI-4 (and the SASSI-A3 for adolescents) indicates whether a client has a high or low probability of having a substance use disorder. It is relatively brief, taking about 15 minutes to complete and score. Although the SASSI instruments cannot confirm a diagnosis of substance use disorder, they do provide additional support to the clinician for diagnostic purposes. The ASI is a comprehensive assessment tool that is administered as a structured interview. It assesses numerous areas of client's life, including alcohol and drug use, legal issues, relationships, and psychiatric problems and has utility in identifying dual diagnoses.

This screening and assessment protocol is rarely accomplished in one 50-minute session, especially if multiple instruments are used. I am upfront with my clients from the start that the assessment process may take up to two to three 50-minute sessions (or one extended session), depending on the presenting issues and what needs clarification. I also may not administer an assessment at the beginning of counseling but suggest it as a possibility as time passes and the client's concerns warrant further investigation. For example, I recently counseled a client who presented with a severe alcohol use disorder and admitted that he had a serious problem. In my opinion, assessment instruments were not going to give us any information that wasn't already obvious. However, as we began exploring his alcohol use, the client had difficulty articulating what alcohol did for him, what benefits he derived from it, and his own style or pattern of use. After several sessions, I introduced the AUI and, to his (and my) surprise, it revealed many aspects about his drinking that guided the treatment direction and approach. Thus, the usual timing for assessment is at the start of counseling; however, circumstances may emerge in which clinicians may either not administer an assessment or decide to introduce it later in the therapy process. Keep in mind that evaluation is an ongoing process.

Other Drug Use

As with the assessment protocol for alcohol use, I begin with a general diagnostic interview for clients who present with other drug use (or there is a suspicion that drug use is a part of the clinical picture). If the client indicates moderate to severe substance use, I typically follow this up by administering the DAST and the SASSI-4. If these results confirm a high risk for substance use disorder, I typically administer the ASI to help clarify the diagnostic picture. Other substance specific instruments may be used as well.

Optional: Personality Inventories

For both alcohol and other drug use, I may consider optional personality inventories such as the Minnesota Mulitphasic Personality Inventory–2 (MMPI-2; Butcher et al., 2006) or the Millon Clinical Multiaxial Inventory–4 (MCMI-IV) (Millon et al., 2009). The MMPI-2 has three supplemental scales: the MacAndrews Alcoholism Scale (MAC-R), the Addiction Potential Scale (APS), and the Addiction Acknowledgment Scale (AAS). Aside from the MAC-R, these scales do not measure direct substance use but assess for characteristics often associated with substance use. In addition to these specific scales, the MMPI-2 provides a wealth of information related to personality style and underlying patterns of interacting with self, others, and the world that may undergird substance use and addiction. The MCMI-IV includes two "clinical syndrome" scales related to substance use: Alcohol Use (Scale B) and Drug Use (Scale T; Groth-Marnat & Wright, 2016). The Alcohol Use scale contains traits and behaviors suggestive of drinking problems related to alcohol. A high elevation on this scale suggests a history of severe drinking, attempts to curb the problem, and considerable disruption at home and work (Groth-Marnat & Wright, 2016). An elevation on the Drug Use scale indicates a history of drug use or addiction, difficulty restraining oneself, and an inability to avoid personal consequences of drug use (Groth-Marnat & Wright, 2016).

The Alcohol Use and Drug Use scales do not assess quantity and frequency of use but are more related to detecting problems related to use. Thus, they are excellent scales to assess consequence of use, and elevations on either one or both suggest a substance use disorder. It is important to note that these scales are considered clinical syndromes and are considered manifestations of "clinical personality patterns" or "severe personality pathology." As with the MMPI, the MCMI can be useful in detecting underlying personality patterns that most likely contribute to one's alcohol or drug use.

The decision to use personality inventories depends on many factors, including the severity of the client's presenting concerns, if administering the assessment will enhance clinical validity (i.e., will this assessment be value added and shed light on the substance use problem, or simply provide information that is already known?), cultural considerations, time, and expense. The clinician must balance usefulness of the test for diagnostic and treatment planning purposes with the cost and time to administer, score, interpret, and provide feedback. In my experience, personality inventories provide a bevy of information regarding underlying client motives, strengths, and personality patterns that provided direction for counseling. However, not all clients need such extensive testing, and forcing them to take lengthy and costly assessments without rationale is unethical.

Assessment Feedback

A critical aspect of any assessment procedure is providing informative and accurate feedback to clients. Some clients have a good idea what an assessment will show; however, many maintain defenses about their substance use and initially become resistant to assessment and treatment. Clinician style and approach to providing feedback becomes vital to how it is received. Assessment results that are utilized to define the client, conclusions that are not supported by the evidence, and feedback styles that are overly directive or argumentative are much more likely to engender client resistance. Rollnick et al. (1999) provided a model of feedback designed to minimize client resistance and open dialogue about what the assessment shows. First, clinicians *elicit* from the client what they want to know, or what they already know, about the problem. Second, clinicians *provide* information and feedback on a portion of the assessment results. Finally, clinicians *elicit* from clients their thoughts and feelings about what was just shared. This process of "elicit-provide-elicit" continues until the client receives all the feedback. The strategy avoids telling clients what they already know, respects their knowledge of their own circumstances, and allows clients to reflect on what was offered as feedback (Rosengren, 2008). Following is an example of how a clinician might use "elicit-provide-elicit" with a client, Ben, who completed the Alcohol Use Inventory.

> **CLINICIAN:** Hello, Ben. Good to see you again. As you know, last week you took the AUI, and I have scored it and taken a look at the results. Before we get to that, though, I was wondering what it is that you would like to know about the assessment or results? (*elicit*)

> **BEN:** Well, I don't really see the point in me taking this test. I mean, as I said I don't think I have a serious problem with drinking. Everyone else thinks I do. But I'll comply. Just give it to me, doc. (*Client is quite resistant about assessments and denies having a serious problem, which the AUI clearly shows. He also has no specific agenda for what he wants to know, suggesting for the clinician to start from the beginning.*)

CLINICIAN: This has been a struggle for you, first having to take the inventory and now having to come in and discuss the results. You're questioning how this is even relevant. (*Client nods in agreement.*) How about I start from the beginning, and we can go from there? (*Complex reflection designed to validate how the client feels followed by question*)

BEN: Okay. Sure.

CLINICIAN: Great. As a point of information, your scores are compared to individuals who are receiving treatment for alcoholism in an inpatient facility; these are people who struggle with serious alcohol-related problems. Taking a look at the first part of the AUI, the results suggest that you are drinking at about the same level as 80% of individuals who are in inpatient care for alcoholism treatment. (*provide*)

CLINICIAN: What thoughts come to mind as you think about that information? (*elicit*)

BEN: Eighty percent?? Wow, that seems high. Are you sure that is correct? I mean, I know I drink but I never thought it was at the level of an alcoholic.

CLINICIAN: This is confusing for you, and it is hard to make sense of. You are wondering if the test if even valid. (*Reflection designed to validate client's thoughts*)

BEN: Yeah, I mean. I guess it is what it is. I am not sure what to make of it, but it has me a bit worried.

CLINICIAN: On the one hand it doesn't make sense, and on the other it's got you thinking a bit. Okay, maybe we can hold that for the moment; How about we move on to the next part, and as we do maybe some things will become clearer. (*Setting up to provide more information*)

As one can observe, the elicit-provide-elicit model allows space for the clinician to use reflection and validate client responses and concerns. The key is to provide information in chunks, separated by checking in with what the client makes of the feedback and information rather than "slamming" them with the results all at one time.

According to Miller and Rollnick (2002), appropriate feedback can be a potent force in motivating change. As an analogy, consider someone who receives medical feedback that their cholesterol is too high. Just this information alone may set in motion a series of behavioral changes in diet and exercise to address the issue. Similarly, if a client learns that they drink more than 80% of those who are in inpatient alcoholism treatment, they may begin thinking more seriously about their drinking and be open to the possibility of change (more on motivational interviewing in Chapter 6).

Substance-Related Diagnoses

The DSM-5 text revision (TR; APA, 2022) provides a compendium of disorders related to substance use. The relevant chapter in the DSM is titled "Substance-Related and Addictive Disorders" and is an excellent resource for clinicians during the assessment and diagnostic process. The Substance-Related and Addictive Disorders chapter is divided into three main categories: substance use disorders (SUDs), which includes substance use problems across several drug classes; substance-induced disorders (SIDs), which includes substance intoxication and withdrawal; and the nonsubstance-related disorder of problem gambling. In general, the substance-related sections provide (a) general descriptions of the substance use and substance-induced disorders applied to all classes of drugs and (b) specific criteria sets of SUDs and SIDs unique to each substance class. Overall, the DSM lists 10 classes of drugs (with an 11th class listed as "other"; APA, 2022).

To record a formal diagnosis, the clinician is asked to write down all relevant diagnoses, in order of clinical importance. Indeed, clients with a substance use diagnosis often have concomitant mental health concerns, such depression or anxiety. All relevant diagnoses should be listed. Whether a substance use disorder or mental health disorder is listed first depends on clinician judgment of the most pressing concern for counseling. Some clients may problematically use multiple substances, in which case each unique substance use disorder would need to be recorded.

Substance Use Disorders

No matter the setting in which they work, clinicians will need to be familiar with criteria for SUDs. In general, SUDs involve the continued use of a substance despite negative consequences. Other indicators include a persistent pattern of substance use, failed attempts at stopping or cutting down, persistently seeking out of the drug, craving, and physiological manifestations of use, such as tolerance and withdrawal. To meet criteria for a SUD, the client must meet only 2 out of 11 criteria within the previous 12 months (APA, 2022). Table 5.2 provides a list of generic criteria for SUDs.

TABLE 5.2 DSM-5-TR Generic Diagnostic Criteria (Adapted) for SUDs*

A maladaptive pattern of substance use leading to clinically significant impairment or distress, as manifested by two (or more) of the following, within a 12-month period:
1. Recurrent substance use resulting in a failure to fulfill major role obligations at work, school, or home (repeated absences, poor work performance, suspensions, or expulsions).
2. Recurrent substance use in situations in which it is physically hazardous (e.g., driving).
3. Continued substance use despite having persistent or recurrent social or interpersonal problems caused or exacerbated by the effects of the substance (arguments, physical fights).
4. Tolerance.
5. Withdrawal.
6. Substance is often taken in larger amounts or over a longer period than was intended.
7. There is a persistent desire or unsuccessful efforts to cut down or control substance use.
8. A great deal of time is spent in activities necessary to obtain/use/recover from its effects.
9. Important social, occupational, or recreational activities are given up or reduced.
10. The substance use is continued despite knowledge of having a persistent or recurrent physical or psychological problem that is likely to have been caused or exacerbated by the substance.
11. Craving or a strong desire or urge to use a specific substance.

Note: Adapted from American Psychiatric Association (2022).
*The exact order of criteria may be different than what is in the DSM.

Substance Use Disorders Specifiers

Diagnostic specifiers are designed to provide the clinician and any interested parties with more information beyond the basic diagnosis. Their value is that they allow the clinician to track progress (as specifiers may change over time), and they assist in case conceptualization when a client has been referred from another therapist. In my experience as a mental health counselor, I have rarely seen specifiers properly added to substance-related diagnoses. This is unfortunate considering the additional information they can provide the practicing clinician.

The first specifier is "in early remission." This specifier is added if the client goes at least 3 months but less than 1 year without meeting any criteria for a SUD, except for the criterion "craving or strong desire to use the substance" (APA, 2022). "In sustained remission" is added to the diagnosis if a client persists for 12 months or longer meeting no symptoms of a SUD, except the craving criterion. You may be wondering why craving is an exception. This "new" component within the DSM-5 is based on the observation that craving for drug use is a common, tenacious symptom that can come about even after years of living substance free. As such, craving is to be expected when clients discontinue after prolonged use and is something that is critical to address in recovery. To insist that all cravings disappear when one stops using substances is unrealistic (APA, 2022).

The next specifier for SUDs is "in a controlled environment." This specifier is used if the client is both in remission (early or sustained) and in an environment where access to alcohol or drugs is limited or restricted (APA, 2022). Examples include inpatient treatment programs, residential treatment facilities, and prison environments. Finally, the DSM-5 asks clinicians to consider the severity level of the SUD. Options include mild, moderate, and severe. A mild specifier includes the client meeting two to three criteria, moderate indicates four to five criteria met, and severe includes six or more criteria met (APA, 2022). Clinicians have some flexibility with severity, however. For example, even if a client meets only two criteria for a SUD, the diagnosis could be considered moderate or severe if the client's use creates major problems and is having serious negative effects. The number of criteria met is a guideline, but the clinician also should consider the degree of disruption when adding a severity specifier.

Substance-Induced Disorders

SIDs refer to substance intoxication and substance withdrawal. These disorders are often not observed in outpatient settings; many individuals enter emergency rooms or other immediate care venues intoxicated after being in an accident or experiencing severe withdrawal after stopping substance use. An important diagnostic note here is that substance intoxication and substance withdrawal are *not* diagnosed unless the client is actively intoxicated or in withdrawal at the time of the evaluation. So, if a client tells the clinician that last week he got intoxicated from alcohol, but in the current session is alcohol free, alcohol intoxication would be an incorrect diagnosis; instead, the clinician should consider and evaluate for an alcohol use disorder to begin the diagnostic process.

Substance Intoxication

Substance intoxication refers to a reversible substance-specific syndrome due to recent ingestion of a substance (APA, 2022). As with any disorder listed in the DSM, it must cause clinically significant behavioral/psychological changes because of the substance on the CNS. The intoxication must develop shortly after ingestion of a substance, making it clear from a diagnostic standpoint what explains the client's behavior.

Substance Withdrawal

Substance withdrawal is a substance-specific syndrome due to stopping (or reducing) substance use that has been prolonged and heavy (APA, 2022). The syndrome causes significant distress/impairment in social, occupational, or other areas of functioning.

Many mental disorders outside of the substance-related disorders in the DSM-5 have a "Substance-Induced" section (e.g., substance-induced depressive disorder, in the depressive disorders chapter). For diagnostic purposes, clinicians should record the specific substance followed by the class of disorder (e.g., anxiety, mood; APA, 2022). Note that for these disorders, the DSM requires specification that the disorder's onset was during intoxication or withdrawal. See these examples:

> F10.980 Alcohol-induced anxiety disorder, with onset during intoxication

> F14.94 Cocaine-induced depressive disorder, with onset during withdrawal

Here, there is no concomitant SUD. If the client had a SUD in addition to the SID, this would be reflected in the diagnosis (e.g., F14.14: Mild cocaine use disorder, with cocaine-induced depressive disorder, with onset during withdrawal; APA, 2022). A good rule of thumb is that if a SID is suspected, consult both the substance-related and addictive disorders chapter *and* the specific mental disorders chapter in the DSM for relevant criteria, specifiers, and recording procedures.

Co-Occurring Disorders

Clients rarely present to counseling with substance use as the only problem in living. Often, they struggle with relationship problems, mood concerns, excessive anxiety, consequences from past abuse, trauma, adjustment issues, and so forth. Whether psychological problems occur before the substance use or are a result of substance use is a matter of philosophical and empirical debate (Miller et al., 2021). Both perspectives are probably relevant. Indeed, many of the clients I counsel often recall feeling bad before turning to substances. However, the substance use certainly plays a role in exacerbating or even leading to these bad feelings.

The term *co-occurring disorders* refers to clients who have one or more substance-related disorders *and* at least one other mental health or personality disorder diagnosis (Miller, 2021). The implication, of course, is that counseling can become quite challenging as clients present with multiple significant problems. Evans (1998) noted that it is important for the counselor to be able to distinguish between symptoms from SUDs, symptoms attributable to other mental disorders, or a combination of both. Failure to do this can lead to misdiagnoses and consequently poor treatment planning.

Miller (2021) provided numerous assessment and diagnosis guidelines for clinicians to consider when they suspect co-occurring diagnoses. In general, observing the client's recovery process can provide clues as to if there is an accompanying mental health problem. For example, if a client is unable to remain substance free after numerous attempts to quit using, there may be a concomitant mental health problem. In contrast, if the client is unable to respond to mental health treatment, the counselor should explore substance use as a possible barrier.

When assessing if a client may have co-occurring disorders, it is helpful to have the client remain substance free for a period of several weeks (Evans & Sullivan, 2001), as what may appear to be a mental health problem may disappear when the client has stopped using substances (Miller, 2021). Client history also may provide important clues to a possible co-occurring diagnosis. According to M. Scott (1995, as cited in Miller, 2021), the following historical evidence suggests a strong likelihood of having co-occurring disorders: (a) history of sexual abuse, (b) persisting mental health symptoms during abstinence, (c) using alcohol/drugs to change how you feel, (d) difficulty staying substance free, (e) later onset of substance use (after age 20), and (f) use of four or more different substances.

According to Thombs and Osborn (2019), co-occurring disorders are considered an expectation rather than an exception. SAMHSA stated that prompt attention is needed to address the problem of co-occurring disorders and would pave the way for significant improvement in the United States public health. Thus, clinicians must prepare to work with clients who present with multiple problems. Unfortunately, co-occurring disorders remain one of the most poorly understood areas in the substance use and treatment services field (Bennett et al., 2017, as cited in Thombs & Osborn, 2019). However, although still developing, some basic guidelines have been established.

In Drake et al.'s (1998) study, traditional treatment approaches for clients who struggle with severe mental health disorders and substance use were based on parallel treatment programs with two different treatment teams. This arrangement meant that a client would see one clinician for substance use issues and another concomitantly for mental health issues. Or, after the client "resolved" the substance use issue, they would begin work on the mental health issue with another clinician. This arrangement, unfortunately, led to ineffectiveness and dissatisfaction, paving way for an integrated treatment model (Drake et al., 1998).

Based on Drake et al.'s (1998) research, several features of integrated treatment were associated with outcome effectiveness. Integrated treatment programs that promoted outreach, effective case management, and were long-term, stage-based, and motivational in their treatment philosophy were seen as offering an optimistic picture of future co-occurring disorder care (Drake et al., 1998). *Long-term* is the key because clients struggling with multiple diagnoses need safe, stable, and substance-free living environments to learn healthy life skills (Brunette et al., 2004). The emphasis of integrated treatment is on building solid relationships with the clients, emphasizing choice, avoiding harsh confrontations and arguments, and establishing flexibility in treatment options (Thombs & Osborn, 2019). For example, in an integrated treatment model 12-step attendance may be encouraged but not forced on the client. Psychotropic medication is seen as a necessary and important component to integrated treatment; such services need not conflict with substance use treatment provided that close monitoring of the client is established (Thombs & Osborn, 2019). Many elements of integrated treatment have support from the National Institute on Drug Abuse (2018), based on a substantive review of the research outcome literature. Thombs and Osborn (2019) outlined 11 principles of the integrated treatment model (see Table 5.3).

TABLE 5.3   Key Aspects of an Integrated Treatment Model

1.   Treatment is not separated into two unique programs but rather provided by a program designed to address both substance use and mental health issues.
2.   Clinician teams are trained to treat the substance use problem and mental disorder concomitantly.
3.   Treatment providers for SUDs move away from traditional terms and practices such as *detox* and *rehab* to tailor treatment to the unique needs of those with concomitant mental health problems.
4.   The traditional practice of "breaking down denial" is de-emphasized with enhanced focus on reducing anxiety about substance use.
5.   Focus on the motivational interviewing principles of avoiding harsh confrontations and argumentation about changing substance use; clinicians attempt to build trust and help clients engage in treatment.
6.   Emphasis is placed on harm reduction and working with client goals, even if they do not include immediate abstinence.
7.   Recognizing that treatment for co-occurring disorders will be long term; the traditional approach of detox and residential care followed by discharge is unrealistic.
8.   Counseling is based on the stages of change and motivational interviewing with minimal confrontation.
9.   Clients should have 24-hour access to treatment staff.
10.   Unlike traditional treatment approaches, 12-step programs are encouraged but not mandatory.
11.   Psychotropic medication use may be indicated based on the client's psychiatric needs; however, close monitoring of medication use is needed and insurance that it does not compromise the goals of substance use treatment.

Note: Adapted from Thombs and Osborn (2019).

Clients with co-occurring disorders may need a longer time in treatment to achieve goals, and clinicians need to prepare for more relapses (Miller, 2021). It is difficult to place a typical timeframe on integrated care, as studies vary, but it usually involves a combination of counseling, medical care, self-help groups, and other adjunct services over a period of months. As Thombs and Osborn (2019) noted, clients tend to become abstinent through gradual harm reduction rather than insistence on immediate abstinence (see Table 5.3). An excellent online resource for clients struggling with co-occurring disorders is Dual Recovery Anonymous (www.draonline.org).

Treatment Planning

The final step in evaluating clients struggling with substance use issues is creating the treatment plan. Treatment planning for substance use issues can be a complex process given the myriad of factors that play a causal or associative role in problematic use. Indeed, a perusal of the red flags and key assessment questions listed suggests that the substance use clinician has many considerations when designing a treatment plan, and as such requires a multifaceted approach (Taylor, 2005).

Substance use disorder treatment should be conceptualized in a similar way as one would treat other chronic conditions like diabetes or cancer (Miller et al., 2019); if someone has complications due to the beginning stages of diabetes, they need immediate care, but the treatment does not stop there. They would meet regularly with a physician to manage their chronic health condition. Traditionally, treatment for substance use disorders has resorted to a finite number of days (e.g., 14-day residential care; 10 sessions of outpatient counseling) to address what is largely considered a chronic problem (Miller et al., 2011). However, Miller et al. (2011) argued that a critical piece of treatment is that, once discharged, that clients *continue* to receive follow-up care, something that has not been the norm. Severe substance use and recovery can be a long journey interspersed with positive changes, backsliding, and more positive changes as one moves through life (Miller et al., 2011). Given the chronic nature of addiction, clinicians should be prepared to identify and coconstruct both short-term and long-term goals with their clients.

To begin the treatment process, it is important to assess the extent and severity of substance use. However, before the clinician and client complete the treatment plan, attention must be given to the most appropriate treatment setting.

Treatment Settings

One of the first considerations when comprising a treatment approach is determining the most appropriate treatment setting. Treatment settings range from most restrictive to least restrictive, *restrictive* referring to the degree of structure provided by the professional mental health staff (Perez, 2005). In general, the more severe the substance use problem, the more restrictive the environment needs to be. The following are typical milieus for clients struggling with substance use problems, listed from most to least restrictive (Fisher & Harrison, 2019; Perez, 2005):

- Medical detoxification and stabilization
- Dual-diagnosis hospital inpatient
- Therapeutic communities and residential programs
- Partial hospitalization and day treatment
- Temporary recovery or halfway homes
- Intensive outpatient and outpatient

Although there are important distinctions among these different settings, there also is considerable overlap in services provided such as prevention, education, counseling, and medication management (Perez, 2005). A brief description of each is provided.

Medical Detoxification and Stabilization

In severe cases of substance use clients may need to go through medically supervised detoxification from substances such as alcohol, barbiturates, opiates, or cocaine. Detoxification is the safe, total withdrawal from a substance, usually supervised in a hospital setting (Smith & Garcia, 2005). Medical detoxification is the most restrictive treatment setting because the client has reached a level of substance use that is dangerous and even life threatening if they were to suddenly stop using the substance. Close monitoring and structure are needed to begin the recovery process. According to Smith and Garcia (2005), medical detoxification settings provide (a) screening for withdrawal and concomitant psychiatric symptoms; (b) on-site medical care to promote safe withdrawal; and (c) staff who structure the environment, protect clients from self-harm or harming others, and educate/counsel clients about substance use and addiction.

Hospital Inpatient

Another restrictive treatment setting is hospital inpatient. Hospital inpatient settings are usually for clients who have severe substance use problems in addition to one or more psychiatric conditions. Clients in inpatient settings may struggle with emotional regulation, have cognitive disturbances, or experience tumultuous interpersonal relationships. These problems in living, combined with substance use, make the potential for self-harm or harm to others high, necessitating a restrictive, structured, inpatient setting. In general, physicians and mental health practitioners help clients withdraw safely from substances, stabilize emotionally, and evaluate and treat co-occurring disorders (Smith & Garcia, 2005). Smith and Garcia (2005) stated that hospital inpatient settings provide (a) 24-hour medical and psychiatric care, (b) secure sections and minimal contact with family, (c) staff with training in co-occurring disorder treatment, (d) crisis stabilization, (e) intensive assessment services, and (f) daily group counseling sessions. Depending on the hospital and other factors, stays in hospital inpatient settings can either be 7, 14, or the more traditional 28 days.

Therapeutic Communities and Residential Programs

Therapeutic communities (TCs) are a type of residential setting usually associated with drug use other than alcohol (Fisher & Harrison, 2018). According to the NIDA (2002),

> TCs are drug-free residential settings that use a hierarchical model with treatment stages that reflect increased levels of personal and social responsibility. Peer influence, mediated through a variety of group processes, is used to help individuals learn and assimilate social norms and develop more effective social skills. (p. 1)

TCs are highly structured environments where the major goal is for residents to let go of their drug-using past and connect with a community group that is positive and supportive of their recovery. A typical day in a TC might include activities from 7:00 a.m. to 11:00 p.m. such as community meetings, job assignments, groups, seminars, individual counseling, and employment services and opportunities (NIDA, 2002). TCs are quite structured but differ from inpatient hospitalization in that the client is stabilized and not an *immediate* risk for harming self or others. TCs also differ in that the length of stay is much longer than inpatient settings, typically 12–24 months (NIDA, 2002), depending on resources, community support, staffing, and financial considerations. Researchers have shown that clients make many positive changes because of living in a TC (NIDA, 2002); however, because of isolation and the long-term nature of TCs, the dropout rates tend to be high (Fisher & Harrison, 2018).

Partial Hospitalization and Day Treatment

Partial hospitalization and day treatment can occur in hospitals or standalone treatment settings; they are considered less restrictive than the other settings covered because the client normally spends evenings or all night at home. The advantage of this treatment setting is that it allows the client to remain connected to daily life while participating in counseling and other forms of treatment during the day. Clients can apply some of the principles and techniques they are learning in individual and/or group counseling in their day-to-day lives (Fisher & Harrison, 2018). This setting also makes barriers to ongoing recovery easier to spot and address, such as a stressful home life, poor relationships, or temptations to use. Unfortunately, the less-structured environment raises concerns about opportunities to use alcohol and other drugs (Fisher & Harrison, 2018), especially if a client returns to a social environment that is not supportive of recovery efforts.

Temporary Recovery or Halfway Homes

Like TCs, a recovery/halfway house is usually a community-based home near a residential facility where clients transition from more restrictive to least restrictive living. Indeed, major differences between halfway houses and TCs are that requirements for the halfway house are fewer in number and less structured. For example, requirements for a halfway house typically include abstinence, employment, attendance at 12-step recovery groups, and possible urine screening (Perez, 2005). Clients can come and go as they reintroduce themselves back into society through employment, religious observation, and other social gatherings. Halfway houses allow clients to save money to live independently (Perez, 2005). Clients benefit from the safe, stable, and supportive milieu as they attempt to get back on their feet.

Intensive Outpatient and Outpatient

Intensive outpatient (IOP) and outpatient programs are typically free-standing programs offered via community mental health centers or even private practices. IOP typically involves counseling (usually the group format) sessions three or four evenings per week for 2 to 4 hours per evening (Fisher & Harrison, 2018). Smith and Garcia (2005) noted that in many IOPs 1 hour of family therapy also is required. Twelve-step group attendance is expected. General outpatient counseling is the least restrictive treatment format. Clients usually attend weekly individual or group sessions. They are living independently, usually well established in recovery, yet understand that relapse is always a possibility. The length, format, and duration of outpatient counseling is usually coconstructed based on client goals, clinician observation, and duration of recovery.

What Treatment Setting Should a Client Choose?

Ideally, clients should be placed in the least restrictive environment that will ensure the highest likelihood of success (Fisher & Harrison, 2018). However, there are guidelines clinicians can use to determine the most appropriate treatment setting for clients struggling with substance-related issues. According to the American Society of Addiction Medicine (ASAM, 2022) there are several placement criteria and considerations in determining the best placement, including (a) acute intoxication/withdrawal potential, (b) biomedical conditions or complications, (c) emotional/behavioral conditions or complications, (d) treatment acceptance and resistance, (e) relapse potential, and (f) the recovery environment. The higher the client "scores" on these criteria (e.g., going through acute intoxication, has numerous medical problems due to use), the more likely a restrictive environment would be the most appropriate level of care.

Clinicians can reformulate these placement criteria into a series of questions to help determine more restrictive versus less restrictive placement:

1. Is the client's condition associated with significant medical or psychiatric conditions or complications? *If yes, lean toward more restrictive.*
2. What is the severity of actual or anticipated withdrawal from drug(s) being used? *If severe, lean toward more restrictive.*
3. Has the client failed multiple times at outpatient treatment? *If yes, more restrictive is probably warranted.*
4. What is the strength of the client's support systems? *If limited or no support system, more restrictive may be best.*
5. How severe is the client's substance use, and is there a possibility of problems across multiple substances? *The more severe, the greater the need for restrictive care.*

As Fisher and Harrison (2018) noted, all these criteria or considerations may not be used in determining client placement. That is, finances, insurance, time, and other client factors also shape what treatment setting a client enters. In my experience, clients who would benefit most from weekly outpatient counseling simply can't afford this frequency of counseling. Believing that some counseling is better than none, I have had to compromise with clients and work within their financial abilities and other potential constraints to find a workable treatment schedule.

The Treatment Plan

In many cases, clinicians must follow agency protocol for treatment planning, especially when it comes to completing paperwork. This usually involves a form or two that must be completed by the clinician and includes spaces to write a diagnosis, problem statement, goals, and objectives. Unfortunately, these forms often are inadequate for documenting a substance use (or dual-diagnosis) counseling or treatment plan as they have limited space to write enough goals, objectives, and diagnoses. Many agencies are open to clinicians using their own forms/models of treatment planning if they comply with and are consistent with legal considerations. I recall in one agency the director allowed me to add my own treatment planning model to what the agency required. It was a bit more work, but in the end, I appreciated having additional latitude to account for the complexity of the client cases I was observing.

The importance of treatment planning is well documented (Miller, 2021; Reichenberg & Seligman, 2016). A comprehensive treatment plan serves as a compass, providing structure and direction to the counseling process, thus keeping clinician and client from becoming overwhelmed (Miller, 2021; Reichenberg & Seligman, 2016). Treatment planning assures counseling with a higher likelihood of success, especially by helping clients and clinicians track progress; it is a way to determine if goals are being met, or if they need revision based on new client developments that inevitably arise during the counseling process. Miller (2021) stated, "The treatment plan serves as a rudder for the client work, assisting both the client and the counselor in keeping a balanced focus on the issues" (p. 127). Each plan must be specific and individualized to meet the client's needs and goals (Perez, 2005).

Treatment planning also facilitates accountability between both clients and clinicians: Is the client working toward goals that they stated are important? Is the clinician using interventions as specified in the plan? Effective treatment planning is important for practical reasons as well, such as assisting in obtaining funding for projects, receiving third-party reimbursements, and providing defense in cases of legal malpractice suits.

Most treatment plans contain four essential components: the problem statement, the goals, the methods, and measurement (Miller, 2005). The four components should be written for *each* presenting problem. The *problem statement* is a sentence or two on what the major problem is that brings the client to counseling. It should be written in clear and behavioral terms. The *goals* are what the client will accomplish to address the problem or, as Miller stated, the flip side of the problem. The *methods* are the interventions or what the clinician will do to intervene and help the client. The *measurement* answers the question "How will we know when the client has accomplished his or her goal?"

Perkinson (2012) outlined a model for substance use treatment planning in which he lists the problem statement, followed by relevant goals, objectives, and interventions related to the problem statement. Clients may have one or more problem statements, and within each problem statement they may have multiple goals, objectives, and interventions. In this context, goals refer to broad changes that the client will make to rectify the problem, and objectives are the actual behaviors he will engage in to accomplish the goals. Interventions are strategies and techniques the clinician will use to help accomplish the objectives. Here is an example of a typical treatment plan based on this description (Perkinson, 2012). Assume that the client has already been through detoxification and a residential facility.

Problem 1: The client consumes alcohol excessively and has experienced numerous negative consequences as a result.

- *Goal 1*: The client will remain abstinent from alcohol use and begin to build a life of recovery.
  - ▷ *Objective 1a*: The client will explore the importance of stopping alcohol use completely.
    - ▪ *Intervention 1a*: Conduct a decisional balance exercise combined with values explorations to enhance importance to change alcohol use patterns.
  - ▷ *Objective 1b*: The client will enhance confidence in being able to remain alcohol free.
    - ▪ *Intervention 1b:* Explore past successes, use confidence ruler exercise, and brainstorm ideas to enhance client's confidence to remain alcohol free.
  - ▷ *Objective 1c*: The client will develop a firm commitment to living a lifestyle free of alcohol.
    - ▪ *Intervention 1c*: Coconstruct and complete a change plan worksheet.

Problem 2: The client experiences intense outbursts of anger toward his family and coworkers.

- *Goal 2.* The client will engage in an anger management plan to help him cope with angry feelings and resolve underlying causes of anger.
  - ▷ *Objective 2a*: The client will reduce subjective experiences of anger by 50% within 4 weeks.
    - ▪ *Intervention 2a*: CBT will address negative cognitions and distortions that lead to angry feelings.

Notice how the goals, objectives, and interventions all flow from the overall problem statement. An advantage of this treatment planning model is that the clinician is encouraged to think through not only what the client will do to change (and accomplish the goal) but tie this change behavior directly into interventions that will help facilitate the change process.

Laban (1997) outlined a more comprehensive model for substance use clients, including nine elements necessary for effective substance use treatment planning:

1. **Type of plan (initial, master, update).** The initial plan is completed within the first 24 hours, the master plan is the main treatment roadmap, and the updated plan is a revision of the master plan(s) as needed.

2. **Problem.** A statement of the problem is written, considering clinical assessment data and client perspective on the problem.

3. **Indicators.** What is the tangible data confirming the problem outlined in the statement (e.g., collateral reports from several sources confirms the clients struggle with alcohol)?

4. **Long-term goals.** What the client hopes to accomplish 6 months to 1 year after discharge.

5. **Short-term goals.** What the client hopes to accomplish during their time in treatment.

6. **Objectives.** What the client will specifically do to accomplish the stated goals. The objectives must be accomplishable, measurable, and behavioral.

7. **Methods.** The tasks and interventions, preferably behavioral, assigned to help the client accomplish stated objectives and goals.

8. **Frequency of services provided.** A statement as to how often treatment will occur and in what format (e.g., individual, group, both).

9. **Signatures.** Signature should be obtained from client to solidify commitment to plan.

Laban (1997) further proposed that the nine elements apply across problem domains including (a) initial treatment, (b) medical/health concerns, (c) emotional barriers, (d) interpersonal issues, (e) recognition versus resistance, (f) relapse potential, (g) social milieu, (h) recovery environment, and (i) home environment. Thus, for a particular client struggling in the medical/health, interpersonal, and home environment domains, three treatment plans would be formulated, with each treatment plan containing the nine elements (i.e., type of plan, problem, indicators, etc.).

Smith and Garcia (2013) have modified Laban's original treatment planning model, especially related to terminology used, to account for developments in the field. For example, instead of recognition versus resistance, Smith and Garcia (2013) used "readiness to change: denial and spirituality outlook" (p. 170). The emphasis on spirituality reflects its importance as part of a client assessment. A strength of Laban's treatment plan model is its comprehensiveness. The clinician must consider a multitude of problem domains negatively impacted by the client's substance use. In addition, for each problem, relevant goals, objectives, methods, and types of services are specified.

DO A CLIENT MAP

One of the most comprehensive treatment planning models available is DO A CLIENT MAP, originally proposed by Seligman (2004). Considering important treatment factors such as clinician characteristics, assessments, and prognosis, the DO A CLIENT MAP is broad, wide-ranging, and flexible. As the acronym suggests, the treatment plan is a "map" or client conceptualization based on 12 key factors. Although DO A CLIENT MAP was not specifically formulated to address chemical dependency issues, it is well suited for substance related and psychological problems. Each letter in the DO A CLIENT MAP stands for one of the key factors.

Diagnosis

The first letter stands for "diagnosis." This is the first step in creating the treatment plan, and the diagnosis should include all relevant codes, disorders, and specifiers. The remaining parts of the treatment plan stem from the diagnosis.

Objectives/Goals[1]

Following the diagnosis, the clinician and client coconstruct treatment objectives (or goals), which refer to what the client will accomplish. Objectives should be written in a clear and measurable way. Reichenberg and Seligman (2016) stressed the importance of clients having a say in what objectives or goals are established. Objectives or goals can be written as short-term (0–3 months), medium-term (4–6 months), and long-term (beyond 6 months).

Assessments

A thorough, comprehensive assessment provides important information related to the client's presenting concerns, extent of substance use and other psychological problems, and attitudes toward treatment. Assessment in this context refers to how the clinician will assess the client's present status and includes everything from diagnostic interviews, mental status exams, and screenings to more formal tests such as the MMPI-2. Assessments of medical status can be listed as well, although with medical specialist support. Under this section of DO A CLIENT MAP, the clinician simply lists all relevant assessment instruments and/or procedures.

Clinician Characteristics

Clinician characteristics such as empathetic understanding, abilities, and skills are necessary and important in the counseling setting and are generally associated with positive client outcomes (Reichenberg & Seligman, 2016). In addition, characteristics include demographic factors such as gender and ethnicity of the clinician, although gender has been found to have little relationship to counseling outcome compared to other factors (Bowman et al., 2001). Experience and professional expertise also fall under clinician characteristics. Under this section, the clinician highlights characteristics that would be particularly important and relevant based on client factors and the presenting concern. For example, an African American client may communicate that they prefer an African American clinician, and this should be reflected in the treatment plan. Another clinician characteristic might be having expertise in the provision of CBT.

Location

This section specifies what treatment setting would best fit the client's circumstances. A simple statement to this effect followed by a brief rationale is all that is needed.

Interventions

The "I" stands for interventions, or what the clinician will do to help the client accomplish stated objectives. Interventions are the heart of the treatment plan and ideally include two elements: theoretical framework(s) from which the clinician intends to counsel and specific strategies based on the theoretical orientation. At minimum, theoretical orientation should be included; specific strategies are optional as they may not be known at the time the original plan is coconstructed.

---

1 Objectives and goals, in this context, refer to the same thing.

Emphasis

Emphasis refers to ways in which clinicians adapt their style of intervention to client circumstances (Reichenberg & Seligman, 2016). Whereas numerous models of psychotherapy exist, each clinician has their own way of using different approaches, largely depending on client issues. Different emphases include level of directiveness, structured versus nonstructured, supportive, confrontation, and exploration (Reichenberg & Seligman, 20016). Emphases also may shift during the counseling process. For example, a client struggling with a severe substance use disorder may need a lot of direction and structure at the beginning of counseling but over time need more support and exploration.

Number

Number entails how many will participate in counseling and what modality will be emphasized. Typical options include individual therapy, family therapy, or group therapy. In the case of substance use, all three could be potential modalities.

Timing

Here, the clinician specifies the length and frequency of each modality of counseling. Length of counseling should include the overall duration (e.g., 9 months) and the length of a typical session (e.g., 50 minutes for individual; 90 minutes for group). Frequency should include how often the client will meet with the clinician, group, or family each week (e.g., twice weekly for individual, once weekly for group, once a month for family).

Medication

The clinician should list all relevant psychiatric and other medications the client is currently taking. If the client is not taking any psychiatric medication but this should be considered, the clinician can simply write, "Will refer to psychiatrist for medical evaluation." In some cases, the client will be taking medication to address their substance use problem (e.g., Vivitrol for alcohol), and these medications should be listed as well.

Adjunct Services

In substance use counseling, adjunct services play an important and sometimes critical role in treatment. For example, Alcoholics Anonymous and other 12-step recovery groups complete a triadic relationship (i.e., the client, the clinician, and AA) critical to the recovery process (Brown, 1995). In some treatment programs, particularly more restrictive environments, 12-step recovery group attendance is required. Other general adjunct services include parent skills training, employment training, and nutritional counseling.

Prognosis

Prognosis refers to the probability that clients will reach their objectives and goals (Reichenberg & Seligman, 2016). As with any client, the prognosis depends on the severity of the problem and client motivation. In general, words to describe prognosis include *excellent*, *very good*, *good*, *fair*, and *poor*.

The DO A CLIENT MAP model provides a wide-ranging structure to the treatment planning process. The model's comprehensiveness makes it an attractive option (although by no means the only option) for substance-related issues. As Reichenberg and Seligman (2016) pointed out, DO A CLIENT MAP should be done in a collaborative fashion and does not require multiple treatment plan forms to be used (although the clinician is free to do so).

SAMPLE DO A CLIENT MAP

Following is a sample DO A CLIENT MAP for Michael, whose case was introduced in Chapter 1.

Diagnosis (at intake, review treatment plan in 90 days)

F10.20 Alcohol Use Disorder, Severe

F14.10 Cocaine Use Disorder, Mild

F33.1 Major Depressive Disorder, Recurrent, Moderate, Provisional

Z63.0 Relationship Distress With Spouse or Intimate Partner

Z56.9 Other Problem Related to Employment

World Health Organization Disability Assessment Schedule 2.0 (WHODAS 2.0)—overall scale average—3.5 (moderate to severe)

Other clinical observations:

Prominent use of displacement and denial

Prediabetic

Objectives

Short-term

1. Michael will undergo an extensive substance use assessment to determine the severity and intensity of his substance use.
2. Michael will undergo a psychiatric evaluation to assess need for medication to manage mood.
3. Michael will commit to and attend Alcoholics Anonymous every day for 90 days.
4. Michael will increase his motivation to abstain from chemical use by exploring consequences, increasing importance, and improving his confidence.
5. Michael will abstain from all chemical use (except for prescribed medications).
6. Michael will no longer be tardy to work or meetings during the day.
7. Michael will practice one form of stress management daily.

Long-term

1. Michael will continue to remain abstinent from chemical use (except for prescribed medications).
2. Michael will undergo a lifestyle assessment to explore how early childhood experiences contribute to his current struggles with mood and anger.
3. Michael will learn to confront and challenge his basic mistakes (i.e., cognitive distortions) that contribute to his substance use and negative moods.

4. Michael will coconstruct an anger management plan with at least six strategies to help him manage his anger.
5. Michael will participate in couples counseling and identify ways that he can make the relationship with his spouse better.
6. Michael will continue to practice one form of stress management daily.
7. Michael will coconstruct a comprehensive relapse management plan.

Assessments

Diagnostic interview

Medical evaluation to address mood symptoms

Substance Abuse Subtle Screening Inventory (SASSI-IV)

Alcohol Use Inventory (AUI)

Addiction Severity Index (ASI)

Adlerian Lifestyle Assessment (Long-term)

Clinician Characteristics

Knowledgeable about the development and symptoms of alcohol and cocaine use disorders

Skilled in setting structure and direction, especially at the beginning of counseling

Able to work with and knowledgeable about dual diagnoses

Culturally competent and sensitive counseling approach

Location

Outpatient counseling to begin; however, intensive outpatient or residential day treatment may be warranted depending on assessment results.

Interventions (both individual and group counseling)

MI to primarily address short-term objectives. MI may be needed beyond this depending on client's motivation level.

A combination of Adlerian and cognitive behavioral counseling to address long-term objectives.

Adlerian couples counseling to address marital conflict.

Education on development of substance use disorders.

Emphasis

Lots of structure and direction at the start of counseling.

Keep focus on alcohol and substance use, especially during the first 3 months.

Mostly supportive and gently confrontational from the start; more exploration as rapport is strengthened (long-term goals).

Number

Individual and group counseling formats. Periodic couples counseling after rapport has been established.

Timing

Treatment will be planned for 6 months' total duration, after which updated recommendations and/or aftercare plan will be provided.

For months 1–3:

Individual counseling—once weekly for 50 minutes
Group counseling—once weekly for 90 minutes
Couples counseling—in collaboration with client, once every 2 to 3 weeks for 50 minutes

For months 4–6:

Individual counseling—once weekly for 50 minutes
Couples counseling—in collaboration with client, once every 2 to 3 weeks for 50 minutes

Medications

Possible referral to staff psychiatrist to discuss medication for alcohol management and mood management

Adjunct Services

Alcoholics Anonymous every day for first 90 days; variable after this
Al-Anon as a possibility for client's spouse

Prognosis

Prognosis is fair. Michael's motivation level is currently low to moderate; improving intrinsic motivation to change is paramount. Successful recovery also depends on commitment to AA attendance, especially the first 90 days. Long-term counseling should focus on marital issues, stress management, resolving early childhood conflicts, managing depressed and angry feelings, and commitment to abstinence. A complete aftercare plan should be established at that time. With these elements in place, the chances for successful recovery improve.

Summary

Proper and accurate substance use screening, assessment, and diagnosis, that together make up an overall evaluation, is a critical first step in working with those struggling with substance use disoders. A proper evaluation sets the stage for appropriate treatment planning and intervention. There are several objective instruments to aid the clinician in determining if a substance use problem exists. The skilled substance use clinician must consider a multitude of factors that underlie the complexity of substance use disorders when formulating evaluations and treatment plans.

References

Alcohol and Drug Abuse Library. (2020). *Substance Abuse Screening and Assessment Instruments Database*. www.http://lib.adai.washington.edu/instruments

American Psychiatric Association (2022). *Diagnostic and manual of mental disorders* (5th ed., text revision). Author.

American Society of Addiction Medicine. (2022, February 21). *About the ASAM criteria*. https://www.asam.org/asam-criteria/about-the-asam-criteria

Barbor, T. F., de la Fuente, J. R., Saunders, J., & Grant, M. (1992). *The Alcohol Use Disorders Identification test*. World Health Organization.

Bowman, D., Scogin, F., Floyd, M., & McKendree-Smith, N. (2001). Psychotherapy length of stay and outcome: A meta-analysis of the effect of therapist sex. *Psychotherapy: Theory, Research, Practice, Training, 38*, 142–148. https://doi.org/10.1037/0033-3204.38.2.142

Brown, R. L., Leonard, T., Saunders, L. A., & Papasoulioutis, O. (1997). A two-item screening test for alcohol and other drug problems. *Journal of Family Practice, 44*, 151–160.

Brown, R. L., Leonard, T., Saunders, L. A., & Papasouliotis, O. (1998). The prevalence and detection of substance use disorder among inpatients ages 18–49: An opportunity for prevention. *Preventative Medicine, 27*, 101–110.

Brown, S. (1995). *Treating alcoholism*. Wiley.

Brunette, M. F., Mueser, K. T., & Drake, R. E. (2004). A review of research on residential programs for people with severe mental illness and co-occurring substance use disorders. *Journal of Drug and Alcohol Review, 23*, 471–481.

Butcher, J. N., Graham, J. R., Ben-Porath, Tellegen, & Dahlstrom (2006). *MMPI-2 overview*. http://tinyurl.com/838cnzp

Cherpitel, C. J. (1999). Screening for alcohol problems in the U.S. general population: A comparison of the CAGE and TWEAK by gender, ethnicity, and services utilization. *Journal of Studies on Alcohol, 60*, 705–711.

Doweiko, H. E. (2019). *Concepts of chemical dependency* (10th ed.). Cengage.

Drake, R. E., Mercer-McFadden, C., Mueser, K. T., McHugo, G. J. & Bond, G. R. (1998). Review of integrated mental health and substance abuse treatment for patients with dual disorders. *Schizophrenia Bulletin, 24*, 589–608.

Evans, K., & Sullivan, J. M. (2001). *Dual diagnosis: Counseling the mentally ill substance abuser* (2nd ed.). Guilford.

Evans, W. N. (1998). Assessment and diagnosis of the substance use disorders (SUDs). *Journal of Counseling and Development, 76*, 325–332.

Ewing, J. A. (1984). Detecting alcoholism: The CAGE questionnaire. *Journal of the American Medical Association, 252*, 1905–1907.

Fisher, G. L., & Harrison, T. C. (2018). *Substance abuse: Information for school counselors, social workers, therapists, and counselors* (6th ed.). Allyn & Bacon.

Groth-Marnat, G., & Wright, A. J. (2016). *Handbook of psychological assessment* (6th ed.). Wiley.

Horn, J. L., Wanberg, K. W., & Foster, F. M. (1986). *The alcohol use inventory: Test booklet.* National Computer Systems.

Jankowski, D. (2002). *A beginner's guide to the MCMI-III.* APA.

Juhnke, G. A. (2002). *Substance abuse assessment and diagnosis.* Brunner-Routledge.

Laban, R. L. (1997). *Chemical dependency treatment planning handbook.* Charles C. Thomas.

Lewis, T. F., & Watts, R. E. (2004). The predictability of Adlerian lifestyle themes compared to demographic variables associated with college student drinking. *Journal of Individual Psychology, 60,* 245–264.

Liese, B. A., & Beck, A. T. (2000). Back to basics: Fundamental cognitive therapy skills for keeping drug-dependent individuals in treatment. In J. J. Boren, L. S. Onken, & J. D. Blaine (Eds.), *Beyond the therapeutic alliance: Keeping drug-dependent individuals in treatment.* National Institute on Drug Abuse Research Monograph. U. S. Government Printing Office.

McLellan, T. A., Luborsky, L., O'Brien, C. P., & Woody, G. E. (1980). *Addiction Severity Index* (5th ed.). Treatment Research Institute.

Miller, G. (1985). *The Substance Abuse Subtle Screening Inventory.* SASSI Institute.

Miller, G. (2005). *Learning the language of addiction counseling* (2nd ed.). Wiley.

Miller, G. (2021). *Learning the language of addiction counseling* (5th ed.). Wiley.

Miller, W. R., Forcehimes, A. A., & Zweben, A. (2011). *Treating addiction.* Guilford.

Miller, W. R., Forcehimes, A. A., & Zweben, A. (2019). *Treating addiction* (2nd ed.). Guilford.

Miller, W. R., & Rollnick, S. (2002). *Motivational interviewing: Preparing people for change.* Guilford.

Millon, T. (1997). *Millon Clinical Multiaxial Inventory-III manual* (2nd ed.). National Computer Systems.

Millon, T., Davis, R., Millon, C., & Grossman, S. (2009). *The Millon Clinical Multiaxial Inventory-III (MCMI-III) with new norms and updated scoring.* https://www.millonpersonality.com/inventories/MCMI-III/

National Institute on Alcohol Abuse and Alcoholism. (2002). Screening for alcohol problems—an update. *Alcohol Alert, 56,* 1–3.

National Institute on Alcohol Abuse and Alcoholism. (2007). Helping patients who drink too much alcohol: A clinician's guide. http://tinyurl.com/2kfvks

National Institute on Drug Abuse. (2002). *Research report series: Therapeutic community* (NIH publication No. 02-4877). https://nida.nih.gov/download/19021/therapeutic-communities-research-report.pdf?v=d9998464105dbc9b3845e22b1969c814c

National Institute on Drug Abuse. (2018). *Principles of drug abuse treatment: A research-based guide* (3rd ed). https://nida.nih.gov/download/675/principles-drug-addiction treatment-research-based-guide third-edition.pdf?v=74dad603627bab89b93193918330c223

Perez, P. J. (2005). Treatment setting and treatment planning. In P. Stevens & R. L. Smith (Eds.). *Substance abuse counseling: Theory and practice* (2nd ed.). Prentice Hall.

Perkinson, R. R. (2012). *Chemical dependency counseling: A practical guide* (4th ed.). SAGE.

Reichenberg, L. W., & Seligman, L. (2016). *Selecting effective treatments: A comprehensive, systematic guide to treating mental disorders* (5th ed.). Jossey-Bass.

Rollnick, S., Mason, P., & Butler, C. (1999). *Motivational interviewing in health care: Helping patients change behavior.* Guilford Press.

Rosengren, D. B. (2008). *Building motivational interviewing skills: A practitioner's workbook.* Guilford.

Seligman, L. (2004). *Diagnosis and treatment planning in counseling* (3rd ed.). Springer.

Seligman, L., & Reichenberg, L. W. (2007). *Selecting effective treatments: A comprehensive guide to treating mental disorders* (3rd ed.). Jossey-Bass.

Seligman, L., & Reicheberg, L. W. (2014). *Theories of counseling and psychotherapy: Systems, strategies, and skills* (4th ed.). Pearson.

Selzer, M. L. (1971). The Michigan alcoholism screening test: The quest for a new diagnostic instrument. *American Journal of Psychiatry, 127,* 1653–1658.

Skinner, H. A. (1982). Statistical approaches to the classification of alcohol and drug addiction. *Alcoholism: Clinical and Experimental Research, 77,* 259–273.

Smith, R. L., & Garcia, E. E. (2005). Treatment setting and treatment planning. In P. Stevens & R. L. Smith (Eds.), *Substance abuse counseling: Theory and practice* (5th ed., pp. 155–187). Pearson

Smith, R. L., & Garcia, E. E. (2013). Treatment setting and treatment planning. In R. L. Smith & P. Stevens (Eds.), *Substance abuse counseling: Theory and practice* (5th ed., pp. 155–187). Pearson.

Taylor, P. (2005). *Diagnosis and treatment of substance related disorders: The declare model.* Pearson.

Thombs, D. L. (2006). *Introduction to addictive behaviors* (3rd ed.). Guilford.

Thombs, D. L., & Osborn, C. J. (2019). *Introduction to addictive behaviors* (5th ed.). Guilford.

Figure Credit

PART II

Theoretical Approaches Supported by Empirical Evidence

In Part II, I cover approaches to substance use counseling that, in general, have been supported by empirical evidence. I begin this part with Chapter 6 on MI. MI is an evidence-based approach that was born out of the addictions field and has amassed an impressive array of research to support many of its principles and applications. CBT, the topic of Chapter 7, is another evidence-based approach that provides the clinician with comprehensive conceptualization of substance use and addiction in addition to a bevy of interventions from which to choose. Any textbook on substance use counseling would be incomplete without a chapter on preventing and managing relapse, a topic of Chapter 8. Many of the relapse-prevention concepts are ground in cognitive behavioral models; relapse prevention is also an approach that has garnered significant empirical evidence for its effectiveness. In Chapters 9 and 10, group therapy and family therapy are reviewed. Group therapy is considered a "standard of care" in substance use treatment, and family therapy can add an important component to any substance use treatment plan. Readers who want to learn about applications of "empirically supported treatments" may find Part II particularly relevant.

CHAPTER 6

Motivational Interviewing in the Treatment of Substance Use Disorders

Introduction

MI continues to receive much attention in the substance use treatment community. An approach born out of the substance use treatment field, MI has been applied to numerous additional problems beyond substance use (e.g., see Arkowitz et al., 2007). Its application is perhaps most effective when there is a clear target behavior to change, such as stopping alcohol or drug use. MI has amassed an impressive array of research, with hundreds of clinical trials that in general support its effectiveness (Miller & Rose, 2009; Miller & Rollnick, 2013). The definition of MI has evolved over the years since the first book on the topic appeared in 1991 (Miller & Rollnick, 1991). Currently, MI is defined as "a collaborative, goal-oriented style of communication with particular attention to language of change. It is designed to strengthen motivation for and commitment to a specific goal by eliciting and exploring the person's own reasons for change within an atmosphere of acceptance and compassion" (Miller & Rollnick, 2013, p. 29). The differing elements of this definition are examined in detail throughout this chapter.

In this chapter, I begin with a basic history of MI to give the reader some background and context for how this approach to helping emerged. I then turn to goals and theoretical influences on MI. Next is coverage on the major tenets of MI, with special emphasis on the MI spirit, principles, and processes. The focus then turns to application of MI to substance use counseling, with emphases on methods (strategies and skills) related to increasing importance, resolving ambivalence, and strengthening commitment to change. The use of MI with diverse populations is considered next, followed by an example of what MI would look like in the case of Michael.

A Bit of History

MI first appeared on the scene in the early 1980s as a response to confrontational approaches to working with clients struggling with substance use and addiction problems. In an interview with Hettema and Langdon (2009), William R. Miller explained that he discovered the building blocks of MI in the early 1980s when training mental health professionals in substance use counseling. When Miller met with participants, they were curious about his approach and why he used a certain technique at a certain time. Much of what Miller was doing, in fact, was consistent with current MI practice: reflecting, asking open questions, and rolling with resistance. Miller (1983) realized after this experience that he had the beginnings of an approach, which culminated in the first article on MI in the *Behavioural Psychotherapy* journal.

MI was a reaction to standard forms of substance treatment at the time. The prevailing therapeutic approach operated under the following assumptions: (a) that substance users are defective, and it is the therapist's job to fix them; (b) substance users have nothing to offer in counseling; (c) harsh confrontation is necessary to break down denial; and (d) patients must admit they are an "addict" or "alcoholic" before any change can take place. What Miller began to observe, however, was that this form of therapy and its assumptions created a huge roadblock toward change: resistance. That is, harsh confrontations, beating down denial, and arguing only seemed to engender resistance rather than lower it. Too much resistance can serve as a major impediment to change. Harsh confrontation created unnecessary tension between clinician and client, which negatively impacted therapeutic rapport, a critical element in any successful therapeutic endeavor. In addition, the idea that one must admit that they are an "addict" or "alcoholic" to improve has no empirical support (Miller et al., 1998).

Goals of MI

What do clinicians hope to accomplish when using this approach to helping? It is safe to assume that most, if not all, MI strategies and techniques can be traced back to assisting with one of four overarching goals. The first goal is to help clients *increase their intrinsic motivation to change*. Intrinsic motivation is like an inner resolve to make changes for the better; clients want to improve their lives, experience internal satisfaction, and enhance meaning. Intrinsic motivation can be contrasted with extrinsic motivation. Extrinsic motivation depends on external rewards; however, when outside rewards are no longer offered, motivation tends to ebb (Kohn, 1999). This is not to say that extrinsic motivation is avoided at all costs. Indeed, researchers have recently revisited the concepts of intrinsic and extrinsic motivation and suggested that they don't necessarily have to be against each other and can be mutually useful in exploring an overall picture of motivation (Locke & Schattke, 2019); however, MI is more about eliciting the clients' own arguments for change rather than being motivated from an outside source. From the MI perspective, intrinsic motivation is thought to lead to more meaningful and lasting change.

The second goal of MI is to *lower the level of discord*[1] within the counseling session. Discordant behaviors can come in all shapes and sizes, but the overall experience is that the counselor and client are not on the same page. A client (or counselor!) may argue, defend, ignore, or interrupt during the session, which are tell-tale signs of discord. In general, too much discord within

---

1 In early writings on MI, the term *resistance* was used instead of *discord*. More recently, Miller and Rollnick (2013) observed that the term *discord* better captured the phenomenon we see in counseling, namely that the counselor and client are not on the same page. That is, discord is inherently a relational issue and is a better term to describe this. Nonetheless, I believe that a client can have inner resistance, but that is usually not related to how the counselor is interacting with them. Although both are important to lower in counseling sessions, within MI the focus is more on lowering discord and building engagement.

a counseling session can thwart clinical progress. As such, a central goal of MI is lower its presence so that space opens for new possibilities.

The third goal of MI is to *resolve ambivalence*. When clients are considering the possibility of change, they often struggle with two (or more) competing perspectives. For example, a client who wishes to stop using cocaine may see several reasons why that may be a good idea *and* reasons why stopping would be difficult. Ambivalence is a key reason clients remain stuck and are unable to change (Miller & Rollnick, 2013). The competing forces (arguments for change and arguments against change) pull back and forth like a psychological tug-of-war. In MI, resolving ambivalence is essential to moving clients forward on the change continuum. Ambivalence regarding change is particularly relevant among clients struggling with substance use problems. Many strategies shared throughout this chapter were designed to help clients resolve ambivalence.

The importance of client change language (called change talk) when assessing the commitment to making positive life changes is a unique contribution from MI. How a clinician responds to it has become and essential ingredient to its effectiveness. As such, a fourth goal of MI is to *emphasize and illuminate client change talk*. The stronger the change language, the higher the probability of change. Indeed, not all change talk is the same. For example, some change talk indicates a client's desire to change but not a full commitment to change ("I would like to cut down on my drinking"). Alternatively, a client may convey a strong commitment to change ("I will cut down on my drinking") and follow through with several activities that promote abstinence. In other words, change talk can come in varying degrees of seriousness and intensity. Change talk and strategies to elicit it will be covered in more depth later in the chapter.

Influences on MI and What MI Is Not

A common misnomer is that MI is simply a version of client-centered counseling. Although there is influence on the development of MI, client-centered counseling is *not* the same as MI. MI is considered a gentle, persuasive style (Miller & Rollnick, 1991) designed to elicit and strengthen motivation to change. The key word is *persuasive*; that is, MI has a directive quality that moves it beyond a client-centered approach. Nonetheless, the impact of empathic listening plays a significant role in what MI looks like in a therapy session.

The transtheoretical model of change, or stages of change model (Prochaska et al., 1992), also influenced the development of MI (Miller & Rollnick, 2002). According to the transtheoretical model, individuals matriculate through a series of stages when behavior change is a possibility. In the first stage, *precontemplation*, clients are usually forced to attend counseling, do not see a need for it, and may be in denial about the seriousness of their substance use. They do not see a need for change and subsequent motivation is low. In *contemplation*, clients display ambivalence about making a change. They see the benefits of cutting down or stopping drinking, for example, and see the disadvantages. Clients in contemplation acknowledge benefits of changing one's behavior, and they are at least thinking about making a change. The next stage is *determination* (or preparation), where clients cognitively recognize the importance of changing but do not know how to change. For example, a client with cocaine use disorder may come to the realization that they need to stop using but are unsure how to go about taking steps toward this goal. When confidence increases, clients move into *action*, where, in addition to making a commitment to change, clients are actively taking steps to realize their goals. After about 6 months of abstinence, clients enter *maintenance*. In this stage, clients maintain their gains made in treatment and, after some time, move out of the change cycle (Prochaska et al., 1992). Relapse is a final stage of the change cycle; its inclusion reinforces the fact that relapse is more the exception rather than the rule. When one relapses, they either enter the change cycle again, or return to full-blown substance use. It is important to note that clients can enter therapy at any stage of the process (i.e., not all clients will be precontemplative when they begin counseling). In addition, clients can and do vacillate the between the stages; motivation is not a static process but rather a fluid internal mechanism that responds to new experiences, events, and stressors.

MI and the transtheoretical model are *not* the same thing; however, they "grew up" together in the 1980s, and each is thought to complement the other (Miller & Rollnick, 2009). The stages of change provided a useful model, one of the first of its kind in substance use treatment, to understand how and why an individual progresses through the change process. MI, on the other hand, provided a clinical tool for how one might move from precontemplation to action, or increase motivation to change (Miller & Rollnick, 2009). Thus, specific motivational strategies correspond to specific stages of change. For example, precontemplative clients may need a different set of motivational strategies than clients who are in the action stage of change. I have found the correspondence between MI and the transtheoretical model helpful when conceptualizing clients; however, it is not essential or necessary to know a client's stage of change to successfully apply MI (Miller & Rollnick, 2009).

Ways to Implement MI

MI can be incorporated in one of three ways. First, it can be used as an approach in and of itself. That is, MI can be used exclusively as a brief therapeutic modality. Second, MI can be used initially, followed by other counseling modalities as appropriate. This use of MI would be appropriate for clients who enter counseling with little or no motivation to change or strong ambivalence regarding whether change is even an option for them. The clinician uses MI to start things off, assessing for motivation and readiness and applying the strategies of MI to enhance and strengthen motivation. Once sufficient motivation has been established, the clinician then moves on to other modalities that may serve the client well, such as CBT, gestalt therapy, and so forth.

Finally, a third way MI can be used is to incorporate it as needed. Client motivation rarely remains fixed, as many people experience fluctuations from time to time in their commitment and readiness to change, even within a session. As an example, consider a client who attends counseling due to opiate use but has little motivation to change their behavior. The clinician begins with MI and over time the client's motivation to change increases. The client makes some progress, only to attend the next session having lost their will and desire to change. The clinician then returns to MI to bolster waning motivation. In essence, clinicians can implement MI whenever motivational issues appear to impede progress.

The Major Tenets of MI: Basic Overview

The major tenets of MI include spirit, principles, and the four processes. These tenets serve as the foundation of MI from which skills and techniques emerge. Clinicians are encouraged to have a firm grounding in these basic MI concepts before applying MI in practice. An in-depth exploration of each tenet follows.

MI Spirit

Miller and Rollnick (2013) discussed how the foundation of MI is a therapeutic posture that is collaborative, evocative, accepting, and compassionate. Taken together, these elements make up what is called MI spirit. Indeed, the principles of MI, as well as many of its techniques, are consistent with MI spirit. MI trainers teach spirit before covering the processes, principles, applications, and techniques of MI.

In an MI session, the clinician takes a stance of curiosity regarding the client's story and sets agendas, goals, and discussions in a *collaborative* nature. In addition, emphasis is placed on what clients know and what ideas they have about changing or not changing (*evocation*). Client *acceptance* is communicated through four components: empathy, affirmation, autonomy, and absolute worth. Finally, *compassion* is where clinicians have a genuine interest in what is best for the client and care about their well-being. MI spirit reminds practitioners that an overreliance on techniques may miss the larger perspective and philosophy upon which MI operates.

Rollnick (2010) likened MI spirit to the ingredients in a recipe. Too much or too little of one or more ingredients upsets to whole recipe, throwing off the taste. For example, too little evocation or not enough emphasis on acceptance/autonomy can give the feeling that something is adrift or just not right about the session. MI spirit is the foundation and energy for good clinical practice (Rollnick, 2010).

Rollnick (2010) outlined three common communication styles that we see in everyday life (as with our friends, families, and coworkers), and within professional helping relationships. First, there is the *directive* style, in which a clinician tends to direct, prescribe, advise, and lead. An example is when a clinician gives a client direct advice about how to get more exercise. The second style, *guiding*, is when the clinician tends to shepherd, encourage, and motivate. An example is when a clinician helps a client explore a dilemma in their life, examining both sides of the argument and supporting the client's choice in whatever direction he chooses.

The third style is *following*, where the clinician permits, lets things be, and simply allows. For example, a clinician might follow a client who recently experienced a traumatic event and simply needs someone to listen. In this instance, the clinician permits and allows to client to share their story without direct intervention. According to Rollnick (2010), the skillful use of guiding style is most consistent with MI spirit.

Clinicians utilize all these styles within their counseling practice. Indeed, even MI clinicians may vacillate between directive, guiding, and following styles depending on the circumstances. For example, sometimes it is appropriate to simply follow a client who is navigating an emotional struggle or provide direction when clients' immediate health is in danger. However, if clients are struggling with change, showing resistance, are ambivalent, and/or need to learn new skills, the guiding style is ideal (Rollnick, 2010). If clinicians are too directive regarding change, discord increases. If they follow too much, clients might feel they are spinning their wheels, and nothing gets done. In essence, the MI style can be thought of as a balance between directive and following. When strategically guiding our clients, we embrace the MI spirit by communicating "we are in this together" (collaboration), "I'll try to elicit important information from you" (evocation), "I accept you as human being and I'll respect whatever decision you make" (acceptance), and "I care about your health and well-being" (compassion; Miller & Rollnick, 2013).

The reader may notice the words "skillful use of guiding" and "strategically guiding our clients" in the previous paragraphs. These phrases are not accidental because not all guiding is considered MI (Rollnick, 2010). It is the *skillful* use of guiding, or a *refined form* of guiding that best exemplifies MI and MI spirit. As such, MI clinicians have intentional conversations directed at specific change goals, pay close attention to what the client says and how they say it, aim to bring out the client's own arguments for change, and show competence in the methods of MI (strategies and skills; Rollnick, 2010).

Principles of MI

Miller and Rollnick (1991) originally outlined five principles of MI. These principles support the underlying philosophy of MI in terms of how to best help individuals strengthen their motivation and commitment to make positive changes in their lives. Although more recent writings on MI (e.g., Miller & Rollnick, 2013) have integrated these principles into the fabric of MI (rather than present them as five separate principles), for didactic purposes the principles, explored separately, provide a broad canvas from which MI is practiced.

The first principle is *avoiding argumentation*. Harsh confrontation, accusations, and labeling build resistance and are to be avoided at all costs. As noted, practitioners of MI adopt a "gentle, persuasive style" designed to increase a client's awareness of a need for change. Arguments are counterproductive and tend to evoke resistance, opposition, and defensiveness (Miller & Rollnick, 1991). At first glance, it may seem obvious that arguing with clients is not a good idea. However, argumentation can be subtle compared to an outright shouting match. For example, clinicians who are adamant about defending the "change" side of the argument, usually through dire warnings, offering unsolicited advice, or using persuasion may unintentionally create an argumentative atmosphere, forcing the client to defend the "counterchange" side.

The second principle is *rolling with resistance*. A central goal of MI is to reduce the amount of resistance in the therapy session. An analogy related to this principle is often helpful. In their 1991 text, Miller and Rollnick likened how MI handles resistance to "psychological judo." In judo and other forms of martial arts such as aikido, opponent attacks are not met head on; rather, the martial artist uses the attackers' own momentum to knock them off balance or come alongside them, so they end up having the same perspective. In MI, resistance also is not confronted directly. The clinician uses strategies to move with resistance in a way that clinician and client end up seeing the situation the same way or with a new perspective. Rolling with resistance implies that the client is not the opponent to be defeated but an ally who has a critical perspective to offer in counseling (Miller & Rollnick, 1991). In MI, there is great respect for the client; reluctance and ambivalence *are not opposed* but acknowledged by the clinician as understandable and natural reactions to biological and environmental demands. Instead of confronting resistance directly, MI counselors "roll" with resistance by reflecting feelings, offering new perspectives, and demonstrating empathy.

The third principle, *expressing empathy*, is what Miller calls the most important ingredient of MI; if you can't be empathetic, you can't do MI (W. R. Miller, personal communication, 1999). Indeed, empathy is an essential and defining characteristic of MI (Miller & Rollnick, 1991). Clinicians who provide an atmosphere of acceptance have a desire to understand the client's perspective. With unconditional acceptance, clients often discover their own reasons and motivations for change in healthy and productive ways. Although empathy can be demonstrated in several ways, a main vehicle from which it is demonstrated is through reflective listening. With reflective listening, the counselor seeks to understand the client's feelings without judging, criticizing, or blaming. Empathy is also demonstrated by the attitude that reluctance to give up a problem behavior is expected; otherwise change would have already occurred already (Miller & Rollnick, 2002).

The fourth principle, *developing discrepancy*, is the idea that for behavior change to take place it is helpful, if not essential, for clients to experience a discrepancy between their values and goals and their current problematic behavior. The idea for developing discrepancy emanates from Festinger's (1957) theory of cognitive dissonance. According to Festinger, individuals experience dissonance when behaviors and values/goals do not line up or move in the same direction; the person remains stuck in terms of motivation. Dissonance is reduced and motivation enhanced when a person develops greater consistency between what they envision for themselves and behaviors that support this vision. Thus, MI uses a subtle form of confrontation by creating and amplifying a discrepancy (i.e., creating cognitive dissonance) between present behavior and values or goals. An example of developing discrepancy may clarify (Hettama & Langdon, 2009). Assume that an adolescent boy, Daunte, smokes marijuana, and he recently got caught on school property with a stash. He is required to attend counseling. To develop discrepancy, the counselor asks Duante what is important to him and what he values. Daunte responds that he likes to play football, he has a younger brother who looks up to him as a role model, and he would like to graduate and attend college. The clinician then asks Daunte what, if any, effect smoking pot has on playing football, being a role model for his younger brother, and graduating from high school and attending college. In essence, the therapist amplified a discrepancy between Daunte's behavior and his goals and values (Hettema & Langdon, 2009).

Often, clients compartmentalize their behavior from their values and goals (Hettema & Langdon, 2009), precluding an honest analysis of how much their negative behavior, such as substance use, impacts their life. In the previous example, the connection between Daunte's behavior and his values and goals was brought to his awareness. There is a greater possibility now for Daunte to examine this discrepancy and possibly make a choice to change it. Ideally, Daunte will change his behavior to better match his goals. In summary, MI practitioners help *develop* discrepancy *within* the client. This is done by (a) clarifying goals and values, and (b) exploring consequences of present behavior that conflict with these goals and values.

The fifth principle of MI is *supporting self-efficacy*. MI practitioners focus on increasing client perceptions of their ability to change and deal with obstacles on the path to change (Miller & Rollnick, 1991). They also seek to assist in reinforcing a client's hope, optimism, and confidence, thus providing a step beyond recognition of the need for change. Self-efficacy is often enhanced by discussing (a) previous success stories and (b) different approaches that have been successful with other clients in promoting change.

As MI has evolved, Miller and Rollnick (2013) have emphasized some elements of their original ideas more than others and refined the approach based on the vast array of MI research. This refining process has been reflected in their discussion of the principles of MI. More recent versions of the MI principles have stressed the acronym RULE (Rollnick, 2010):

1. **Resisting the righting reflex.** It is human nature to want to help people and make things right, especially in the helping professions. However, it is the method of helping where clinicians can get into trouble. Clinicians must resist the temptation to "make right" what is going on in the client's life. Usually, this reflex involves giving unsolicited advice, coming across as the "expert" on the client, warning, prematurely focusing on a topic, and arguing.

2. **Understanding client's own motivations.** This principle is consistent with the importance of evoking from our clients their own motivations, ideas, and thoughts about change. Part of clients creating their own motivations for change depends on clinicians skillfully eliciting their ideas and reflecting these back to clients.

3. **Listen with empathy.** A defining characteristic of MI that will always be a foundation of the approach.

4. **Empower the client.** Perhaps like "supporting self-efficacy."

The Four Processes of MI

Miller and Rollnick (2013) outlined four key processes in MI that helps us with the question "What does MI look like in clinical practice?" The first process is *engaging*. Engaging involves building rapport by the strategic use of open questions, affirmations, reflections, and summaries (OARS). Engaging is more than simply being "nice" or "friendly"; it involves intentional listening and avoiding the "righting reflex." Engaging also entails exploring the broader goals and values of the client: What interests the client? What do they value? What is important to them? With engagement, there is a sense that the counselor and client are moving in the same direction. Although engaging with clients can take some time, do not underestimate how quickly this can take place with intentional listening and empathy.

The next process is *focusing*. One of the features of MI that I most appreciate is the emphasis on getting more focused in counseling sessions. We, as clinicians, can always work on getting more focused! In my teaching experience, counseling students and new counselors notoriously struggle in this area. Whereas clients certainly do come in with a broad range of difficulties that can make it difficult to know where to begin, the focusing process can help. With focusing, the clinician homes in on something the client would like to change. It may be a specific behavior (reducing drinking), or something broader such as building a successful recovery plan. Once the area of focus is determined, the conversation centers on that for the session. Simple questions such as "What change(s) are we going to focus on today? And what is the topic of our focus?" can help clinicians establish focus. If the conversation veers off course, the clinician gently moves the discussion back to the daily topic (for some additional strategies to establish focus, see Miller & Rollnick, 2013).

The third process is *evoking*. As noted, evocation is part of MI spirit. Here, clinicians elicit from clients their own ideas about change. In addition, evocation plays a major role in eliciting change talk. Indeed, assessing the client's own thoughts about change is at the heart of MI (Miller & Rollnick, 2013).

The processes of engaging, focusing, and evoking are important for building motivation, importance, confidence, and readiness to change (Lewis et al., 2017) and defining the MI approach. That is, MI serves the purpose of helping people resolve ambivalence to create movement toward making positive changes in their lives. Planning, the fourth process, is not an *essential* process of MI (i.e., MI can be fully defined without planning; Lewis et al., 2017); however, Miller and Rollnick (2013) did acknowledge that once sufficient motivation is established, clinicians must take an additional step with their clients to see change through cocreating/negotiating a plan for change.

Clients are usually ready to move to planning when change talk is heightened, sustain talk is lessened or absent, and there is strong commitment language (i.e., client statements suggesting a solid commitment to make a change). Planning should entail exploration of barriers to change, activities, supports, goals, and markers for knowing change has happened.

With the MI spirit, goals, principles, and process as our foundation, we are now ready to examine the application of MI in the treatment of substance use problems. The following sections will focus more on the skills of MI within substance use counseling, within the context of the aforementioned tenets of the approach.

Application of MI in the Treatment of Substance Use Disorders

With a strong grounding in the MI approach, we are now ready to apply skills and techniques to enhance our practice. As you will see, the strategies that follow serve to promote spirit, carry out the processes, and follow the key principles. When practicing MI, it is important to keep these connections in mind. MI is an intentional process, with skills that link directly with its underlying philosophy. Using skills without this grounding makes MI seem too technical and places the alliance at risk.

Increasing Importance

Miller and Rollnick (2013) explored the need to assess how important change is to clients. Clearly, if clients do not believe that changing their substance use patterns is very important, little effort will be exerted inside and outside of the counseling session. Clients who are low on importance would fit into the "precontemplation" stage of change: They see little importance in making a change in their substance use, deny the seriousness of their use, and may question why they are in counseling. In MI, an imperative early assessment is to determine how important change is to the client. Specific components and techniques that facilitate increasing importance are presented next.

Reflective Listening

Reflective listening is at the heart of MI technique (Cole, 2008). Used strategically, reflections minimize resistance, convey understanding, and express empathy. Although reflective listening is a critical skill through all levels of client motivation, it is particularly relevant when a client is low on importance. In reflective listening, the clinician seeks to summarize client meaning in the form of a guess or hypothesis. Reflections are statements, rather than questions, and encourage clients to continue forward in discussing a concern (Cole, 2008). There are generally two types of reflections, simple and complex.

A simple reflection (SR) states back to clients what was said, usually by paraphrasing. A complex reflection (CR) adds meaning to client statements in the form of underlying emotion, body language, or other nuances. Complex reflection emanates from the question "What is the client experiencing?" As an example of each type of reflection, consider the following client statement:

> **CLIENT:** I don't know. I just can't seem to muster the energy to go to those stupid meetings. I mean, are they really that helpful, anyway?
>
> **SR:** You are wondering if the AA meetings are even beneficial.
>
> **CR:** You feel drained when thinking about going to those meetings, and you are frustrated because you don't get a lot out of them.

Notice with the simple reflection the clinician is simply paraphrasing what the client stated; there is no attempt to add meaning. In the complex reflection, the clinician adds meaning to move the conversation forward. For example, "and you are frustrated because you don't get a lot out of them" was not specifically stated by the client. The client would likely respond, "Heck yeah, I am frustrated, and here is why ..." Or the client might say, "No, frustrated is not the right word, but anger is!" Either way, the clinician gains valuable information about the client, even if the reflection is off the mark. Client responses to reflections tell us if we are on track with our hypotheses, paving the way to greater rapport and empathy.

OARS+I

The acronym OARS+I stands for *o*pen-ended questions, *a*ffirmations, *r*eflections, *s*ummary, and *i*nformation exchange. OARS+I encompasses basic counseling strategies designed to build rapport, demonstrate empathy, and assist in moving the client up the importance ladder. These are excellent skills for opening sessions with clients. As Rosengren (2018) noted, strategic use of these skills can have a dramatic effect on how a client responds during an interaction (e.g., with enhanced or lowered resistance). Although these skills were not created by MI they are used strategically and given emphasis throughout one's work with clients. Let's briefly take each in turn.

Open-Ended Questions

In MI, therapists attempt to stay in preponderance of open-ended questions (Cole, 2009). Open questions allow for greater exploration and set the stage for clients to respond beyond one-word answers. This skill fits with the MI spirit component of "evocative" in that open questions help to elicit from clients thoughts, beliefs, attitudes and feelings about their own behavior, the possibility of change, and so forth. Arguments for change are more likely to be explored with open-ended questions. Although open questions are a basic counseling skill across all therapeutic approaches, in MI there is a directive quality to them in that they are strategically used to elicit change talk and move the client closer toward resolving ambivalence.

Asking a preponderance of open questions is what a good guide does (Rollnick, 2010). Strategic and skillfully used open-ended questions convey a searching, curious, respectful, and simple quality that clients appreciate: "What concerns do you have about your drug use?" "How would you really like to change this?" "How might you do this?" are examples (Rollnick, 2010).

Affirmations

Affirmations are statements of appreciation related to client effort, internal characteristics, and behavior. For example, a clinician might affirm to a client, "You have a lot of strength coming in and talking to me today given all that has happened." Affirmations are essentially reflections, although designed to anchor clients in their own strengths and resources. To borrow a term from narrative therapy, clients often enter counseling with *problem-saturated stories*. Affirmations counter these stories with words of encouragement and strength. Rosengren

(2018) pointed out making affirmations can be surprisingly tricky, as it is easy to slip into the trap of coming across as patronizing or insincere. To avoid this trap, Rosengren suggested that MI practitioners should, among other suggestions, use affirmations that (a) focus on specific behaviors and internal attributes instead of decisions, goals, and so forth; (b) avoid using the word "I"; and (c) nurture a competent rather than deficient worldview of clients. These suggestions increase the likelihood that affirmations will be well received; however, they still must come from a place of genuineness.

Suggestion (b) deserves a bit more focus. It is sometimes difficult to avoid "I" statements, as they come so natural to clinicians. Statement such as "I think" or "I really appreciate" are common ways that helpers convey optimism or hope for their clients. However, "I" statements also have an evaluative element to them and are more about complimenting/praising rather than affirming (Rosengren, 2018). Stating affirmations as "you" statements makes them less evaluative and places them squarely on the client's own internal resources and strengths (Rosengren, 2018). Here are some other examples of affirmations:

> "You are someone who cares deeply for your children and are willing to fight to keep them."

> "You have great determination, despite setbacks, to make your life be different."

> "You have a lot of resolve to come today, despite your strong reservations about treatment."

Reflections

Reflections were discussed previously; however, there is an additional guideline that should be mentioned. As a rule, reflection to question ratios should be around 2:1 (although for advanced practitioners, a ratio of 3:1 is often considered the gold standard). The reason for this is that too many questions can pull clinicians into *the question and answer trap* (Miller & Rollnick, 2013). The question and answer trap is when the clinician primarily relies on questions to get information, many of which are close. Too many questions can seem like an interrogation and at times come across as judgmental, resulting in increased resistance. Using more reflections to every question helps avoid these potential pitfalls.

Summaries

Session summaries are designed to help keep the momentum of counseling moving forward (Cole, 2009; Rosengren, 2018) and should include two primary elements when possible: the client's ambivalence about making changes, and change talk, or client statements that suggest change is being considered (more on this later; Rosengren, 2018). In general, summaries are considered complex reflections involving anywhere from 3 to 10 small sentences (Cole, 2009).

Summaries are useful to keep the discussion focused and help clients reflect on their own ambivalence and change. Although the number of session summaries may vary depending on the topic, stage of change, or client characteristics, a general guideline is to use them when needed and it feels natural to the counselor. Miller and Rollnick (2002, as cited in Rosengren, 2018) cautioned about the overuse of summaries, which can seem artificial. Thus, it would be wise to use no more than one per session, and even consider one every few sessions. Ideally, summaries are used as needed, usually in the middle or toward the end of a session. In my experience, making intentional use of summaries is a strategy that often is neglected in counseling practice. However, strategic use of summaries can be a powerful way to convey empathy, keep things on track, and reflect client feelings/thoughts about change. An example of a session summary might look like this:

> **CLINICIAN:** You have been under a lot of stress recently and alcohol has usually provided an escape. At the same time, you do recognize how drinking as negatively impacted your family and work life. You're really trying hard to be a better father, husband, and employee, and cutting down or stopping drinking is something you are considering. Anything I've missed?

In this example, both recommendations for a good summary are met: The client's ambivalence is noted (alcohol provides an escape and drinking has negatively impacted their life) and change talk is reinforced (trying hard to be a better). Rollnick (2010) and Miller and Rollnick (2013) suggested that clinicians need to gather the key parts of what the client has stated, analogous to picking out the flowers in a wild meadow. The summary is likened to a "bouquet" of key information that is provided for the client to digest. In addition, summaries should use "you" language as much as possible and the clinician's own words (i.e., don't simply repeat back what the client said). Finally, summaries are a great strategy to use when the clinician is lost or wants to change direction (Rollnick, 2010). After a good summary, a simple "Where would you like to go from here?" or "What do you make of that?" can often be enough to move in fruitful directions.

Information Exchange

Information exchange is a relatively new addition to the OARS skill set, although it has always been part of the MI process. At first glance, providing information may seem like delivering advice inconsistent with MI. However, sometimes therapists need to give information depending on client circumstances. Giving information about previous treatments that have been successful with other clients, on the potential dangers of continued use, or on alternative resources for recovery such as Alcoholics Anonymous can correct inaccurate information and thus boost confidence. In addition, information exchange is not a one-way path (Rosengren, 2018). Clients can and do offer expertise on themselves and their situations. The give and take of information exchange can lead to new ideas and compromise.

Rollnick et al. (1999), however, cautioned that providing information should be done in an MI-consistent manner. In Rollnick et al.'s (1999) view, the elicit-provide-elicit model accomplishes this task. The basic idea is to find out what the client already knows (elicit), then provide information that the client doesn't know, or correct misinformation (provide), and then check in with the client in terms of what they make of that information (elicit). This pattern, elicit-provide-elicit, continues for however long is necessary. Elicit-provide-elicit respects what clients know and what they think about the information the clinician just told them.

Importantly, information exchange can be useful with most processes of MI, including focusing, eliciting, and planning (Rosengren, 2018) It can be helpful for clients who are low on confidence and want ideas to help them reach their recovery goals. The question is not so much whether information should be given but how it is given to maximize its effectiveness. Rosengren (2018) provided several guidelines for giving information:

1. Ask permission.
2. Offer ideas. Don't try to persuade.
3. Ask if clients want the information in the first place.
4. Give clients permission to disagree with you.
5. Be concise. Don't ramble or offer too many concerns.
6. Use a menu if possible. A menu stands for "menu of options." The idea is to suggest two or three options from which the client can choose to bolster a sense of freedom and responsibility. For example, clients may be offered a choice among psychoeducation, individual counseling, or group therapy in a substance use treatment facility.
7. Solicit what clients think or what the information means to them.

Specific Strategies to Increase Importance

Listed are several strategies that clinicians can utilize to increase importance. Following each strategy is a brief explanation as to why it can assist in this effort.

- **Develop discrepancies between behaviors and goals/values.** As discussed previously, developing discrepancies can be a powerful way for clients to gain insights into how their substance use fits (or doesn't fit) with their goals or values. For example, a client who sees that her drinking interferes with her goal of being a better mother may give greater importance to stopping or cutting down.

- **Ruler exercise.** "On a scale of 1–10, with 1 being not important and 10 being very important, how important is changing your cocaine use to you?" If the client says "5", the clinician follows up with "And what makes it a 5 instead of a lower number? What would it take to move it from a 5 to a 5.5 or 6?" The ruler exercise can be quite helpful in getting a sense of where the client is in terms of importance. If the client is relatively low, this signals that more time should be spent on importance. If the client gives a high rating, then moving on to other topics may be more valuable.

- **Roll with resistance.** A general MI principle, rolling with resistance tends to lower rather than engender client defensiveness. Clients are more likely to consider change and increase importance if they do not feel attacked, blamed, or criticized.

- **Worst case/best case outcomes (Cole, 2008).** This technique involves a series of questions that query clients on extremes of maintaining the status quo and extremes of making a change in substance use. Examples include "What would be the best-case scenario if you did not change your substance use? If you did?" and "What would be the worst-case scenario of you did not change your substance use? If you did?" These questions tend to elicit statements about the possibility of change, especially if the consequences of the client's substance use are severe. In such cases, clients often state that the worst case of continuing to use is injury or death, and the best case is continuing to be miserable. Clients would be hard pressed not to give a little more weight (importance) to the direction of change after considering these questions.

- **Find out what is important. Negotiate for change.** For clients who continue to find little motivation to change (and higher resistance toward change), inquiring about what is important for the client to talk about can often help get things started. For example, a client may have little interest in looking at their drinking but does want to talk about how their boss at work is out to get them. Although talking about the client's employer may not be an optimal avenue to pursue, such a discussion allows the clinician to honor what is important for the client and consequently builds rapport. By using OARS+I, it is almost certain that the subject of drinking will eventually present itself, especially if there is a relation between the client's drinking and poor performance at work. Another strategy is to negotiate what the clinician and client will talk about. In this example, the clinician could agree to talk about the client's employer for half the session, but the second half would need to focus on and explore the client's drinking and how that fits into their life.

  Some readers may disagree with the notion that something other than substance use be discussed, given the obvious trouble it causes. This point is well taken; however, in my experience a premature focus on substance use before sufficient rapport has been built can often backfire, engendering more resistance. It may be better to explore what is on the client's mind, knowing that eventually substance use will emerge in the discussion or that clinicians can negotiate later if needed.

- **Explore the meaning of events that brought the client in to counseling.** This strategy is like the previous bullet point in that the goal is to explore, from the client's perspective, what meaning they give to why they came to counseling. What perspective do they have about the issue? Many clients with substance use disorders do not have an opportunity to share their side to others. They may be viewed as manipulative and deceitful and cannot be trusted, so they are not listened to by law enforcement, the courts, family, or other social systems. It is unfortunately true that many of their actions created these reactions in others; however, the point is that if they are heard and accepted in the therapy setting, the door opens to the possibility of change (because resistance is lowered). An excellent way to develop rapport, lower resistance, and encourage change is to ask for the client's perspective about what brought them in to counseling and how they view change. Give them a chance to tell their side.

Resolving Ambivalence

Ambivalence plays a major role in why someone remains stuck in their substance use or other problem behavior. From the MI perspective, ambivalence about giving up substance use, for example, is considered normal and expected rather than pathological. A major goal of MI is to help clients reduce ambivalence so that they no longer are immobilized by feeling two ways about something (e.g., giving up versus not giving up substances). Although it is true that a client might choose to keep using substances, MI practitioners focus on and explore the change side of the equation, with the underlying belief that if clients are provided an atmosphere consistent with the MI spirit, the decisional balance will "tip" in favor of behavior change, health, and wellness. Specific components and techniques that facilitate resolving ambivalence are presented.

Eliciting Change Talk

In their 1991 edition of *Motivational Interviewing: Preparing People to Change Substance Using Behavior*, Miller and Rollnick stressed the importance of client statements that appeared to signal an increased motivation to change substance using behavior, calling them "self-motivational statements." However, in their most recent edition (2013), they refer to self-motivational statements as *change talk*, a term that better captures the intention behind client language when motivation increases: the desire to change in a positive direction. Change talk has become a significant and defining concept in MI, based on the premise that the more a client talks about change, the more likely that change will be realized. Rollnick et al. (2008) stated,

> In successful MI, the change talk statements you collect from the patient are like little weights placed on the "pro-change" side of a balance. Helping patients to voice pro-change arguments gradually tips the balance in the direction of change. (p. 42)

MI clinicians listen for change talk, reflect it, and reinforce it whenever possible. If change talk is not happening, then MI clinicians use open questions to *elicit* it from clients.

Methods for Eliciting Change Talk

Based on research by Amrhein et al. (2004), there are six main types of change talk. The first represents a client's *desire* to change and is indicated by statements such as "I really want to change my substance use." The second type of change talk reflects client *ability* to change; "I know I can do it if I put my mind to it." The third type includes *reasons* for change, such as the statement, "If I cut back on my drinking, my wife won't get so angry with me." Finally, the fourth type includes the *need* for change; "I have to change my cocaine use, or I will die." The reader will notice that each first letter of the first four types of change talk spell the acronym DARN. The components of DARN indicate preparatory change talk (Miller & Rollnick, 2013). Preparatory change talk suggests the client is considering change but has not yet made a strong commitment. Clinicians can use DARN as a quick mnemonic for remembering questions for eliciting change talk:

D—"Why do you want to change your cocaine use?"

A—"What abilities within you suggest you could cut down on alcohol use?"

R—"What are some reasons for stopping your heroin use?"

N—"Why would you need to make a change in your substance use?"

In addition to DARN, MI practitioners attempt to elicit mobilizing change talk, which includes *commitment language*, *activation*, and *taking steps* toward change, spelling the acronym CATS:

C—"How strong is your commitment to changing your marijuana use?"

A—"What are you willing to do at this point?"

T&S—"What steps have you taken to already to curb your drinking?"

Mobilizing change talk is a form of language that strongly conveys clients are ready and willing to change. The change process has gained momentum, and their commitment is high. This would be an appropriate time to consider moving to the planning process.

Using an analogy, Miller and Rollnick (2013) noted that preparatory change talk is like the client trudging up a big hill. On the way up, their motivation is slowly but surely increasing and strengthening, with some possible backsliding here and there. Once they reach the peak and start to descend the hill, motivation gains momentum through mobilizing change talk and a strengthening resolve and commitment. This analogy, of course, is the ideal scenario. Many times, clients will remain stuck going up the hill (i.e., preparatory change talk), never really committing to change. In addition, clients can, within a few sessions, convey relatively strong mobilizing change talk.

You will notice that the previous questions related to each letter in DARN CATS command a response that will increase the likelihood of change talk. If a client responds with change talk, therapists have several strategies from which to draw. They can elaborate on the change talk (e.g., "Tell me more about your use"), affirm the change talk (e.g., "It is not easy to stop using and you are seeing the importance of doing so"), reflect (e.g., "You can see many reasons to stop drinking"), and summarize. Ending counseling sessions with summaries allow clients to leave with their own change language fresh in their minds. The important consideration is that clinicians do not ignore change talk, but rather use it to build and strengthen motivation to change.

Additional Strategies

In a sense, the previous strategies for eliciting change talk assume that the client has at least some motivation for change. For example, the question "Why do you want to make this change?" suggests that the client has already considered changing, but the talk about change needs to be strengthened. However, what about clients who are clearly precontemplative and do not see any need for change despite numerous negative consequences? In such cases, additional strategies for eliciting change talk can be used (Miller & Rollnick, 1991). These strategies, like DARN CATS, are in the form of open questions:

1. Problem recognition: "In what ways has this been a problem for you?"
2. Expression of concern: "What is it about your substance use that you and others see as a concern?"

3. Intention to change: "I can see that you are stuck now. What's going to have to change?"
4. Optimism: "What gives you the hope that you could change if you wanted to?"

Statements of problem recognition, concern, intention to change, or optimism can be followed up in a similar manner as outlined (elaborate, affirm, reflect, or summarize).

Handling Discord

Before clients can resolve their own ambivalence about making a change, they must be in an atmosphere where discord is lowered. From the MI perspective, discord occurs when the counselor and client are not in agreement; it is *between* people rather than *in* clients. Somehow, things just aren't working. Discord is "lively" in that it forces the clinician to do something different. Indeed, the implication is that clinician style can have a tremendous impact on the level of discord. Clinicians who operate inconsistent with the MI spirit (noncollaborative, argue, harshly confront, or ask too many questions), may unintentionally engender discord rather than help to lower it.

There are two main strategies for handling discord, reflective responses and strategic responses. These strategies are somewhat "quiet" in practice; however, when used consistently over time they can have a profound impact on lowering discord. Table 6.1 lists these strategies and provides a brief definition, uses, and tips related to each, followed by examples.

TABLE 6.1 Reflective and Strategic Strategies for Handling Discord

Reflective Responses	Definition/Uses/Tips	Examples
Simple reflection	Stating back what the client just said; paraphrase	**CLIENT:** I am not happy being here talking about my substance use. **CLINICIAN:** This isn't the most joyful experience for you.
Amplified reflection	Slight exaggeration *or* increase in intensity of client statements Amplify resistant element, no sarcasm or hostility Can allow student/client to become aware of extremity of position and back away from this Can be a bit playful Use when relationship is strong	**CLIENT:** They would make fun of me at school if I didn't drink like I normally do at parties. **CLINICIAN:** People would be *rolling on the floor* if you didn't drink like you do now! **CLIENT:** I will never succeed at this abstinence thing. **CLINICIAN:** It is *hopeless*, I guess.

(continued)

TABLE 6.1   Reflective and Strategic Strategies for Handling Discord (*Continued*)

Reflective Responses	Definition/Uses/Tips	Examples
Double-sided reflection	Captures both sides of the client's ambivalence Try to end on the change side in your reflection	**CLIENT:** I know that smoking pot isn't the best thing to do for my health. But I don't see the big deal in doing it occasionally with friends. **CLINICIAN:** Yeah, it's kind of perplexing. On the one hand you like to hang out and smoke with friends, and on the other hand you may see some real positives about the benefits of stopping.
Strategic Responses	**Definition/Uses/Tips**	**Examples**
Shifting focus	To shift client's attention away from stumbling blocks precluding the movement toward progress (labels, blaming others, stating what client thinks counselor is thinking, etc.) Introducing other areas of concern Moving away from labels; "let's not worry about that now, let's focus on this" If you get too focused on convincing, you move away from exploring ambivalence	**CLIENT:** I know you probably think I am some kind of alcoholic or something. **CLINICIAN:** Your experience of drinking has you concerned. Tell me more about what happened when you got the DUI.
Emphasizing personal choice and control	Autonomy in action Only client can decide; client determines what happens	**CLIENT:** I'm not sure how you will take this, but I'm just not going to quit using. **CLINICIAN:** My hope for you would be to reconsider; however, what decision you make is up to you—nobody can make it for you.
Reframe	Seeing things in a different way; turning negatives into strengths Validates client's observations, but adds new information	**CLIENT:** I really want to remain off this stuff (opiates), but I'm sick of trying. No matter how hard I try, I just keep failing. **CLINICIAN:** We can always learn something from what we consider failures. R. H. Macy failed several times before his department stores took off. Tell me something you have learned from these setbacks.

TABLE 6.1   Reflective and Strategic Strategies for Handling Discord (*Continued*)

Strategic Responses	Definition/Uses/Tips	Examples
Agreement with a twist	To initially side with the client but introduce a new consideration or direction, usually in a positive direction Reflection followed by a reframe (a different way of viewing things that is in a more positive direction) Tricky to do; may be more complex than other responses	**CLIENT:** I hate this whole abstinence thing. I hate everything about it. **CLINICIAN:** You are not happy with how difficult abstaining can be, and yet finishing this program is one way you can see your family and benefit you in the long run.
Coming alongside	Defending the counterchange side may elicit change talk from client Counselor defends not changing at the time, but queries when the right time might be Use strategically as a last resort, when all else fails	**CO:** I can't handle this abstinence thing. I am just not up to it. **CLINICIAN:** Maybe you are right. Maybe all this alcohol-free stuff is too hard. At this time, you would rather drink, even with some consequences, than go through an alcohol-free program. I hear that now may not the right time; when would be the right time?

Note: Examples based on Miller and Rollnick (2002) and Cole (2008).

Specific Strategies to Resolve Ambivalence

Listed are several strategies that clinicians can utilize to explore and/or resolve ambivalence. Following each strategy, a brief explanation is offered as to why each may be useful toward this end.

- **Continue OARS+I.** Remember that OARS+I includes foundational skills of MI. They should be incorporated throughout MI treatment because they aid in exploration of the client's perspective and ambivalence.

- **Clarify target behavior.** It can be difficult to use MI without establishing a clear target behavior. Clarifying the target behavior (e.g., cutting down on drinking, stopping cocaine use, no longer hanging out with friends who use) sets the stage for exploring and working through ambivalence. Examples of questions to elicit a target behavior are "What is it that you would like different?" and "What is it that you would like to work on/change?" Sometimes the target behavior may need to be defined collaboratively if the client is unsure.

- **Ruler exercise.** This ruler exercise also can be useful for resolving ambivalence. If a client records a "5" they are ambivalent about changing her substance use. The two sides of the equation can then be explored.

- **Explore both sides of ambivalence.** Once a target behavior has been established, and the clinician determines where a client falls on the 1–10 importance ruler exercise, momentum is set for exploring parts of the client that want to change and parts that do not. The clinician adopts a position of curiosity about both sides of the change equation, with emphasis on where the client stands on the change side of things.

- **Decisional balance (pros/cons exploration).** Sometimes it is helpful for clients to talk through or even write out their own ambivalence. In the decisional balance exercise, the clinician asks about the pros and cons of making a change and pros and cons of *not* making a change. Admittedly, clients are sometimes taken aback by being asked about what is good about using drugs. It is essential, however, that both sides be explored. As Miller and Rollnick (2002) noted, the experience of ambivalence can be confusing and frustrating. Exploring ambivalence in this manner helps clients sort out their confusion and provides some level of understanding as to why they remain stuck in self-defeating substance use patterns. Clients are in a better position to assess their own predicament and make choices to change them.

  More recent research, however, has called into question the relevance of the decisional balance exercise in some circumstances (Miller & Forcehimes, 2015). That is, if clinicians do this exercise with clients who are already ambivalent, it can actually increase their ambivalence, leaving clients stuck. If they have a clear direction from which to change, then why do the decisional balance in the first place? Miller and Forcehimes suggested that when clinicians are neutral about a decision (i.e., showing equipoise), the decisional balance may be useful. The key is intentionally not steering the client in one direction or the other. In cases of substance use, the direction of change from using to not using seems clear. However, there may be many other decisions in the client's life where the clinician can remain neutral, facilitate exploration of ambivalence, and encourage the client to make their own choice. Overall, I have found the decisional balance exercise quite helpful in simply exploring a client's use, without insisting that it lead to a decision.

- **Reinforce/reflect/summarize change talk.** Any statements about change should be reflected to the client. Doing so facilitates building their own arguments for change and may propel them to feel less ambivalence.

Enhancing Confidence

Many times, clients will know that stopping or changing their substance use is important and feel relatively little ambivalence. Nonetheless, they keep engaging in harmful use and still can't seem to stop. In these situations, the issue is not importance or ambivalence, but confidence. I have had many clients with opiate use disorder come to me and report a 9 or 10 on the importance ruler, yet still cannot seem to stop. They are fully aware of the negative consequence so of using. It is ultimately a question of *how* to stop.

At first glance, one may consider building confidence as relatively easy, given that the client is most likely high on importance and less resistant; The hard part is over. To the contrary, building confidence is surprisingly difficult to do. This may resonate with you; Can you think of a behavior or habit you would like to change only to persistently "fail" at change attempts. Knowing something needs to change is not the same as knowing how to go about doing it. If building confidence were easy, clients would be able to stop using substances without any problems. We know this is not the case.

Specific Strategies for Building Confidence

Listed are several strategies clinicians can utilize to build confidence. Following each strategy, a brief explanation is offered as to why it may be useful for that purpose.

- **Open-ended questions focused on ability and strengths.** Helping clients explore what abilities and strengths they possess and can call on to help them in their recovery builds confidence. Sometimes, simply reminding clients of abilities that they have talked about, that others see in them, or that the clinician sees in them is helpful.

- **Ruler question/exercise focused on confidence.** This technique is the same as the importance ruler exercise, except that the focus is on confidence about changing substance use.

- **Personal supports.** In my practice, I often like to ask, "Who is in your corner?" or "Who is on your side?" The purpose of these questions is to assist the client in clarifying who can be an ally in their recovery. Knowing someone has their back can be reassuring for clients and help build confidence.

- **Past successes at change.** This strategy is based on the popular quip "success begets success." Clients often minimize or simply forget about previous times they were able to overcome difficulties. Exploring past successes, what clients learned from these successes, and how they can bring this information to their current substance use problem can help in supporting self-efficacy and confidence. The mantra is "I did it before, and I can do it again."

- **Information and advice that is MI consistent.** See discussion under the "Information Exchange" section.

- **Hypothetical change, envisioning change and anticipating challenges.** Clients often struggle with what a change in substance use will "look like." Encouraging clients to envision change, or to think hypothetically how their life would be different when not using drugs, can help them think through what thoughts and behaviors are important or consistent with recovery. Any anticipated challenges, and methods to overcome those challenges, should be discussed. When the path of how one might change is clarified, momentum and confidence is increased.

- **Explore barriers to change.** Making note of and anticipating barriers to the change process is another way to strengthen confidence. Many clients would feel more confident in remaining substance free if they knew how to handle what gets in their way. Barriers to change include negative peer relationships, stress, psychological problems, and so forth. Exploring these barriers may open space for clients to consider possible remedies and thus move the positive change process forward.

Strengthening Commitment

When clients are high on importance and confidence, they are ready to change their substance use; in other words, they are beginning to make a commitment to change. MI practitioners focus on strengthening this commitment. Clinicians switch from exploring ambivalence to encouraging action when the client indicates a decision to make a change. Clinicians assist in developing a plan for change (i.e., negotiating a change), not imposing a plan. The goal at this stage is to get and secure commitment with questions such as "How will you go about that?" "When will you start?" and "How likely will you do it?"

How Do You Know Clients Are Ready to Change?

Clients are ready to change when there is an abundance of change talk, and they are high on importance, confidence, and readiness. They may be starting to envision change, and discord noticeably decreases as they may portray a "quiet resolve." The focus of therapy moves form exploration to action (Cole, 2008). Incorporating techniques from other theoretical models may be useful at this stage.

One must be cautious, however, of moving ahead too quickly and pushing for change before the client is ready. Clinicians might slip into the trap of taking too much of a lead, which is inconsistent with the collaborative spirit of MI. They may make change plans that are too big, which become overwhelming for clients or may fail to account for the number and type of client resources to help carry out the change plan (Cole, 2008).

Creating Change Plans

Change plans can be completed during the entire therapy session or in small pieces (e.g., completing one piece per session). Good change plans are specific and include barriers to change and ways to overcome them. Goals are written in measurable, behavioral terms. Good change plans also include a time frame as to when clients will start and who in their life will support them.

Change plans can be a written exercise (e.g., using the change plan worksheet in Miller & Rollnick, 2002) or discussed verbally. The written exercise adds a bit more formality to the process, and clinicians can even treat it as a sort of contract between clinician and client. The written change plans also can be placed in or around the client's home as a reminder of one's commitment toward change.

MI in the Treatment of Diverse Populations

The basic tenets of MI, in particular its affirming, respectful stance toward clients, seem to be well suited and applicable across a diverse sample of client populations. Emerging research within the past 2 decades confirms this initial view. Indeed, MI has amassed an impressive array of research that, in general, supports it as an effective approach with *various client problems*, such as substance use. Given that MI is a relatively new counseling approach compared to traditional psychotherapies, researchers have been focused on assessing its effectiveness as a legitimate therapeutic intervention. It seems reasonable and only a matter of time that scholars will place greater attention on the applicability of MI across multicultural populations.

There is no doubt that MI is having global reach. For example, Thevos et al. (2000) found that MI enhanced water disinfection practices in Zambia compared to standard health education practices. The Motivational Interviewing Network of Trainers (MINT), an association of individuals who have been trained in the teaching of MI, hold annual workshops worldwide. These workshops attract educators, therapists, teachers, and others in the helping professions from around the world, including the Americas, Canada, Australia, Europe, the Middle East, and Asia (Motivational Interviewing Network of Trainers (2021)). The first video demonstration of MI, the *Motivational Interviewing Professional Training Videotape Series* (Miller et al., 1998), now includes translations in Chinese, Italian, Slovenian, French, Portuguese, Spanish, German, and Swedish. Stephen Rollnick stressed the success of using MI to address HIV/AIDS prevention among South African women (Rollnick, 2010). Clearly, no current therapy approach is "hotter" than MI, and it appears to have acceptance as a legitimate approach across many regions of the world.

The effectiveness of MI with diverse populations has support in the literature. Dickerson et al. (2016, as cited in Morris et al., 2021) noted that the underlying philosophy of MI is consistent with Native American beliefs and found that urban Native American and Alaska Native youth appreciated the open style and collaborative nature of MI and the approach helped them feel more connected. In a 5-year randomized control trial (RCT), Morris et al. (2021) found that a culturally adapted MI (CAMI) brief intervention may be effective in reducing marijuana use among Native American teens at 3 months. The adaptation included a partnership in which Native American values were integrated into the treatment implementation, while maintaining the integrity of MI, and strong Indigenous community involvement occurred in every phase of the study. In a study with African American participants, Longshore and Grills (2000) sought to learn if community health interventions were more effective when they incorporated cultural values congruent with the community. The authors conducted a randomized field trial using a motivational intervention to promote recovery from illegal drug use among a sample of 269 African Americans. The "culturally congruent intervention" incorporated elements of MI, the transtheoretical model (TTM) of behavior change, and activities fitting with African American values (e.g., communalism). At the 1-year follow up, drug use was significantly less likely in the experimental group. The implication from this finding is that using MI with African American clients may be enhanced if cultural values are included as part of the counseling process.

Field and Caetano (2010) explored the connection between ethnic matching between patient and provider and its effect on brief alcohol interventions. They found that Hispanics who were matched ethically with their counselor, and who received a motivational intervention, experienced significant reductions in drinking outcomes at 12-month follow-up. Although ethnic matching may not be possible at all substance use treatment centers or mental health agencies, these results suggest that, at least among Hispanic clients, arranging to work with a counselor of similar cultural background may be beneficial.

Other studies have shown that MI is effective, but not necessarily more so than other approaches. For example, Arroyo et al. (2003) sought to determine the role of Hispanic ethnicity on long-term outcomes in three alcohol treatment approaches (motivational enhancement therapy, CBT, and 12-step facilitation therapy). The sample was comprised of 105 non-Hispanic White and 100 Hispanic participants in Project MATCH (Albuquerque, New Mexico, treatment site). In both the CBT and MET groups, Hispanics and non-Hispanic White participants showed similarly favorable outcomes. The results suggested that motivational approaches were not superior to CBT in this study.

Adapting MI to the cultural context of clients appears critical to its effectiveness with diverse clientele (Cordisco Tsai & Sebellos-Llena, 2020). Cultural adaptation means more than being aware of the cultural differences between client and counselor. The change or adaptation to an approach can include surface level (or surface structure) or deeper, core level (or deep structure). Surface-level adaptations include changing interventions to better fit the client's cultural background, such as providing therapy in the client's language. Deep structure adaptation entails have a solid understanding of the cultural variables and experiences that have shaped the client's life and how these can impact the effectiveness of counseling. The client's view of counseling and the process of change from their cultural background, for example, may need additional reflective listening and evocation to ease fears, promote collaboration, and foster understanding.

Adapting MI does not mean that the integrity of the approach is compromised. Rather, culturally adapted MI can result is an intervention that is intellectually and emotionally associated to client's values and goals. Overall, the goal of many researchers studying MI interventions is to competently adapt MI to the cultural background of clients while also keeping the integrity of approach, namely MI spirit, the helping skills, expressing empathy, and evoking client ideas about change. Of course, there will always be broad questions about how best to integrate culture into any psychotherapeutic approach. Researchers are currently doing just that with MI.

These reviews are not intended to be a thorough review of MI and it use with diverse clientele. Overall, researchers have found MI useful with diverse populations; in some cases, cultural adaptation in conjunction with MI appears to boost its effectiveness (see Diverse Perspectives and Examples). More outcome-based research is needed to better understand the use of MI with diverse samples and how it might be adjusted to fit with clients from different cultural backgrounds.

CHAPTER 6 Motivational Interviewing in the Treatment of Substance Use Disorders | 135

DIVERSE PERSPECTIVES AND EXAMPLES

◇◇◇◇◇◇◇◇

In my university work, I was fortunate to be a part of a large "health disparities" research grant, based on a study to test the effectiveness of MI in the prevention of diabetes among at-risk African Americans. Whereas the target behaviors for change are eating healthier and exercising, many of the participants continue to struggle with substance use. The study protocol for the experimental group included seven MI sessions across a period of about 6 months. My primary responsibility was to train research assistants in the application of MI and to apply MI myself. Although I am confident in my ability to use MI, I became increasingly aware that MI may not have been what many of the participants needed to eat better and exercise more. For example, I would dutifully apply the principles of MI and convey the MI spirit, but some participants wanted information. Many were already motivated and wanted me to give advice on healthy food choices and exercises. Giving advice is appropriate when using MI; however, I avoided giving advice too early. Over time, I came to realize that my use of MI could be enhanced by being more intentional about incorporating cultural perspectives and activities. For example, many of my African American participants have large families and a strong tie to communal living. I tried to bring the perspectives of others into our discussions, reflecting their thoughts, and perhaps even developing discrepancies between what others hope for the participant and how the participant is behaving (unhealthy eating, not exercising). I also found myself freer to give information that clients wanted, albeit in an MI-consistent manner. I honored my participants' wish for advice, presented it in an MI-consistent way, and found that participants improved both their diet and exercise habits. The value of education in the African American community provided a conduit for health information that gave energy to our sessions. Certainly MI, as with any approach, that strays from cultural considerations "misses the boat." In essence, I do not believe that I compromised the use of MI (which would have compromised the study!) by being more culturally sensitive and aware; in fact, the exact opposite has happened. That is, my use of MI in a culturally sensitive manner only enhanced the results. It's a good cultural counseling lesson that I will take with me whenever I apply MI.

CASE STUDY

Using MI With the Case of Michael

In the following demonstration, I describe a session with Michael using MI (see Chapter 1 for the full case study). In this session, Michael is high on importance related to his drinking (cocaine use has not been addressed yet) but still feels a lot of ambivalence about cutting down or stopping, which is what "everyone" wants him to do. This analysis breaks down the strategies for resolving ambivalence, working with resistance, and using OARS+I as the foundation. The session began with the counselor setting the agenda for the hour.

CLINICIAN: Michael, I appreciate that you came in today. I'd like to start by proposing an agenda if that is all right. I want to make sure we talk about your drinking and how that is going in your life right now. However, I also want to be sure we talk about whatever is on your mind. So, where should we start? (affirmation, setting the agenda)

MICHAEL: Well, I guess I'll start. I had a pretty tough week at work. My boss continues to be on my case. Everyone is so "concerned" about my drinking—why can't they just get off my case?

CLINICIAN: It's been a difficult week, and the fact that everyone is in your face about this drinking thing hasn't made it any easier. (OARS+I — reflection)

MICHAEL: No, it isn't easy. I mean, like we discussed last time, I know I should probably take a look at my drinking, but it is nobody's business.

CLINICIAN: Changing your drinking is on your mind, and it's important that it's done on your own terms. (complex reflection; reinforcing change talk)

MICHAEL: Yes, I have always done things on my terms; it is my life.

CLINICIAN: You stated that you should probably look at your drinking behavior. One way to do this is to think about the pros and cons of using alcohol. Tell me, what is good about your drinking? What does it do for you? (introducing decisional balance/pros/cons exercise)

MICHAEL: That is kinda weird getting that question from you. I guess that alcohol helps me relax. It is nice to come home to a few beers after a hard day of work. I also like to have a few with my buddies. I'm more sociable with a few drinks in me.

CLINICIAN: You drink to help you relax, both after a difficult day from work and in social settings, such as with your buddies. What else? (simple reflection followed by open question)

MICHAEL: Hmm. I guess I drink because I can! I mean, it is something I can control, something that no one can take away from me.

CLINICIAN: I see, you also drink because it gives you a sense of freedom that your boss, wife, or anyone cannot take away from you. (complex reflection)

MICHAEL: Exactly.

CLINICIAN: Okay. What are the not so good aspects of drinking?

MICHAEL: Oh, that's easy. Obviously, I've gotten in trouble with the law a few times. Although I think my boss is out to get me, I have shown up to work drunk, so I guess interfering with work. My wife has threatened to leave me because of my drinking. That is probably about it.

CLINICIAN: On the one hand you use alcohol to help you relax and be more sociable when out with buddies, and other hand there is this negative side of drinking: legal problems, difficulties at work, and your wife threatening to leave. (double-sided reflection)

MICHAEL: Yes, that's pretty much it. I feel stuck in some ways. Definitely can see the pros and cons.

CLINICIAN: As you think about the pros and cons of drinking, what would be the worst-case scenario if you maintained the status quo, didn't change a thing? (worst-case scenario question)

MICHAEL: I probably would get fired, but that might happen whether drinking was involved or not. I don't know, my wife might leave me, and I guess if the legal stuff continues, maybe go to jail. Life would be pretty bad.

CLINICIAN: What would be the best-case scenario if you did not make any changes to your drinking?

MICHAEL: Okay. I see what you are getting at. I really don't see any. I mean, I have a good time with my friends when I drink, so that would stay the same. But the negatives seem to outweigh the positives right now.

CLINICIAN: How would you like your life to be different related to drinking? (open question designed to elicit more change talk)

MICHAEL: I just need to cut down, I mean, stop, I guess. It's like I have no choice.

CLINICIAN: You feel you don't have a lot of wiggle room here; stopping seems like the best choice for you. (simple reflection)

MICHAEL: I've thought about stopping before, but I can't imagine not drinking at all.

CLINICIAN: Something has bothered you about your drinking before, and when you think about stopping completely, you get overwhelmed. (complex reflection)

MICHAEL: Yeah, overwhelmed. I mean, I can only imagine what my buddies would say if I told them I was not going to drink anymore.

CLINICIAN: So, your buddies would laugh hysterically at you if you told them. (amplified reflection, designed to help Michael reevaluate how his friends might respond)

MICHAEL: No, not hysterically. Probably some minor "ribbing," but that is about it.

CLINICIAN: You can imagine that initially it would be difficult with your friends, but after that they would still hang out with you. (complex reflection)

MICHAEL: Yeah, that is probably true. When I first tell them, it will be difficult, but over time they would just forget about it.

CLINICIAN: Let me see if I can tie some things together before we move on. You started today by talking about how your boss has been on your case, especially this week. You wish that everyone would just get off your back about this drinking thing because you like to take care of things yourself. You can see the pros of drinking, including being more sociable and helping you relax, and there is the not so good side of drinking, which has led to legal, job, and marital problems. I really hear that something needs to change, and you acknowledge that you probably need to stop drinking even though thinking about that is a bit overwhelming. Is that about right? (summary with an emphasis on reflecting change talk)

MICHAEL: Yup, that sounds good.

At this point, Michael has a clear idea of the pros and cons of his drinking behavior and, although he is ambivalent about stopping his drinking, he is leaning toward the change side of the argument. Thus, importance of making a change does not seem to be the issue for Michael; rather, he is struggling with visualizing how not drinking will fit in his life, especially related to how his friends might respond. In other words, Michael is struggling with confidence about changing his drinking, and this became the focus for the rest of the session.

CLINICIAN: It sounds like changing your drinking, in point of fact, stopping your drinking, is something you are really considering. On a scale of 1–10, with 1 being not confident and 10 being very confident, how confident are you that you can stop alcohol use if you wanted to? (simple reflection followed up with open ruler exercise question)

MICHAEL: That is a good question; I would say probably a 5.

CLINICIAN: I see, so there is some confidence in your ability to stop drinking. What makes it a 5 rather than a 3? (simple reflection followed by open question)

MICHAEL: Well, I have cut down before, and this legal situation I am in is no fun. That is enough to make anyone think about what they are doing.

CLINICIAN: It would be absurd not to do something about your drinking at this point. (complex reflection)

MICHAEL: Yeah, good way of putting it.

CLINICIAN: How might you increase your confidence, even just a little bit, say from a 5 to a 5.5 or 6?

MICHAEL: I could start going to AA. I don't like big groups, but I do know a buddy at work who attends every night. I also could come clean with my wife, you know, try to be a better husband and father.

CLINICIAN: You have a lot of courage to look at this and have some really good ideas. What else? (affirmation followed by open question)

MICHAEL: I could cut down on hanging out with my friends at the bar. I end up spending too much money anyway, and that is a big reason my wife gets so upset. So, maybe cut down from every night to a couple times a week. And only drink coke or O'Doul's, of course.

CLINICIAN: You mentioned going to AA, committing to becoming a better father and husband, and cutting down on the time at the bars as ways to increase your confidence. As you think about these, where does your confidence lie now? (simple reflection followed by open question)

MICHAEL: It is still pretty low, probably still at a 5 because I haven't tried these things yet.

CLINICIAN: Your confidence would increase if you could use these ideas in practice, out in the real world. (simple reflection)

MICHAEL: Exactly.

CLINICIAN: If you were to implement these changes—going to AA, being a better father and husband, and cutting down the bar time—what do you envision that being like?

MICHAEL: I don't know; I see it being tough to maintain.

CLINICIAN: It is easier to talk about but harder to envision what, exactly, your life would be like without alcohol. (complex reflection)

MICHAEL: Yes, that is it. I have told myself time and time again the reasons I should stop or cut down, but that has accomplished nothing.

CLINICIAN: What else do you envision? (open question)

MICHAEL: Well, aside from being difficult, I am interested in how AA might help. I always can contact Jim at work and go with him if needed. Checking out what they offer kinda has caught my interest.

CLINICIAN: You envision AA being a possible avenue to help you remain alcohol free. (simple reflection)

MICHAEL: Yeah, but listen, though. At the same time I know the AA "type." I mean at least I am not an alcoholic; I think. Do you think I'm an alcoholic?

CLINICIAN: Well, it doesn't concern me whether you or I think you are an alcoholic. However, what I am interested in is your emerging plan to help you build confidence that you could stop your drinking if you wanted to. It is true AA may or may not work for you. Tell me a little more about contacting Jim. How would you go about doing this? (shifting focus)

MICHAEL: Jim works on the second floor in our plant. He is a pretty nice guy. All I would have to do is pull him aside and ask him about AA and how to get involved.

CLINICIAN: You are sounding confident that you can do that. (affirmation)

MICHAEL: Yeah, I'll talk to him this week.

CLINICIAN: We are about out of time, so let me see again if I can tie things together. You realize the importance of stopping your drinking, and your confidence to do this is at a 5 because of the legal issues you are facing and the possibility of your wife leaving. To increase your confidence, you mentioned that going to AA may help, as well as committing to being a better father and husband and cutting down on the time spent at bars with friends. Although you may get some "ribbing" by your buddies, overall they would understand. The AA possibility is really intriguing to you, and in fact you intend to talk to Jim this week to explore this possibility. How does that sound? (summary)

MICHAEL: Sounds like I am on my way. But still lacking in some confidence.

CLINICIAN: If I may ... that feeling is very common for individuals who are thinking about making a big change in their life. I would hope for you that we could continue to talk about confidence and how to increase it if that is what you want. (offering information with permission)

MICHAEL: Okay, sounds good.

CLINICIAN: See you next week.

In this session, the clinician stayed true to the MI spirit by asking open questions, affirming, reflecting, and summarizing. Notice also how the clinician did not go down the path of exploring his troubles with anger, depression, or even cocaine use, which would have gotten off the target behavior of alcohol use. However, these other issues could eventually be worked through in a similar manner. In addition, the stopping of alcohol use may go a long way in curbing other life problems.

Strengths, Limitations, and Ethical Issues Related to MI

MI is an approach designed to (a) increase intrinsic motivation to change, (b) resolve ambivalence, (c) decrease discord, and (d) increase change language. Within these broad goals, several strategies were discussed to help increase importance and confidence, strengthen commitment, and handle discord. MI was born out of working with clients struggling with substance use, and it is an approach that is well suited for this population. To use MI well, therapists must try to establish a target behavior and develop some discrepancy between goals and values and behaviors. MI represents an alternative to "old-school" approaches to substance use counseling where the focus is more confrontational. From the MI perspective, clients who are approached collaboratively, whose ideas are respected and elicited, and whose autonomy is emphasized, naturally have lower resistance and are more likely to consider changing problematic substance use.

MI has many strengths and is one that I favor in my own counseling practice; however, it is certainly not the only approach that "works" with clients struggling with substance use. As with any counseling approach, there are limitations to its use and scope. In addition, some writers have acknowledged ethical "itches" (Miller & Rollnick, 2002) inherent in the use of MI. Table 6.2 provides a summary of the strengths, limitations, and potential ethical issues that might arise when using MI in the treatment of substance use problems.

TABLE 6.2   Summary of Strengths, Limitations, and Ethical Concerns of MI in the Treatment of Substance Use Problems

Strengths	<ul><li>MI has a global reach and appears to be applicable with diverse populations (although more empirical research is needed in this area).</li><li>Respectful, strength-based approach in which client has significant say in their own substance use treatment.</li><li>Applicable across a wide range of behavioral problems, especially those in which a clear target behavior can be established (like lowering/stopping substance use).</li><li>Places greater responsibility on clinician when resistance/discord is high.</li><li>Offers numerous skills for working with "difficult" clients (e.g., court-ordered, "resistant," defiant adolescents).</li><li>Impressive empirical base suggesting that MI is effective with some populations, including those struggling with substance use.</li><li>MI can be effectively integrated into several other treatment approaches for substance use.</li></ul>
Limitations	<ul><li>In some contexts, it may be entirely appropriate to be "anti-MI" and educate, offer clear advice, teach, coerce, or make decisions (Miller & Rollnick, 2002). That is, MI is not a panacea, nor will it be effective in all situations.</li><li>Not much is known about when MI is most and least effective. We cannot answer yet, "Whom should MI not be used with?" (Miller & Rollnick, 2002).</li><li>More research is needed in the application of MI with diverse populations. Is MI effective as a standalone strategy with diverse clients? How can it be enhanced with diverse clients? Does incorporating cultural congruent interventions strengthen MI with some diverse clients?</li></ul>
Ethical Issues	<ul><li>There is some concern about undue influence or manipulation when counselor's wishes for the client are different than the client's. Is "motivating" clients to change their wishes ethical?</li><li>According to Miller and Rollnick (2002), MI would be ethically questionable if the clinician has (a) a clear opinion as to which direction the client should proceed, (b) has different aspirations from the client, (c) has a personal investment in the outcome, (d) has a personal investment that is in conflict with what the client wants, and (e) has power to influence which direction the client takes.</li><li>For an excellent review of ethical issues and MI, see Miller and Rollnick (2002).</li></ul>

References

Amrhein, P., Miller, W. R., Yahne, C. E., Knupsky, A., & Hochstein, D. (2004). Strength of client commitment language improves with training in motivational interviewing. *Alcoholism: Clinical and Experimental Research, 28,* 74A.

Arkowitz, H. Westra, H. Miller, W. R., & Rollnick, S. (Eds.). (2007). *Motivational interviewing in the treatment of psychological problems.* Guilford.

Arroyo, J. A., Miller, W. R., & Tonigan, J. S. (2003). The influence of Hispanic ethnicity on long-term outcome in three alcohol-treatment modalities. *Journal of Studies on Alcohol, 64*(1), 98–104.

Cole, C. (2008). *Advanced training motivational interviewing.* Cathycoletraining, Inc.

Cole, C. (2009). *Supervision/peer consultation for motivational interviewing.* Cathycoletraining, Inc.

Cordisco Tsai, L., & Sebellos-Llena, I. F. (2020). Reflections on adapting motivational interviewing to the Filipino cultural context. *Practice: Social Work in Action, 32,* 43–57.

Festinger, L. (1957). *A theory of cognitive dissonance.* Stanford University Press.

Field, C., & Caetano, R. (2010). The role of ethnic matching between patient and provider on the effectiveness of brief alcohol interventions with Hispanics. *Alcoholism: Clinical and Experimental Research, 34,* 262–271.

Hettema, J. (Producer), & Langdon, L. (Director). (2009). *Motivational interviewing training video: Instructional information and demonstrative clinical vignettes, a tool for learners.* United States: Langdon Productions.

Kohn, A. (1999). *Punished by rewards: The trouble with gold stars, incentive plans, A's, praise, and other bribes.* Houghton Mifflin.

Lewis, T. F., Larson, M., & Korcuska, J. (2017). Strengthening the planning process of motivational interviewing using goal attainment scaling. *Journal of Mental Health Counseling, 39,* 195–210.

Locke, E. A., & Schattke, K. (2019). Intrinsic and extrinsic motivation: Time for expansion and clarification. *Motivation Science, 5,* 277–290.

Longshore, D., & Grills, C. (2000). Motivating illegal drug use recovery: Evidence for a culturally congruent intervention. *Journal of Black Psychology, 26,* 288–301. https://doi.org/10.1177/0095798400026003002

Miller, W. R. (1983). Motivational interviewing with problem drinkers. *Behavioural Psychotherapy, 11,* 147–172.

Miller, W. R., & Forchimes, A. A. (2015, February 16–17). *Integrating motivational interviewing in addiction treatment* [Presentation]. The Change Companies, Scottsdale, AZ.

Miller, W. R., & Rollnick, S. (1991). *Motivational interviewing: Preparing people to change addictive behavior.* Guilford.

Miller, W. R., & Rollnick, S. (2002). *Motivational interviewing: Preparing people for change* (2nd ed.). Guilford.

Miller, W. R., & Rollnick, S. (2009). Ten things motivational interviewing is not. *Behavioural and Cognitive Psychotherapy, 37,* 129–140.

Miller, W. R., & Rollnick, S. (2013). *Motivational interviewing: Preparing people for change* (3rd ed.). Guilford.

Miller, W. R., Rollnick, S., & Butler, C. C. (2008). *Motivational interviewing in health care. Helping patients change their behavior.* Guilford.

Miller, W. R., Rollnick, S., & Moyers, T. B. (1998). *Motivational interviewing: Professional training videotape series.* University of New Mexico.

Miller, W. R., & Rose, G. S. (2009). Toward a theory of motivational interviewing. *American Psychologist, 64,* 527–537. http://dx.doi.org/10.1037/a0016830

Morris, S. L., Hospital, M. M., Wagner, E. F., Lowe, J., Thompson, M. G., Clarke, R., & Riggs, C. (2021). SACRED connections: A university-tribal clinical research partnership for school-based screening and brief intervention for substance use problems among Native American youth. *Ethnic and Cultural Diversity in Social Work, 30,* 149–162. https://doi.org/10.1080/15313204.2020.1770654

Motivational Interviewing Network of Trainers (2021). *Trainer listing.* https://motivationalinterviewing.org/trainer-listing

Prochaska, J. O., DiClemente, C. C., & Norcross, J. C. (1992). In search of how people change: Applications to addictive behaviors. *American Psychologist, 47,* 1102–1114.

Rollnick, S. (2010). *Motivational interviewing for mental health disorders.* PESI Continuing Education Seminars.

Rollnick, S., Mason, P., & Butler, C. (1999). *Motivational interviewing in health care: Helping patients change behavior.* Guilford.

Rosengren, D. B. (2018). *Building motivational interviewing skills: A practitioner's workbook* (2nd ed.). Guilford.

Thevos, A., Quick, R., & Yanduli, V. (2000). Motivational interviewing enhances the adoption of water disinfection practices in Zambia. *Health Promotion International, 15,* 207–214.

CHAPTER 7

Applying CBT in the Treatment of Substance Use Disorders

Introduction

Cognitive therapy lends itself well to the treatment and counseling of substance use and addiction issues. Indeed, the origin and persistence of many substance-related problems can be traced to maladaptive, irrational thinking as only one, albeit significant, component in their development. Behavior therapy serves as the foundation for many approaches to substance use counseling. For example, controlled drinking programs, contingency contracting, enhancing compliance, and token economies all rely on principles of operant conditioning to influence behavior (Thombs & Osborn, 2019). Taken together, cognitive therapy and behavior therapy have each broadened and enriched each other, culminating in the development of *cognitive behavioral therapy* (Reichenberg & Seligman, 2016). Well-established substance use intervention models such as rational emotive behavior therapy (REBT) and dialectical behavior therapy (DBT) use cognitive and behavioral principles as key ingredients in helping clients change substance use patterns. According to Dattilio (2000), CBT has generated more empirical research across a spectrum of psychological problems than any other psychotherapy approach.

It generally does not take long when working with clients struggling with substance use problems to realize that their thinking patterns are off kilter. Irrational thinking can be related to substance use or life in general, or both. Distorted thinking has been shown to lie at the heart of several psychological problems (Beck, 1976), including depression, anxiety, PTSD, eating disorders, psychosis, and substance use. In the case of substance use, these distorted patterns serve to maintain and justify one's substance use behavior. For example, a client who struggles to control their alcohol use may state, "If I don't have my six pack of beer for the game, what fun can I possibly have?" In this instance, the client is maintaining their drinking by clinging to the belief that if they do not drink, they will get bored and not be entertained. This pattern of thinking is evident despite the negative consequences that may accompany this behavior.

The connection between our thinking, feeling, and behaviors is at the heart of CBT, providing a framework from which clinicians can assess and help clients struggling with substance use problems. Although maladaptive thinking patterns do not tell the whole story of why clients use substances, they can play a major role as to why clients remain stuck in this self-defeating behavioral pattern.

In this chapter, I present a broad overview of both cognitive and behavior therapy, with specific examples and applications related to substance use and addiction. The major thrust of this chapter is about cognitive therapy due to the multitude of principles and techniques available to the clinician; behavior therapy is subsequently introduced as an application to broaden cognitive concepts and interventions. However, both therapy approaches augment each other, and in some cases CBT strategies are added to the separate cognitive and behavioral therapy sections. Indeed, one would be hard pressed to find literature using a purely cognitive or purely behavioral model. This fact is especially evident among the outcome study research in substance use, where almost all studies test the efficacy of CBT rather than either alone. Following this analysis, I present two prominent CBT strategies that have grown in application and empirical support in the treatment of substance use problems: REBT and DBT. Finally, I examine CBT as applied to substance use issues within a multicultural context and demonstrate what CBT might look like when counseling Michael, the case study in the text.

The Major Tenets of Cognitive Therapy: Brief Overview

Cognitive theory rests on the assumption that our thoughts, thought patterns, and cognitive themes, or *schemas*, play a large role in psychological distress and behavior problems (Beck, 1976). In his clinical work, Aaron Beck, the founder of cognitive theory, noticed that many of his patients (mostly depressed) had a particular internal dialogue that contained themes of self-blame, self-criticism, judgment, and negative interpretations (Sharf, 2004). These negative themes, he reasoned, were at the heart of why his patients were experiencing negative emotions and problems, such as depression and anxiety. From this basic premise, Beck reasoned that individuals could be helped if biases, distortions, and negative thinking were pointed out to them and corrected within the context of a safe, collaborative therapeutic relationship. Indeed, Beck created the notion of the *cognitive shift*, where individuals tend to ignore positive events in their lives and instead dwell on the negative. The tendency to dwell on the negative creates the perception that negative events happen all the time; however, the ratio of positive to negative is often lopsided. That is, a person typically experiences several positive events in 1 day as opposed to one or two negative events.

It is important to note that these cognitive processes are not considered the cause of all psychological disorders; however, they do play a major component. The development of these maladaptive thinking patterns most likely emerges in early childhood, when individuals receive, interpret, and store positive and negative messages from significant others in their world. Distorted cognitions then begin to develop as the individual progresses through life (Seligman & Reichenberg, 2014). Often, there is interplay between "critical incidents" and one's thinking patterns that essentially activate schemas and basic beliefs about oneself. If these schemas or basic beliefs tend to be negative, the stage is set for unhealthy coping mechanisms and symptoms, including anxiety, depression, substance use, or other psychological or behavioral problems.

For example, a client struggling with cocaine use recalls that they first experimented with it when they were bullied in high school; the incessant teasing and getting picked on exceeded their typical coping mechanisms of denial and avoidance. Upon further inquiry, the clinician realized that the client had a difficult upbringing as a child, experienced numerous negative events, and thus developed the schema that they were worthless and deserved punishment. The bullying became the "critical incident" that triggered their underlying schema of worthlessness and deserved punishment. The client turned to cocaine use as an escape, to punish themself, consistent with their maladaptive schema.

Cognitive Schemas

Schemas are considered "core beliefs" that are set in motion early in life (Archer & McCarthy, 2007). Like Adler's notion of "private logic" that is part of one's lifestyle or personality, schemas can exert a major influence on how we perceive self, others, and the world. In Beck's original conceptualization of cognitive theory, schemas or core beliefs were the foundation from which automatic thoughts, negative interpretations and, consequently, behavioral, and emotional problems emerged. This became particularly evident with clients struggling with depression. Often, such clients would present with schemas reflecting negative views of self, the world, and the future, called the cognitive triad (Archer & McCarthy, 2007). An example of a schema might be "I have nothing to contribute to the world." As a foundation for interpreting and acting upon the world, such a schema pervades one's relationships with others and precludes a more optimistic, happy approach to life.

Schemas among clients who use substances often resemble the same themes as clients with other mental health or behavioral struggles. However, once schemas become activated, their automatic thoughts, cognitive distortions, and other thinking errors often revolve around the substance as providing relief (more on this later). Beck et al. (1993) noted that addressing these schemas and other thought processes are at the core of substance use treatment through a cognitive lens.

Automatic Thoughts

Automatic thoughts emanate from schemas that have been activated from one's environment. That is, schemas often lie dormant in the person's consciousness but become activated when situations in the environment confirm their premise (Archer & McCarthy, 2007). From one's core belief or schema arise automatic thoughts, which are types of thoughts that are consistent with the schema. The thoughts are "automatic" in the sense that they confirm one's schema and occur without much, if any, conscious awareness. For example, taking the schema in the previous example, "I have nothing to contribute to the world," automatic thoughts might be "I am worthless," "Nobody will love me," and "I have nothing interesting to say."

Cognitive Distortions

Beck's (1976) cognitive theory also focuses on thinking distortions, which are thinking errors that occur when one is interpreting events from the environment. Such distortions are often directly associated with negative mood states, which may lead to problematic behaviors, such as substance use. Following is a brief list of common cognitive distortions.

Overgeneralization

Overgeneralization occurs when one interprets the meaning of an event as if it applies to all events or situations. For example, a person who is turned down for two jobs in a row concludes that it is hopeless and that they will never get a job.

All-or-Nothing Thinking

A common problem facing those struggling with substance use is the tendency to interpret events and behaviors dichotomously. For example, a person may think that "unless I resist all temptation to use, I am a complete failure as a person." Such rigid thinking can work against the person's recovery in that if a slip should happen, they become emotionally devastated, propelling a cycle of continued use.

Selective Abstraction

Focusing on one event to the exclusion of others is called selective abstraction. This distortion serves to maintain the integrity of one's core belief or schema. For example, assume a client who uses alcohol has several difficulties with the law, including arrests for driving under the influence (DUI). Recently, they were out with their buddies, consumed a lot of alcohol, and were able to drive home without getting caught by the police. They selectively abstracted this event as opposed to other negative events, interpreting it as a "success" of not getting caught, which served to maintain their schema that "I must have alcohol to have fun."

Magnification or Minimization

This distortion involves magnifying the negative and minimizing positive events or characteristics (Seligman & Reichenberg, 2014). A person struggling with addiction may tend to magnify or minimize events in such a way to maintain negative schemas about the self. For example, a person whose manager made suggestions for work improvement interprets this as a severe rebuke of his work, feeling lousy as a result, and seeking substances to self-soothe. Such thinking maintains the schema "I suck at everything I do and need an escape."

Mind Reading

Mind reading is a common cognitive distortion in which a person "knows" what another person is thinking about them, often leading to false conclusions (Leahy, 2003). For example, a person who drinks too much alcohol may think that a potential mate approves of this behavior because of all the laughing they did together at a recent party. However, the mate was turned off by the other's obnoxious behavior. In this instance, mind reading led to a false conclusion that maintained heavy drinking.

Cognitive Models of Substance Use Disorders

The *cognitive model of substance abuse* was first proposed by Beck et al. (1993), and then updated to the *cognitive behavioral model of addictive behaviors and SUDs* by Liese and Beck (2022).[1] According to this model, a major roadblock to elimination of problematic substance use is the dysfunctional beliefs about substances and their effects (Liese & Beck, 2022). Examples of such beliefs include "I cannot function without cocaine" or "drugs are the only way to handle my stress." These dysfunctional beliefs are problematic in that they often distort reality, create negative mood states, and justify using substances to handle problems. Interestingly, clients' dysfunctional beliefs often intensify when they experience deprivation (Beck et al., 1993). For example, the client might believe "I can't stand being without heroin" or "These cravings are too strong for me to handle." In essence, such beliefs become self-fulfilling in that the client believes they can't control their use or cravings, leading them to give up trying, which then leads to relapse, thus confirming the original belief. CBT provides the foundation for well-supported theories of relapse prevention, a topic covered in Chapter 8.

As any person severely using substances can attest, cravings and urges present formidable problems when trying to cut down or stop using. Whereas cravings and urges are typically conceptualized as physiological phenomena, Liese and Beck (2022) suggested that dysfunctional beliefs contribute to the formation of urges. This process starts with a belief, which leads to an expectation, which then creates the internal urge to use. For example, a client with cocaine use disorder might hold the belief "If I use cocaine, I can accomplish so much more in my job." This belief sets up an expectation that if they use cocaine they will do a good job and receive praise from coworkers and their manager. As a challenging job assignment looms, the client's expectations of reward for using cocaine (increased productivity) lead to the urge to take the drug to cope and "succeed" at the task.

According to Beck et al. (1993), most substance-related beliefs center around pleasure seeking, problem solving, relief, and escape. The authors pointed out that components of these dysfunctional beliefs include (a) the expectation that drugs will maintain internal balance, (b) the belief that drugs will make one more sociable and smarter, (c) the expectation that drugs will give one pleasure and fun, (d) the belief that drugs will increase energy and make one feel powerful, (e) the conviction that drugs will calm stress and tension, (f) the idea that drugs will relieve boredom and depression, and (g) the belief that the only way to manage cravings is to take the drug.

---

1   This change in the title of the model reflects the growing confluence between cognitive and behavioral clinical interventions and how the two together provide a comprehensive conceptualization and treatment philosophy for those struggling with substance use disorders. The Liese and Beck (2022) book is a follow-up to their classic 1993 text. In this discussion, both resources are valuable and will be used throughout.

Many of these beliefs correspond to the specific physiological effects each drug produces. For example, cocaine, a central nervous system stimulant, produces a physiological effect of increased energy along with feelings of invincibility. As such, clients who use cocaine may do so because they believe it will give them an edge in the workplace, or on the field, or in life in general.

Importantly, Liese and Beck (2022) identified two sets of additional beliefs common in those who use substances. The first, called *permission-giving beliefs*, serve to promote justification, risk taking, and entitlement. Examples of such beliefs include "I deserve a break after such a hard day," "One little hit isn't going to hurt anyone," and "I'll just take some now and begin my abstinence plan on Monday." The second, called *anticipatory beliefs* (also referred to as positive outcome beliefs), relate to thoughts about what one expects when thinking about taking drugs or drinking. For example, a person may think, "If I drink tonight, I'll be more relaxed and confident to approach others." Thus, the anticipation of social facilitation from drinking alcohol may set the stage for alcohol use.

As you can see, the central tenant of the cognitive perspective on substance use is that thinking, perceiving, and interpreting strongly impact one's choice to use or not use substances. Beck et al. (1993) proposed that people become vulnerable to substance using behavior based on a cluster of beliefs. This cluster can be interpreted as a sequence that emanates from core beliefs (or schemas), which give rise to negative emotional states, which then lead to substance using beliefs. This sequence of beliefs and emotions is illustrated by my client John (not real name), a client whose substances of choice were alcohol, opiates, and marijuana. John also experienced significant depression. John's core belief was "I am so worthless, I won't ever get out of this," which led to feelings of sadness, anger, and depression, triggering the substance-related thoughts "Drugs are the only way to feel better" and "Given the crap I have gone through, I deserve an escape." These beliefs ultimately lead to the substance using behavior.

Cognitive Behavioral Model of Addictive Behaviors and SUDs

The cognitive behavioral model of additive behaviors and SUDs (Liese & Beck, 2022) relies heavily on the impact of beliefs in the development of substance use and addiction. However, before core beliefs are activated, one must encounter an "antecedent event," which can be internal (feeling stressed, depressed, or anxious) or external (hanging out with friends, feeling awkward at a party). The stimulus serves as a trigger to addiction-related thoughts, setting in motion a series of additional thoughts, emotions, and cravings, ultimately leading to substance use behavior. The complete cognitive behavioral model is illustrated in Figure 7.1.

Therapy can be used to intervene at any point in the cognitive behavioral model process, including modifying core beliefs and addressing anticipatory or permissive beliefs, that place one on the fast track to substance use and associated problems (Liese & Beck, 2022). Indeed, the nature of automatic thoughts is that they occur spontaneously. As a result, a vulnerable person can become entangled in substance-related problems quickly and without much

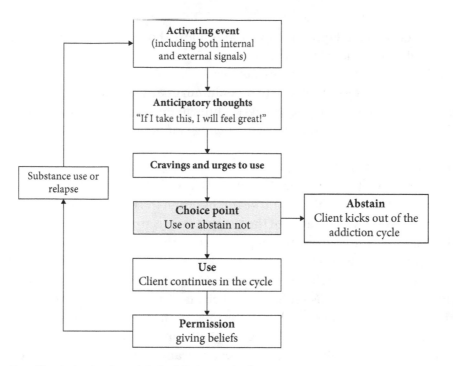

FIGURE 7.1 Cognitive behavioral model of addiction and substance use.

warning. One goal of cognitive therapy, expanded on in the next section, is to help clients become more aware of their automatic thoughts and how they create cognitive vulnerabilities toward using substances.

Application of Cognitive Therapy With Substance Use Disorders

According to Beck (1976) cognitive therapy is an approach to psychotherapy and counseling that aims to reduce emotional turmoil and deleterious behavior by modifying faulty schemas, automatic thoughts, and thinking distortions that are believed to be at the root of such problems. When used as a framework for working with those struggling with substance use problems, cognitive therapy is active, structured, and focused on goals that are generated in a collaborative manner. Also, the spotlight of therapy is primarily on reducing faulty thought processes that contribute to both emotional struggle and substance using behavior. In essence, the therapist keeps the following question at the forefront of their mind: What thought processes seem to be maintaining this client's substance use problems? Cognitive techniques and strategies also help reduce cravings and concomitantly promote a stronger system of intrinsic control (Beck et al., 1993). According to Beck et al. (1993) and Liese and Beck (2022), put simply, cognitive therapy, and CBT for substance use, is designed to decrease pressure and increase control. In a broad sense, the vehicle to accomplish these objectives is challenging and helping the client to modify maladaptive schemas, automatic thoughts, cognitive distortions, and problematic behaviors related to substance use.

In cognitive therapy for substance-related problems, attention is centered on addressing underlying thought patterns that lead to or maintain one's use (Beck et al., 1993). The energy of sessions is geared toward helping clients to think more rationally and logically about their lives. In CBT, additional focus is given to managing emotions and behavior.

Therapeutic Relationship

A misperception about cognitive therapists is that they have little interest in developing the therapeutic alliance. Nothing could be further from the truth. In fact, Beck (1976) made specific mention of the importance of the therapeutic relationship with cognitive therapy. In addition, specific mention on the importance of the therapeutic relationship is given significant attention in Beck et al. (1993) and Liese and Beck (2022). Liese and Franz (1996) and Liese and Beck (1997) acknowledged that building therapeutic rapport is especially important with clients who use substances because they may not enter treatment under their own volition and hold negative feelings toward therapy in general. Motivation levels may be particularly low. Westra and Dozois (2008) proposed that techniques such as MI could be successfully combined with cognitive therapy and CBT to address some of these relationship issues.

Assessment

Cognitive therapy and CBT offer a wealth of strategies and tools to aid in assessment and diagnosis of substance related problems. Whereas assessment is an important clinical skill across the spectrum of mental health disorders, it is particularly relevant when ascertaining the extent of problematic substance use. The cognitive and cognitive behavioral therapist also takes a survey of emotions and behaviors that may play a role in maintaining problematic substance use. Although emotions and behaviors are not the central focus of cognitive therapy, they are associated with automatic thoughts and are incorporated with the cognitive behavioral approach; cognitive techniques are often combined with behavioral interventions to help clients struggling with substance use disorders. Specific cognitive behavioral methods, such as REBT and DBT, are explored later in the chapter.

The overall goal in the assessment process is to integrate significant clinical data into a comprehensive case conceptualization (Liese & Beck, 2022). The case conceptualization is comprised of many elements designed to aid the clinician in developing treatment plans and goals. Major elements of the case conceptualization include (a) the main problem(s), including concomitant mental health issues; (b) social context; (c) past and current antecedents (triggers) to use; (d) cognitive, emotional, and behavioral patterns; (e) motivation level and readiness; (g) integration of a–e; and (h) CBT treatment strategies (Liese & Beck, 2022).

Session Structure

Many clinicians use cognitive therapy because of its emphasis on structuring the counseling session. Structured sessions are especially important for those who use substances because topics can quickly spiral into nonproductive discussions. Cognitive therapists place a premium on maximizing time and efficiency. Structured sessions are necessary to realize this aim (Liese & Beck, 2000).

Although there will be great variability from client to client and session to session, there are common elements that operate in a cognitive therapy session with someone using substances. The first element is *setting the agenda* (Liese & Beck, 2022). Rollnick et al. (1992) discussed how agenda setting is an important skill, especially when the therapist is pressed for time. In Rollnick et al.'s view, it is appropriate for the clinician to share their agenda with the client as well as provide an opportunity for the client to share what is on their mind. This strategy respects what the client brings to the session and facilitates a collaborative atmosphere.

Clients who use substances may indeed come to sessions with numerous problems other than their use of drugs. This can make focusing on what is the most pertinent a challenge. The danger of not setting an agenda, from the cognitive viewpoint, is that discussions may steer in directions where not much is accomplished. Setting an agenda is illustrated in the case of Ramona (name disguised), a female client of Hispanic descent, who was struggling with a recent cocaine relapse:

CLINICIAN: Hello Ramona; thank you for coming in today. What would you like to focus on for today's session?

RAMONA: Well, I'm not sure. I was hoping we could talk about how to handle stress and stuff like that.

CLINICIAN: You struggled a bit this past week, felt overwhelmed, and want to talk more about that. Okay. Let's put that on the agenda. Anything else?

RAMONA: Not really, I guess. The usual family stuff. Maybe how to better communicate with my daughter? I'm having some problems there.

CLINICIAN: Yes, I remember you mentioned that a while ago. Your relationship could be better. Okay. That sounds like something we can add, too.

RAMONA: I think that's it.

CLINICIAN: Great. I also have a couple of items that I would like to address as well, Ramona, and would like to share those with you. As you know, we have been working on skills related to preventing relapse, since you had a slip last month. However, we haven't had much time to practice those skills, and I would like to do that today. I also would like to talk more about cravings and how you might better manage those. So, to summarize, our agenda today is (writing on a flip chart) handle stress, relationship with daughter, practice skills, and manage cravings. Oh, and we need to review last week's homework. We may not get to all these today, but this looks like a place to start. What do you think?

RAMONA: Okay. Sounds good to me.

In this exchange, notice how Ramona offered nothing for the agenda directly related to her substance use; instead, she wanted to focus on better managing stress and her relationship with her daughter. The clinician, however, strongly believed that her recent slip, as well as managing cravings, needed more attention, and placed these on the agenda. In a collaborative fashion, all items were placed on the agenda. Although four items may be a lot to cover in one session, they give the session focus, should the discussion meander off track.

Liese and Beck (2022) suggested that negative mood states, such as depression, anxiety, and hopelessness are stimuli that can easily trigger continued use or relapse and thus are important items to cover in *every* session. The link between negative emotional states and substance use is well established (Amendola et al., 2022; Prentiss, 2007), and thus a *mood check* is considered a second element in the structure of a cognitive therapy session for substance use. The most formal way to assess for mood status is to encourage clients to complete one or more short assessment instruments, such as the Beck Depression Inventory (BDI), the Beck Anxiety Inventory (BAI), the Symptom Checklist 90, or the Beck Hopelessness Scale (BHS). Each of these instruments takes little time to administer, score, and interpret (except for the Symptom Checklist, which may take a little more time to hand score, and thus probably would not be conducive to do every session). The advantage of using these instruments is that they provide an objective, quick way of "checking in" with clients regarding difficult emotions they are currently experiencing. Scores in the moderate to high range indicate that the client may be in a vulnerable state and at higher risk for relapse. The clinician can use this information to either place on the agenda or to at least check in with the client about their mental and emotional state.

There is, of course, a less formal but effective way to conduct a mood check: Simply ask clients how they are feeling. One way to accomplish this is through a simple scaling-type question, such as "On a scale of 1 to 10, where would you rate your mood, with 1 being not so good and 10 feeling great?" Ultimately, the mood check can be done several ways, depending on clinician preference and time.

The third element of the structure of a cognitive therapy session for substance use is *bridging from the last session*. Many clients with substance use problems lead chaotic lives where the potential exists for them to bounce from one issue/problem to the next between therapy sessions. To establish continuity from one session to the next, clinicians can summarize the last session(s) and ask if there is any unfinished business or unresolved issues the client would like to cover (Liese & Beck, 2022). As the counseling session begins, clinicians need to ask themselves, "How does our current topic connect to what we discussed the last time we met?" Rather than a formal technique, making a bridge from the last session is more about awareness on the clinician's part of where the discussion was previously and how that connects to the current discussion. If the client veers too far astray from therapy goals and/or agenda items, the clinician can gently refocus the session in a more productive direction.

The next steps in the session are the *exploring of agenda items* followed by *guided discovery* (Liese & Beck, 2022) and other cognitive-based techniques. Guided discovery moves beyond information gathering and entails asking questions that promote self-discovery, decision-making, and thoughtfulness (Liese & Beck, 2022). Example questions might be "What thoughts did you have when you decided to use?" or "What emotions came up for you when you thought about using?" These elements comprise the "heart" of the session, in which the most teaching and learning take place. Ideally, most of the session is allocated to exploration, discussion, and teaching of cognitive interventions. Specific techniques unique to cognitive therapy for substance use are presented.

Finally, the clinician and client should recap what has been discussed, processed, and learned in every counseling session via a *capsule summary* (Liese & Beck, 2022). Liese and Beck recommend that therapists provide a minimum of three capsule summaries per session; however, three summaries may be too difficult to fit into one session. In addition, too many summaries can seem forced and redundant (see Chapter 6 for more about using summaries and guidelines), especially when sessions are moving along slowly and not much information has been shared. In my experience, the beginning and end of sessions are natural opportunities for summaries. Capsule summaries are usually done by the clinician, at least initially. As time passes and rapport builds, summaries can be the responsibility of the client as well (Liese & Beck, 2022).

Cognitive-Based Techniques

Many of the cognitive techniques used with clients in general also are applicable to clients struggling with substance use. The techniques range from focusing on modifying dysfunctional thoughts to mindfulness and meditation training. Some of the more common cognitive techniques used to address substance use are discussed in the coming sections. For a comprehensive list of cognitive and cognitive behavioral techniques effective for substance use issues, see Liese and Beck (2022).

Daily Thought Record

When clients who use substances become aware of their automatic thoughts, they are better able to see their dysfunctional patterns and how they contribute to substance use. This awareness also sets the stage for intervention; if clients are more aware of their negative thinking styles, they can choose to substitute negative thoughts with more positive or adaptive ones. The daily thought record is based on Davis Burns's (2020) popular daily mood journal and is one of the most common and fundamental techniques in cognitive therapy.

The daily thought record is recorded on a sheet of paper, generally with five or so columns (Liese & Beck, 2022). First, clients are asked to notice when they are experiencing negative emotions and, consequently, feel like using substances to cope. In the first column, clients are asked to record the situation that most likely triggered the negative emotions. Second, clients list their automatic thoughts that preceded these emotions, along with their belief or confidence in that thought (0%–100%). In the third column, clients list their associated emotions and rate the intensity of these emotions (from 0%–100%). In the fourth column, clients are instructed to write out rational (or alternative) responses to their negative automatic thoughts, followed by a rating or level of belief or confidence in this response. In the final column, clients report the outcome of substituting that rational response in place of the automatic thought (Liese & Beck, 2022).

The daily thought record has two main components: (a) asking clients to monitor their automatic thoughts and concomitant feelings and (b) substituting more preferred, positive ways of thinking and then recording how emotions change. Liese and Beck (2022) noted that many iterations of the daily thought record may be needed for clients to eventually make changes in thought and behavior. The critical skill in this exercise is generating the rational or alternative response. Clinicians should help clients develop strong, healthy responses to their automatic thoughts. For example, the automatic thought "I must have a hit of cocaine, or I'll feel terrible" could be replaced with "I'm going to strengthen my recovery and there are many healthier ways to feel good." The goal of using the thought record is to help clients identify the situations, thoughts, and emotions that may trigger substance use.

Pros–Cons Analysis

Liese and Beck (2022) pointed out that many clients who use substances overestimate the advantages of using and underestimate the disadvantages. The pros–cons analysis is designed to help clients identify a more balanced picture of their substance use. If successful, clients begin to see that there are disadvantages about using that they had not considered or that the advantages are not as great as they once thought. Pros–cons analysis can simply be discussed in the therapy session or written out on a piece of paper or flip chart.

In general, it is helpful to ask about the pros of using substances first. The reason is clients are usually aware of the negatives of using, as these have probably been hammered into them from outside the therapy office (from the law, friends, well-intentioned relatives). At first, clients might be taken aback at the exploration of the pros of using, assuming clinicians would explore the negatives of using and communicate dire warnings about the dangers of drug use. Exploring the pros first conveys to the client that the clinician acknowledges that there are good things about using as perceived by the client, which aids in building rapport. After an exploration of the pros, the clinician turns attention to the cons. When the cons have been explored, it is helpful to reflect the analysis back to the client and follow up with "Where does this leave you?" or "What do you make of seeing the pros and cons of using like this? Again, if used successfully clients will modify their previous beliefs about the advantages and disadvantages of using. This technique can also be applied to automatic beliefs one holds about substance use in general (Leahy, 2003).

Downward Arrow Technique

The downward arrow technique (Burns, 2020) can be a powerful avenue to get at one's core belief or schema. As an analogy, it is like peeling an onion, layer after layer, until one arrives at the core. In cognitive therapy, the "peeling" is moving away surface thoughts that cover deeper, more central thoughts that are leading to distress and problematic behavior. The strategy is to identify an automatic thought, usually through simple discussion or from the daily thought record. The clinician encourages the client to repeat the thought and then asks the question "If that were true, why would that be upsetting?" (Burns, 2020, p. 277; a simpler question to ask is simply "And then what?") The client then shares another, related thought (although a little closer to the core schema), and the therapist follows with "If that were true, why would that be upsetting?" (or "And then what?") and so on until a mutual stopping point is achieved. This stopping point should be at or near core belief or schema.

The case of Terrence (named disguised) illustrates this technique. Terrence presented to counseling with alcohol and related anger problems and appeared to take well to a cognitive approach to counseling. Terrence worked two jobs that barely paid him enough money to keep his family afloat. He described how his children would hide when he was around due to his drinking and angry outbursts. His spouse placed tremendous pressure on him to bring in the money. Using a daily thought record, it was discovered that Terrence had the automatic thought of "We will never have enough money, so I must work two jobs." Terrence and I began with this thought and used the downward arrow technique. The sequence looked like this:

TERRENCE: We will never have enough money, so I must work two jobs.

TFL: And then what?

TERRENCE: Well, our house will go into foreclosure.

TFL: And then what?

TERRENCE: We will be kicked out on the street, and my family will have no place to live.

TFL: And then what?

TERRENCE: I will feel like a failure.

TFL: And then what?

TERRENCE: It's proof that I am inadequate.

TFL: And then what?

TERRENCE: A man who doesn't provide for his family and therefore dishonors them.

Bingo! Through the downward arrow technique, we were able to sort through all the fears and automatic thoughts that served to cover the core belief "I am a failure to my family." When Terrence recognized this core belief, he experienced a surge of sadness. I now understood from where his anger and excessive drinking sprang: a deep seated belief that he was inadequate and a failure to his family because he could not provide enough for them. Terrence's cultural upbringing sent the message that he was to provide for his family and failure to do so disrespects his family values and church. While respecting these positive cultural messages, we were able to process his feelings and begin focusing on ways to explore the evidence against these negative core schemas.

Examining and Challenging Cognitive Distortions

Leahy (2003) outlined several techniques to address the many cognitive distortions people hold about themselves, others, and the world. Many of these techniques are in the form of Socratic questioning, where the clinician asks a series of 10–13 questions designed to help the client better examine the distortion they hold. For example, a client who engages in dichotomous thinking might be asked, among other questions, to rate the degree of belief and emotions about the belief, conduct a cost-benefit analysis, and examine the evidence for and against their dichotomous thinking.

Imagery

Imagery can be a potent cognitive technique in helping a client prevent relapse (see Chapter 8). Making use of client imagination helps clients visualize working through difficult high-risk situations in which they might be tempted to use substances. Imagery is a type of cognitive rehearsal technique in which the client visualizes an upcoming situation (or any situation in which they would most likely be tempted to use) and concomitantly how he would handle this challenge. In essence, they are taught to restructure their images in more positive directions (Prochaska & Norcross, 2007) The client rehearses in their mind several of the techniques they have been taught in counseling, leading to a satisfactory resolution to the situation (Beck et al., 1993).

For example, a client who is going to a party on the weekend might be worried that they will be tempted to use cocaine. The clinician encourages the client to relax and close their eyes and picture themself in a situation in which they feel tempted. He then instructs the client to practice modifying their beliefs and attitudes about cocaine and substitute rational responses in their place. The client might hold the following attitude about cocaine use: "What the hell, I have had a tough week and I deserve a hit." Craving level increases as the client imagines imminent use. The clinician then asks the client to modify this belief to "I have had a tough week, and I also have learned some great strategies to help me relax other than drugs." In response, the cravings are reduced to manageable levels and the client can take this opportunity to shift focus or distract themself by talking to someone else (who doesn't use) or simply leave the party.

Imagery can be used in several different ways. Beck et al. (1993) discussed the case of a client who visualized how his life would look different if he created alternatives to using drugs. Using imagery, the client was able to imagine jogging as a suitable replacement for smoking. He discovered how this activity would bring him the joy of being outside in nature and how smoking was clearly inconsistent with this image.

There are numerous cognitive techniques that can be useful when counseling clients struggling with substance use. Cognitive techniques are not only used to correct negative thought patterns, but also to help clients modify dysfunctional schemas and process difficult emotions. An exploration of each technique is beyond the scope of this chapter. For an excellent resource on description and application of cognitive therapy techniques, see Leahy (2003).

In the remainder of the chapter, I will turn our attention to behavior theory, behavioral counseling and techniques, how these are combined with cognitive therapy to create contemporary CBT, and provide two examples that represent variations of CBT. Application to substance use and addiction issues also will be the focus.

Behavior Theory, Counseling, and Techniques

To be historically accurate, behavior therapy had its origins in the 1950s and 1960s well before the emergence of cognitive therapy (Corey, 2009); indeed, it wasn't until the 1970s that cognitive therapy emerged as a "second wave" in behavioral approaches to counseling (Corey, 2009). Strict behaviorists, such as B.F. Skinner, believed that cognition or "inner events" had no place in the science of behavior. However, theorists, such as Albert Bandura and Aaron Beck, pointed out the critical nature that cognition, interpretation, and belief systems had on mediating the relationship between the environment and behavior. Let's take a closer look at behavior theory and therapy.

Behavior theory rests largely on the conditions of human learning and developing strategies for behavior change. According to Thombs and Osborn (2019), behaviorists believe that most, if not all, human behavior is learned. Based on this assumption, human beings can learn adaptive coping responses to their environment as well as maladaptive responses, such as substance use and addiction. A foundational assumption of behavior psychology is that underlying laws shape the initiation, maintenance, and cessation of human behavior, especially overt behavior (Thombs & Osborn, 2019).

Learned behavior can be classified as to whether it emanated from (a) classical (or respondent) conditioning, (b) operant conditioning, or (c) social learning theory (Corey, 2017; Thombs & Osborn, 2019). For purposes of this analysis, I will focus on operant conditioning as this appears to have substantial theoretical application to substance use. The premise for operant conditioning is rather straightforward: Behavior is conditioned if followed by a consequence. *Positive* reinforcement refers to the increased likelihood of a behavior occurring again following a positive consequence. *Negative* reinforcement also refers to the increased likelihood of a behavior occurring again; however, it is the *removal* of noxious stimuli that creates this effect. For example, if a person with heroin use disorder suddenly stops using, they will experience severe withdrawal symptoms. If they return to heroin use, the withdrawal symptoms disappear, and they feel better. Thus, drug use is reinforced by the removal of the noxious stimuli, in this case nausea, lethargy, and depression associated with heroin withdrawal. Negative reinforcement is often confused with punishment. *Punishment* refers to the decreased likelihood of a behavior occurring again following a negative consequence. If a person with alcohol use disorder were to receive an ultimatum to stop drinking from their spouse, this punisher may have the effect of decreasing or eliminating their drinking behavior.

According to the behaviorists, four key elements need to be in place to define an addiction. First, there must be availability and access of substances in the person's environment. Second, the person experiences positive reinforcement from drug use. An obvious example of this is their impact on the reward pathways of the brain, creating the immediate "high" or "rush." The third element is the lack of positive reinforcement for alternative behaviors. For example, a client who has made a commitment to abstinence following years of significant substance use may find a skeptical and unforgiving social environment during their abstinence journey. Broken relationships may take years to mend, employment opportunities may be limited, and the stigma from others may further alienate the client. Reinforcement for positive, antidrug behaviors may not be realized until years down the road. Finally, the lack of immediate punishment for using drugs and alcohol is the fourth element in the development of an addiction (Thombs & Osborn, 2019).

Many who use substances do not experience significant negative consequences until several years after use. Indeed, some may maintain good jobs and decent relationships with family members, showing no obvious or outwardly signs of problems. However, one thing we know is that eventually heavy substance use will take its toll in a myriad of negative ways.

Based on the behaviorist analysis, one can see why relapse rates are so high among those those struggling with substance use. As noted, many of the rewards of being substance free and recovery are delayed, leading to increased risk for relapse. According to the behaviorist idea of addiction, a person stops using when (a) punishers that follow ingestion become immediate and (b) the rewards for abstinence are realized and more immediate (Thombs & Osborn, 2019).

Behavioral Techniques

There is a plethora of behavioral techniques at the substance use clinician's disposal. One popular approach is "contingency management" or "contingency contracting." In contingency management, the clinician uses the principles of operant conditioning to shape behavior, using the following key questions as their guide:

1. What behavior is maladaptive? What behaviors should be increased or decreased?
2. What environmental contingencies currently maintain or support the behavior?
3. What are the rewards of maintaining drug use? Are there punishers associated with avoiding drug use?
4. What environmental changes can be manipulated to alter the behavior?

Based on these questions, the clinician and client coconstruct a treatment plan that considers environmental contingencies that serve to maintain the substance using pattern. Contingency management has been the foundation of many substance use intervention programs and has demonstrated success in reducing substance using behaviors and increasing/supporting abstinence times (Carroll et al., 2006; Lake et al., 2022; Petry et al., 2007; Rawson et al., 2006). In addition, several common applications of contingency management under the guise of other names exist, such as controlled drinking, contracting for initiation of maintenance of abstinence, community reinforcement, and token economies (Thombs & Osborn, 2019).

Another set of techniques from the behavioral school is relaxation training and other related methods. Relaxation training can be particularly useful for clients who tend to relapse when under a great deal of stress. Teaching clients how to breathe deeply, relax tense muscles, and engage in behaviors that promote relaxation (e.g., listening to a relaxing audio) can sometimes diffuse tense situations in which the client is at greater risk of relapse. Progressive muscle relaxation has gone through many variations but generally entails progressively tensing and relaxing different muscles of the body. I have had encouraging results with relaxation principles in my work with clients, presumably due to the lessening of concomitant anxiety often associated with problematic substance use. Exercises in breath work and breathing, a variant of relaxation strategies, can help calm an anxious, compromised brain, without the use of medication. Clients who engage in persistent practice of these methods often create a state of calm in which drug obsessions are minimized and the intensity of cravings reduced. Wim Hof methods (www.wimhofmethod.com) and Stig Severinsen (www.breatheology.com) are excellent breathwork resources for both clinicians and clients.

Another behavior strategy that is quite popular and has garnered significant empirical support (Corey, 2017) is systematic desensitization, created by Joseph Wolpe. Systematic desensitization entails a lengthy initial interview to identify the nature of fears and anxieties followed by relaxation training. The clinician and client then cocreate an anxiety hierarchy (typically ranging from 1–10) from least anxiety-provoking situation (1) to most anxiety-provoking situation (10). The client is asked to relax as the clinician slowly guides the client up the hierarchy. To be effective, the client is asked to imagine the situation at each step and experience it fully, as if it were happening in the moment. If the client experiences anxiety, the clinician helps them apply previously taught relaxation and breathing strategies until little or no anxiety remains. The goal is to help the client imagine the most anxiety-provoking situation with calm and focus, which is thought to then translate into real-life situations. Systematic desensitization should not be rushed; indeed, the amount of time from the initial behavioral interview and assessment to completion takes time (Corey, 2017).

One can see how useful systematic desensitization might be for clients struggling with substance use. For example, a client who anticipates an unavoidable high-risk situation coming up might create a hierarchy such as the following:

1. Thinking about the family gathering coming up this weekend.
2. Two days before the weekend I start to picture my relatives drinking.
3. The day of the event I wake up and fear I might relapse.
4. I have a conflict between not buying beer and yet having some on hand for my relatives.
5. As my family arrives, I start to experience alcohol craving.
6. Everyone is laughing and having a good time; most are having drinks.
7. Family members begin to wonder why I don't have a drink in hand.
8. I start to get teased and laughed at.
9. I fear they will find out I drink too much and am trying to stay alcohol free.
10. A relative approaches to hand me a beer. When I refuse, he says, "What is the matter with you?" I am craving alcohol now.

For this client, working through the anxiety and fear associated with these images may translate to less anxiety when the event happens. Additional skills, such as positive self-talk and cognitive restructuring, can be applied as the client moves up the hierarchy (e.g., repeating a positive phrase at step 6 to counteract the negative thoughts such as "Everyone but me is having a good time").

The full range of behavior techniques is beyond the scope of this text. However, it is important to keep in mind that contemporary behavior therapy almost always has a cognitive component and vice versa. Cognitive and behavior therapy pretty much go hand in hand nowadays, with each perspective augmenting and supporting the other. As we will see, CBT approaches have considerable applicability to the treatment of substance use problems.

Specific CBT Approaches

Although numerous variations of CBT exist, two approaches have amassed a conceptual, research, and clinical base in the treatment of treatment substance use problems: REBT and DBT. A brief description of each approach, as well as application to substance use treatment, is provided.

Rational Emotive Behavioral Therapy

REBT was one of the first CBTs (Corey, 2009). Never one to avoid stating it like it is, Albert Ellis (1982), the founder of REBT, said "Humans are brilliantly talented at devising fiendishly clever rationalizations for their abominable behavior" (p. 15). Ellis strongly believed that the *real* cause of suffering, crime, hate, war, and substance use was human choice. Responsibility for self-destructive behaviors, including substance use, falls squarely on the shoulders of the self-destroying individuals themselves, a philosophy expounded by great thinkers such as the likes of Epictetus and Marcus Aurelius. REBT assumes that client did not *get* an addiction, nor were they made to be a person with a substance use disorder, nor did anything cause them to severely use substances (Ellis, 1982). Rather proponents of REBT believe that individuals drove themselves to addiction primarily through their philosophical belief systems. And, if their belief systems drove them to addiction, they have the power to change their pattern of thinking and basic beliefs to become emotionally happy and free from substances (Ellis, 1982).

The REBT model of substance addiction places a premium on cognitive dynamics that maintain a substance using and self-destructive cycle. Specifically, these dynamics are the irrational beliefs related to abstinence combined with low-frustration tolerance (LFT; the abstinence–LTF pattern; DiGiuseppe & McInerney, 1990). The familiar "ABCs" of behavior from the REBT model are illustrative. First, "A" stands for *activating event*, which refers to a client making the decision not to consume or use substances (DiGiuseppe & McInerney, 1990). "B" stands for *belief* or the irrational belief system the client holds about "A." "C" is the *consequence* that follows from "B," low frustration tolerance. Later writings on REBT extended this basic model to include "D," or *disputing*, and "F," which stands for *new feeling* (Archer & McCarthy, 2007). The key element in this model, however, is "B," the irrational belief system, something that Ellis (1982) looks for immediately when a client comes complaining about A. When a person struggling with addiction makes the decision to stop using, irrational beliefs may emerge about the abstinent effort, such as "I can't stand not having a drink, I am too weak and tired to resist drugs," or "I cannot function completely without alcohol"

(DiGiuseppe & McInerney, 1990). These irrational beliefs lead directly to LFT and concomitant anxiety. The increased emotional discomfort then increases the risk of continued substance use (Ellis, 1985).

Clients can overcome the LFT by adopting one of three strategies: (a) waiting for the urge to use pass, (b) immediately returning to substance use, or (c) disputing irrational beliefs that cause the discomfort (i.e., anxiety from the LFT). Clearly, when a client is attempting to stop using substance, (a) and (b) are not ideal; from the REBT perspective, (c) offers the best hope to help clients resist temptation to return to substance use.

One of the main reasons substance use disorders are so easy to maintain is that no cognitive or behavioral strategy can eliminate the increased anxiety from the LFT better than substances (DiGuiseppe & McInerny, 1990). Indeed, from an operant conditioning perspective, lack of immediate reinforcement from abstinence plays a large role in why relapse rates are so high. For REBT to be effective, clinicians need to help clients identify specifically what emotions they are feeling when deprived. Unfortunately, clients often struggle with this important process due to years of hiding from or avoiding their emotions. Ellis (1980) used the term *discomfort anxiety* to capture the emotional struggles that result from LFT. However, many clients might not experience anxiety or have a difficult time understanding what discomfort anxiety means (DiGuiseppe & McInerny, 1990). Clinicians need to encourage clients to specifically describe all negative emotions that arise when abstaining from drugs. Doing so enables client and clinician to identify the irrational beliefs more precisely behind the emotion.

REBT Techniques

REBT techniques generally fall into three categories: cognitive methods, emotive methods, and behavioral methods (Corey, 2017). As such, there are several strategies that clinicians can employ for uncovering LFT, identifying emotions, and disputing irrational beliefs. Cognitive methods were discussed extensively earlier in the chapter. Emotive methods include a variety of vivid and evocative strategies designed to facilitate disputation of irrational thinking. Examples of emotive strategies include the following:

- **Imagery.** Clients practice visualizing themselves thinking, feeling, and behaving exactly how they would like (Maultsby, 1984). Or, clients can imagine being deprived of something, experience the emotion in its entirety, and then practice disputing irrational beliefs that lead to the difficult emotion. One can see how this might be helpful for clients who struggle with LFT.

- **Role playing.** Although this strategy has cognitive, emotional, and behavioral elements, the clinician focuses on the emotions that the role play brings out to assess the cognitions behind them (Corey, 2017). A client struggling with peer pressure to use substances may benefit from this exercise. During a role play, for example, a client might discover the irrational belief, "If I say no to drugs, I will never have any friends." The REBT clinician would quickly challenge this irrational belief.

- **Shame-attacking exercises (Ellis, 1999).** People who harbor lots of shame often feel miserable. Ellis believed that individuals can absolutely refuse to feel shame by convincing themselves that it is not the end of the world if someone thinks they are foolish or stupid. Shame-attacking exercises involve the client doing something out of the ordinary or silly in public (but not illegal or hurtful!), such as singing out loud in line, wearing attention-getting clothing, or yelling a friend's name in public (Corey, 2017). The purpose of these exercises is to help clients realize that others are not as interested in their behavior as they think and to become sensitized to shaming, even though they may feel judged by others. Clients who have substance use disorders may experience significant shame from their families and friends. Helping clients lessen the amount of shame, either through exercises or vigorous disputation of irrational beliefs, may open space for a happier, healthier existence.

One technique outlined by DiGuiseppe and McInerny (1990) is to simply talk to clients about what they feel when deprived of their substance of choice. Often, clients will struggle with this question. If this is the case, then clinicians can generate emotional reactions by helping clients imagine that the substance is right in front of them, but they are not allowed to indulge. Clients are encouraged to give labels to their discomfort anxiety, and clinicians subsequently help clients dispute the irrational thoughts that lead to these upsetting emotions.

The process of REBT has a strong educational component. Indeed, another strategy is to teach clients alternative ways to accomplish desired physical states, such as relaxation. It is common for clients to hold inaccurate perceptions as to the effects certain drugs have on coping with stress. For example, many clients who use alcohol report that it helps them mellow out and relax, yet one of its physiological effects is to increase heart rate, which is the exact opposite of relaxation. Correcting these misperceptions and pointing out that clients are deluding themselves by their own biased thinking patterns may help to clarify that chemical forms of coping come with side effects and hidden costs (DiGuiseppe & McInerny, 1990). Techniques to address the irrational beliefs ("B" in the ABC model) can be any of the cognitive strategies addressed earlier in this chapter.

A unique contribution of the REBT model is the LFT; simply put, most clients in the throes of a substance use disorder do not tolerate feelings of depression, anxiety, or anger very well. The emergence of these difficult emotions taxes the client's already low coping resources. In essence, LFT stops clients from creating, selecting, and reaching their goals. Clinicians have a bevy of cognitive and behavioral interventions to help clients increase their ability to handle frustration. Disputing irrational beliefs and engaging in philosophical persuasion about the benefits of abstinence can go a long way to ease difficult emotions. Behavioral strategies such as relaxation training, diaphragmatic breathing, and meditation can help clients "sit with" the frustration, which over time dissipates or even passes.

Dialectical Behavior Therapy

DBT is a treatment approach for individuals who struggle with multiple severe psychological problems (Dimeff & Linehan, 2008). Developed by Marsha Linehan, DBT was originally created as a comprehensive treatment approach to address extreme emotionality and self-injurious/suicidal behaviors among those with borderline personality disorder. More recently, DBT has been empirically demonstrated to be effective in the treatment of suicidal and parasuicidal behaviors, eating disorders, depression, and substance use (Adams et al., 2021; Koerner & Dimeff, 2007; Linehan et al., 1991, 1999; Salsman, 2020; Smith, 2010; Telch et al., 2001).

DBT is a comprehensive, highly structured intervention protocol that rests strongly on cognitive behavioral principles with elements of Zen mindfulness. A key underlying philosophy of DBT is *biosocial theory*, or the interaction between biological dysfunction of the emotional regulation system with an invalidating social environment (Koerner & Dimeff, 2007). DBT has emerged as an evidenced-based approach for substance use disorders, especially when these issues are comorbid with borderline or other dramatic, emotional personality disorders.

The "dialectic" in DBT is a guiding principle to the approach; in general, a fundamental principle of DBT is to "create a dynamic that promotes two opposite goals for clients: change vs. acceptance" (Dimeff & Linehan, 2008, p. 39.). The treatment of severe disorders, including substance use disorders, requires synthesis of many dialectic polarities, but acceptance (i.e., accept life's inevitable pain) versus change (desire to eliminate all painful experiences) is at the core (Dimeff & Linehan, 2008). Other dialectic polarities can reach synthesis through the art and practice of arriving at the "truth" through exchange of both sides of an argument (Smith, 2010). For example, many clients who struggle with substance use issues see benefits to the "change side" as well as benefits to the "not change" side. Progress is achieved when voice is given to both sides of the argument and, over time, the "truth" presents itself via a "dialectical synthesis" (Smith, 2010).

Hierarchy of DBT Stages and Targets

The principles of DBT are used as the basis for clinician intervention and client skill development. The first stage of DBT is called the pretreatment stage, and the primary target is to orient the client and the environment to treatment and obtain commitment to partake in counseling. Activities in this stage might include assessment and treatment planning, review of biosocial theory, overview of the treatment protocol, skill acquisition, and overview of the stages of treatment (Smith, 2010). Stage 1 of DBT is comprised of four targets based on a hierarchy of highest to lowest priority. The highest priority target is decreasing *life-threatening behaviors*, such as suicidal or parasuicidal behavior. Once these are addressed (or they are not a problem in the first place), the next priority is decreasing *therapy interfering behaviors*, which include tardiness, not showing for sessions, or not completing homework assignments. The next target on the hierarchy is decreasing *quality of life–interfering behaviors*. Quality of life–interfering behaviors may include school problems, depression, anxiety, relationship problems, impulsive/acting out problems, and substance use. Finally, *increasing behavioral skills* (DBT skills) represents the fourth target in stage 1 (Smith, 2010). Notice that when clients first enter counseling, substance use may not be discussed immediately or at least until the first two targets are met. That is, the client must not be suicidal, and they must show commitment to therapy and avoid sabotaging their own counseling work before other issues are addressed.

In stage 2 of DBT, the target is to decrease the posttraumatic stress response (Smith, 2010). Many clients may not experience this type of response, in which case the clinician can move on to stage 3. However, for those who are dealing with trauma and experiencing associated symptoms of distress and anxiety, therapeutic time is needed to address these issues so the client can respond with greater equanimity related to the trauma as well as other stressful environmental events. The targets for stage 3 DBT include increasing self-respect and accomplishing individual goals. In stage 4, the target includes helping clients find greater freedom, joy, and completeness in life (Smith, 2010).

DBT Skills Training

A significant part of DBT practice is teaching clients critical skills designed to help them lead more productive and preferred lives. Regular practice leads to skill acquisition and strength, which leads to less extreme emotional and behavioral reactions to the environment. The DBT skills fall under four overarching skill categories: mindfulness, interpersonal effectiveness, emotion regulation, and distress tolerance. The skills can be taught in any order, with mindfulness being a foundational skill from which all others are practiced.

The goal of mindfulness skills is to help clients enhance awareness of their thinking and emotions, which decreases impulsivity. Clients are taught to rely on both the "emotional mind" and "rational mind" when making decisions. The synthesis of emotional mind and rational mind is the "wise mind" (Smith, 2010). Rather than relying on emotions or logic exclusively, clients are taught to access wise mind when they feel emotionally overwhelmed (i.e., "What would wise mind tell you in this situation?). One skill taught to accomplish these goals includes helping clients to "observe" or be aware of thoughts and feelings without reacting to them.

The goal of strengthening distress tolerance skills is like the goal of managing LFT in REBT. Distress tolerance skills were designed to help clients tolerate crises and prevent clients from engaging in behaviors that would make the situation worse (Linehan, 2014). An example of a distress tolerance skill is "self-soothing" or encouraging clients to engage in activities that are soothing to each of their five senses (e.g., listening to calming/relaxing music). Emotion regulation skills are designed to help clients identify an emotion, label it, and act the opposite of what the emotion is trying to get them to do. As an example, Linehan (2014) encourages clients to practice the acronym, PLEASE: treat *p*hysical i*ll*ness, balance *e*ating, *a*void mood-altering drugs, balance *s*leep, and *e*xercise. Interpersonal effectiveness skills address problems in interpersonal relationships that often characterize clients struggling with borderline personality disorder, substance use, or both. One skill related to interpersonal effectiveness includes focusing on self-respect through FAST, which stands for being *f*air, making no *a*pologies, *s*ticking to values, and being *t*ruthful.

Originally designed for clients who were suicidal and experiencing extreme emotional regulation problems, DBT practitioners have a bevy of skills to teach clients and, when applied in its entirety, leave them with an arsenal of strategies to help better manage their lives. A full analysis of each skill used as part of a DBT intervention is beyond the scope of this chapter.

Interested readers are encouraged to refer to two excellent DBT based workbooks (Linehan, 2014; McKay et al., 2019).

DBT Applied to Substance Use Disorders

The attractiveness of DBT with those using substances is that it has built-in mechanisms to address client behaviors that clearly interfere with clinical progress. For example, a clinician would be hard pressed to work on substance use issues when the client is indicating they are going to harm themself (life-threatening behaviors). In addition, it is difficult to make counseling progress when the client consistently shows up late and "forgets" to do homework (therapy-interfering behavior). In DBT, there is a structure in place to nip these issues in the proverbial bud before they sabotage therapy, preclude progress, and increase both clinician and client frustration.

Many of the DBT skills appear face valid for use with clients struggling with substance use. For example, what substance use clinician has not observed clients struggle with emotional regulation, handle distress poorly, or have disastrous interpersonal relationships? In addition, clients who struggle with substances often have limited insight and awareness into their problems, especially early in treatment. Increasing mindfulness can go a long way to help clients develop greater awareness of their behavior, how their behavior sabotages their life, and alternative actions that can lead to greater fulfillment. When DBT is successful, the client learns to create, envision, and pursue goals that transcend their history of out-of-control behavior and is better able to handle life's challenges (Dimeff & Linehan, 2008).

The dialectical approach to abstinence involves pushing for immediate cessation of substance use (change), while at the same time understanding that if relapse does happen, it is not the end of the world (acceptance). This DBT-based approach helps the client focus on the unrelenting goal of total abstinence and yet allows for nonjudgmental problem solving related to relapse should it occur (Dimeff & Linehan, 2008). Indeed, the DBT clinician establishes the expectation of complete abstinence from the very first session, encouraging the client to commit to this goal for any agreeable length of time. As the client meets shorter abstinence goals, new commitments are made with increasing time intervals of abstinence (Dimeff & Linehan, 2008).

DBT clinicians teach clients to "cope ahead" to address potential problems in one's environment (Dimeff & Linehan, 2008). In coping ahead, the client learns to anticipate probable risk factors in the environment (e.g., an upcoming social gathering) and practices skills and strategies ahead of time to prepare for the event. If the client were to slip or engage in a full-blown relapse, the clinician emphasizes the "acceptance" side of the dialectic. In other words, rather than perceiving the client as being a treatment failure and incapable of change, the clinician treats the lapse as a problem to be solved by taking stock of what happened and analyzing the events that led to the mishap. In essence, the DBT clinician helps the client "fail well" (Dimeff & Linehan, 2008) by accepting what happened, learning from it, and moving ahead with a new plan.

In DBT, the target of "therapy-interfering behaviors" takes on a prominent role. Dimeff and Linehan (2008) liken many drug-using individuals as butterflies, flittering to and from counseling, in and out of the therapy process, only to become lost over time. Typical butterfly behaviors are all too common when working with clients struggling with substance use disorders: episodic engagement in counseling, not returning phone calls, failure to fully participate in sessions, not showing up for sessions, and terminating prematurely (Dimeff & Linehan, 2008). DBT clinicians are actively involved in helping clients understand the butterfly problem from the beginning of treatment. They may discuss the problem openly with clients, encourage clients to make a phone list of all possible places they could be if they become "lost," and increase contact with clients during the first months of counseling (e.g., once-a-week phone call check-in; Dimeff & Linehan, 2008).

Researchers have demonstrated that several components of DBT targeting therapeutic alliance (e.g., frequent contact with clients, addressing therapy interfering behaviors) keep substance-using clients in treatment longer (Bornovalova & Daughters, 2007). In addition, several clinical trials of DBT have demonstrated success in reducing symptom severity of clients with comorbid borderline personality disorder and a substance use disorder (Harned et al., 2008; Linehan et al. 1999, 2002; Van den Bosch et al., 2002). Salsman (2020) noted the DBT has garnered considerable empirical support as a treatment for substance use problems. The author noted that DBT with substance use problems surpasses an important threshold of quality by having at least two independent, controlled, and well-designed studies in support of a treatment compared to another.

CBT in the Treatment of Diverse Populations

In general, cognitive therapy has been criticized for emphasizing dysfunctional thinking and biased cognition to the exclusion of social and contextual issues that may contribute to client difficulties (Archer & McCarthy, 2007). Ivey et al. (2002, as cited in Archer & McCarthy, 2007) suggested that any exploration of cognitions, emotions, or behaviors should be made considering racial, social, cultural, and other contextual frameworks and even suggested that additional columns be placed on the *daily thought record* labeled, "gender" and "culture."

Corey (2017) noted the numerous strengths that CBT has in working with clients from diverse backgrounds, including using the client's core belief system when engaging in self-discovery. Culturally diverse clients appear to appreciate the focus on both thoughts and behavior, as well as ways to handle stress (Corey, 2017). The skills that are taught and learned in CBT can be put to immediate use. The collaborative nature of CBT is also a strength from a multicultural perspective (Corey, 2017).

According to Corey (2017), behavior therapy has many advantages over other therapies in counseling clients from diverse backgrounds. For example, behavior counseling usually does not emphasize the sharing of feelings or expression of emotion, activities that clients may shy away from given their cultural or ethnic backgrounds. The emphasis on action orientation, staying on task, dealing with the present, and teaching behavioral skills may appeal to many clients whose cultural values are based on concrete methods for solving problems. Behavior therapists stress the uniqueness of the individual given their specific cultural background.

The strong focus of behavioral therapy on behavior change, shaping the environment, and thought processes may dwarf critical client factors such as gender, race, ethnicity, and sexual orientation. The tendency may unfortunately be to overlook or otherwise ignore these factors, making counseling less effective (Corey, 2017). Clients from diverse backgrounds come from unique situations that may be quite different than the counselor's background. As such, behavior change is likely to have an impact, positive or negative, on the environment; clients need to be aware of and prepare for such an impact, and the counselor needs to discuss the inherent challenge that often accompanies change (Corey, 2017).

Most research supporting the effectiveness of CBT across a range of psychological disorders was conducted with samples consisting mainly of White European Americans (Horrell, 2008; Windsor et al., 2015). Research on the applicability of CBT to diverse populations, however, is growing. Jackson et al. (2006) sought to determine if (CBT) was a suitable model of treatment for Native Americans. Both Native Americans and European Americans (each group had 95 participants) were recruited and asked to complete the Cognitive Behavioral Therapy Applicability Scale (CBT-AS). The CBT-AS is composed of three scales that represent major tenets of CBT to assess suitability and client preferences for this form of therapy. European Americans rated "focused in session behavior" (e.g., counselor works with client to uncover relationship between thoughts and feelings) as more appealing than did Native American participants. "Active stance" (e.g., client actively participates in counseling by completing homework) was accepted by both groups; however, "structured therapeutic stance" (e.g., it is the responsibility of the client to change) was rated as more desirable by European Americans. The authors described how these differences reflect Native American culture and suggest ways in which clinicians can implement a culturally appropriate form of CBT with this population.

Milligan et al. (2004) investigated the results of two previous studies to determine if White and African American participants differed in posttreatment cocaine use outcomes. The studies were randomized controlled clinical trials that evaluated CBT, 12-step facilitation, and pharmacotherapy for cocaine dependence. An analysis of posttreatment cocaine use outcomes (e.g., cocaine-positive urine specimens and percentage of days abstinent from cocaine use) found no difference between ethnic groups. However, in both studies African American participants were significantly less likely to complete treatment than were White participants. The authors recommended the inclusion of medication because this addition enhanced treatment retention among African Americans in Study 1. More research is needed to clarify treatment retention issues when using CBT with African American clients struggling with substance use problems. Similar findings related to retention were found by Windsor et al. (2015).

Horrell (2008) sought to specifically explore the efficacy of CBT with non-White populations. The researcher identified 12 studies in which researchers used CBT with adults of African American, Hispanic American, or Asian American descent. Overall, CBT was found to be a promising approach for the treatment of PTSD, agoraphobia, panic attacks, and depression with these populations. However, the authors noted that there is limited research supporting the efficacy of CBT to treat substance use with African Americans. Jankowska (2019), in a systematic review, found that CBT with "modest" cultural modifications was an effective treatment for social anxiety disorder.

Research on the use of CBT with substance use problems among diverse clientele is also increasing. Windsor et al. (2015) conducted a meta-analysis comparing the impact of CBT in lowering substance use between non-Hispanic White and Black and/or Hispanic participants. Their results demonstrated similar effect sizes at posttest; however, effect sizes taken before the posttest indicated that CBT had a stronger impact on the non-Hispanic White sample and reduced retention rates within the Black and Hispanic sample. The authors called for additional research on CBT's impact on substance use among Black and Hispanic individuals. In a randomized trial comparing standard CBT with culturally accommodated CBT among Latina/o adolescents with SUDs, Burrow-Sanchez and Hops (2019) found a significant difference at 12-month follow-up between the two groups. Specifically, the culturally accommodated CBT group had lower levels of substance use compared to the standard treatment, with parental familism as a moderator. Cultural accommodation included the use of "Spanish names in examples, implementation of culturally relevant role-plays, ... and providing opportunities to discuss real-life stressors" (p. 315). It also included developmental and identity issues for Latina/o adolescents and significant parental/family involvement.

Clinicians are encouraged to place all clients' cognitive distortions, biased thinking, and destructive behavior patterns within cultural and social context. For example, a Latino client may be struggling with alcohol use to cope with racism rather than any inherent thinking flaws or problems with interpreting situations. This client's drinking probably results from a combination of both factors (i.e., internal thinking and external/contextual factors); the overemphasis on one to the exclusion of the other may undermine recovery.

CASE STUDY

Using CBT in the Case of Michael

In the following demonstration, I describe a session with Michael using CBT (see Chapter 1 for the full case study). At this point, Michael has already gone through the cognitive assessment process, in which triggering events, core schemas, and automatic thoughts have been discovered. Key emotional factors also were assessed. For context, Figure 7.2 shows Michael's substance use pattern through the lens of the cognitive behavioral model. Assume that Michael is at the beginning stages of recovery and has attended regular counseling each week for about a month. He is currently abstinent from substances and has not relapsed, although he has had urges to use. The agenda has been set for the session, in which the focus will be on challenging and modifying Michael's automatic thoughts. The behavioral element to his treatment will consist primarily of guided imagery and practicing skills outside of the counseling office.

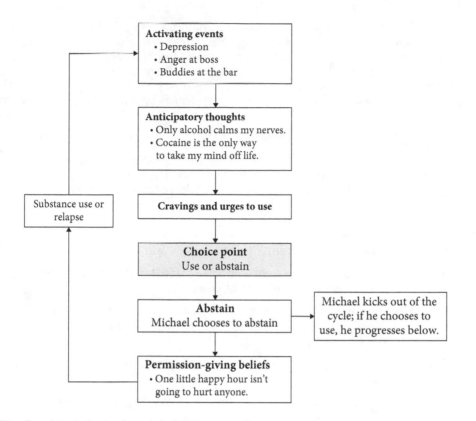

FIGURE 7.2 Cognitive behavioral model of addiction and substance use related to Michael.

CLINICIAN: Hello, Michael. As you know we already set the agenda over the phone. Is there anything else you would like to add? (setting the agenda)

MICHAEL: No, not really. Maybe ways to handle stress at work. And anger management.

CLINICIAN: Okay, I'll put those on the agenda. If we don't get to those today, we can for sure cover them next week.

MICHAEL: Sounds good.

CLINICIAN: Great. Before we begin, I would like to check in today with how you are feeling. On a scale of 1–10, with 1 being feeling not so good and 10 feeling great, where would you put yourself? (mood check with scaling question)

MICHAEL: I am actually doing pretty good, so I would say a 7.

CLINICIAN: That is a lot better than last week, so you are seeing some improvement in your life.

MICHAEL: Yeah, my boss was not on my case as much, although I still feel a lot of stress at work.

CLINICIAN: Yes, I do recall that work has been stressful for you, and that can sometimes be a trigger. However, it sounds like work, at least for the time being, is going better for you.

CLINICIAN: Michael, I would like to take a minute and summarize what we talked about in the last session and how that can tie into what we talk about today. If you recall, last week I explained to you the cognitive behavioral model of substance use, and we identified several triggers to your using substances. We also discussed how schemas, automatic thoughts about substance use, and permission giving thoughts can lead to using. We talked about how these thoughts relate to your feelings, which then relate to behavior, such as substance use. Taken together, we came up with a model that explains your substance use, and I would like to revisit that today (bridging from the last session).

MICHAEL: Okay. Sure. I remember something that you drew on the flip chart related to this.

CLINICIAN: Yes, here it is. (turning flip chart over to show the diagram of Michael's pattern of use) Today I would like to focus on your automatic thoughts about substance use and how they relate to actual use. (beginning discussion of agenda items)

MICHAEL: Okay.

CLINICIAN: Well, when we look at this diagram, one of your automatic thoughts is "Cocaine use is the only way to take my mind off life." Tell me more about that.

MICHAEL: I mean, I just don't know what I would do without it. When I go to a bar with my buddies, I just don't know if I could ever refuse a hit.

CLINICIAN: I'm curious, what is the evidence that this thought is true, that cocaine use is the only way to take your mind off life? (beginning of Socratic questioning to help Michael explore automatic thoughts)

MICHAEL: Cocaine is an escape; it takes my mind of things; I mean, I come home or go to the bar stressed and when I have had a hit, I feel better.

CLINICIAN: But what is the evidence that cocaine is the *only* way to distract your mind? (continuing with Socratic dialogue)

MICHAEL: I am not sure when you put it that way. I guess there are other methods people use to help calm nerves and stay focused: medication, relaxation, stuff like that.

CLINICIAN: So, you can see that there are other ways to help take your mind off things. How does that realization fit with your automatic thought, "Cocaine use is the only way to take my mind off life?"

MICHAEL: I see where you are going. That is an extreme statement. I guess I haven't tried any of that other stuff.

CLINICIAN: So, now that you see that your automatic thought is biased, what is the effect of continuing to believe in this thought?

MICHAEL: It seems like I am limiting myself, unwilling or unable to explore other avenues to calm my nerves and take my mind off things. Maybe there are some ways that aren't so harmful.

CLINICIAN: Right, maybe that is something we can explore together: ways to take your mind of off life for a bit that do not involve cocaine or substances.

At this point in the session, the clinician introduced Michael to the daily thought record. He explained its purpose and how to record triggering events, automatic thoughts, feelings after the automatic thoughts, rational responses, and feelings after the rational responses. The clinician explained that Michael was to complete this record every day for the next week and that an exploration of his automatic thoughts would proceed as was done previously (i.e., in a Socratic dialogue).

MICHAEL: I do have a situation coming up this weekend in which there will be cocaine, I am sure of it, and I am scared to death about my own using, especially given this DUI and legal mess I am in.

CLINICIAN: Okay. Let's look at that. Would you mind if we try an exercise? (Michael nods affirmatively.) I would like you to sit back and relax, close your eyes, and think about the upcoming situation. Try to be at the place you are going; really get into it. Are you there? (behavioral imagery technique)

MICHAEL: (closing his eyes) Yup, I'm there.

CLINICIAN: Great. Now, think of any situation in which you may be tempted to use cocaine. Who would be around you? Where are you? And so forth. Tell me when you feel really tempted to use, when the craving is high.

MICHAEL: Okay. I'm there. I can almost taste it.

CLINICIAN: Now, think about your automatic thought, "Cocaine is the only way to take my mind off life." Repeat it in your mind repeatedly. What do you feel?

MICHAEL: I feel like I want to use now. I had a hard week, and this will help me forget it all.

CLINICIAN: After repeating your automatic thought, say to yourself as a substitute, "There are other strategies to distract me that are just as effective minus the problems."

MICHAEL: Got it! I am now repeating the substitute thought.

CLINICIAN: (after several minutes) Let's check in with how you are feeling now. Do you still have a craving or desire for cocaine?

MICHAEL: Yes, moderate, but it is not as strong. The fact that there are other ways to take my mind off life is a bit relieving. I almost feel that I have choice in the matter, whereas before everything was so automatic.

CLINICIAN: The substitute thought is often called the "rational response." I say "rational" because it is a more accurate statement than an automatic thought. In the daily thought record, I would like you to generate as many rational responses as possible for each automatic thought.

MICHAEL: Okay. I see how this might work. But I am going to need a lot more rational responses, I think.

CLINICIAN: Yes, and that is the point of the daily thought record. In essence, you will be building a collection of rational responses that you can apply in tight situations. We only have a few moments left. How about we take a moment to review the session. When you came in today, you agreed with today's agenda, and if time permitted, we would talk about stress at work. We did not get to that, so I will make sure to put that on the agenda first thing next week. You reported that you were feeling a "7," which was higher than previously reported. I then talked more about the cognitive model of substance use, and we discussed your first automatic thought about cocaine use. Through the imagery exercise, you were able to see that substituting rational responses in place of the automatic thoughts can reduce your craving for cocaine and buy you some time to get out of a tight situation. I also introduced the daily thought record, and I would like you to complete it every day and then bring it in for the next session. Is that about right? Anything to add? (capsule summary)

MICHAEL: No, that seems pretty on target about what we discussed.

CLINICIAN: Okay. I look forward to seeing you next week.

This session set the stage for further exploration of triggering events, schemas, and automatic thoughts using the daily thought record. The use of the imagery exercise is a classic behavioral strategy that blends nicely with cognitive base therapies. As an additional intervention, the clinician could have used systematic desensitization as way to deepen behavioral change. Other behavioral interventions, such as relaxation training, could be done at later times as new skills and techniques are acquired through counseling.

Strengths, Limitations, and Ethical Issues Related to CBT

CBT is a general therapeutic approach that incorporates both cognitive theory and behavior theory principles to maximize the change process. The cognitive and behavioral components both augment and support each other. CBT has many variations, and the clinician has a range of flexibility when using this approach. CBT is a promising treatment for those struggling with substance use issues, as irrational thinking and deleterious coping patterns pervade many clients' lives. However, more research is needed on the efficacy of CBT with those struggling with substance problems as well as those from diverse backgrounds. In addition, some elements of CBT may not be particularly useful for some minority populations. A review of the strengths, weaknesses, and ethical issues using CBT are presented in Table 7.1.

TABLE 7.1   Summary of Strengths, Limitations, and Ethical Concerns of CBT in the Treatment of Substance Use Problems

Strengths	• CBT is based on the interrelationship and reciprocal nature of thinking, feeling, and behaving and how these contribute to substance use. It is an integrative practice. • Most variations of CBT allow for flexibility in their use of therapeutic strategy and technique, something critical for working with clients struggling with substance use disorders. • Great value in confronting clients regarding core assumptions, beliefs, and values (Corey, 2009), which often maintain persistent substance use. • Allows for placing newly acquired insights into action via homework assignments (Corey, 2009) so clients can practice abstinence supporting skills. • CBT strategies allow clients to become their own best therapists outside of the counseling office. • CBT is not a mysterious or complicated approach; it is effective, focused, and practical, which can appeal to a wide range of clients presenting with substance use problems. • Education is a strong component of CBT; clients struggling with substance use disorders can benefit from a combined educational/therapeutic model such as CBT.

TABLE 7.1   Summary of Strengths, Limitations, and Ethical Concerns of CBT in the Treatment of Substance Use Problems (*Continued*)

Limitations	• Perhaps true with any approach, but especially CBT, clinician's level of training, knowledge, and skill correlates to how well it is implemented. Many clinicians may simply not have this level of training and continuing education. • Corey (2009) pointed out the questionable assumption that exploration of the past is ineffective in helping clients change behavior. • More research is needed in the application of CBT with diverse populations as well as its application to substance use problems.
Ethical Issues	• The nature of many CBT approaches, especially REBT, create a power differential by the clinician's imposing ideas as to what is rational thinking (Corey, 2017). Would clients who use substances feel pressured to adopt the goals/values of the clinician? • Many aspects of substance use disorders, such as denial, rationalization, physical dependence, and so forth, would theoretically not be addressed by many CBT approaches. • There is some concern about undue influence or manipulation from directive approaches such as CBT: Ethical issues may arise when the wishes for the client are different than the client's own wishes.

References

Adams, G., Turner, H., Hoskins, J., Robinson, A., & Waller, G. (2021). Effectiveness of a brief form of group dialectical behavior therapy for binge-eating disorder: Case series in a routine clinical setting. *International Journal of Eating Disorders, 54,* 615–620.

Amendola, S., Hengartner, M. P., Ajdacic-Gross, V., Angst, J., & Rossler, W. (2022). Longitudinal reciprocal associations between depression, anxiety, and substance use disorders over three decades of life. *Journal of Affective Disorders, 302,* 315–323.

Archer, J., & McCarthy, C. J. (2007). *Theories of counseling and psychotherapy: Contemporary applications.* Pearson.

Beck, A. T. (1976). *Cognitive therapy and the emotional disorders.* Meridian.

Beck, A. T., Wright, F. D., Newman, C. F., & Liese, B. S. (1993). *Cognitive therapy of substance abuse.* Guilford.

Bornovalova, M. A., & Daughters, S. B. (2007). How does dialectical behavior therapy facilitate treatment retention among individuals with co-morbid borderline personality disorder and substance use disorders? *Clinical Psychology Review, 27,* 923–943.

Burns, D. B. (2020). *Feeling great: The revolutionary new treatment for depression and anxiety.* PESI Publishing.

Burrow-Sanchez, J. J., & Hops, H. (2019). A randomized trial of culturally accommodated versus standard group treatment for Latina/o adolescents with substance use disorders: Posttreatment through 12-month outcomes. *Cultural Diversity and Ethnic Minority Psychology, 25,* 311–322.

Carroll, K. M., Easton, C. J., Nich, C., Hunkele, K. A., Neavins, T. M., Sinha, R., Ford, H. L., Vitolo, S. A., Doebrick, C. A., & Rounsaville, B. J. (2006). The use of contingency management and motivational/skills-building therapy to treat young adults with marijuana dependence. *Journal of Consulting and Clinical Psychology, 74*, 955–966. https://doi.org/10.1037/0022-006X.74.5.955

Corey, G. (2009). *Theory and practice of counseling and psychotherapy* (8th ed.). Brooks/Cole.

Corey, G. (2017). *Theory and practice of counseling and psychotherapy* (10th ed.). Cengage.

Dattilio, F. M. (2000). Cognitive-behavioral strategies. In J. Carlson & L. Sperry (Eds.), *Brief therapy with individuals and couples* (pp. 33–70). Zeig, Tucker, & Theisen.

DiGiuseppe, R., & McInerney, J. (1990). Patterns of addiction: A rational-emotive perspective. *Journal of Cognitive Psychotherapy: An International Quarterly, 4*, 121–134.

Dimeff, L. A., & Linehan, M. M. (2008). Dialectical behavior therapy for substance abusers, *Addiction Science and Clinical Practice, 4*(2), 39–47. http://www.ncbi.nlm.nih.gov/pmc/articles/PMC2797106/pdf/ascp-04-2-39.pdf

Ellis, A. (1980). Discomfort anxiety: A new cognitive-behavioral construct (part II). *Rational Living, 17*, 25–30.

Ellis, A. (1982). The treatment of alcohol and drug abuse: A rational-emotive approach. *Rational Living, 17*(2), 15–24.

Ellis, A. (1985). *Overcoming resistance: Rational-emotive therapy with difficult clients*. Springer.

Ellis, A. (1999). *How to make yourself happy and remarkably less disturbable*. Impact.

Harned, M. S., Chapman, A. L., Dexter-Mazza, E. T., Murray, A., Comtois, K. A., & Linehan, M. M. (2008). Treating co-occurring Axis I disorders in recurrently suicidal women with borderline personality disorder: A 2-year randomized trial of dialectical behavior therapy versus community treatment by experts. *Journal of Consulting and Clinical Psychology, 76*, 1068–1075.

Horrell, S. C. V. (2008). Effectiveness of cognitive-behavioral therapy with adult ethnic minority clients: A review. *Professional Psychology: Research and Practice, 39*, 160–168.

Jackson, L. C., Schmutzer, P. A., Wenzel, A., & Tyler, J. D. (2006). Applicability of cognitive-behavior therapy with American Indian individuals. *Psychotherapy: Theory, Research, Practice, Training, 43*, 506–517. https://doi.org/10.1037/0033-3204.43.4.506

Jacobsen, E. (1938). *Progressive relaxation*. University of Chicago Press.

Jankowska, M. (2019). Cultural modifications of cognitive behavioral treatment of social anxiety among culturally diverse clients: A systematic literature review. *The Cognitive Behavioral Therapist, 12*, e7, 1–25. https://doi.org/10.1017/S1754470X18000211

Koerner, K., & Dimeff, L. A. (2007). Overview of dialectical behavior therapy. In L. A. Dimeff & K. Koerner (Eds.), *Dialectical behavior therapy in clinical practice: Applications across disorders and settings* (pp. 1–18). Guilford.

Lake, M. T., Krishnamurti, T., Murtaugh, K. L., van Nunen, L. J., Stein, D. J., & Shoptaw, S. (2022, April 28). Decision-making tendencies and voucher spending independently support abstinence within contingency management for methamphetamine use disorder. *Experimental and Clinical Psychopharmacology*. Advance online publication. http://dx.doi.org/10.1037/pha0000574

Leahy, R. L. (2003). *Cognitive therapy techniques: A practitioner's guide*. Guilford.

Liese, B. S., & Beck, A. T. (1997). Back to basics: Fundamental cognitive therapy skills for keeping drug-dependent individuals in treatment. *NIDA Research Monograph, 165*, 207–232.

Liese, B. S., & Beck, A. T. (2022). *Cognitive-behavioral therapy of addictive disorders*. Guilford.

Liese, B. S., & Franz, R. A. (1996). Treating substance-use disorders with cognitive therapy: Lessons learned and implications for the future. In P. M. Salkovskis (Ed.), *Frontiers of cognitive therapy* (pp. 470–508). Guilford.

Linehan, M. M. (2014). *Skills training manual for treatment borderline personality disorder* (2nd ed.). Guilford.

Linehan, M. M., Armstrong, H., Suarez, A., Allmon, D., & Heard, H. (1991). Cognitive-behavioral treatment of chronically parasuicidal borderline patients. *Archives of General Psychiatry, 48*, 1060–1064.

Linehan, M. M., Dimeff, L. A., Reynolds, S. K., Comtois, K. A., Welch, S. S., Heagerty, P., & Kivlahan, D. R. (2002). Dialectical behavior therapy versus comprehensive validation therapy plus 12-step for the treatment of opioid dependent women meeting criteria for borderline personality disorder. *Drug and Alcohol Dependence, 67*, 13–26.

Linehan, M. M., Schmidt H. I, Dimeff, L. A., Craft, J. C., Kanter, J., & Comtois, K. A. (1999). Dialectical behavior therapy for patients with borderline personality disorder and drug- dependence. *The American Journal on Addictions, 8*, 279–292.

Maultsby, M. C. (1984). *Rational behavior therapy*. Prentice-Hall.

McKay, M., Wood, J. C., & Brantley, J. (2019). *The dialectical behavior therapy skills workbook: Practical DBT exercises for learning mindfulness, interpersonal effectiveness, emotion regulation, and distress tolerance* (2nd ed.). New Harbinger.

Milligan, C. O., Nich, C., & Carroll, K. M. (2004). Ethnic differences in substance abuse treatment retention, compliance, and outcome from two clinical trials. *Psychiatric Services, 55*, 167–173. https://doi.org/10.1176/appi.ps.55.2.167

Petry, N. M., Alessi, S. M., & Hanson, T. (2007). Contingency management improves abstinence and quality of life in cocaine abusers. *Journal of Consulting and Clinical Psychology, 75*, 307–315. https://doi.org/10.1037/0022-006X.75.2.307

Prentiss, C. (2007). *The alcoholism and addiction cure: A holistic approach to total recovery*. Power Press.

Prochaska, J. O., & Norcross, J. C. (2007). *Systems of psychotherapy: A transtheoretical analysis* (6th ed.). Brooks/Cole.

Rawson, R. A., McCann, M. J., Flammino, F., Shoptaw, S., Miotto, K., Reiber, C., & Ling, W. (2006). A comparison of contingency management and cognitive-behavioral approaches for stimulant-dependent individuals. *Addiction, 101*, 267–274. https://doi.org/10.1111/j.1360-0443.2006.01312.x

Reichenberg, L. W., & Seligman, L. (2016). *Selecting effective treatments: A comprehensive, systematic guide to treating mental disorders* (5th edition). Jossey-Boss.

Rollnick, S., Healther, N., & Bell, A. (1992). Negotiating behavior change in medical settings: The development of brief motivational interviewing. *Journal of Mental Health, 1*, 25–37.

Salsman, N. L. (2020). Dialectical behavior therapy for individuals with substance use problems: Theoretical adaptations and empirical evidence. In J. Bedics (Ed.), *The handbook of dialectical behavior therapy: Theory, research, and evaluation* (pp. 141–174). Elsevier.

Sharf, R. S. (2004). *Theories of psychotherapy and counseling: Concepts and cases* (3rd ed.). Brooks/Cole.

Smith, J. (2010). *Dialectical behavior therapy*. PESI Seminars.

Telch, C. F., Agras, W. S., & Linehan, M. M. (2001). Dialectical behavior therapy for binge eating disorders. *Journal of Consulting and Clinical Psychology, 69,* 1061–1065.

Thombs, D. L. (2006). *Introduction to addictive behaviors* (3rd ed.). Guilford.

Thombs, D. L., & Osborn, C. J. (2019). *Introduction to addictive behaviors* (5th ed.). Guilford.

Van den Bosch, L. M. C., Verheul, R., Schippers, G. M., & van den Brink, W. (2002). Dialectical behavior therapy of borderline patients with and without substance use problems implementation and long-term effects. *Addictive Behaviors, 27,* 911–923.

Westra, H. A., & Dozois, D. J. A. (2008). Integrating motivational interviewing into the treatment of anxiety. In H. Arkowitz, H. A. Westra, W. R. Miller, & S. Rollnick (Eds.). *Motivational interviewing in the treatment of psychological problems*. Guilford.

Windsor, L. C., Jemal, A., & Alessi, E. J. (2015). Cognitive behavioral therapy: A meta-analysis of race and substance use outcomes. *Cultural Diversity and Ethnic Minority Psychology, 21,* 300–313.

Figure Credits

CHAPTER 8

Applying Relapse Prevention in the Treatment of Substance Use Disorders

Introduction

I was once told by one of my professors that much of substance use counseling is essentially about preventing relapse. When clients come to see a substance use clinician, many have usually hit rock bottom and have tried to remain drug and alcohol free, or have at least reduced use, before entering treatment. A key task then is to help clients prevent returning to problematic use. This entails either helping them avoid alcohol and/or drugs for the rest of their lives or to better manage their use as in the case of controlled drinking or other harm reduction programs. Regardless, relapse prevention is *critical* in the treatment and care of those struggling with substance use disorders.

As many substance use clinicians will attest, regardless of type of drug, many clients who receive alcohol and/or drug treatment return to use after leaving treatment (Fisher & Harrison, 2018). Indeed, there is a high degree of consensus that relapse is a very common aspect of recovery (Dobmeier & Stevens, 2013). Some time ago Miller and Hester (1980), in a review of alcohol outcome-based studies, found that 26% of clients were "successful" at 1 year follow-up from treatment, which was defined as abstinent plus improved functioning. McLellan et al. (2000) estimated over a 60% relapse rate after substance use treatment. More recently, Hser et al. (2007), in a study examining relapse among those with heroin use disorders, found nearly 60% of individuals continued regular use throughout their study. Estimates suggest that individuals will attend treatment up to three to four occasions (suggesting three to four relapses) over a period before maintaining abstinence (Dennis et al., 2005). Clearly, research findings and the general agreement among substance use professionals warrants effective, empirically supported strategies to prevent and manage relapse.

Relapse prevention (RP) is "a generic term that refers to a wide range of strategies designed to prevent relapse in the area of addictive behavior change" (Marlatt & Gordon, 1985, p. xii). Relapse prevention is not a theory per se; however, many relapse prevention models are grounded in theory, primarily cognitive behavioral ideas. Thus, the strategies of RP can be the sole focus of therapy or incorporated into any theoretical approach and modality. RP groups, with a specific focus on building skills to prevent relapse, have been used in several agencies across the United States (Center for Substance Abuse Treatment [CSAT], 2005). The development of RP strategies has provided greater conceptualization and organization for substance use treatment protocols (Rawson et al., 1993). The techniques of RP are appealing to clinicians and clinical researchers because they have a strong conceptual foundation (e.g., cognitive behavioral) and many have been empirically validated (Rawson et al., 1993).

In this chapter, I discuss the major tenets of RP by outlining what a relapse is, how it is different from concepts such as lapse, and how it fits in the recovery process. I also explore the determinants of relapse and three popular models of relapse. Numerous RP strategies are offered to readily incorporate into your work with clients. Finally, I discuss diversity issues and RP, followed by RP in the case of Michael. It is my hope that after reading this chapter you will have a good understanding of what relapse is (and isn't), the key models of relapse, and strategies that can be applied immediately in your practice.

The Major Tenets of Relapse Prevention

What Is a Relapse?

Before I define relapse, it is important to explore similar terms such as *slip* or *lapse*.[1] Miller (2005) and Fisher and Harrison (2018) defined slip/lapse as the return to drug usage after a period of abstinence; it generally refers to one-time use that may or may not generate much guilt. For example, someone with an alcohol use disorder may have sip of wine at a family wedding but subsequently does not have any more alcohol. This one-time occurrence may seem benign, but from the perspective of the individual can cause much consternation. A *relapse* refers to a period of uncontrolled drinking or other drug use following a period of abstinence (Fisher & Harrison, 2018; Thombs & Osborn, 2019). In general, the person regresses to pre-treatment levels of use, where they have fallen of the proverbial wagon.

Clinicians must plan for a slips or relapse as it is to be expected. I agree with Fisher and Harrison (2018) that abstinence is the safest and healthiest plan for most clients; however, it is foolish to ignore the reality of slips and to leave clients unprepared for how to manage slips from becoming worse (more on relapse management later). Substance use clinicians should be aware that in many cases clients might relapse three, four, or more times before establishing firmly into recovery. That is, they may cycle through the stages of change several times before behavior change is firmly established (Miller, 2021).

Many clinicians believe that a lapse after a period of abstinence does not constitute a relapse because it is not a return to pretreatment levels of using. This perspective refers to the *process* view of relapse, which is consistent with MI and harm reduction strategies. The process view comes from social learning theory (SLT) and considers a lapse/relapse as an act of backsliding or worsening in the recovery journey; relapse does not mean one is stupid or lazy but rather an opportunity to learn from the experience (Thombs & Osborn, 2019). Viewing

---

1 Although some may see slight differences in the terms *slip* and *lapse*, my preference is to use them interchangeably and as essentially meaning the same thing.

relapse on a continuum from minor use (slip) to full-blown use (relapse) has been an underlying assumption of many RP models and is a useful talking point with clients. Proponents of the *traditional* view of relapse (those who subscribe to disease model thinking) and some AA venues, however, have little to say about RP (Thombs & Osborn, 2019) and may see relapse as a myth. This is because they define addiction as a disease in which victims lose control once they consume even a drop of alcohol or hit of drugs. Either the person is ill and has symptoms or is well and does not; they are either abstinent or using. Thus, taking even a sip places the individual with an alcohol use disorder on the inevitable return to problematic drinking (i.e., relapse). Relapse, then, is seen as an end state, a negative outcome equal to treatment failure (Larimer et al., 1999). This is not to say that the traditional view is necessarily "bad." Indeed, in some instances clients need to remain completely substance free, and any hint of alcohol or drugs may send them in a quick and dangerous downward spiral. As we will see, approaches to RP pull from both the process and traditional viewpoints.

Regardless of how one feels about slips/lapses, they can and do lead to more intense substance use, especially if (a) the attribution of the slip is internal, stable, and global; (b) the client has a strong self-image as a person in recovery who has made a long commitment; and (c) letters (a) and (b) combined lead to the abstinence violation effect (AVE; Dimeff & Marlatt, 1998; Thombs & Osborn, 2019). Attributions refer to explanations for why something happened. For example, if a person struggling with addiction slips and views it as a temporary "hiccup" and as a response to peer pressure that they are confident they can avoid in the future, the slip will most likely have little impact. However, if the same person views their slip as related to an internal flaw, as something they will never be able to control, and as a reflection of their total failure as a human being, they will most likely be on the path to full-blown relapse. In addition, clients who have invested a significant amount of time and sacrifice toward their recovery might see a slip as devastating, again placing them at risk for relapse. Those who engage in problematic substance use often assume a fatalistic stance toward their slip (Ford, 1996); the AVE refers to an experience of shame, guilt, and other difficult emotions when a slip occurs; it is a mind-set in which the person believes their slip has blown their recovery and so they might as well go all out. In contrast to loss-of-control mechanisms that define the disease model of addiction, the AVE is based on psychological mechanisms such as cognitive and emotional reactions to a lapse. A "harsh" reaction generally leads to uncontrolled use (Dimeff & Marlatt, 1998). I will say more about the AVE in later sections.

Marlatt et al. (2002) noted that a key factor in RP is helping clients reframe the notion of a lapse/relapse with the goal of preventing over-reaction and a cascade of negative feelings. In the authors' view, a lapse/relapse can be observed as a temporary setback with potential for positive outcomes. Clients can learn from their mistakes, develop strategies to prevent them from happening again, and gain confidence from their successes. Instead of using the term *relapse*, which has negative connotations, Marlatt et al. (2002) suggested *prolapse*, which is defined as "mistakes that clients learn from that improve their eventual chances of success" (p. 9). Ford (1996) argued that clients must recognize their own abilities and capacity to control the magnitude of a lapse before it turns into something far worse.

Recovery and Its Relation to Relapse

Regardless of the nature and extent of the relapse, it should be perceived as a temporary setback and sign that something within the recovery plan has gone awry (Miller, 2021). Recovery refers to the period or state of deliberate and intentional nonuse of substances. It includes efforts to abstain *and* begin new and positive behaviors to live a productive and healthy life. Recovery is a step beyond abstinence; although in many cases abstinence is a prerequisite to recovery from substance use, recovery refers the presence of something, not just the absence of something. Recovery is a *process* that has a definite beginning but no definite ending. This process can be difficult and lifelong. Indeed, individuals often make several attempts in striving for a goal before it is successfully reached (Dimeff & Marlatt, 1998). The expectation that recovery and RP is a constant forward moving, linear process can inadvertently engender negative and hopeless thoughts and feelings when slips occur (Dimeff & Marlatt, 1998). Although failures in recovery are to be expected, they also can be great learning opportunities for growth.

Ford (1996) noted that clients tend to focus so much energy on not using drugs or alcohol but fail to address what they will do with the rest of their lives. That is, recovery is about broadening one's life and cultivating a meaning and purpose from which they can derive satisfaction. The implication is that clients will not be successful if their only goal in life is negative (i.e., trying to *not* use drugs). Without a positive purpose or goal, the client is on a slippery slope toward relapse. Indeed, lifestyle growth, in addition to behavioral RP skills, is critical to successful recovery.

The path of recovery can look different for each client, but a typical pattern is often *not* a nice, linear progression from stopping use to being fully recovered. Recovery often includes changes in the patterns and intensity of drinking or drug use, binges, long stretches of living substance free, with eventual stabilization in the maintenance stage of change. The process of recovery can take years, and in some cases a lifetime. Thus, relapse may be a part of one's recovery journey. How they respond to this relapse, and continue to work to prevent future occurrences, plays a large role in the success of recovery.

Models of Relapse

The first model of relapse can probably be traced to AA and their initial (and still current) perspective on recovery. The foundation of AA is that individuals must paradoxically give up control of drinking to gain control of one's life (Dobmeier & Stevens, 2013). Members of AA work through the 12 steps that focus on giving up control (to gain control), self-examination, and making amends. They encourage group participation and that each member have a "sponsor" who listens, supports, and, when necessary, confronts. Many clients who I have counseled regard AA as the single most important component in recovery. Yet, AA is not for everyone. Since the initiation of AA, several RP models and programs have been proposed that deviate from the AA perspective. These additional models see relapse not as a failure but as a chance for the individual to learn new coping strategies (Dobmeier & Stevens, 2013).

The primary theoretical foundation for many RP models is cognitive behavioral. In addition, several models have been developed and/or empirically tested for use with only one substance (e.g., Annis's [1990] RP model for alcoholism). For our purposes, we will focus on three primary models of RP that have stood the test of time: Gorski's developmental model of recovery (CENAPS), Marlatt and Gordan's RP model, and the more recent dynamic model of relapse. Although Gorski's model lacks a specific methodology that can be assessed through empirical research (Rawson et al., 1993) it is well known and has been incorporated into many chemical dependency treatment agencies (Miller, 2021). Marlatt and Gordan's model is based on CBT principles and has been influential to many other RP programs (Miller, 2021). The dynamic model of relapse is a reformulation of Marlatt and Gordan's earlier model. Empirical research supports many of the constructs in both models. In addition to the major models of relapse, we also will examine RP from REBT and DBT perspectives.

CENAPS Model of Relapse Prevention

Gorski's developmental model of recovery, also known as the CENAPS model of relapse prevention (Gorski 1989, 1990), is an integration of developmental theory and the disease model of addiction (Dobmeier & Stevens, 2013). It also incorporates cognitive behavioral elements of addiction, although RP is generally conceptualized via biopsychosocial perspectives. As such, although the disease model is how addiction and recovery are conceptualized, the techniques of RP are eclectic (Fisher & Harrison, 2018). The model places a premium on noticing relapse triggers, how relapse happens, and alternative coping behaviors (Miller, 2021). Gorski (1989) proposed that clients struggling with substance use disorders progress through six developmental stages on the path to recovery:

1. **Transition.** The individual experiences greater problems and symptoms related to substance use and comes to the realization that they have lost control.

2. **Stabilization.** The client begins treatment, usually with detoxification to manage withdrawal. The client is stabilized, and short-term issues are addressed.

3. **Early recovery.** The client identifies the negative effects of drugs on thinking and feeling and learns healthy methods to address these.

4. **Middle recovery.** The focus is on establishing lifestyle balance.

5. **Late recovery.** The client experiences personality changes because chemicals are out of the system. Intimacy may increase, in addition to having more energy and enhanced self-esteem. Client becomes aware of some of the psychological triggers that can lead to relapse.

6. **Maintenance.** Abstinence is the only goal; maintaining this is a lifelong commitment.

There are several principles that underlie the CENAPS model, which reflect disease model, developmental, and cognitive behavioral ideas. These principles include (a) self-regulation and stabilization; (b) teaching client self-assessment as a means to understand the recovery-re-lapse-recovery process; (c) relapse and dependency education; (d) identification of relapse warning signs (RWSs); (e) the teaching of coping skills in the management of RWSs; (f) review of the recovery plan; (g) morning and evening problem inventories to anticipate RWSs (morning) and review progress (evening); (h) cultivating social supports from significant others; and (i) consistent follow-up care reinforcement of living substance free (Gorski, 1989).

Each principle is complemented with a clinical procedure or technique that allows for application of the principle in clinical practice. For example, in recovery planning (c), the clinician might help the client create a set of activities to engage in when experiencing warning signs of relapse. Dobmeier and Stevens (2013) noted that problems and warning signs will change as the client progresses from transition to maintenance. Thus, such changes will require a reconsideration/reworking of each of these principles across each developmental stage of recovery. An important consideration with Gorski's model is that clients need to prepare for RP by attaining primary goals of treatment. These primary goals include acceptance of their substance use as a biopsychosocial disease, recognizing the need for lifelong abstinence, having a recovery plan to maintain a substance-free lifestyle, and addressing other mental health concerns that can derail abstinence (Fisher & Harrison, 2018).

Marlatt and Gordon's Relapse Prevention Model

The RP model (Marlatt & Gordon, 1985) is perhaps the most well known in the field of substance use and addiction. The late G. Alan Marlatt dedicated his professional life to exploring the intricacies of the relapse process and strategies to minimize or prevent relapse from happening. The RP model is based on both cognitive behavioral theory and social learning theory (Larimer et al., 1999; Rawson et al., 1993). For Marlatt, substance use problems are a set of habitual patterns that has been reinforced by biological and environmental contingencies (Rawson et al., 1993). Severe substance use is primarily seen as learned behavior, and thus relapse is a failure of coping rather than a bodily loss of control over substances (Stephens et al., 1994). Essentially, then, preventing a return to use requires a change in thinking and behavioral habits. The RP model emphasizes enhancing healthy coping habits and self-efficacy via social learning and cognitive mechanisms. According to Miller (2021), the model is based on four assumptions:

1. Severe substance use is an over-learned, maladaptive habit.
2. Behavioral modification principles (e.g., reinforcement, punishment) have a major impact on substance-using behavior.
3. It is understandable why people develop a bad habit and why they simply cannot stop.
4. Escape from severe substance use requires changing habits. (p. 210)

The last point needs emphasis. According to the RP model, individuals develop the maladaptive habit of substance use to cope with life. As such, they can learn positive habits as a substitute for substance-using behavior. The cornerstone of the RP model is identifying high-risk situations, identifying and modifying deficiencies in coping skills, supporting confidence, and challenging positive outcome expectancies (Stephens et al., 1994; Witkiewitz et al., 2005; see Figure 8.1).

Relapse Taxonomy

Marlatt (1996) and Marlatt et al. (2002) identified several "determinants" (i.e., a taxonomy) that contribute to substance relapse. In general, factors fall into two main categories: immediate determinants and covert antecedents (Larimer et al., 1999). Immediate determinants include high-risk situations, a person's coping skills, outcome expectancies, and the AVE. Covert antecedents refer to lifestyle imbalances, urges, and cravings (Larimer et al., 1999). Marlatt et al. (2002) further broke down determinants into intrapersonal-environmental and interpersonal types. Intrapersonal-environmental determinants include (a) coping with negative emotional states, (b) coping with negative physical-physiological states, (c) enhancement of positive emotional states, (d) testing personal control, and (e) giving in to temptations or urges. Interpersonal determinants include (a) coping with interpersonal conflict, (b) social pressure, and (c) enhancement of positive emotional states.

Any one or combination of these determinants (immediate, covert, intrapersonal-environmental, or interpersonal types) can trigger a return to use. Indeed, stress is a major contributor to relapse (Larimer et al., 1999; Lin et al., 2020), and much of relapse prevention includes strategies to mitigate stress. Another significant predictor of substance use, especially alcohol, is negative affect (i.e., depression). Witkiewitz et al. (2011) found that negative mood was a key predictor of alcohol use disorders and relapse following treatment and that decreases in negative mood were significantly associated with decreases in heavy drinking behavior. Clinicians may wish to assess each of these determinants with their clients to identify potential triggers and develop strategies to lessen their influence.

A key focus of the RP model is to help individuals conceptualize lapses/relapses as mistakes rather than irrefutable evidence that they are failures (Miller, 2021). Viewed as mistakes, clients are less likely to self-punish and more likely to put a return to use into perspective. As one might imagine, such an idea did not initially go over well with those who took the more traditional view toward relapse, prompting Marlatt to infuse his ideas gently and strategically into the mainstream substance use treatment (for an excellent history of relapse, see Dimeff & Marlatt, 1998; Marlatt, 1996). By making the distinction between lapse and relapse, the dichotomous, all-or-nothing disease model perspective of relapse was challenged (Marlatt, 1996). Today, the RP model and related constructs serve as the foundation for RP programs across the United States and internationally.

The RP model begins when one encounters a high-risk situation. At this juncture, a person can go in one of two directions. Direction A is to incorporate an effective coping response, leading to an increase in self-efficacy, followed by a decrease in the probability or risk of relapse. Direction B is to incorporate an ineffective (or no) coping response, leading to decreased self-efficacy combined with positive expectancies of drug use, which leads to the initiation of use, followed by the AVE plus perceived positive effects of the drug, culminating in an increased risk of relapse (Marlatt & Gordon, 1985). An adapted diagram of the model is presented in Figure 8.1.

The RP model is designed to offer those struggling with substance use a set of tools and information to better equip them when confronted with high-risk situations or when they have

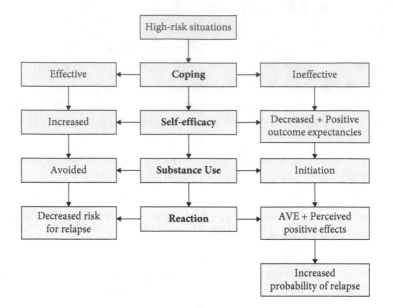

FIGURE 8.1   The RP model of relapse (also called the cognitive behavioral model of relapse).

slipped back into use. In general, there is no underlying causal mechanism that is assumed; instead, clinicians and clients attack the drug-using behaviors themselves. The clinician is provided with a set of strategies that encourage clients to engage in practices that are incompatible with substance use (Rawson et al., 1993). Many of the RP strategies discussed later are based in the RP model. Substance use researchers have generally validated many of the components of the RP model, and outcome studies have demonstrated that it has been applied with some success across several of substance-using behaviors (for excellent studies and reviews, see Irvin et al., 1999; Kouimtsidis et al., 2014; Larimer et al., 1999; Rawson et al., 1993; Stephens et al., 1994; Witkiewitz & Marlatt, 2007).

The Dynamic Model of Relapse

The RP model of relapse served as the foundation for subsequent research and clinical intervention. However, a weakness of the original model may be in its simplicity: Relapse is now thought to be a complex process in which numerous factors contribute to a return to use. For example, Witkiewitz and Marlatt (2009) noted the critical role that interpersonal factors play in the relapse process, factors that are not explicitly part of the original RP model. In response to empirical research that highlighted relapse complexity, Witkiewitz and Marlatt (2007) reconceptualized the original RP model of Marlatt and Gordon (1985) to account for this complexity. The new, revised RP model, called the *dynamic model of relapse*, has high-risk situations (or "contextual factors") as a central component and which are critical to identify. The model includes several interacting relapse risk factors and considerations as one progresses toward a "transgressive behavior" (i.e., substance use) (Witkiewitz & Marlatt, 2007). Following is a list of key components of the dynamic model of relapse.

- **Distal risks.** These refer to factors that predispose a person toward relapse such as family history, social support, and personality (Witkiewitz & Marlatt, 2007). Distal risks can lead directly to substance use, impact coping behavior, influence cognitive processes, and influence how one experiences physical withdrawal.

- **Cognitive processes.** Cognitive processes include self-efficacy, outcome expectancies, cravings, and motivation level. These processes play a key role in the original RP model and are also important in the dynamic model. As we observed with the RP model, cognitive processes can play a direct role leading to substance use.

- **Coping behavior.** Coping behavior remains an important component in the dynamic model. One's ability to cope and self-regulate can be a determining factor in whether one relapses. The greater the ability to cope, the greater the chances of avoiding a return to substance use.

- **Tonic processes.** Tonic activity is a term borrowed from medical science and neuroscience, but in this context is referred to as chronic vulnerability (Witkiewitz & Marlatt, 2007). Within the dynamic model of relapse, tonic processes refer to distal risks, cognitive processes, physical withdrawal, coping behavior, and affective state. These components tend to be long-term characteristics that have the potential to lead to relapse.

- **Phasic responses.** Phasic responses are risk factors that tend to be more transient and state- (instead of trait-) based characteristics that precede a relapse (Witkiewitz & Marlatt, 2007). Phasic responses include coping behavior, cognitive processes, affective states, and substance use itself. Note that cognitive processes, affective states, and coping behaviors are partially tonic *and* phasic processes, indicating overlap in the dynamic model. Indeed, the interrelationship between tonic processes and phasic responses has been supported by research on posttreatment outcomes (Witkiewitz & Marlatt, 2007).

- **Perceived effects.** Perceived effects refer to processes that occur after a slip or relapse that feed back into the substance use behavior. For example, a client might perceive the slip or relapse as providing much needed comfort and pleasure, leading to a reinforcing effect and continued use. A goal of both the RP model and dynamic model is help clients see a slip as part of a growing process and something that, with the right skills, can be avoided down the road.

It is worth repeating that at the core of the dynamic model is high-risk situations that span across both tonic and phasic processes. These contextual factors must be considered in any successful relapse management and prevention plan. The components of the dynamic model might appear as a linear progression from distal risks to substance use. However, the dynamic model shows relapse as a multidimensional, nonlinear process with many overlapping components. Empirical research that supports many of these individual components and their association with substance use continues to build (Krenek et al., 2017; Maisto et al., 2017).

REBT and Relapse

The REBT model of substance use (Ellis & McInerney, 1988), discussed in depth in Chapter 7, has implications for both understanding how relapse comes about and preventing relapse. Because there is overlap with the presentation in Chapter 7, only the essential elements to relapse and RP from an REBT perspective will be reviewed here.

The REBT model begins with the assumption that the client has made the decision to stop using substances. The client then enters high-risk situations or is exposed to cues for using substances (e.g., entering a bar, hanging out with old using buddies, seeing someone using). These cues to drinking or using then lead to an increased desire to consume substances. However, because the client has already made the decision not to drink or use, they experience a cascade of irrational beliefs *related to the abstinence* (e.g., I cannot stand not having a drink; I am too weak to control my urges). These irrational beliefs lead to discomfort anxiety, which then leads to a crossroads: Either the client can dispute the irrational beliefs and subsequently avoid a relapse, or they can give in to the desire to use, reduce anxiety, and strengthen their LFT (Ellis & McInerney, 1988).

There are several points of intervention from the REBT model. First, clinicians may wish to work with clients to avoid cues to substance use in the first place. A thorough assessment of high-risk situations can help clients prepare for and avoid potentially risky events. If clients find themselves in risky situations, they can practice disputing their irrational beliefs about remaining abstinent. For example, in response to "I am too weak to resist this urge," clients might be taught to counter this thought with "I know it seems difficult, and I have overcome these feelings before and been just fine." A third potential intervention point is helping the client cope with discomfort anxiety. Substituting rational for irrational thinking can mediate the connection between choosing not to use and anxiety. Additional strategies include relaxation training, deep diaphragmatic breathing, and practicing mindfulness.

The various models of RP provide a framework from which to understand the mechanisms of relapse as well as points of intervention. Research has shown that RP models provide a viable treatment option for a significant number of individuals struggling with substance use problems (Rawson et al., 1993). In addition, the success of RP models may depend on the type of drug the client is consuming. For example, those with cocaine and alcohol use disorders seem to respond well to outpatient models of RP, but those with opiate use disorders appear to respond better when relapse prevention is part of an aftercare program (Rawson et al., 1993).

Application of RP in the Treatment of Substance Use Disorders

Whether using RP as an intervention in and of itself or using part of it to supplement one's theoretical approach, the practical, skill-based focus on preventing a return to problematic use has great appeal to clinician and client alike. In general, RP strategies include seven overarching content areas: (a) psychoeducation, identification of high-risk situations,

(b) development of coping skills, (c) development of new and balanced lifestyle behaviors, (d) enhanced confidence, (e) avoiding the AVE, and (f) drug and alcohol monitoring (e.g., urine and breath testing; Rawson et al., 1993). The several strategies and applications discussed fall under one or more of these seven content areas.

Fisher and Harrison (2018) outlined essential RP components, drawing from the CENAPS model and cognitive behavioral social models. In general, these components are necessary to successfully manage or prevent relapse:

- **Assessment of high-risk situations.** Examples of high-risk situations are numerous but include anything from social gatherings where drugs are present to negative emotions and interpersonal troubles. High-risk situations can be interpersonal (problems with relating to others), intrapersonal (negative inner states or traits), or environmental (social stress) and place the client at heightened danger of relapsing.

- **Coping with high-risk situations.** Once situations are identified, clients need to have tools for how to cope with them (Fisher & Harrison, 2018). Education and information can be quite helpful. Daley and Marlatt (1992, as cited in Fisher & Harrison, 2018) suggest that clients need to understand the process of relapse; for example, relapse often begins with mini decisions, which can lead one down a slippery slope toward a return to substance use. Exploring the connections between thoughts, feelings, attitudes, stressors, behaviors, and substance use can help clients identify any triggers or warning signs from which to be aware.

- **Establishing support systems.** As noted elsewhere in this text, addiction can be very isolating. Clients cannot accomplish the tasks of recovery alone, and it is incumbent upon them (as well as clinicians) to find a stable support system that they can lean on in difficult times.

- **Lifestyle changes.** Fisher and Harrison (2018) highlighted leisure time, support systems, good social and communication skills, self-care, educational and vocational guidance, financial planning, and relationships as key areas of change that clients struggling with addiction can embrace. Clinicians and clients should not try to tackle all these areas at once but rather address problems in each area in increments.

RP Goals, Style, and Strategy

Marlatt et al. (2002) encouraged a nonconfrontational stance when working with relapse issues. They also encouraged clients to be objective when examining their substance-using behaviors. Incorporating the client's perspective into their own relapse plan fosters objectivity by reducing defensiveness and encouraging self-monitoring and support. The overall goals of RP are to increase clients' awareness and choice, develop coping skills, and increase confidence, mastery, self-efficacy (Marlatt et al., 2002).

Larimer et al. (1999) and Marlatt et al. (2002) outline several strategies clinicians can adopt when working with relapse potential, including both specific and global prevention strategies.

Specific intervention strategies include focusing on the immediate precipitants of relapse, including cognitive distortions, high-risk situations, and negative reactions to the environment. They are usually the focus early in treatment, where the client is trying to prevent a single lapse. Global strategies include broader elements of the client's recovery, such as establishing lifestyle balance, identifying and handling early warning signs, and managing the AVE. Specific strategies can be implemented across five domains: assessment, insight/awareness raising techniques, coping skills training, increasing self-efficacy, and cognitive strategies (Marlatt et al., 2002), and are considered next.

Assessment and Insight Awareness Strategies

Relapse prevention–based interventions usually start with a thorough substance use assessment. As noted in Chapter 5, substance use assessment is a complex process that entails both subjective and objective methods. Aside from providing basic information such as types of drugs used, frequency of use, and quantity of use, a substance use assessment helps the clinician get a sense of the triggers for use, the strength of cravings, what has worked in avoiding drug use in the past, and the client's skill base in addressing and coping with stress. All these factors, as well as others, provide an informal risk factor profile for relapse.

Insight and awareness strategies help raise consciousness about the extent of substance use and associated consequences. Marlatt et al. (2002) advocated an MI-based approach in which client stage of change is assessed, followed by the decisional balance exercise consistent with MI philosophy. Helping clients increase importance and confidence related to behavioral change minimizes the risk of relapse. During this step, clinicians also teach clients about relapse and provide a "big-picture" perspective (Larimer et al., 1999). Clients develop alternative perspectives on their substance use and become aware of the thoughts, feelings, and behaviors that interfere with change (Marlatt et al., 2002).

Another assessment and insight strategy is to encourage clients to write an "addiction/ex-user autobiography" (Marlatt et al., 2002, p. 28). In this strategy, clients are encouraged to write about their life as someone who uses substances, focusing on triggers, emotions, behaviors, consequences of use, and self-perception as a substance user. Indeed, the goal of this exercise is to identify high-risk situations, thoroughly confront and vet consequences, and assess the client's self-image as substance user. Clients also are encouraged to write an essay about their future lives as ex-drug/alcohol users.

Coping Skills Training

As noted previously, a key part of the RP approach is learning how to successfully cope with high-risk situations (Fisher & Harrison, 2018; Larimer et al., 1999; Miller, 2005). When an person struggling with substance use faces a high-risk situation, they can either use an effective coping response and subsequently avoid relapse or not use a coping response and thus greatly increasing the probability of relapse. One of the first set of skills a substance use clinician should assess is the client's ability to cope. If coping skills are lacking, the clinician should endeavor to teach new skills and help the client practice them in therapy.

Although it is important to respect and utilize client resources, clinicians should avoid assuming that clients have all the skills necessary to cope with high-risk situations. I have encountered clients who thought they could resist temptation only to be disappointed at their subsequent loss of control. At other times, clients are all too aware of their inability to cope. I recall counseling a 62-year-old woman who struggled with chronic alcoholism and who simply did not know how to cope with stress. She reported a relatively normal upbringing; however, she had the insight to recognize that his mother and stepfather never allowed her to make decisions on her own. They were overprotective and created an environment where she failed to generate her own internal resource against stress. Her drinking and substance use spanned years, often spurred on by difficult times or seemingly insurmountable stress. A large part of our work together was helping her find ways to better cope with life.

The substance use clinician assesses for strengths and limitations across several areas—family, work, recreation, diet, exercise, stress management—and helps promote behavioral action to expand the client's life. If a client possesses strong coping skills and uses them proficiently, then their self-efficacy increases, and the risk of relapse is low. If they possess poor or nonexistent coping skills, the chances of relapse increase greatly.

Enhancing Self-Efficacy

We learned from the RP model that self-efficacy plays a critical role in whether one will relapse. Specifically, lack of coping skills combined with low self-efficacy can set the stage for increased risk of continued drug use. In MI, self-efficacy is listed as one of its core principles related to behavior change.

One strategy to enhance self-efficacy is to explore with clients their past successes with either substance use or some other behavior that they had difficulty stopping but were able to. Another strategy is to break down the overall task of behavior change into smaller, more manageable parts that can be addressed one at a time (Larimer et al., 1999). For example, a client might have an overall goal of repairing their marriage but start with a sub-goal of communicating something positive to their spouse every day for a week. Essentially, clients are taught that changing a habit is a matter of skill acquisition rather than forging enough willpower (which, in substance use, often fails; Larimer et al., 1999).

Marlatt et al. (2002) proposed enhancing self-efficacy through imagery exercises. Here, the clinician invites the client to imagine being in a tough situation and incorporating a coping skill learned in counseling. This exercise can be effective for clients who are anxious about maintaining their abstinence; in essence, through their imagination they can strengthen their refusal skills and approach situations with renewed confidence.

Cognitive Strategies

Cognitive strategies involve helping clients to restructure or reframe their perspectives and attributions regarding relapse (Larimer et al., 1999). The primary point of intervention is when a client experiences a lapse. Clients are taught to reframe lapses as mistakes or errors in the learning process rather than failures. A lapse is a sign that some skills need strengthening or greater focus in therapy. Additional cognitive strategies include coping imagery and cognitive restructuring (Marlatt et al., 2002). Coping imagery might include clients visualizing a successful experience in which they coped effectively with a high-risk situation. Cognitive restructuring might include self-talk in which positive, affirming statements are substituted for negative talk consistent with maintaining the substance use pattern.

Global RP Strategies

Global relapse strategies are designed to assess and help clients navigate broader lifestyle issues related to relapse. These strategies include promoting a balanced lifestyle, stimulus control methods, urge/craving management techniques, and relapse road maps (Larimer et al., 1999). Each of these will be considered in turn.

Lifestyle Modification and Balance

Individuals struggling with substance use often live unbalanced lives in which significant external demands lead one to feel deserving of pleasure and fulfillment through drug use (Thombs & Osborn, 2019). Recovery from severe substance use requires changing lifestyle habits with the goal of achieving some measure of balance. Being physically off alcohol and other drugs (or successfully controlling use, such as alcohol) is an important first step in any recovery plan, but failure to attend to other lifestyle issues can lead to repeated relapse (Dobmeier & Stevens, 2013).

High-risk situations become even more problematic when a person has a lifestyle imbalance. Lifestyle imbalance is defined as having more "shoulds" in life than the "wants" (Marlatt, Parks, & Witkiewitz, 2002). In other words, clients place too much pressure on themselves and carry around too much negative emotion (shoulds) to the exclusion of simple, everyday pleasures (wants). A focus on lifestyle balance encourages clients to infuse more wants into their lives. Imagine a client who attends two AA meetings a day, is trying to gain full employment, is trying to repair their relationships with family, is serving a probation sentence, and is trying to get out of debt. The shoulds in this client's life are usurping all their time, energy, and resources. Over time, they may grow discouraged and think, "Hey, I am working hard, and I deserve a break." If they encounter a high-risk situation, the chances of relapse substantially increase. Although their shoulds are important, such as attending AA, this client could benefit from more wants—more time to relax, enjoy life, and doing something pleasurable without drugs.

Clinicians can incorporate a shoulds versus wants activity with clients to drive home the idea of the importance of greater balance (Marlatt et al., 2002). For example, clinicians could draw a straight line down a dry erase board and label one column "shoulds" and the other "wants." Clients then list all their shoulds and wants and get a visual for how their life may be currently unbalanced. Exploration and discussion may help clients see a need for more wants (and less shoulds) in their lives. Clinicians also could explore the should side and the want side by having the client have a dialogue with the two competing parts. For example, a client could role-play the should voice to the clinician (or an empty chair) and then role-play the want voice. The client may gain several insights from an experiment like this, such as becoming more aware of how strong the should voice is and the need to strike greater balance with wants.

Lifestyle modification programs can be a part of any agency or private practice work where substance use issues are addressed through counseling or psychotherapy. In general, these programs include educational and therapeutic components. Clients are taught, for example, the importance of exercise, diet, and meditation for an overall balanced lifestyle. Marlatt, Parks, and Witkiewitz (2002) suggested helping clients to create substitute indulgences in the form of positive addictions such as running, meditation, hiking, and other hobbies. Building life skills and mastery and enhancing well-being go a long way in helping clients stay off substances.

Stimulus Control

Gaining control of one's environment is an essential component in RP. Whereas it is impossible to control every element in one's environment, there are many actions an individual can take to minimize risk. One of the simplest strategies is to encourage clients to remove all items directly related to substance use from their home, car, and office (Larimer et al., 1999). This may include supplies, paraphernalia, pictures, and other objects associated with use. The importance of this step cannot be overstated. I recall counseling a relatively young client, age 25, who had an alcohol use disorder and had made steady progress in his recovery. As we began to discuss relapse and RP, I was surprised to learn that his roommate kept a stash of alcohol in the refrigerator and in various places in the kitchen. The client rationalized that the alcohol was his roommate's and that he is not at liberty to tell him what to drink. This rationalization did not hold up, though. The client relapsed and was not seen at the agency until a year later. When counseling resumed, he admitted that keeping alcohol so close was one of the triggers that led to full-blown use.

Teaching stimulus control refers to three primary activities: avoidance, escape, and delay (Marlatt et al., 2002). The most obvious way to help prevent relapse is to *avoid* the environments or situations in which drug use occurs. This may be easier said than done; however, clients must understand that it is much safer for them to stay away from situations that place them at increased risk of a return to substance use. Many clients recognize the importance of staying away from high-risk situations but are lacking in confidence that they can do so. Indeed, building confidence becomes an important task in the therapeutic work between clinician and client.

Escape refers to removing oneself from a high-risk situation should clients find themselves in trouble. Clients may not always be able to avoid experiences in which drugs and/or alcohol are present. Consider a client with alcohol use disorder, who decides to go to a class reunion in his hometown. He sees many of his old high school friends and has a good time. Soon after, he is invited out to the bars to continue the party. He decides to go, thinking that he will just have a Coke or water, that he has been alcohol free for 9 months, and that the risk of relapse is low. When he gets to the bar, however, he experiences surprise cravings and a strong urge to use. Although difficult to manage, the client must escape the situation. Of course, he should have never placed himself in this position in the first place; however, high-risk situations can be underestimated by many people. Clinicians should discuss an "escape plan" with clients should inevitable high-risk situations arise. Escape plans can be as simple as removing oneself from the situation for a moment or two, calling one's sponsor, or having someone come pick the client up. If avoidance or escape seems difficult or impossible, the client might *delay* action to interrupt negative cognitions and flow of experiences toward relapse. To delay action simply means to "hold off" on taking a drink until RP strategies can be used effectively.

Urge/Craving Management

One of the main reasons many clients relapse is the failure to manage cravings for drug use. Even clients who have been substance free for years may occasionally need to work through a spontaneous craving. Although advances in neuroscience are helping us understand the biological mechanisms behind craving, it remains one of the least understood concepts related to substance use. The traditional view of craving is that it is primarily a physiological phenomenon, based on biological susceptibility and exposure of the brain to drugs. However, Tiffany (1990, as cited in Thombs & Osborn, 2019) has made a strong argument that craving has many cognitive elements, thus casting doubt on a total biological explanation. Craving is most likely a complex interaction involving neurobiological and psychological elements. Regardless of how cravings happen, managing them goes a long way in helping clients avoid relapse. Given their ubiquitous nature in substance use disorders, Holt (2021) argued that SUD clinicians need to provide psychoeducation to clients about likely causes and management strategies related to craving.

A first step in managing cravings is to help clients understand that they do occur and to anticipate and even accept these reactions as normal learning responses (Larimer et al., 1999). In addition, helping clients reframe the craving as the dopamine back-up phenomenon (see Chapter 3), and that this is just their brain reacting to old patterns, but it will pass, can be useful. It is a mistake to attribute the urge or craving as a signal of the desire to drink or use (Larimer et al., 1999). Another method for avoiding or minimizing cravings is teaching the client stimulus control, as discussed. Cravings strengthen when one is exposed to sights, sounds, environments, or situations that either include drugs or strongly remind the client of previous using behaviors.

Another coping strategy is "urge surfing" (Larimer et al., 1999). Urge surfing refers to teaching clients how to "sit with" or "ride out" a craving experience. Indeed, much like a wave in the ocean that builds up and then comes rolling down into the shore, a craving builds in intensity but eventually recedes into the background. The trick is to help clients "ride" the highest part of the "wave" until the craving lessens.

Reminding oneself that a craving will eventually recede may offer little comfort when the intensity is high. Some clients may tolerate cravings well and are thus able to ride them out, while others have limited psychological resources and ego strength and thus struggle mightily. Additional strategies, such as relaxation training, breathing exercises, and removing oneself from the situation, may offer additional benefit. For example, clients can learn to do deep diaphragmatic breathing during a craving episode to help them ride the experience until it is diminished.

Cue exposure (Drummond et al., 1995, as cited in Marlatt et al., 2002) is another strategy that has shown some success in managing cravings. This behavioral-based intervention involves systematically exposing clients to contextual cues for substance use. Like systematic desensitization, the procedure is used in the safety of the therapeutic setting. Drummond et al. suggested that cue exposure is maximized when paired with strategies designed to help the client resist high-risk situations in their day-to-day lives.

Self-monitoring strategies can be an effective way for clients to monitor and have some control over their craving experiences. Marlatt et al. (2002) suggested use a craving diary in which clients jot down their experiences with drug cravings throughout the day. Clients are encouraged to write down internal and external cues, situations, the people they are around, what they are thinking, and so forth. Reviewing the diary can be an effective intervention as clinician and client look for themes and design strategies to prevent relapse.

Finally, several medications have been developed to help ease cravings for certain drugs. For example, buprenorphine (Suboxone) is an effective medication to lessen opiate craving. Vivitrol, administered as a monthly shot, has been shown to reduce alcohol craving. Medication may or may not be a component of RP. The substance use clinician is encouraged to consult with available medical addiction specialists and discuss all options with clients to see which aspects of treatment fit best for them.

Relapse Roadmaps and Seemingly Irrelevant Decisions

A relapse roadmap (Larimer et al., 1999) refers to a global analysis of high-risk situations, available choices, and associated consequences with each choice. During this activity, client and clinician can "map out" the likely scenario if the client chooses to go to a party, for example. The consequences of going to the party and not going to the party can be clearly articulated and visualized. Clients can see firsthand the relative risk associated with certain choices.

Relapse road maps also can help clients identify "seemingly irrelevant decisions" (SIDs). SIDs refer to subtle choices a client makes that may on the surface seem innocent but indicate a small step toward relapse (Dimeff & Marlatt, 1998). Often, clients are unaware of these mini decisions and why they make them. As an example, consider Devon (name disguised), an African American client I counseled related to cocaine use. Devon was committed to a substance-free lifestyle given the mounting pressures in his life such as work, family, and health issues. Being abstinent from cocaine, not surprisingly, was a huge step toward healing. During one relapse episode, it was discovered that Devon was still in contact with an old using buddy and would often travel to his former neighborhood to see him. In Devon's mind, the decision to visit his friend seemed innocuous enough; after all, he made a firm commitment to remaining abstinent from cocaine. In addition, his friend "understood" that he was substance free and would not push the issue of using with Devon. This SID, however, had disastrous consequences for him. Just driving by the old neighborhood triggered cravings, and his friend continued to use in front of him. Eventually, Devon relapsed. After an analysis of what happened, we discovered the SID (among others) and how it was one step on the path to relapse.

SIDs may not be as obvious as hanging out with an old friend who uses. In fact, relapse can be the culmination of several subtle SIDs that build like a snowball rolling down a hill. Keeping beer in the refrigerator "just in case" friends stop by, listening to music associated with past use, and making the choice to isolate oneself seem, on the outside, to be relatively minor but in reality may be the first step toward relapse. It might be argued that relapse does not begin with actual use but when one engages in an SID. The implication for the substance use clinician is to educate clients on what SIDs are and perhaps help them generate some examples. Continual assessment of clients' choices, via the relapse road map, can help them avoid operating on autopilot; becoming aware of one's SIDs can help clients identify problematic choices, take a step back, and choose a different action.

Relapse Management

Relapse management refers to helping clients manage a lapse so that it does not spiral out of control, leading to a full-blown relapse. Relapse management differs from relapse prevention in that the focus is on *managing a return to use, however, small*. Relapse management principles rest on the assumption that a lapse is a form of backsliding rather than a failure that will inevitably lead to uncontrollable use. The goal of relapse management strategies is to minimize the degree of setback and help clients "right the ship." Relapse management strategies are general, which involve helping clients to shift perceptions of a lapse, and specific, which involve taking behavioral actions to minimize the psychological impact of a lapse (Weingardt & Marlatt, 1998).

General Relapse Management Strategies

One of the greatest risks for full-blown relapse is when a client returns to drug use, however small, and cognitively appraises the situation as confirmation that they are a complete failure and can never achieve abstinence (i.e., the AVE). Such cognitive mechanisms, as we have discussed, place a person at significant risk for pretreatment levels of use. General relapse management strategies help clients place a lapse into perspective. For example, a client might be told that a lapse is like a mistake or error in the learning process (Weingardt & Marlatt, 1998) and that it is a specific, unique event in time and space. The AVE occurs because attributions of lapses are internal, stable, and global; management of relapse involves teaching clients that lapses can be reattributed to external, specific, and controllable factors. For example, it might be pointed out to a client with alcohol use disorder who took a sip at a ball game that he was in a tough situation being surrounded by family and friends, that it was only one incident, and that next time he can prepare a little more in advance. Clients can be taught that abstinence or control is always a moment away; while they might be in the throes of a lapse, they can decide to stop at any time. It may be helpful for the clinician and client to write these reminders on a 3×5 card so the client can have easy access to them when confronted with a risky situation.

Specific Relapse Management Strategies

Specific relapse management strategies involve behavioral skills and interventions that the client can do to avoid "falling off the wagon." In the case of a lapse, the client is instructed to do the following (Weingardt & Marlatt, 1998):

- **Stop, look, and listen.** Here, the client is coached to enhance awareness of their surroundings and tune in to their behavior. If the client slips, they are instructed to stop what they are doing, look around, and listen to interrupt the negative flow of events.

- **Make an immediate plan for recovery.** Clients who slip and who do not have a plan to address the aftermath are climbing up a slippery slope. Lowered self-efficacy, positive expectancies, and the AVE all combine as powerful factors that pull the individual toward heavy drug use. Clinician and client should coconstruct an immediate plan for recovery. Preferably, a plan is written down so that the client can take it with them and keep it in important places such as their car, workspace, or home. The sooner the client can implement the plan, the better chances a full-blown relapse is avoided. There is no one right template for a plan, as they will vary depending on the client circumstances. In addition, it is ideal to coconstruct a plan that is realistic to the client. If a client does not feel confident they can perform an action on the plan, they will most likely ignore the plan when it is needed. My preference is to keep plans relatively simple and to always include phone numbers where appropriate. Here is an example of a plan based on a client I was counseling who struggled with alcoholism:

  Relapse management plan for "Fred":

  a. Call sponsor immediately after slip. His number is _____.
  b. If possible, remove yourself from the situation.
  c. Call and make an appointment to see clinician as soon as possible. The agency number is _____.
  d. Repeat and practice the general strategies (e.g., "Lapse is like a mistake or error in the learning process"; "It is a specific, unique event in time and space").

- **Stay calm.** After a slip, the client is likely to experience a rush of negative emotions. It is important that they stay calm both physically and emotionally. Clients can be taught breathing exercises or brief relaxation methods to stem the tide of negative thoughts and feelings. Repeating some of the general strategies discussed may also help with this process.

- **Renew commitment.** Clients are taught to "shake it off" like how an athlete is instructed to shake off a mistake while playing. Reaffirming one's commitment can empower clients and is effective in blocking negative and self-defeating self-statements. It can be helpful for clients to remove themselves from a situation, even for a brief time, to renew their commitment to abstinence. For example, I encourage clients who attend social gatherings to go to the bathroom to get away from a tight situation. While there, they can have a moment of privacy to renew and strengthen their commitment.

- **Review the situation leading up to the slip.** Marlatt et al. (2002) suggested that the client pose questions to self, such as "What events led to the slip? What warning signs preceded the relapse? or What was the high-risk situation that led to the return to use?"

- **Use a support network.** It is well known among substance use professionals that healthy human relationships provide a strong antidote to the isolating the impact of addiction. Clients must seek out and find those who will support them in their recovery. Obvious examples of this include fellow members of 12-step mutual help groups and sponsors. However, other supportive individuals include family members, members of a religious organization, and nonusing friends. I like to ask clients "Who will be in your corner as you take this journey into recovery?" Encourage them to make a list of key people and their phone numbers to hold onto in case of a slip. If other people in the client's life are willing to help and be supportive, the client has a much greater chance of moving successfully through a lapse.

- **Work through/process guilt and other negative emotions related to the AVE.** Using many of the general strategies mentioned can help minimize the AVE. Other self-statements that reaffirm recovery and address negative thinking also can be helpful. As noted, clients can keep a 3 × 5 card full of positive self-statements with them and pull it out to read over as necessary.

Relapse management strategies are designed to mitigate a slip and help the person get back on track as soon as possible. Both general and specific strategies rely on cognitive and behavioral skills and interventions to accomplish this goal.

Behavioral Chain Analysis: Breaking Down What Happened

The behavioral chain analysis (BCA) is one of the most effective strategies in the practice of DBT (Smith, 2010b). Originally adopted for clients who engage in high-risk behavior, such as self-injury, suicidal, or parasuicidal behavior, it has a great deal of applicability in the case of substance use and relapse. The underlying function of a BCA is to determine (a) the nature of the problem; (b) what is influencing the target behavior (problem), based on both operant and classical conditioning principles; (c) what is getting in the way of more adaptive behavior; and (d) what resources the client has (or doesn't) to effectively handle the problem (Smith, 2010b). For our purposes, the target behavior that Smith discussed refers to "a return to substance use." To be clinically useful, a proper BCA is performed collaboratively within the context of a strong therapeutic alliance.

According to Smith (2010b), there are six steps to carrying out a BCA when one engages in the target behavior:

1. **Identify the target behavior.** This step is an easy one for substance use clinicians; the target behavior is a return to substance use after a period of abstinence. However,

the target behavior should be defined in clear, measurable behavioral terms (Smith, 2010b). Thus, instead of the client reporting that they "returned to drinking," a behaviorally specific target behavior might be "drank a fifth of liquor alone on my couch." The thoughts and emotions leading up to the target behavior form part of the chain of events that led up to a return to use.

2. **Identify prompting events.** At this step, the clinician explores when the relapse began as well as environmental, cognitive, and emotional factors that contributed to a return to use. Smith (2010a) encouraged clinicians to try and elicit responses that may have been out of the client's awareness. For example, a prompting event may have been driving by the liquor store on the way home from work. The client, however, may not have made the connection between this behavior and a relapse. Through the BCA, the client and clinician essentially retrace the steps that led to a return to use. As such, the client begins to see how seemingly innocent events, such as driving by a liquor store, actually were part of the overall chain of events that led to a relapse. Key questions to pose at this step include "What went on that started the chain of events?" and "When you first thought about using, what was going on in your life (thoughts, feelings, actions, other people around you, etc.; Smith, 2010a)?

3. **Identify vulnerability factors.** In assessing relapse, it is important to note what made the client vulnerable to the prompting event that led to continue drug use. This idea is the foundation of the RP model discussed: assessing high-risk situations (i.e., situations that make the client *vulnerable*). The type and number of vulnerability factors vary with each client; however, some common ones include fights, arguments, job stress, health problems, poor sleep, daily hassles, and financial problems. At this point in the BCA, clients should become more aware of how these issues make them vulnerable to use. If multiple BCAs are completed with a client, a pattern may emerge in which only certain situations or stressors trigger a relapse.

4. **Link the chain of events.** In this step of the BCA, the clinician helps the client bridge the gap between the prompting event and the target behavior (Smith, 2010a), thus linking the chain. Smith (2010a) recommended getting as much detailed information as possible from the client about what was going on behaviorally, emotionally, and cognitively before the relapse. The more severe the relapse (e.g., a return to pretreatment use versus a slip), the more extensive the BCA should be (Smith, 2010a). For example, in assessing a full-blown relapse, the client might state that the prompting event was when they got up in the morning and felt "bad." The clinician should then probe for specific details about what, specifically, the client was feeling and what was happening around them when they got up in the morning. It may be, for example, when they got up the client felt depressed and entertained thoughts of using. Without probing for these details, the clinician and client can miss an important link in the chain of events, leading to little direction for how the client could intervene to help themselves.

Smith (2010a) outlined the following tasks to be accomplished at this stage of a BCA: (i) probe for emotional reactions to events leading up to a relapse; (ii) determine where the client might be lacking in behavioral skills that could have contributed to a return to use; (iii) identify environmental and psychological occurrences, such as hanging out with old friends, negative cognitions, attitudes, and so forth that interfere with healthier behaviors; and (iv) assess for themes in how client engages in persistent problematic use.

5. **Identify consequences of substance use.** The final portion of the BCA addresses the fallout from engaging in the target behavior (i.e., substance use). Here, the focus is on consequences of use, both positive and negative, that serve to preserve (or weaken) the substance use behavior (Smith, 2010a). Consequences can be environmental or internal such as negative thoughts and feelings. An analysis of the consequences of use can help the clinician and client figure out the purpose of the substance use (Smith, 2010a). For example, if one of the consequences of using was that it helped the client "mellow out" or "relax," then the function of the substance use is probably to dampen down intense emotions, such as anger or fear.

6. **Generate hypotheses.** Once the BCA is complete, the clinician and client explore both events leading up to the relapse and consequences following the relapse. Places for intervention are identified and skills, if lacking, are suggested and taught to the client. Theory should be a guide during this phase of the BCA (Smith, 2010a). Although the BCA emanated from DBT, other theoretical approaches and perspectives could be used to help interpret what led up to the relapse as well as how to intervene before that point. From the DBT point of view, a return to substance use is essentially a learned behavior, based on anticipated benefits (e.g., feeling good) and positive reinforcers. The clinician should be aware of the power of intense negative emotions that can derail any recovery process (Smith, 2010a). A critical point of intervention, then, is to help clients better manage these emotional experiences. Exercises in mindfulness, interpersonal effectiveness, emotional regulation, and distress tolerance, all grounded in DBT, are examples of strategies that clients can use prevent relapse. The goal in a BCA is to help the client break the chain of events leading to the target behavior (Smith, 2010b).

The process of doing a BCA involves mapping out a chain on a piece of paper or, preferably, on a dry-erase board. Circles are drawn, resembling a chain, which represents each decision, thought, feeling, or behavior (i.e., antecedents) leading up to the relapse. A second group of circles, representing consequences of the target behavior follows. An abbreviated example of a BCA diagram related to substance use is shown in Figure 8.2.

I have found the BCA a useful and appropriate strategy after a client has slipped or relapsed. Many times, clients may have some sense of why they used again but are largely unaware of the seemingly inconsequential mini decisions that make up the chain of events (i.e., SIDs). The

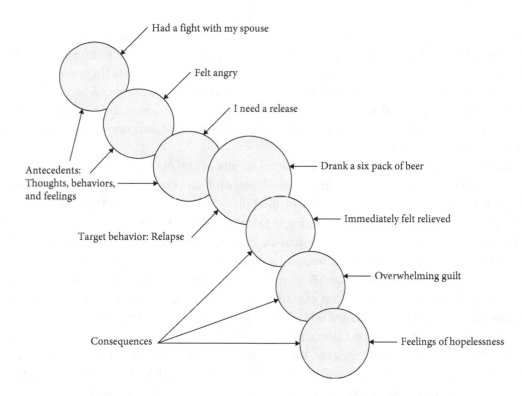

FIGURE 8.2   An (abbreviated) example of a behavioral chain analysis.[2]

BCA can empower clients and increase awareness of their choices, thoughts, behaviors, and emotions that led to using again. From a clinical perspective, the BCA can provide direction and insight for treatment planning. Smith (2010a) cautioned clinicians that it may take doing several BCAs on one target behavior for substantive changes to occur, and this certainly may be the case with substance use.

Emerging Relapse Prevention Strategies

The primary theoretical underpinning of many RP models is cognitive behavioral, especially related to strategies to address issues such as cravings, high-risk situations, and the AVE. Over the years, however, new and emerging strategies have been proposed, either to supplement traditional RP approaches or to be used as standalone strategies. DBT, discussed at length in Chapter 7, is one such approach. Another approach is to use mindfulness as a tool to treat substance use and prevent relapse (Fernandez et al., 2010). Mindfulness is thought to help in

---

2   This is a simple example of what a BCA diagram might look like and is for illustrative purposes. Each circle is a "link" in the chain. A full BCA would have many more "links" in both the antecedents and consequences.

substance use behavior treatment by enhancing awareness of triggers to substance use and by using cognitive mechanisms to simply observe cravings without reaction (Bowen et al., 2010; Marlatt, 2002). Indeed, developing an attachment to one's craving places them on a trajectory toward renewed use of substances. Observing cravings but not reacting can help clients "ride out" difficult times (Dimeff & Marlatt, 1998). Mindfulness through meditative practices also is thought to induce feelings of well-being and relaxation that can serve as substitutes for substance use (Marlatt, 2002).

Research supports the long-held notion that mindfulness and meditation enhances awareness and precludes mindless, automatic, and compulsive behaviors (Marlatt, 2002). Neurobiological findings now support the role that mindfulness plays in reducing an individual's proclivity to act spontaneously without much thought (Marlatt, 2002). Given the impulsive nature of substance use behavior, strategies to combat such tendencies have widespread clinical appeal.

Combined with the RP model of relapse, mindfulness strategies may be an attractive option for clients. Witkiewitz et al. (2005) and Bowen et al. (2009) discussed mindfulness-based relapse prevention (MBRP) as a combination of traditional RP strategies (e.g., assess high-risk situations, develop coping skills, enhance self-efficacy) and mindfulness strategies (raise awareness of triggers, monitor internal reactions, foster skillful behavioral choices). Mindfulness thus adds practices that help clients focus on increasing acceptance and tolerance of difficult states, such as urges and cravings. By accepting and tolerating these difficult emotions and physical tensions, the need to release through substance use is lessened (Bowen et al., 2009). Mindfulness also helps clients process situational cues and monitor one's reaction to environmental stimuli (Witkiewitz et al., 2009). Whereas traditional cognitive therapy techniques focus on changing the content of thoughts, mindfulness-based interventions are designed to change a client's attitude toward their experiences—thoughts, feelings, sensations, and perceptions (Witkiewitz et al., 2005).

An example of a mindfulness strategy is to help clients direct their attention to the breath to calm their mind and emotions. Called "breath awareness" (Nuernberger, 1997), this strategy can be remarkably effective in slowing down one's thoughts and remaining relaxed during a high-risk situation. The client is instructed to pay attention to the feel of the breath as it enters the nose (cool sensation) and exits the nose (warm sensation). Practicing breath awareness for 5 minutes can be just enough to help a client stop a progression toward relapse.

The enthusiasm for the potential of mindfulness training in the prevention of relapse has grown over the years with a small but growing research base to support its use in clinical settings. Bowen et al. (2009) and Bowen and Marlatt (2009) found that participants who received training in mindfulness, meditation, and RP skills experienced greater reductions in use and cravings. Fernandez et al. (2010) found a significant link between "experiential awareness" and reduced levels of alcohol use. In this study, awareness was believed to play a role in reduced use, implying that some thinking styles related to substance use occur outside of conscious awareness. The ability to bring these cognitive tendencies to the forefront of one's conscious experience avoids operating on "automatic pilot" and cultivates choices for how to move forward in a healthy way. The authors concluded that "the ability to observe one's thoughts and feelings without judging them is a marker of behavioral restraint that is related to [less] alcohol related behavior and risk taking" (Fernandez et al., 2010, p. 614). Witkiewitz and Bowen (2010) found that MBRP mediated the relationship between depressive symptoms and post-intervention substance use. Finally, Bowen et al. (2014) found that, compared to treatment as usual (TAU), those who received MBRP and cognitive behavioral relapse prevention (CBRP) had significantly lower risk of relapse to substance use and heavy drinking. At 12-month follow-up, MBRP offered additional advantages over CBRP and TAU in reducing drug use and heavy drinking.

RP in the Treatment of Diverse Populations

RP encompasses a diverse set of strategies and techniques designed to help people prevent a return to substance use. A potential concern, however, is the applicability of RP to diverse populations. Given that many of the concepts of relapse prevention (e.g., self-efficacy, attribution bias, etc.) come from Western psychology, there is concern that pertinent cultural factors may be ignored when using such strategies with diverse clients. RP models may be more useful for middle-class clients compared to lower income clients (Rawson et al., 1993).

Across many substance use treatment programs in the United States today, clients are diverse on many dimensions, including racial/ethnic heritage and identity (Castro et al., 2007). Such diversity speaks to the challenges substance use treatment facilities face and the need for culturally sensitive interventions. Castro et al. (2007) noted that the NIDA 13 principles for effective drug abuse treatment does not mention cultural factors as important for effective outcomes. It also is noteworthy that across much of the RP literature, cultural factors are not given much attention or weight. The dynamic model of relapse comes closest to incorporating context and, by proxy, cultural issues as distal risk factors for substance use and relapse.

Rawson et al. (1993) noted that RP techniques *could* be applied to a wide range of populations, although cultural and gender issues must be competently addressed. For diverse clients, effective RP and treatment includes an understanding of early life and familial influences within their broader culture, and how current political, sociocultural, and environmental situations can serve as high-risk triggers for relapse (Castro et al., 2007). If these political and cultural elements are ignored in counseling, clients may not find treatment relevant to their lives and feel turned off by treatment programs ignoring their cultural heritage.

Castro et al. (2007) identified several key cultural factors in the substance use treatment and RP work among Hispanic clients. For example, familism, or close family ties and expectations, can play an important role in recovery. Ethnic identity and harmonious social relations (called *simpatia*) are other examples of cultural factors that can play an integral role in RP. Bilingual and bicultural as well as low acculturated Hispanic clients may prefer traditional cultural approaches and benefit from culturally relevant interventions in their recovery programs (Castro et al., 2007). Sensitivity and understanding on the part of the clinician create an atmosphere where Hispanic clients (as well as clients from other cultural backgrounds) build culturally relevant skills to avoid relapse (Castro et al., 2007).

Cultural resilience, or traditional cultural strengths that safeguard against disease and mental problems, has received some attention in the literature as a potent force against heavy drug use and mental illness (Alderete et al., 2000). Shon and Ja (1982, as cited in Castro et al., 2007) stated that among Asian Americans particular cultural norms promote self-regulation, inner peace, and pro-social behaviors that resemble the idea of cultural resilience. These norms, which are based on the three philosophical/religious traditions of Confucianism, Buddhism, and Taoism, include elements such as discipline, proper relationships, restraint, and the use of shame in motivating good behavior. Clearly, this pattern of self-regulation and restraint is counter to the impulsive, reckless, risk-taking behavior observed in substance use. Thus, Asian American clients who struggle with substance use issues may find solace in these traditional cultural values and norms.

Substance use clinicians need to explore cultural and social norms for self-regulated behavior and harmonious relationships to help promote pro-social behavior that is compatible with the client's cultural background. To ignore clients' cultural resilience would do a great disserve; fortitude and connection can be re-discovered when clinicians assist their clients in exploring important cultural strengths and how these can be adapted into their recovery plan.

One of the first assessment tasks in RP work is assessing for high-risk situations and helping clients to cope with these potentially stressful times. However, clients from diverse backgrounds may not find "typical" high-risk situations as particularly problematic. For example, a common high-risk situation such as "hanging out with old using friends" may be completely irrelevant to a Latino client who feels completely marginalized and disenfranchised in their current society. Clinicians need to be mindful of assessing for multiple high-risk situations from a cultural context such as considering the client's level of acculturation, the client's experience of disenfranchisement and racism, conflict between their cultural beliefs and the society in which they live, and so forth. Assessment for relapse also should include life history, linguistic preferences, the client's cultural orientation, and the process of acculturation (Castro et al., 2007). Failure to successfully assess for these cultural elements can set the clinician up for failure, as illustrated in Diverse Perspectives and Examples.

DIVERSE PERSPECTIVES AND EXAMPLES

◇◇◇◇◇◇◇

As a counselor in a community agency, I make it my intention to seek out wisdom of other therapists with whom I work. I recall speaking with Charles, a seasoned and excellent therapist, about his experiences with Khanh, a 30-year-old Vietnamese woman, and her husband, Jethro, when he was a new therapist. Khanh and Jethro did not have any children. Khanh presented with severe alcohol use disorder and had been hospitalized on her most recent drinking binge. When she and Jethro came to counseling, she was clearly uncomfortable in the session, denied any problems with alcohol, and simply did not know why she was there. Charles could not fully understand Khanh as she did not speak very clear English. Jethro did most, if not all, of the talking while Khanh sat looking confused and not understanding the conversation. According to Charles, she probably felt very isolated and misunderstood as he and Jethro went on talking about Khanh's alcohol problem. Charles, limited in his experience at this point, moved right in to helping mode, focusing prematurely on fixing the marriage between Jethro and Khanh, which other than the alcohol abuse, was relatively strong. Charles did not understand Khanh and vice versa, which again made the sessions awkward and of limited focus. Meanwhile, Khanh's alcohol problem was only tangentially addressed.

Jethro and Khanh came to only a few additional sessions before quitting with Charles and seeking other treatment options. Upon reflection, Charles told me that he made several mistakes with Khanh, and most of them had to do with not understanding or respecting her cultural background and situation. He spoke about how he could have put Khanh in touch with Vietnamese support groups in the community (such as AA) and incorporated a translator in the sessions to help with language and understanding. He could have taken more time to understand her culture and its general view toward alcohol and alcoholism. He could have respected her discomfort in the session and addressed this instead of continuing to talk with Jethro, which seemed to alienate Khanh. Charles stated that he likes to share this experience to beginning therapists to help them avoid some of the mistakes he made with this client. "Knowledge of cultural background and other salient differences, and the client's worldview in general, need to be respected and explored for successful counseling to ensue." Good advice indeed!

A large portion of one's recovery from substance use may involve AA or other mutual help recovery programs. Whereas AA has helped millions of individuals with their drinking problems, criticism has been issued by women's and minority groups who feel many of the 12 steps and philosophy disenfranchise them (Dobmeier & Stevens, 2013). For example, from a feminist perspective, AA "perpetuates the powerlessness of women in steps 1 through 3" (Dobmeier & Stevens, 2013, p. 276). Some minority groups believe that AA is best suited for White, middle-class men who struggle with alcohol use and fails to recognize the social and contextual factors in minority substance use. However, it is important to note that little research exists predicting successful membership in AA; many clients from diverse backgrounds have benefited from its philosophy and recovery approach.

Castro et al. (2007) noted that research on RP with diverse clients is lacking, although some researchers are beginning to explore this issue in more depth. As more research accumulates, clinicians will have a better understanding of how cultural factors impact the relapse process and how they can better intervene to help their clients. Understanding the client's worldview and cultural context is an important and critical first step.

CASE STUDY

Using RP Strategies in the Case of Michael

As noted, RP can be used as a supplement to other treatment approaches or as a standalone approach in working with substance use issues. In the case of Michael, assume that he has been substance free for several months. He is firmly committed to AA, has been coming regularly to individual and group counseling sessions, and has gained more confidence in his ability to avoid drug use. However, he still experiences occasional cravings for cocaine and the stress in his work and home life has not dissipated much over this time. Relapse remains a real threat. The clinician, realizing that issues of relapse and RP need to be addressed, broaches this topic in Michael's next counseling session, outlined here. Notice that several components of the RP model are illustrated in this vignette:

CLINICIAN: Hey Michael, thanks for coming in today. How have things been going?

MICHAEL: Hey doc. Well, things have been going okay. I'm still struggling at work a bit. I like some aspects and others just tick me off. My boss is still on my case a lot!

CLINICIAN: I see, yes, maybe we can talk about some of that today. How is the AA and group counseling coming along? (checking in to see if Michael has remained committed to his recovery)

MICHAEL: No problems, there. I have grown to enjoy my AA groups—5 days a week—and the group gives me a chance to vent a bit. I guess, despite this I still think of using every now and then. You know how we talked about cravings before? Well, I can't say that I have been free of them completely.

CLINICIAN: You're struggling a bit with cravings and not sure what to do about it. Maybe even scared a bit. Well, I was wondering how you were managing these, since we haven't talked about them in awhile. (reflection followed by continued focus on cravings and beginning introduction to RP)

MICHAEL: Can we talk about that a bit more today, and maybe about some of the stress I have been experiencing?

CLINICIAN: We sure can, and that actually leads into what I have been thinking about for our sessions: relapse and RP. To begin, I would like to draw a diagram on the board here, and then we can discuss those issues. I think you will find it relevant to what your concerns have been. Does that sound good? (introduces RP and draws the RP model on the dry-erase board)

MICHAEL: Sure. Sounds good.

After drawing the RP model on the dry-erase board, the clinician explains what a relapse is and how it is different from a lapse. He then goes through and explains each component of the RP model. Thus, Michael was taught the importance of coping skills, self-efficacy, positive expectancies, the AVE, and perceived positive effects. He became more aware of what factors lead to a greater risk of relapse and what factors lead to less risk.

CLINICIAN: After reviewing this model, I would like to start here (pointing to the board) talking about high-risk situations. The essence of RP is knowing what these are and learning how to cope with them. What do you think are some high-risk situations/triggers for you related to substance use? (assessing for high-risk situations)

MICHAEL: I always used when I hung out with some old friends, but I think I have taken care of that trigger for the most part. They really weren't buddies but using acquaintances now that I think about it. I don't know; I guess when I get this overwhelmed feeling. That is very uncomfortable, and I just want a release—want to feel good.

CLINICIAN: Okay, so one trigger is when you start to feel overwhelmed and restless. Let's start with that. When you feel overwhelmed, what are you thinking and feeling? (exploring the high-risk situation)

MICHAEL: Well, I get this way when work and home life seems to be one big stress ball. I am thinking that this [situation] sucks and that my life lacks joy. Drug use gave me pleasure. I get this empty feeling in me, and I also feel irritable and tense. I haven't felt these in awhile, but when I do I notice my craving and urge to use increases.

CLINICIAN: Let's look at that. Your thinking and thoughts seem to get you in trouble. What might be some positive messages you can tell yourself when feeling overwhelmed?

MICHAEL: Yeah, this is what AA means by "stinkin' thinkin.'" I guess I could remember how lucky I am to have a job, a caring family. The ability to experience joy should return the longer chemicals are out of my body. Saying that the situation sucks is probably too harsh. Difficult, yes, but it doesn't suck.

CLINICIAN: When you think about it, you feel fortunate with what you have. You understand that joy will return in time, and that your life is difficult but not overwhelming. Let me write some of these thoughts down on 3 x 5 cards for you. (begins writing the following on 3 x 5 cards with the help of Michael):

I am fortunate to have a job, a caring family.

Joy will return in time. Hang in there and try to find small joys in the moment.

It is difficulty now, but I am getting better and less overwhelmed day by day.

CLINICIAN: Michael, I would like you to keep these cards with you everywhere you go. When the overwhelmed feeling comes about, pull these out and read through them. Feel free to create your own card, a whole stack even, of positive statements that you can say to yourself to interrupt the "stinkin' thinkin.'" What do you think? (suggesting coping strategy)

MICHAEL: I never thought of that, but I guess I could give it a try.

CLINICIAN: Great. And, let me know how it works for you, the statements need to come from you and make sense to you. I also would like to provide some information to go along with this. You mentioned that sometimes your life lacks joy. I wonder if your "shoulds" in life are greater than your "wants," and that has created some lifestyle imbalance. (introducing the idea of lifestyle balance)

MICHAEL: What do you mean?

CLINICIAN: Most of us have too many "shoulds" in our lives—the demands that are placed on us and that we place on ourselves. We do not take advantage of or cultivate our "wants," the activities that give us pleasure, leisure, and relaxation, without drugs, of course [Michael chuckles]. From our discussions, I have noticed that you take your recovery very seriously, your work very seriously, and your relationship very seriously. You place tremendous demands on yourself and leave little time for the "wants." Don't get me wrong, "shoulds" are a necessary part of life and *are* important. However, too many shoulds lead to lifestyle imbalance, which also can be a trigger for relapse.

MICHAEL: I can see how that fits. But the challenge is in how to get more "wants" into my life. I have wanted to take that online class in finance; although it is work, I know I would enjoy it.

CLINICIAN: Yes, that is the idea. And, they don't have to be big wants. Taking a walk, enjoying the outdoors, going on a small trip, shopping, reading, and so forth can all be wants. The trick is to find balance, and I encourage you to drop some of the shoulds if you can, and increase more wants. (explaining more about wants and shoulds)

MICHAEL: Okay. I guess I never thought of it like this. It is just hard to relax with this recovery thing.

CLINICIAN: You hear this message to relax, to increase the wants, yet you struggle because recovery is such a serious matter. That is something we can definitely talk more about: *how* to increase the wants. Michael, there is a lot more we can discuss related to relapse and relapse prevention, and let's see if we can continue this discussion next time and beyond. In the meantime, I would like to do a quick check in regarding AA and your support system in general. In what ways have you felt supported in your recovery? (reflection followed by assessing strength of support system)

MICHAEL: No real problems there. AA is a good support, and I like my sponsor—someone who tells it like it is. When I first started at AA, I was worried about not fitting in given my racial background and, despite some small issues here and there, it hasn't been too bad. Can't get anything past him. There are a couple members of the group that I really connect with, and they said that I could call them anytime. I wish I had more support at home and with my family and maybe that is something else we can discuss down the road. I think my wife holds a lot of resentment based on the damage my addiction has caused.

CLINICIAN: Well, as we have discussed along the way, social support and connection is important in your recovery and for relapse prevention. I admire that you have some really strong supports and acknowledge that you can still improve in that area with your family. (affirmation and reinforcing point of social support being important in recovery)

This case vignette illustrated several basic elements of RP, including assessing high-risk situations, development of coping skills, lifestyle balance, and assessing strength of social supports. It is important for the reader to know that this session with Michael could have gone in any number of directions. For example, the clinician and Michael may have chosen to focus on relapse management principles rather than RP. Which direction is chosen depends on the mutual collaboration between clinician and client. My general approach is to always start with high-risk situations and coping skills and then see where the discussion takes us. I also usually draw the RP model on the board for clients to see there is some element in the model that strikes a chord with the client, leading to a productive discussion.

With Michael, future sessions could continue to focus on other high-risk situations and development of coping skills. At some point, Michael's self-efficacy would need to be assessed and strengthened, as this is a key component to resisting cravings. Because cravings were a struggle for him, I also might suggest breathing, relaxation training, and the "urge surfing" technique.

Strengths, Limitations, and Ethical Issues Related to RP

Unfortunately, substance use relapse is considered the rule rather than the exception. As such, RP is an essential part of any substance use treatment program. The methods of RP are based largely on cognitive behavioral principles. Many components of Marlatt and Gordan's RP model have been supported by empirical research.

RP strategies may not work for clients whose substance use is not based on cognitive deficits. Indeed, substance use may be the result of many other factors such as genetic predisposition, emotional self-regulation problems, and negative early childhood influences. In addition, RP strategies appear to encourage first-order change but may fail to address deeper issues (i.e., second-order change) or root causes related to the client's substance use. For example, keeping a card with positive self-statements on it may help some individuals avoid a relapse, but it may do little to address changes in personality, attitude, and traits that may be needed and at the heart of substance use recovery. RP alone may be insufficient for lasting change; ideally, both first-order and second-order change variables are addressed in treatment. Many of the models of relapse other than the RP model have limited empirical support.

A full list of strengths, limitations, and ethical issues related to relapse prevention work is presented in Table 8.1.

TABLE 8.1 Summary of Strengths, Limitations, and Ethical Concerns of RP in the Treatment of Substance Use Problems

Strengths	<ul><li>RP strategies can be used as a standalone intervention or infused throughout the counseling process.</li><li>RP was born out of the substance use field and thus incorporates the language of substance use through cognitive and behavioral means.</li><li>The concepts of RP, especially based on Marlatt and Gordan's original model, has received an impressive record of research support.</li><li>Recent developments in RP suggest a broadening of the influence of contextual factors in the return to substance use (see the dynamic model of relapse). This greater emphasis on context can improve delivery of services to clients from all backgrounds.</li><li>RP is relatively straightforward to understand and implement. Clients readily understand the concepts of high-risk situations, coping, self-efficacy, and the AVE. They can easily apply these ideas into their recovery plans.</li></ul>
Limitations	<ul><li>Many RP models rely heavily on cognitive behavioral concepts. Hence, the limitations inherent in CBT could apply to RP as well.</li><li>The difference between a slip/lapse and a relapse is seen as a myth by some circles who subscribe to the strict disease model of addiction. This may cause some friction between the client's individual counseling and other supportive services such as AA.</li></ul>

(*continued*)

TABLE 8.1   Summary of Strengths, Limitations, and Ethical Concerns of RP in the Treatment of Substance Use Problems (*Continued*)

	• RP involves a strong educational component, which may turn off some clients who are more process oriented. Clients may need to process their emotions and experiences related to substance use rather than be lectured on RP topics. • RP strategies work at the level of cognition and behavior but may do little to address fundamental disorders of personality that may significantly contribute to substance use.
Ethical Issues	• Some adherents to the disease model may argue that conceptualizing a slip as a "mistake" or "backsliding" is not a good idea and may be an ethical concern. From the disease model perspective, such a stance is irresponsible and places the client at risk: Clients must realize they have a disease and stop substances completely. A slip, no matter how small, should be conceptualized as a full-blown relapse and handled accordingly, disease model proponents argue.

References

Alderete, E., Vega, W. A., Kolody, B., & Aguilar-Gaxiola, S. (2000). Lifetime prevalence of and risk factors for psychiatric disorders among Mexican migrant farmworkers in California. *American Journal of Public Health, 90,* 608–614.

Annis, H. M. (1990). Relapse to substance abuse: Empirical findings within a cognitive-social learning approach. *Journal of Psychoactive Drugs, 22,* 117–124.

Bowen, S., Chawla, N., Collins, S. E., Witkiewitz, K., Hsu, S., Grow, J., Seema, C., Garner, M., Douglas, A., Larimer, M. E., & Marlatt, G. A. (2009). Mindful-based relapse prevention for substance use disorders: A pilot efficacy trial. *Substance Abuse, 30,* 295–305.

Bowen, S. Chawla, N., & Marlatt, A. G. (2010). *Mindfulness-based relapse prevention for substance use disorders: A clinician's guide.* Guilford.

Bowen, S., & Marlatt, G. A. (2009). Surfing the urge: Brief mindfulness-based intervention for college student smokers. *Psychology of Addictive Behaviors, 23,* 666–671.

Bowen, S., Witkiewitz, K., Clifasefi, S. L., Grow, J., Chawla, N. Hsu, S. H., Carroll, H. A., Harrop, E. Collins, S. E., Lustyk, M. K., & Larimer, M. E. (2014). Relative efficacy of mindfulness-based relapse prevention, standard relapse prevention, and treatment as usual for substance use disorders: A randomized clinical trial. *Journal of the American Medical Association, 71,* 547–556.

Castro, F. G., Nichols, E., & Kater, K. (2007). Relapse prevention with Hispanic and other racial/ethnic populations: Can cultural resilience promote relapse prevention? In K. Witkiewitz & G. A. Marlatt (Eds.), *Therapist's guide to evidence-based relapse prevention* (pp. 259–292). Elsevier.

Center for Substance Abuse Treatment. (2005). Substance abuse treatment: Group therapy. *Treatment Improvement Protocol (TIP) Series, No. 41.* SAMHSA.

Dennis, M. L., Scott, C. K., Funk, R., & Foss, M. A. (2005). The duration and correlates of addiction and treatment careers. *Journal of Substance Abuse Treatment, 28,* S51–S62. https://doi.org/10.1016/j.jsat.2004.10.013

Dimeff, L. A., & Marlatt, G. A. (1998). Preventing relapse and maintaining change in addictive behaviors. *Clinical Psychological Science Practice, 5,* 513–525.

Dobmeier, R. A., & Stevens, P. (2013). Retaining sobriety: Relapse prevention strategies. In P. Stevens & R. L. Smith (Eds.), *Substance abuse counseling: Theory and practice* (5th ed., pp. 261–286). Prentice Hall.

Ellis, A., & McInerney, J. F. (1988). *Rational-emotive behavior therapy with alcoholics and substance abusers*. Allyn & Bacon.

Fernandez, A. C., Wood, M. D., Stein, A. R., & Rossi, J. S. (2010). Measuring mindfulness and examining its relationship with alcohol use and negative consequences. *Psychology of Addictive Behaviors, 24,* 608–616.

Fisher, G. L., & Harrison, T. C. (2018). *Substance abuse: Information for school counselors, social workers, therapists, and counselors* (6th ed.). Pearson.

Ford, G. G. (1996). An existential model for promoting life change: Confronting the disease concept. *Journal of Substance Abuse Treatment, 13,* 151–158.

Gorski, T. T. (1989). Special issue: Relapse: Conceptual, research, and clinical perspectives. *Journal of Chemical Dependency Treatment, 2,* 153–169.

Gorski, T. T. (1990). The Cenaps model of relapse prevention: Basic principles and procedures. *Journal of Psychoactive Drugs, 22,* 125–133.

Holt, R. W. (2021). A vehicle to pass through substance use craving and navigate the addiction recovery cycle. In R. Miller & E. T. Beeson (Eds.), *Neuroeducation toolbox: Practical translations of neuroscience in counseling and psychotherapy* (pp. 125–131). Cognella.

Hser, Y.-L., Huang, D. Chou, C.-P., & Anglin, M. D. (2007). Trajectory of heroin addiction: Growth mixture modeling results based on a 33-year follow-up study. *Evaluation Review, 31,* 548–563. https://doi.org/10.1177/0193841X07307315

Irvin, J. E., Bowers, C. A., Dunn, M. E., & Wang, M. C. (1999). Efficacy of relapse prevention: A meta-analytic review. *Journal of Consulting and Clinical Psychology, 67,* 563–570.

Kouimtsidis, Stahl, D., West, R., & Drummond, C. (2014). Path analysis of cognitive behavioural models in substance misuse. What is the relationship between concepts involved? *Journal of Substance Use, 19,* 399–404.

Krenek, M., Prince, M. A., & Maisto, S. A. (2017). Life events and alcohol use disorder clinical course: Modeling the dynamic association. *Drug and Alcohol Dependence, 180,* 137–143.

Larimer, M. E., Palmer, R. S., & Marlatt, G. A. (1999). Relapse prevention: An overview of Marlatt's cognitive-behavioral model. *Alcohol Research and Health, 23,* 151–160.

Lin, S-Y., Fried, E. I., & Eaton, N. R. (2020). The association of life stress with substance use symptoms: A network analysis and replication. *Journal of Abnormal Psychology, 129,* 204–214.

Maisto, S. A., Xie, F. C., Witkiewitz, K., Ewart, C. K., Connors, G. J., Zhu, H., Elder, G., Ditmar, M., & Chow, S-M. (2017). How chronic self-regulatory stress, poor anger regulation, and momentary affect undermine treatment for alcohol use disorder: Integrating social action theory with the dynamic model of relapse. *Journal of Social and Clinical Psychology, 36,* 238–263.

Marlatt, G. A. (1996). Taxonomy of high-risk situations for alcohol relapse: evolution and development of a cognitive-behavioral model. *Addiction, 91,* 37–49.

Marlatt, G.A. (2002). Buddhist philosophy and the treatment of addictive behavior. *Cognitive and Behavioral Practice, 9,* 44–49.

Marlatt, G. A., & Gordon, J. R. (Eds.) (1985). *Relapse prevention: Maintenance strategies in the treatment of addictive behaviors.* Guilford.

Marlatt, G. A., Parks, G. A, & Witkiewitz, K. (2002). *Clinical guidelines for implementing relapse prevention therapy: A guideline developed for the behavioral health recovery management project.* Addictive Behaviors Research Center, Department of Psychology, University of Washington. http://www.bhrm.org/guidelines/ RPT%20guideline.pdf

McLellan, T. A., Lewis, D. C., O'Brien, C. P., & Kleber, H. D. (2000). Drug dependence, a chronic medical illness: Implications for treatment, insurance, and outcome evaluation. *Journal of the American Medical Association [JAMA], 284,* 1689–1695.

Miller, G. (2005). *Learning the language of addiction counseling* (2nd ed.). Wiley.

Miller G. (2021). *Learning the language of addiction counseling* (5th ed.). Wiley.

Miller, W. R., & Hester, R. K. (1980). Treating the problem drinker: Modern approaches. In W. R. Miller (Ed.), *The addictive behaviors: Treatment of alcoholism, drug abuse, smoking and obesity* (pp. 11–141). Pergamon Press.

Nuernberger, P. (1997). *The quest for personal power: Transforming stress into strength.* Penguin.

Rawson, R. A., Obert, J. L., McCann, M. J., & Marinelli-Casey, P. (1993). Relapse prevention strategies in outpatient substance abuse treatment. *Psychology of Addictive Behaviors, 7,* 85–95.

Smith, J. (2010a). *Master the behavioral chain analysis.* PESI Seminars.

Smith, J. (2010b). *Advanced dialectical behavior therapy.* PESI Seminars.

Stephens, R. S., Roffman, R. A., & Simpson, E. E. (1994). Treating adult marijuana dependence: A test of the relapse prevention model. *Journal of Consulting and Clinical Psychology, 62,* 92–99.

Thombs, D. L. (1999). *Introduction to addictive behaviors* (2nd ed.). Guilford.

Thombs, D. L., & Osborn, C. J. (2019). *Introduction to addictive behaviors* (5th ed.). Guilford.

Weingardt, K. R., & Marlatt, G. A. (1998). Sustaining change: Helping those who are still using. In W. Miller & N. Heather (Eds.), *Treating addictive behaviors* (2nd ed, pp. 337–351). Plenum.

Witkiewitz, K., & Bowen, S. (2010). Depression, craving, and substance use following a randomized trial of mindfulness-based relapse prevention. *Journal of Consulting and Clinical Psychology, 78,* 362–374.

Witkiewitz, K., Bowen, S., & Donovan, D. M. (2011). Moderating effects of a craving intervention on the relation between negative mood and heavy drinking following treatment for alcohol dependence. *Journal of Consulting and Clinical Psychology, 79,* 54–63.

Witkiewitz, K. & Marlatt, G. A. (2007). High risk situations: Relapse as a dynamic process. In K. Witkiewitz & G. A. Marlatt (Eds.), *Therapist's guide to evidence-based relapse prevention* (pp. 19–33). Elsevier.

Witkiewitz, K., & Marlatt, G. A. (2009). Commentary: Further exploring the interpersonal dynamics of relapse. *Addiction, 104,* 1291–1292.

Witkiewitz, K., Marlatt, G. A., & Walker, D. (2005). Mindfulness-based relapse prevention for alcohol and substance use disorders. *Journal of Cognitive Psychotherapy: An International Quarterly, 19,* 211–228.

Figure Credits

Fig. 8.1: Adapted from Mary E. Larimer, Rebekka S. Palmer and G. Alan Marlatt, "Relapse Prevention: An Overview of Marlatt's Cognitive-behavioral Model," *Alcohol Research and Health,* vol. 23, no. 2. 1999.

Fig. 8.2: Adapted from Josh Smith, "Master the Behavioral Chain Analysis," *Master the Behavioral Chain Analysis.* Copyright © 2010 by PESI, Inc.

CHAPTER 9

Applying Group Theory in the Treatment of Substance Use Disorders

Introduction

If there is one theme that I have consistently observed among clients who struggle with substance use is isolation from others. Many clients struggling with substance use disorders are not forthcoming about the extent of their isolation, but eventually the topic comes up because of its obvious nature: They speak of few or no friends, have destructive family relations, struggle with colleagues at work, and withdraw more and more as their life breaks down. In essence, they report that they are lonely and bored. Why is isolation such a predominant symptom of substance use disorders?

In response to client isolation, I often explain that addiction is a process that slowly eats away at one's ability and desire to connect with other people; the reason is because connection to other people is part of the *antidote* to substance using behavior. Speaking metaphorically, the addiction doesn't want the client to connect to others and build relationships because to do so would be incompatible with the maintaining of the addiction. The only relationships that are "allowed" are with using buddies. The more and more one moves away from others, the more likely the client can sit quietly with the addiction, as if it were a best friend—always available and always ready to numb the pain.

A striking similarity among substance use clients is their disconnection from the important people in their lives. Adler recognized that "friendship" was a key task of life, and social interest is the engine of a healthy community and individual. Notice how Adler called friendship a "task," implying that it takes effort and work to build relationships of value. Let's face it: Building relationships with others is not always easy and is sometimes filled with anxiety, fear of failure, and social discomfort. Many individuals feel vulnerable putting themselves out there, and so turn to substances to lower inhibitions. The strange irony is that for many people the drug becomes the "friend" that demands nothing from them, is always there, comforts them, and unfortunately, slowly destroys their lives. Clients who struggle with substance use disorders often are uncomfortable in social situations because they have not learned the social skills needed to build healthy relationships. This is not to say that clients need to be social butterflies, but healthy connection and social support appear to be necessary for a strong recovery (Burkey et al., 2011).

Thankfully, there is a counseling modality that can effectively address isolation, has grown in popularity, and has come to be regarded as a robust approach to substance use counseling (CSAT, 2005): group therapy. Indeed, one of the main reasons group therapy can be so effective in treating clients with substance use disorders is because of curative social forces such as affiliation, support, and appropriate peer confrontation (CSAT, 2005). These curative forces allow clients to bond with one another in a *culture of recovery*. A bonus of group counseling is that clients can also work on concomitant problems associated with substance use such as relationship difficulties, depression, anxiety, or other mental health issues. In addition, group therapy increases participation in formal substance use treatment and 12-step attendance when used as a "low-threshold outreach intervention" (Rosenblum et al., 2005, p. 91).

Group therapy for substance use and addiction offers unique advantages over individual counseling. First, the ever-present defense mechanism of denial has a more difficult time surviving in the group setting. Substance use groups can be compelling sources of persuasion, confrontation, and insight where phoniness and excuse making will not be tolerated. This level of confrontation is more difficult to achieve in individual counseling. Group members become keen observers and, because they have used similar defenses and had similar experiences, they tend to call out members who appear to be disingenuous, faking, or making excuses. In individual counseling, the counselor, although well intentioned, may miss client defenses that need attention. The group format is cost effective because it is an efficient use of clinician time and lowers the cost for clients (Miller et al., 2019). Quality also is maintained; instead of seeing one client at a time, the clinician can see several clients without loss of effectiveness. Another advantage is that group members can benefit from others' experiences and support each other through the group process. Finally, the group format may allow clients to be more open to peer feedback and information than they would in an individual session, especially if they struggle with those in positions of authority (Miller et al., 2019).

Group therapy is considered a treatment of choice for those struggling with substance use issues (Brooks & McHenry, 2015) and is the most common form of substance use treatment across inpatient and outpatient settings (Miller et al., 2019). Given its prevalence as a treatment approach for substance-related issues, it is essential that counselors and other mental health professionals have a basic understanding of group theory, process, and technique (Miller, 2021). In some cases, special types of groups for substance-related issues require additional training beyond general academic coursework (CSAT, 2005).

Some may wonder why this chapter is in a book about theoretical applications to substance use counseling. There are three primary reasons for its inclusion. First, group therapy is based on theoretical principles. In the classic text, *The Theory and Practice of Group Psychotherapy*, Yalom and Leszcz (2020) outlined the theoretical parameters and theory-driven concepts of group therapy. Second, as already stated, group therapy is a common form of chemical dependency treatment in the United States (Brooks & McHenry, 2015; Capuzzi & Gross, 1992) and is effective in terms of cost (Vannicelli, 1996) and psychological improvement (Yalom & Leszcz, 2020). Third, every theory in this text can be applied in a group format. For example, SFT, Adlerian, and CBT are all popular approaches to use in a group setting. The reader is encouraged to gain a basic understanding of group therapy and envision how particular theories can apply using a group counseling setting.

Before we proceed, it is important to note the differences between group *counseling* or *therapy* as applied to substance use compared to mutual support groups, such as AA and Narcotics Anonymous (NA). The distinction is an important one. Group therapy is facilitated by a trained specialist, focuses on skill building and interpersonal process (depending on the type of group), has an associated fee, has an attendance maximum around 12 members, and holds to a certain number of sessions. In support groups, members rotate as leaders and there is sharing of experiences and strengths but no questioning or confrontation (Brooks & McHenry, 2015). There is not a focus on skill building or enhancing interpersonal process. There are no dues or fees, no size limit, and no time limit (Brooks & McHenry, 2015). Many clients may opt not to participate in support groups, and they typically are not mandatory but encouraged. In this chapter, the major focus will be on group therapy and its applications in substance use counseling; however, I do want to stress that *both* group therapy and support groups are important components of substance use treatment. Accordingly, I provide information at the end of the chapter on mutual support groups and how they can complement one's substance use care.

Specifically, this chapter entails an overview of the main tenets of group therapy. This is followed by the application of group therapy in substance use counseling, focusing on working with defenses, the most common types of substance use groups, and techniques. The chapter concludes with commentary on support groups, the use of group therapy with diverse populations, and group therapy as applied to the case of Michael. Throughout all sections, clinical examples and supportive evidence from the literature are provided as appropriate.

The Main Tenets of Group Therapy: Brief Overview

In this section, I will cover the main tenets of group therapy, including inpatient vs. outpatient care, the therapeutic factors, and stages of group therapy. After this review, the reader should have a solid foundation from which to apply group therapy and process in the substance use counseling setting.

Inpatient Versus Outpatient Substance Use Group Counseling

Substance use groups are conducted in both inpatient and outpatient settings. Outpatient groups allow clients to live at home, go to work, and keep a regular schedule (Brooks & McHenry, 2015). They occur one to several times a week and generally last 90 minutes (although some may be as long as 3 hours). With outpatient groups, the group leader needs to be aware that clients leave the group setting to return to their normal lives. Processing how clients are feeling after the group and ensuring they feel able to control triggers and urges that inevitably come up is important (Brooks & McHenry, 2015).

Inpatient group therapy tends to be brief and intense, with regular, frequent meetings. Clients who attend these groups generally have more severe problems compared to clients in outpatient groups, such as dual diagnoses, medical concerns, or extreme life-threatening substance-related or psychological problems. Groups tend to occur throughout the day, which leads to continuity from morning to afternoon or day-to-day sessions (Brooks & McHenry, 2015).

Therapeutic Factors

Yalom and Leszcz (2020) asserted that group therapy allows for 11 key experiences, called therapeutic factors (or curative factors), that serve as the foundation for therapeutic change. As any mental health clinician can attest, change is a complex process that depends on the interplay between personal characteristics and environment. In group therapy, the therapeutic environment is such that clients gain much more than learning social skills. For example, well-formulated groups can be a powerful way for clients to develop hope, correct early negative family experiences, and receive/engage in altruism. The curative factors include the following: installation of hope, universality, imparting information, altruism, the corrective recapitulation of the primary family group, development of socializing techniques, imitative behavior, interpersonal learning, group cohesiveness, catharsis, existential factors. A brief description of each factor, with a focus on application to substance use groups, is presented next.

Instillation of Hope

Instilling and cultivating hope are important in any therapeutic endeavor and are especially applicable to substance use counseling. Many clients struggling with substance use issues teeter on the precipice of hope versus hopelessness. With relapse a common experience in the change process, it can unfortunately be easy for clients to slip into discouragement. The group environment, however, is a unique setting in which members can encourage hope with other, less experienced members (Brooks & McHenry, 2015). There will be some clients in the group who have been successful on their road to recovery, and these individuals can be inspirational to others who may be struggling or a bit more skeptical.

Miller (2021) noted that instillation of hope is uniquely related to clients struggling with substance use issues and is thus one of the more powerful factors to take advantage of in treatment. Leaders who instill hope within their clients provide the motivation and support needed for clients to begin changing their behavior. Members who make substantive changes provide models for those who continue to struggle. Seeing another group member offers hope that one can also change.

Universality

Universality is an especially important factor for clients who use substances. Many clients who attend substance use counseling are demoralized and see no hope for a better future. Some may believe that they are useless individuals destined to a life of addiction and associated problems. In many clients' minds, no one on earth has experienced what they have. They believe they are alone in their suffering, which makes the suffering even worse. Group therapy offers a potent antidote to this state of thinking: universality. After learning of other members' concerns, fears, and anxieties, clients in group therapy report feeling more connected to the world and that others do indeed share similar experiences (Yalom & Leszcz, 2020). They are, after all, not alone and part of humanity.

Revealing one's struggles, hopes, and fears and then learning that others in the group share those same struggles, hopes, and fears can be an enormous relief. A necessary ingredient for incorporating universality in the substance use group is self-disclosure. Indeed, group members should be encouraged from the start to share their story and disclose experiences and what they want from the group. Through self-disclosure, universality begins to emerge as members connect with others and realize that they are not alone in their substance use struggles.

One of the reasons universality can be such a powerful factor is because members of groups can speak to each other with authenticity and experience, something that clinicians may not be able to do (Yalom & Leszcz, 2020). Members, over time, learn to trust each other and respect their *real-world* experiences. On the other hand, suggestions, techniques, and strategies that come from the group leader may be met with resistance: After all, if the clinician is not in recovery how can they know what it is like to have a substance use disorder and what to do about it? (However, group members often do seek out and respect help from clinicians even if they have not been through a substance use disorder.) The point is that feedback, advice, suggestions, and information from member to member is just as powerful, or perhaps more so, than what the clinician offers. This member-to-member feedback should not be underemphasized.

Substance use groups are usually homogeneous groups who are naturally connected through the "universal theme of addiction" (Brooks & McHenry, 2015, p. 215). Recovery is a lifelong journey, and the thought that one is not alone in their quest for a better life can be immensely comforting. In general, universality is something that can naturally develop in the group as members learn the group process, appropriately disclose information, and come to feel more connected. However, group leaders can be intentional about enhancing universality with awareness and strategic questions. For example, leaders can listen for common themes that group members discuss and then make explicit mention of the commonality between group members. Another strategy is to openly comment about how a group member feels (e.g., lonely, disconnected, shameful) and then ask if anyone else in the group can relate to what they are feeling (Brooks & McHenry, 2015).

Imparting Information

Imparting information is a factor that is closely aligned with psycho-educational groups. In these groups, didactic instruction, clinician advice, and suggestions form the main therapeutic interventions and thus serve as the primary influences for clients (psycho-educational groups are discussed in more detail later). In groups that are more interactional or process oriented in nature, didactic instruction is usually not offered or provided on a limited basis.

In substance use groups, imparting information is particularly relevant in that clients benefit from learning about the process of substance use, how drugs impact the brain and body, why it is so difficult to stop using drugs, and strategies to prevent relapse. Imparting information is more than simply providing education to clients; explicit instruction on the nature of substance use and associated problems may help clients examine long-held cognitive distortions, misconceptions, and self-defeating behaviors related to their drug use problems (Yalom & Leszcz, 2020).

Human beings from time immemorial have craved certainty. We worry less about events that are predictable and controllable. The unpredictable nature of substance use, however, begets much fear and anxiety. According to Yalom and Leszcz (2020), this fear and anxiety clouds a client's ability to rationally explore the meaning, purpose, and cause of symptoms. Imparting information provides structure, explanation, and clarification that can ease emotions based on uncertainty. The adage "knowledge is power" seems quite relevant in this instance.

Altruism

One of the sad realities among clients who use substances is their belief that they are "losers" and have nothing of value to offer anyone in their lives. A life consumed by substance-related processes eventually withdrawals from others and becomes centered on getting the next high, regardless of who is hurt in the process. Group therapy is a unique setting in which clients help other clients through listening, providing support, making suggestions, and simply being there week after week. In the group therapy milieu, members not only receive help from others, which itself is therapeutic, but also gain by giving (Yalom & Leszcz, 2020). The reciprocal giving–receiving process provides yet another powerful group therapy process from which clients can heal.

Of course, the intrinsic benefit and value of the act of giving is nothing new, as altruism has been the philosophical foundation for many religious and spiritual traditions across the world. Group members may start group therapy believing they have nothing to offer but over time realize that they indeed may be able to offer something important to another member. Even if a client cannot offer specific information, they can be present, participate, and support other members. The simple act of providing a supportive comment may seem of limited value to a new group member and yet have a powerful effect on the one receiving the support. The act of altruism, no matter how small, is a win-win situation: The giver benefits from an inherently kind act, and the receiver benefits from the act itself.

Altruism is a natural factor that emerges in substance use group therapy and 12-step mutual support groups, such as AA (Brooks & McHenry, 2015). The foundation of AA, as envisioned by its founder Bill Wilson, is based on altruism. Many of my clients, at first reticent to try AA, develop an affinity for the group and appreciate the simple premise that people are there simply to provide support and help others.

Corrective Recapitulation of the Primary Family Group

Some clients who struggle with substance use disorders recall childhood experiences that were traumatic, neglecting, abusive, and negative. Of course, these experiences are not limited to only clients who use substances. However, I have found it remarkable how widespread early family problems are among clients struggling with substance use issues. Yalom and Leszcz (2020) noted that in psychotherapy groups, the setting resembles a family with "authoritarian/parental figures, peer/sibling figures, deep personal revelations, strong emotions, and deep intimacy as well as hostile competitive feelings" (p. 15). Working through problems with the leader and members is also working out unfinished business from negative early childhood experiences.

Naturally, if a group resembles the relationships that develop in a family, members are probably going to have various reactions to other members, either positive or negative, and sometimes with significant energy. For example, if one member reminds another of their father, who they grew to hate growing up, they may relive this anger in the here and now of the group by directing it toward the other member. Indeed, that is the point: Interpersonal group therapy provides an immediate family situation in which the past is recreated, and repaired, in the now. Early family conflicts are relived in the group so that they can be corrected in the moment (Vannicelli, 1996). A group leader might ask the client above if the group member reminds them of anyone in their life. They may admit that a member reminds them of their father. The leader and members can then help the client become aware of the genesis of their anger, work through their negative emotions, and practice new behaviors toward the other member. It might be pointed out, too, that excessive anger is inconsistent with a substance-free life.

Group leaders can attract the brunt of transference because of their position of authority and power. They may be perceived as playing the "parental role" and dig up particularly difficult feelings in clients whose parents were abusive, autocratic, or inflexible. Brooks and McHenry (2015) noted that group leaders need to constantly attend to transference issues and how they play out in the session. Of course, transference does not occur only between leader and member. Member-to-member transference should be monitored as well.

Socializing Techniques

The development of social skills is often a specific focus in substance use groups. As noted earlier, many clients with substance use disorders have significant relationship problems, failing to honor the customs and nuances of healthy social connections, such as giving and receiving. In addition, for some clients the drug has literally taken the place of other people. Social skills never fully develop, which consequently drives others further and further away.

The group therapy milieu, however, offers a setting where social skills—connecting with other people—can be observed, taught, and practiced. A client, for example, who complains of persistent relapses may come to understand through group feedback how they don't make sincere attempts to connect with other members. They may then practice connecting with others in the group, initiating conversation and being altruistic. The therapy group may be the only occasion where the client has experienced receiving interpersonal feedback (Yalom, 1998).

Imitative Behavior

In my master's in counseling program, we had a professor who looked like Sigmund Freud in his later years: white head of hair slicked back, round glasses, and full beard that was closely trimmed. He had everything but the cigar (although we would see him walking around campus with a pipe from time to time). Pretty soon, the males in my cohort (including, I am embarrassed to say, myself) were beginning to talk like him, walk like him, and some even took up pipe smoking. Looking back, I realize this was a classic example of imitative behavior. People learn from watching other people perform some action from which they have some interest. Albert Bandura, the eminent social cognitive psychologist, coined this phenomenon observational learning or modeling, and it can have a potent impact on behavior.

Individuals who are successful in their recovery efforts naturally serve as good role models for new group members. Group members learn from watching one another address stumbling blocks on the road to recovery. They learn, for example, that telling oneself to simply cut back on heroin or cocaine use to once a week does not work. Clients new to recovery learn quickly that pro-recovery behaviors, such as going to meetings, attending therapy, reconnecting with others, and the building healthier lifestyles ought to be imitated; after all, they can see the proof of their effectiveness by the success of clients more advanced along the path of recovery.

Imitating behavior is not, however, limited to what the more experienced can teach the new. It works the other way as well. The result is a group factor that benefits all members as they struggle to remain substance free.

Interpersonal Learning

Interpersonal learning is at the heart of group psychotherapy, as most psychological problems are, at their essence, relational problems (Yalom & Leszcz, 2020). Improvement in interpersonal relations equates to healthy human functioning. In the group setting, the client often perceives others with interpersonal distortion (Brooks & McHenry, 2015); interpersonal learning entails correcting these biased and distorted perceptions of others. Mental health and symptom improvement come with awareness and working through these interpersonal dynamics within the group (Brooks & McHenry, 2015).

Yalom and Leszcz (2020) noted that clinicians can facilitate interpersonal learning by creating an environment that provides a corrective emotional experience. For example, a client may feel animosity toward the group and thus shuts down or provides cynical comments in response to other members' statements. When confronted, they may admit that they don't feel they belong in the group, that they feel they are among losers, and that they can't take anything away to improve their life. The leader and other members may wonder if their attitude toward the group is the same attitude they display outside the group, and if this is why they have so much trouble with relationships, experiencing intense loneliness. It might also be pointed out that acts of kindness from other group members, such as recent compliments, seem to be inconsistent with their harsh evaluation. In this short example, the client has a distorted view of the group, and this distortion probably occurs in most of their interpersonal relations outside of the group. The awareness of how they distort relationships with others is a key learning moment for this client. The group leader might encourage them to let the group know when they are feeling cynical and impatient. Group members can then respond to confirm or disconfirm these perceptions to help the client see things more accurately.

Group Cohesion

Group cohesion generally refers to feelings of attraction, affiliation, and support between and among group members, although nuances of definitions exist (Toseland & Rivas, 2001).

It is analogous to the relationship between clinician and client in individual therapy (Yalom & Leszcz, 2020). The clinical research literature has been consistent in the finding that the therapeutic relationship accounts for a significant amount of variance in individual counseling outcomes (Duncan et al., 2010). A strong therapeutic bond between clinician and client allows for greater receptivity to theoretical approaches and techniques. A client who connects with their therapist is more likely to try out different suggestions, feel validated, and benefit from psychotherapy.

In group therapy, the relationship plays an equally important role (Yalom & Leszcz, 2020). However, the concept of therapeutic relationship is more expansive because there are more relationships to consider. For example, there is the relationship between clinician and client, client and other group members, and client to the entire group (Yalom & Leszcz). Thus, the process of leading a group becomes more complex, and this can make for a challenging experience for group leaders who need to attend to a multitude of relationship dynamics.

Cohesiveness is not only a critical factor for successful groups, it also is essential for the other factors to successfully operate in the group (Yalom, 1998). Group members who lack cohesiveness, for example, will be less likely to accept information, engage in altruistic behavior, or minimize resistances to the group process. Cohesiveness is enhanced when the level of trust in the group is established and demonstrated. Trust lays the foundation for self-disclosure, which then leads to empathy from others, reinforcing trust, and so forth (Yalom & Leszcz, 2020). Sharing one's personal struggles combined with the *acceptance by others* (Toseland & Rivas, 2001) strengthens cohesion and by proxy the entire group is enhanced.

Catharsis

Catharsis refers to the intense emotional release that *may* occur because of therapy. Although opportunities for catharsis present themselves in individual and group therapy, the intensity of emotional expression in group therapy may be greater due to the level of transference and reactions to other group members. Group members do not have to experience a catharsis to profit from group counseling (Brooks & McHenry, 2015). What seems to be important, however, is that if a group member experiences an intense emotional release, cognitive processing immediately follows to preclude the emotional release from becoming a damaging experience (Brooks & McHenry, 2015; Yalom & Leszcz, 2020).

Substance use clients often live in a world of intense emotions. Their drug use is associated with negative consequences that hurt themselves and others. In some cases, the client may bury negative feelings and cut themself off from their emotions. When drug use is stopped, these emotions come barreling to the surface and in need of expression. However, simply allowing the client to blow off emotional steam may be counterproductive and leave them feeling vulnerable (Brooks & McHenry, 2015). Again, catharsis in combination with group processing places the emotional reaction into perspective, gives the client a sense of hope, and forces the client to make meaning of these intense feelings and what they can do to improve their life.

An example from my own clinical experience illustrates the factor of catharsis. The client, Travis (name disguised), struggled with alcohol for many years. His rock-bottom moment came when he was arrested in his home after a day and a half–long alcohol binge with intense vomiting, blackouts, and physical symptoms such as palpitations (he had stolen some beer at a local convenience store). He was taken to an inpatient hospital where he was evaluated, treated for several weeks, and then released with a referral to continue outpatient counseling. During one group session, Travis became quite emotional, sharing the following story:

> Blacking out was the last straw when I hit rock bottom. It scared the hell out of me. I didn't know where I was, what I was doing. I suddenly felt deep sadness for what I had become, how I let my family down, myself down. Nothing could be worse than watching your life slip right through your fingers. [Starting to cry] I, I want to connect with my children again, but how can they respect me for what I have done? I guess being in treatment gives me some hope [crying intensely].

Travis's emotional release was intense, and I knew that he should sit with his emotions while at the same time elicit the group to help him cognitively process the catharsis. To begin this process, I invited the group to offer any thoughts or suggestions for how Travis can make sense of these difficult emotions. I also helped Travis by reinforcing two important points he made: wanting to connect with his children and having hope. I asked him how he might use this emotional experience to provide the motivation to make these a reality for him.

Existential Factors

Existential factors refer to certain "givens of existence" that all humans must face. Yalom and Leszcz (2020) listed five existential themes that often emerge in group therapy:

1. Recognizing that life is at times unfair and unjust.
2. Recognizing that ultimately there is no escape from some of life's pain and from death.
3. Recognizing that no matter how close I get to other people, I must still face life alone.
4. Facing the basic issues of my life and death, and thus living my life more honestly and being less caught up in trivialities.
5. Learning that I must take ultimate responsibility for the way I live my life, no matter how much guidance and support I get from others (p. 131)

In my experience, existential issues strongly resonate with clients struggling with substance use. Clients with substance use problems indeed struggle with finding meaning and purpose, teeter with death (sometimes daily), loathe isolation, and struggle with the great responsibility that comes from freedom. The inability to successfully navigate through these existential issues can be a catalyst for substance use and other problems. Existential concerns crop up over and over in my work with clients, so much so that I regularly incorporate discussions of these issues in my individual and group work (see more on the connection between existential issues and substance use in Chapter 14).

The 11 factors serve as the foundation for group therapy. Even within theoretical application, such as cognitive therapy groups, these factors are operating at some level. These factors are curative in their ability to promote healthy interpersonal relationships, which leads to healthier choices and functioning outside of the group.

Stages of Group Therapy

Several models exist regarding the sequence of stages a typical group proceeds through on its way from beginning status to advanced functioning (Corey, 2016; Tuckman & Jensen, 1977; Yalom & Leszcz, 2020). All groups will experience beginning apprehension, resistances, periods of impressive productivity, and termination. Miller (2021) used Corey's (2016) framework as a suitable model for substance use groups. In Corey's (2016) model, there are four general stages:[1] (a) orientation and exploration, (b) transition, (c) working stage, and (d) final stage. It is important to keep in mind that these stages are not mutually exclusive or fixed in any way (Miller, 2021). Groups can and do move back and forth between stages depending on group membership, type of group, and leader skill. A group also may straddle between two stages. Let's take each of Corey's (2016) stages in turn.

Initial Stage: Orientation and Exploration (Stage 1)

Stage 1 entails much anxiety and apprehension as members are new to each other and are not sure what to expect. Corey (2016) labeled this stage "orientation and exploration" because members are familiarizing themselves to each other and the group as a whole and discovering what is expected of them. The development of trust is crucial in this stage: Members begin to get a feel of the group and if they belong (Miller, 2021).

Transition Stage: Dealing With Resistance (Stage 2)

Conflict is inevitable in group development as members try to sort out if they belong in the group, if the leader is competent enough to lead the group, and if the group is a safe place to share deeply personal information (Corey, 2016). Argumentation between members may occur as misunderstandings abound. Group members may challenge leaders in a multitude of ways. For example, the leader may be challenged in terms of how they handle group conflict. If leaders are not recovering from substance use disorders themselves, members may question their knowledge and experience with substance-related issues (Miller, 2021).

Resistance unique to substance use groups also occurs when members complain that the group is not using enough "recovery talk," members distract attention from the group, or members avoid talking about serious issues (Vannicelli, 1996). They may, for example, joke around to the point of distraction rather than discussing important topics (Vannicelli, 1996). Group leaders become the target of resistance, especially if they have not experienced a 12-step program. Their competence is called into question (Miller, 2021). Group leaders need to be aware of this tension in the group and redirect the energy toward the anxiety in the group and process it to move forward in a therapeutic manner (Miller, 2021).

---

1 Corey (2016) proposed "pregroup issues" (stage 1) and "postgroup issues" (stage 6) as the first and final stages in his model, respectively. For brevity and ease of presentation, I have only included stages 2–5.

Working Stage: Cohesion and Productivity (Stage 3)

Over time, a comfort level is established among group members, leading to enhanced cohesion and productivity (Corey, 2016). In well-functioning groups (i.e., high in cohesiveness), productivity levels can be extraordinary. Members feel they can trust each other and are more willing to share deep, personal information that they would not reveal earlier in the group (Miller, 2021). Conflict turns into appropriate confrontation, as members learn how to make and take constructive suggestions. Leaders are seen as competent, professional, and evaluated more realistically (Miller, 2021).

Superficial discussions of types of drugs used and the "good ole' times" give way to deeper revelations about shameful actions used to obtain drugs or early childhood experiences that were defined by drug-using parents (Miller, 2021). Members reach new levels of vulnerability and exposure (Miller, 2021). At the same time, members strengthen their support of each other.

Final Stage: Consolidation and Termination (Stage 4)

The focus of the final stage is on how well members can integrate the group experience into their lives (Corey, 2016). Members consolidate information and experiences they gained from the group and negotiate what will work for them in the real world. Strong emotions may emerge as the termination date is in sight (Miller, 2021). It is important for the group leader at this stage to facilitate consolidation, help members apply what they have learned in the group, and address concerns that rise in doing so.

Understanding the stages of group development prepares group leaders for what to expect during the beginning, middle, and end stages of a group. Leaders should understand, for example, that small, chit-chat type of talk is normal during the beginning stages and that challenges to competence are to be expected. Awareness of these stages can help keep negative emotions and counter-transference reactions in check.

Application of Group Therapy With Substance Use Disorders

Group therapy with clients who use substances shares many similarities with group therapy in general (Southern & Thornton, 2013). One of the strengths of group therapy for substance use is that the group is homogeneous in nature, leading to greater cohesion in less time than heterogeneous groups (Brooks & McHenry, 2015). Substance use groups also tend to crystallize more quickly than other groups because they share a particular vernacular, most members are in some type of crisis due to their substance use, and members are unified by the "disease" of addiction (Vannicelli, 1996). Indeed, research has supported the basic premise that individuals who are in contact with others who have experienced the same or similar crisis has substantial value ("Group Therapy Works Well," 1997, as cited in Brooks & McHenry, 2015). Kinney (2003) stressed that group therapy for substance use helps clients learn about the self in relation to others, receive feedback and advice, and share hope for change, making it the preferred model of treatment for substance use issues. In addition, "enhanced group therapy," defined as counseling *and* educational interventions three times per week, has been shown to improve the efficacy of naltrexone, a commonly used medication for opiate use disorder (Rawson et al., 2001). Specifically, Rawson et al. found that length of time in treatment, amount of naltrexone taken, support services accepted, measures of affect, and opioid use were superior in the enhanced group compared to a "standard group" (monthly visits to monitor medication). Apparently, intensive group work has the benefit of being "value added" to other treatment protocols, such as medication for substance use.

Yalom and Leszcz (2020) stressed the importance of a pre-group interview to ensure clients are appropriate for the group format. However, Vannicelli (1996) suggested that specific information is needed for substance use clients who have attended 12-step mutual help groups but have not participated in group therapy. Clients who are familiar with 12-step mutual help groups may not be comfortable with the more stringent norms of group therapy. In addition, expectations in group therapy include keeping appropriate boundaries, minimizing outside group contact, greater expression of emotions, and explorations of the past. Margolis and Zweben (1998) asked that substance use clients not come intoxicated, be ready to discuss alcohol and/or drug use in the group, and commit to a minimum of 3 months' group therapy, requirements that are not established for nonsubstance use groups.

Another issue unique to substance use groups includes the ever-present reality of relapse. Even though RP may not be the specific focus of a group, elements of RP should part of the process, including how the group will handle a member relapsing (Miller, 2021). Indeed, RP becomes an even greater focus for clients who struggle with dual diagnoses. As noted in Chapter 5, integrated treatment protocols have been recommended for dual-diagnosis clients, and group therapy has been infused within integrated treatment regimens. Researchers have demonstrated that "integrated group therapy" is superior in reducing substance use compared to group drug counseling among clients with concomitant bipolar disorder and substance dependence. Specifically, Weiss et al. (2007) found that 20 weeks of integrated group therapy produced significant reductions in substance use but no difference in number of days with bipolar disorder compared to the group drug counseling intervention. Apparently, integrated group treatment has a positive impact on substance use but is not superior in reducing bipolar symptoms (this doesn't mean it wasn't effective, just that there was negligible difference in terms of bipolar symptoms).

Leaders of substance use groups will discover that clients often struggle with authority figures, trusting others, and controlling their emotions and impulses (Miller, 2021). Extra care is needed to encourage members to be as open, honest, and respectful with one another as possible—the only way to enhance the level of trust.

Working With Client Defenses

For most people, anxiety, whatever its source, is uncomfortable. And, if it begins to exceed the boundaries of our coping resources, it becomes downright unbearable. Anxiety is omnipresent, even among emotionally well-adjusted people. It serves as the foundational symptom for several psychiatric diagnoses in the DSM-5. Anti-anxiety medications were listed in nine of the top ten prescribed psychiatric drugs in the United States (Kuebrick, 2012).

Indeed, anxiety plays a key role in psychoanalytic theory (Thombs & Osborn, 2019). Freud first coined the term *ego-defense mechanisms* when referring to how individuals manage anxiety. When people experience anxiety, there is generally one of two choices for how to handle it (excluding counseling and medication therapy). First, we could confront the source of the anxiety directly, work toward a solution, and move on with our lives. Second, and perhaps more commonly, we distort reality to lessen the anxiety we feel. This distortion of reality is what Freud referred to when he spoke of defense mechanisms: Essentially, the person changes the rules of the game (i.e., reality) to feel less discomfort about their behavior. Use of defense mechanisms is widespread and considered normal if used within reason. However, overuse of defense mechanisms weakens the person's ability to cope with the demands of reality. That is, if a client continually distorts their drinking and associated consequences (reality) by rationalization or denial, their capacity to see their drinking as a problem will diminish and they will continue their deleterious behavior. Common defense mechanisms among substance use clients include the following (Thombs & Osborn, 2019):

- **Compensation.** The individual substitutes one addiction for another (e.g., a client who started an abstinence only program becomes compulsive about internet porn use).

- **Denial.** The individual fails to observe or acknowledge an unacceptable reality (e.g., a husband, when confronted harshly by his spouse about his drinking, denies he has a problem.).

- **Rationalization.** The individual justifies one's mistakes by making increasingly elaborate excuses for the misconduct (e.g., a client admitted taking a hit of cocaine because they had a hard day and deserve to relax).

- **Undoing.** The individual repents and makes up for an unacceptable or hurtful action (e.g., a client who relapses says that they will never use again and then mows the lawn, cooks dinner, and gives their wife a backrub the next day.).

- **Displacement.** The individual directs hostility and anger toward objects, animals, or people that appear less threatening than what originally aroused the anger (e.g., a client whose drug use has been challenged in therapy comes home and is irritable to their family the whole night).

All the examples generate anxiety on some level. Individuals use defense mechanisms to assuage anxiety related to their situation and behavior. People are usually not aware that they are using defense mechanisms, as they operate at an unconscious level (Thombs & Osborn, 2019). Part of helping individuals "come back to reality" is to enhance their conscious awareness of how they distort reality. Traditional substance use counseling uses this fact as the bedrock of therapy: Harsh confrontation of denial and admittance of being an "addict" or "alcoholic" are necessary conditions to change. Unfortunately, these strategies have had the unintentional effect of engendering resistance and are simply ineffective for many clients (Miller & Rollnick, 2002). More contemporary approaches, such as MI, use gentler methods to help clients recognize their distortions.

Recognizing Denial

Perhaps one of the most common defense mechanisms among clients who use substances is denial. Denial occurs when one does not see their substance use as problematic. Clients who harbor strong denial tendencies are absolutely convinced they do not have a problem. Its effects can be pervasive as they also convince family members, clergy, colleagues, friends, and even clinicians that they do not have a problem. I once counseled a 34-year-old male client who struggled with alcohol use. He and his wife came to the first session and the scenario was typical: He was sullen and resistant, sunk down in the couch as if life was unfair. She, on the other hand, was angry and teary-eyed and went through all the typical problems with alcohol use: He was not the same person when he drank, he became violent and ugly, and if he did not stop his drinking, she and their two young children (ages 5 and 7) would leave him. I agreed to see the client for several sessions, and his denial was extraordinarily effective that even I was wondering if he really had his drinking under control (he did not). We decided to try a controlled drinking program, and he would come to counseling on an agreed-on schedule for up to a year. Sure enough, after a couple months, his wife emailed me in great distress, convinced that he is an alcoholic. She wanted to meet with me separately and, with the client's permission, I saw her for one session. I stated that intensive therapy may be necessary, but first wanted to talk with him to see what was going on. As one might imagine, he downplayed his drinking, stating his wife was upset that he had "one or two" drinks and that everything was fine. The last straw came a few months later, when the client left me a phone message that he was going to inpatient residential care and thanked me for my services. I wondered what had happened for him to abruptly go from outpatient to a residential program, especially for someone who was not that excited about therapy. My guess is that he hit rock bottom (again) and concluded along with his family that he could not continue the path he was on. My failure with this client was underestimating the extent of his denial and how convincing he was that his drinking wasn't that bad. Recognizing and confronting denial is difficult work for all clinicians, especially in individual therapy. However, in group therapy the chances of denial surviving greatly diminish.

When new clients are referred to group therapy with other clients struggling with substance use issues it becomes much more difficult to maintain denial and other defenses because the more experienced group members have seen it all and even used the same defenses. If the group is skillfully led, clients grow by making the connection between their defenses, emotional consequences, and substance use (Brooks & McHenry, 2015). Group members who have been in recovery for a period can help new group members gain greater insight and awareness of how their use impacts them physically and emotionally as well as how it impacts others. Helping clients become aware of their defenses is an important aspect of substance use group therapy and recovery (Brooks & McHenry, 2015).

Other Considerations in Substance Use Group Counseling

Clients who use substances often struggle with setting boundaries in their personal lives. One of tasks of the group leader is to help members create appropriate boundaries by establishing group rules. Interpersonal skills and relationships are strengthened when the group leader and members establish structure and ground rules related to attendance, general etiquette, and participation (Gladding, 2011). This process should be collaborative in nature: rules and boundaries that come directly and forcefully from group leadership sets the wrong tone and will be greeted with discord.

As part of any treatment plan, including those involving groups, goal setting is an important component. Many clients who have struggled with substance use may have little practice in setting goals. Their life goals are either nonexistent, revolve solely around getting the next high, or vague, such as "I just want to feel better." When I help clients develop goals in individual and group therapy, I like to borrow from solution-focused therapy or CBT where objective, measurable, and behavioral goals are emphasized. Being clear on goals allows substance use clients to strive for something positive to start things off, no matter how small.

Common Substance Use Group Formats

The following group models are commonly used in substance use counseling settings (CSAT, 2005). These models should not be seen as mutually exclusive; some groups may include several elements from each model. For example, in one group session a clinician may begin the group with educational material and then proceed to skill building. In other cases, there may be a singular purpose to the group, such as when the leader focuses the entire session on interpersonal process. Finally, the following is not an exhaustive list of group models to help clients with substance use problems. Other group models, such as culturally specific treatment groups or expressive arts groups, function as unique entities within substance use treatment (CSAT, 2005) but will not be covered here.

Psycho-Educational Groups

Psycho-educational groups are designed to educate clients on substance use issues, consequences of use, and related behaviors (CSAT, 2005). Topics might include effects of drugs on the body and brain, developmental trajectories of substance use problems, issues related to relapse maintenance and prevention, and theories of addiction. These groups are highly educational and designed to present clients with information that they can apply in their own life to make better choices. Psycho-educational groups are not aimed at making long-term intrapsychic or personality changes, although thinking and behavioral changes may occur as clients gain new insights (CSAT, 2005). The primary mode of delivery is through mini lectures, video recordings, movie clips, and case studies.

A second, often overlooked, component of psycho-educational groups is helping clients process the material that has been presented. This involves taking time either during a mini lecture or at the conclusion of a lesson for group members to discuss the topics amongst themselves and how the information might apply in real life. Failure to bridge the gap between theory and practice runs the risk of leaving clients with interesting information but with few ideas for how it should be applied.

Psycho-educational groups help clients in early recovery learn more about substance use disorders, triggers related to use, relapse, and the pathway to recovery (CSAT, 2005). These groups also may help precontemplative clients enhance motivation to change as they learn about consequences of use, the impact that drug use has or could have on their lives, and possible avenues toward change (CSAT, 2005). Psycho-educational groups also work well for families where a member abuses substances. In my experience, family members often are unaware of the progressive, deteriorating nature of severe substance use and struggle to understand why their loved one just can't stop. Family members need information that can help them better support their loved one in recovery as well as gain suggestions for their own care and growth.

Techniques

Undergirding the many techniques of a psycho-educational group are two overarching considerations: (a) how is information to be presented and (b) how leaders can assist clients in applying the material to make better choices and live healthier lives (CSAT, 2005). Leaders need to be cognizant of what modality would best present the information to the group, including mini lectures, videos, movie clips, podcasts, and so forth. In my experience as an educator, using multiple modalities, if possible, allows for a richer learning experience among students and clients. In addition, some clients might prefer learning through one modality as opposed to another. Using a variety of modalities ensures that all learning styles are respected and that, ideally, maximum learning takes place.

Group leaders can help clients apply the educational material by asking reflective and process-based questions. For example, after presenting on the topic of relapse prevention, a group leader might ask, "From the strategies we discussed thus far, which one(s) seem to be a good fit for you?" Or to be a bit more reflective, "Think ahead 6 months for now and imagine that you have stopped using drugs; which one of these strategies helped you reach this point?" Whether processing questions are asked during or after the presentation is up to the preferences of the leader and, in some cases, the group. For example, if the material to be presented is substantial, forging ahead with an hour-and-a-half lecture would probably lead to clients tuning out. However, breaking up the material with "check-in" periods that allow for processing and discussion can strategically avoid this problem.

Other techniques that often accompany psycho-educational groups include role playing, cases studies, problem-solving exercises, and writing exercises, all designed to solidify learning and enhance application of material. These techniques are performed in an atmosphere of mutual respect, sensitivity, and encouragement. Of course, the group leader's attitude and approach significantly contribute to this type of learning environment.

Psycho-educational groups are highly structured and often follow a manual or planned curriculum (CSAT, 2005). This format requires significant preparation on the part of the group leader. The leader must also be aware of cutting-edge research and clinical applications that emerge in the substance use field. Staying abreast of the most recent developments ensures that information and educational material is accurate.

Skill-Building Groups

Skill building (or skill development) plays a major role in substance use groups, with some group leaders making this the primary focus. Many clients struggling with substance-related issues have lost skill in how to live in a healthy and effective manner. Most skill-building groups rely on cognitive behavioral strategies, although any theoretical orientation can provide the foundation from which to teach clients healthy life skills.

The capacity to build new skills and relearn old ones is especially important in recovery (CSAT, 2005). Recall that recovery is more than simply stopping substance use; it also refers to building a positive lifestyle by making healthy choices. Many of the skill deficits in those struggling with substance use are interpersonal in nature, making group therapy a natural fit for social skill development (CSAT, 2005).

The types of skills taught in skill-building groups are many and varied. Some groups may focus on helping clients better manage difficult emotions, while others might help clients balance a checkbook. In most cases, a combination of life skills forms the content of the group. Members benefit from practicing refusal skills so they can resist temptation from old buddies who use or relaxation skills to help them better manage stress, a common trigger for relapse.

Techniques

Specific techniques used in skill-building groups will vary as a function of what is being offered by the group. In general, however, group leaders rely on several common strategies that are endemic to all skill-building groups: didactic instruction, group practice, role play, demonstration, processing, and feedback. An example may be illustrative.

I once counseled a group of African American adolescent boys in an urban group home who were struggling in school as reflected by expulsions, violence, and substance use. When we met as a group every week, I incorporated several cognitive behavioral–based exercises to help these boys enhance their skill development. For example, for 1 week I provided a case study for every group member to read. The case study was a story in which the protagonist was confronted by a bully who used expletives and was verbally aggressive, taunting him for a fight. One member volunteered to play the protagonist, another volunteered to play the bully, and two other members agreed to represent the protagonist's rational and irrational thoughts. (Because of the cultural context of this group, what constituted rational and irrational thoughts was discussed before the exercise.) The protagonist and bully were then instructed to relive the scene in the case study, while the members who played the protagonist's thoughts repeated rational and irrational comments, respectively. The member representing irrational thoughts would say, "I hate this loser, and I have to take him out" and "Fighting is the only way to solve this." The member who played the rational thoughts would say the following: "It is not worth it," "I am the better man," and "I have higher goals for myself than to get in a fight." The experiment was designed so the irrational thoughts gradually faded into the background as the rational thoughts grew in intensity. The protagonist was then instructed to pay attention to the rational thoughts and describe how he felt.

Even though this exercise was not directly related to substance use, learning how to "tune in" to rational self-messages and thoughts became a valuable skill that these clients could take with them in any number of difficult situations.

Cognitive Behavioral Groups

As noted, CBT serves as the foundation for many skills development groups. Aside from this application, CBT groups also focus on more substantial change, sometimes impacting change at the deeper personality structures. All in all, a common thread in CBT groups is cognitive restructuring followed by behavioral application of what has been learned (CSAT, 2005).

Cognitive behavioral group therapy has similar goals to individual CBT: to change learned behavior by changing thought processes, beliefs, perceptions, and behaviors (Beck et al., 1993). The idea is for group members to examine their assumptions, thoughts, attitudes, decisions, and opinions that serve to maintain substance-using behavior. This feature of CBT group therapy makes it an appropriate choice for those in early recovery (CSAT, 2005). The concreteness of CBT provides a good starting place for clients to make positive changes in their lives. Once a foundation of cognitive and behavioral change has been established, clients may be ready to move on to more introspective or expressive forms of therapy.

CBT groups for substance use are designed to enhance cognitive and behavioral coping skills so that the client can better handle life stressors and live a more productive, happy life (Miller et al., 2019). One of the strongest empirically supported group approaches for substance use is CBT coping skills. Here, clients learn skills to recognize their substance use problems and apply self-monitoring based on behavioral principles (Marques & Formigoni, 2001). CBT coping skills groups are also designed to prevent relapse once the client has stopped using substances (see Chapter 8). Leaders of CBT groups often adopt the "tell-show-try" method of skill development (Miller et al., 2019): The clinician provides information about a skill (tell), demonstrates how it is done, possibly via role play (show), and then encourages members to practice the skill with each other (try).

Techniques

The techniques used in individual CBT often can be applied to the group format. This may entail having all group members participate in a technique or focusing on one member followed by group feedback, processing, and discussion. Most CBT group techniques generally include (a) didactic instruction in how thinking leads to emotions, which leads to behavior; (b) an emphasis on problem solving and reasonable short- and long-term goal setting; and (c) helping clients to self-monitor thoughts, feelings, and behavior (CSAT, 2005).

Support Groups

The genesis of support groups comes out of the 12-step mutual help group traditions such as AA. Such groups can be an indispensable aspect to one's recovery (for some clients, however, they are not as effective, or the client is not as interested). The focus of support groups can range from a directive, problem-solving emphasis to a nondirective, process-oriented, and interpersonal emphasis (CSAT, 2005). The underlying theme in these groups is providing *support*. That is, members offer other members help with maintaining abstinence and living day to day without drug use. Specific kinds of support may be offered, such as providing suggestions, volunteering to help a member take an important step, or simply listening. Support groups tap into the curative factor of altruism, and members usually notice improved self-esteem and self-confidence.

Support groups may dabble in processing experiences and emotions, but this is not the main interest as the goal is not personality change. If processing of issues does occur, it is usually on a smaller, less complex, more directive scale than interpersonal process groups (Toseland & Rivas, 2001). Indeed, the very nature of support groups is to destigmatize the treatment process, which is helpful for reluctant or fearful clients. Clients in support groups often appreciate the nonthreatening milieu that such groups provide. The focus of these groups is on practical matters such as staying substance free and avoiding legal difficulty (CSAT, 2005).

One of the factors that make support groups effective is members holding other members accountable for their own abstinence. Guidance is provided via member-to-member exchange as well as leader input and direction. Confrontation is minimized to keep levels of anxiety low.

Techniques

In most situations, theoretical orientation of the leader will dictate specific techniques used in support groups. In general, leaders actively facilitate discussion, maintain group norms and boundaries, facilitate working through conflict, and provide acceptance for members (CSAT, 2005).

Support groups are not technique-laden groups. Techniques are of less importance because leaders tend to be less active and directive. Interventions may be more about facilitating hope and introspection than is typical of other, more directive groups (Toseland & Rivas, 2001). As such, leaders of substance use support groups need to be keen observers and skilled at providing supportive, empathetic comments and reflections to maximize potential healing.

Interpersonal Process Groups

Interpersonal process groups (IPGs) closely resemble the theory and practice of group therapy as outlined in Yalom and Leszcz's (2020) classic text. IPGs focus on both intrapersonal and interpersonal change. However, the primary mechanism of change is through interpersonal dynamics. In fact, Yalom and Leszcz argued that improving interpersonal relationships through the group therapy process is *the* conduit for intrapersonal change. Underlying psychological symptoms, then, reflect interpersonal pathology, and so the task of the leader is to convert the psychological into the interpersonal (Yalom, 1998).

IPGs can be enormously helpful for individuals struggling with substance use because poor interpersonal relationships characterize many of these clients. As noted previously, the group therapy format is a social microcosm in which dysfunctional relationship patterns eventually play themselves out (Yalom & Leszcz, 2020). Through immediacy, here-and-now work, and feedback, clients begin to reexamine their tendencies to push others away and create chaos in relationships outside the group. Clients are encouraged to become aware of how they preclude connection to others, practice new skills, and develop mutually satisfying relationships with group members (hopefully translating to others outside of the group). Satisfying relationships with other people takes much of the power and appeal away from drugs and alcohol (CSAT, 2005).

Interpersonal process groups place greater importance on process rather than content. The reason is that group members sometimes get bogged down with content, which often is of limited therapeutic value. A classic example of this is a group "complaint session" in which members argue and complain about anything under the sun. This venting may help clients feel somewhat better, but it does little to promote therapeutic change. Focusing on the group process yields greater fruit from which clients can increase awareness, practice new ways of relating, and improve their lives. To emphasize process, the group leader in an IPG observes (a) the psychological functioning of each member, (b) the way members are relating to one another, and (c) how the whole group is operating (CSAT, 2005). What a leader focuses on depends on what the group needs in the moment, although how members relate is where IPG leaders place much of their effort. Leaders focus on the present and need to be observers of how members are re-creating their past in the here and now of the group.

As an example of focusing on process, consider a group member who comments in the beginning of the group about a story on the news the other night. Several other group members chime in, and soon the group is engrossed in opinion and debate about the story. A group member then asks the leader what they think. Responding to this question has the risk of continuing an unproductive dialogue that can take precious time away from group work. To stay in process, the leader could simply state they are not sure about the story and then refocus the group on some process-oriented issue (e.g., that one group member is missing or how everyone feels about being in the group today, etc.). This is not to say that leaders need to consistently avoid small talk and pleasantries in the group, as they can serve to build rapport and cohesion; however, focusing too much on content is an effective way for members to avoid difficult therapeutic work.

Techniques

The IPG group clinician usually does not rely on skill-based or problem-solving techniques. Instead, they may offer interpretations of group dynamics or interpersonal functioning between two members. The techniques used in IPG include interpretation of group dynamics and discussion of interpersonal process through a focus on the here and now (Yalom, 1990). Emphasizing the here and now might include asking members their current impressions, who members think they are most like/least like, who will be the easiest/more difficult to relate to, and how members feel about one another in the moment (Yalom, 1990).

Yalom (1990) noted two key steps in establishing a here-and-now focus: expressing feelings and looking at what just happened in the moment. Individuals cannot hide difficult emotions in the moment, and such feelings become grist for the therapeutic mill because they can be brought to the forefront and explored now. Group leaders need to be constantly aware of what happens between group members and comment on significant dynamics. There is usually a significant correspondence between the here and now of the group and outside relationships (Yalom, 1990); providing clients feedback in terms of how they are perceived by other group members followed by "Is this reflective of how others might view you outside the group?" or "Are you satisfied with how others view you?" (Yalom, 1990) can set in motion social and personal change.

IPGs may not focus exclusively on substance use during group meetings. This is because psychological symptoms are translated into interpersonal issues. Thus, it is believed that clients who work on improving how they relate and connect to others will consequently either give up or cut down on their drug use. They come to realize that substance use is incompatible with healthy family, work, and other relations. Strong bonds to others and a drug-free life go hand in hand.

Other Group Techniques

Other useful techniques in group therapy for substance use clients include linking, blocking, and conveying focus and discipline (Miller, 2021). Linking refers to making intentional connections between group members based on interests, actions, or words. For example, two members may struggle with peer pressure to use drugs, and over time their discussions encompass similar experiences and even words. The astute leader will point out this connection and link these two members. Linking enhances group cohesion, which, as we have seen, improves group outcome (Yalom & Leszcz, 2020). Blocking refers to precluding certain members from sabotaging the group process or overtaking discussion with inappropriate comments or actions (Miller, 2021). Too much talking, asking too many irrelevant questions, or irritating other members needs to be addressed. Shifting focus, discussed in Chapter 6, is a strategy that can facilitate blocking. When a leader shifts focus, they gently guide the discussion and focus of the group into a more productive direction. Finally, Miller (2021) advocated a directive approach, emphasizing focus and discipline, with clients who use substances. Focus and discipline are important for clients who have probably learned few boundaries while under the influence of drugs. Gentle confrontation can help clients address self-defeating behaviors and thoughts (Miller, 2021). "By being directive, respectfully confrontative, tolerant, and nondefensive, leaders can assist groups in becoming more cohesive" (Miller, 2021, p. 142). The way the group leader responds to challenges and opportunities in the groups provides a model to group members for how to interact with others outside the group (Miller, 2021).

Substance Use Group Counseling Through the Lens of Theory

Many of the theories discussed in this book can be adapted to the group counseling format. Indeed, Corey (2016) discussed general group counseling approaches from Adlerian, existential, Gestalt, behavioral, and CBT perspectives, among others. An extensive amount of literature has been written on the application of solution-focused group therapy as applied to substance use issues (Sharry, 2001; West, 2010). Relapse prevention, discussed in Chapter 8, is the sole focus of many groups in substance use treatment facilities (CSAT, 2005).

Theoretical orientation is an important consideration for substance use clinicians and agencies to consider when forming a substance use group. This is because theory has a strong impact on the tasks the group will be doing, its focus, the topics of discussions, and clinician techniques (CSAT, 2005). Theoretical considerations should be thought through before a particular model is decided on. For example, if an agency shifts from a traditional treatment approach to a solution-focused approach, an educational model would probably not be the best fit for this SFC theory. Correspondence between theoretical approaches and group therapy model increases the chances for effective substance use group work (CSAT, 2005).

Theoretical techniques can be applied to the entire group or a single member who would like some concentrated work with the help of the group members. As an example, consider a group with solution-focused counseling as the theoretical approach. A technique for the entire group might be for all members to construct their own miracle based on the miracle question. Each member then shares aloud their miracle. The leader can choose one or two miracles to explore further, with the help of the other group members.

The adaptation of theoretical techniques to group counseling should never be done in a haphazard manner. Just because a technique works in individual counseling does not guarantee that it will be effective with groups. When planning group activities, leaders should reflect on the purpose of the technique, how the group might respond, if it can be used with all members or just a few, and what potential drawbacks might arise from its use. The technique should have clear relevance to the group and be consistent with the group model (psycho-educational, skill development, etc.).

Mutual Support Groups

In probably no other area of mental or public health is there a stronger emphasis on mutual help groups than in the substance-related disorders. I agree with Miller et al. (2019) that the term *mutual* help groups is preferred to *self*-help groups and consequently has been used throughout this text. On close examination, these groups are indeed mutual in that members rely on each other in a reciprocal fashion for support, guidance, and fellowship. As noted earlier, mutual help groups are *not* the same as therapeutic groups conducted by a professional clinician. The key differences have already been stated. They are best thought of as an adjunct to one's substance use treatment (Miller et al., 2019). A full review of all the mutual help groups available is beyond the scope of this chapter. However, Table 9.1 lists the most common mutual help groups as well as contact information.

According to the Alcoholics Anonymous (n.d.), it is estimated that there are approximately 116,000 AA groups and over 2,000,000 members across 180 countries. It has been my experience that AA or similar groups provide a strong foundation for recovery and, for some, is the most significant influence in helping them to remain alcohol free. This observation is

TABLE 9.1 Common Mutual Help Groups, Contact Information, and Their Primary Focus

Group	Contact	Focus
Alcoholics Anonymous	www.aa.org	For those who engage in problematic alcohol use and have a desire to stop drinking
Narcotics Anonymous	www.na.org	For those who engage in problematic drug use; NA makes no distinction between drugs, including alcohol
Cocaine Anonymous	www.ca.org	For those who engage in problematic cocaine use; for those who want to stop using cocaine and any other mind-altering drug
Rational Recovery	Conduct internet search with keywords "rational recovery" for a bevy of useful resources	Alternative to AA; like cognitive and cognitive restructuring methods; lots of information and classes on website
SMART	https://www.smartrecovery.org/	Nonspiritual approach to recovery; evidence-based motivational, behavioral, and cognitive methods; for individuals seeking abstinence from substance using behaviors
Moderation Management	www.moderation.org	For those who want to cut down on alcohol use but not necessarily remain abstinent. Behavioral methods and national mutual support group network; promotes early self-recognition of problem drinking, where moderate drinking is a reasonable and achievable goal
Women for Sobriety	www.womenforsobriety.org	Dedicated to helping women overcome alcohol use disorders as well as other substance use disorders; emphasis on growth, self-esteem, and generating a positive lifestyle

not uncommon; Stephanie Brown (1995), a respected researcher in problematic alcohol use, considers AA attendance an essential component of alcoholism treatment. For Brown, successful alcoholism treatment is built on the foundation of a triadic relationship: the client, the clinician, and AA. On the other hand, Miller et al. (2019) noted that many others view mutual help groups skeptically, and even as unhelpful and dangerous. Indeed, I also have observed that some clients do not benefit from mutual help groups, perceive them with suspicion, or for some reason are simply not a good fit. My general approach to mutual help groups is to encourage their attendance but not make it a mandatory part of treatment. It is unrealistic to expect that all clients will want to attend these groups, benefit from them, or find them a useful adjunct to formal substance use treatment. Clinicians need to respect client decisions about their own treatment. When talking about mutual help groups, I have found that the best approach is an encouraging tone that respects and understands clients' resistances. Often, providing information, clarifying misunderstandings, responding to resistance with reflection and empathy, and gaining permission to revisit the topic later can go a long way toward enhancing motivation to give mutual help groups a try.

There is substantial research that suggests that mutual help group attendance, in general, is connected to more positive outcomes (Miller et al., 2019; see also Chi et al., 2009 and Tonigan, 2001 for an excellent example of this research). Most research is on AA, with less known regarding other 12-step groups (Miller et al., 2019). One could make a reasonable assumption, however, that other mutual help groups also aid in promoting better treatment outcomes. For the substance use treatment professional, it is well worth the effort to become acquainted with the range of mutual help groups available to clients who wish to stop using substances. There is an abundance of mutual help group information online, including contacts and resources in most communities.

The Range of Mutual Help Groups

Since the founding of AA in 1935, numerous other groups based on the 12 steps of AA have emerged. Narcotics Anonymous (NA) is parallel in structure to AA and follows the 12-step tradition. The term *narcotics* generally refers to opiate drugs, although NA is accepting of members who wish to stop using any drug. Other mutual help groups focus on providing information and support for family members whose loved one's struggle with drug use, such as the Al-Anon family groups; a component of Al-Anon family groups is Alateen, where teen-agers whose family member(s) struggle with substance use can talk with each other, provide support, and offer information.

Some of the criticism of 12-step mutual groups, especially AA, is the emphasis on spiritual development. Although AA is adamant that spirituality can and should be defined by the individual, many clients feel uncomfortable with an emphasis on spirituality or discussions that have religious themes. As a result, nonspiritual mutual help groups have been created such as Moderation Management, Rational Recovery, and Self-Management and Recovery Training (SMART). These programs do not emphasize the spiritual aspects of traditional 12-step groups and often rely on evidence-based methods (i.e., CBT) as the foundation of recovery (Miller et al., 2019). Women for Sobriety (WFS) was created as an alternative to AA to address the unique needs of women in recovery, including the need to foster self-worth and feelings of self-value and to heal shame, guilt, and humiliation (www.womenforsobriety.org). WFS is nonspiritual and places a premium on self-acceptance (Miller et al., 2019). For example, instead of admitting one is powerless over alcohol (step 1 in traditional AA), WFS offers "acceptance statements" such as "I am in charge of my mind, my thoughts, my life." One can readily see how these aspects of WFS run counter to some traditional components of AA. Kaskutas (1994) found that most women who decided to leave AA said that they never felt they fit in, it was too negative, there was too much focus on the past, and it was too biased toward men's needs. On the other hand, Miller et al. (2019) noted that some women end up choosing both AA and WFS with great benefit, finding them complementary. Substance use clinicians would best serve their female clients by understanding their unique needs and preferences for mutual help group support, whether that involves only WFS, only AA, or elements of both.

Incorporating Mutual Help Group Attendance Into Therapy

Mutual help groups are an important part of recovery for many clients struggling with substance-related issues. Clinicians would be mistaken to avoid integrating these into their therapeutic work. This does not need to be the entire focus of therapy; something as simple as checking in with the client regarding mutual group attendance shows interest and opens the possibility for further exploration. Anxieties and fears can be explored and, if possible, allayed. More intentional integration would allow the clinician to explore which of the 12 steps the client is currently "working on" and frame sessions to promote a deeper exploration of each step.

Some clients may be reluctant at first to attend a 12-step mutual help meeting. Stereotypes usually pervade the client's consciousness such "only a certain kind of person goes there" or "AA is for the down-and-out drunks, and at least I am not that bad." I have found that clients hold many misconceptions about AA, but after attending a few meetings, their preconceived notions are seriously challenged. It is important to note that not all mutual help groups are the same. Some, for example, might have an open and welcoming atmosphere, whereas others might appear less open and more businesslike. This is critically important for clients to understand; if a client does not feel right after going to one meeting, clinicians can encourage them to search around for a home fellowship that meets their needs. Many communities have several AA or other 12-step venues from which the client can choose. Table 9.2 lists other common problems or forms of resistance that clients hold regarding mutual help groups, possible strategies to address this resistance, and what clinicians might say in these circumstances.

TABLE 9.2   Forms of Resistance to Attending 12-Step Mutual Help Groups, Strategies to Address the Resistance, and Selected Comments to Tell Clients

Problem or Form of Resistance	Strategies	How to Say It
Client's views and attitude toward 12-step meetings are negative.	Use these attitudes and feelings to get at feelings about substance use and recovery; explore in nonjudgmental manner.	
Client shows low motivation to attend 12-step meetings.	Assess stages of change; utilization of MI.	"AA is open to anyone who wants to look at their drinking, not just alcoholics." "You are not required to say anything that you don't want to say. AA doesn't force you to do something you don't want to. They actually are tolerant of many perspectives and beliefs."

TABLE 9.2   Forms of Resistance to Attending 12-Step Mutual Help Groups, Strategies to Address the Resistance, and Selected Comments to Tell Clients (*Continued*)

Problem or Form of Resistance	Strategies	How to Say It
Client feels two ways about attending 12-step groups.	Use MI: Explore both sides and strike balance between attending and exploring barriers.	Dialogue with ambivalence; develop discrepancies; conduct cost/benefits analysis.
Client believes stereotypes about people who attend 12-step groups.	Ask clients what their perception is as to what happens at meetings and how AA members behave; correct any misperceptions.	Supply information such as "All different kinds of people, from differing backgrounds, attend AA. Some do have severe alcohol problems, and some less severe problems but still want to improve their lives."
Client cannot engage in action stage of change.	Work through importance and confidence issues (see Chapter 6); encourage small steps such as getting information on meeting times, asking to go with a friend, and reading information online and then processing.	Negative feelings can change over time and need not be a barrier. The following AA statements (Zweben, 1995) can be helpful: "Bring the body, the mind will follow"; "It's OK to do the right thing for the wrong reason"; "Take what you need and leave the rest" (p. 129).
What do I go to, AA, NA, CA?	What is the client's drug of choice? Start there. Many clients who do not have an alcohol use disorder go to AA and apply to their lives. Encourage clients to shop around until a suitable home fellowship is found.	
Resistance to having to make the statement "I am an alcoholic." What is the use of going if I have to state this?	As noted in Chapter 6, labels should be avoided, and clinicians should not try to convince clients they are "addicts" and must accept this label. Reframe discussion as an exploration with the "not using" side of the equation to see how abstinence does or does not fit for them.	Meeting attendance can be a learning experience to find out more about how substance use progresses. Bring "others" into the conversation: "I know others have found that attending AA meetings have provided many useful insights that have helped them on the road to recovery."
I don't like groups or the concept of fellowship.	Respect client's feelings. Invite client to revisit the topic later. If the client reluctantly goes, encourage attending with another person. Stress that each visit becomes easier.	"I understand your reluctance. Perhaps we can revisit down the road?"

(*continued*)

TABLE 9.2   Forms of Resistance to Attending 12-Step Mutual Help Groups, Strategies to Address the Resistance, and Selected Comments to Tell Clients (*Continued*)

Problem or Form of Resistance	Strategies	How to Say It
		"That says a lot about you that you can push your feelings aside and attend this evening. It may be that you will get more comfortable the more you go."
I'm afraid of losing my identity to the group.	The client gets to choose their relationship with AA. AA is accepting of anyone who attends.	"That is perhaps the good thing about these groups. You can take what fits for you and dump the rest."
Client can't talk about feelings of their AA experience with other members.	Clinicians serve an important role here. They can provide a venue for discussing both positive and negative feelings.	
What is a sponsor? How do I select a sponsor?	Provide information. Encourage client to select someone who has had significant time substance free and who appears happy with their role. Counselor must attempt to reconcile potential conflicts between sponsor's philosophy and counselor's philosophy of recovery.	
I don't agree with the spiritual aspects of AA. They make me uncomfortable	Explore spiritual barriers and clarify misconceptions. Open possibility of attending alternative 12-step groups.	

Note: Based on J. E. Zweben, "Integrating Psychotherapy and 12-Step Approaches," *Psychotherapy and Substance Abuse: A Practitioner's Handbook,* ed. A. M. Washton. Copyright © 1995 by American Psychiatric Association Publishing.

Group Therapy in the Treatment of Diverse Populations

Consensus exists among leading experts in group therapy that ethnicity, culture, and other client differences (e.g., gender, sexual orientation) are significant clinical considerations, and failure to acknowledge these differences can have a profound negative impact on the effectiveness of group treatment. Therapy groups, by their very nature, may include a mix of ethnicities and other individual differences that need to be acknowledged and accepted by leaders and members. The greater the mix of cultural differences, the more likely prejudice and biases will emerge that need intervention (CSAT, 2005). Unfortunately, matching the ethnicity of the group leader and members is usually not feasible. Group leaders need to understand how ethnicity, culture, and other differences influence substance use behavior and how diverse clients interact in group therapy. Research has shown that homogeneous groups generally have a positive impact on symptom reduction. For example, McHugh and Greenfield (2010) found that substance use group therapy produced significant symptom reduction through 6 months after follow-up among a group of women.

Taking a multicultural stance is imperative for group leaders, as diversity affects important components of the group process (CSAT, 2005), such as how clients view the process of disclosure, what is expected of those in authority (i.e., the leader), and how clients from different backgrounds interpret other members' behaviors. For example, an Asian American client, whose culture values modesty and restraint in human affairs, may be put off by the member who harshly confronts their substance using behavior. Without leader intervention, such an experience may preclude further group attendance by the client.

The therapeutic factor of universality becomes especially salient when leading multicultural groups (Yalom & Leszcz, 2020). Clients from backgrounds other than the majority may feel uneasiness about attitudes toward disclosure, connection, and emotional expression that pervade Western societies. Yalom and Leszcz recommended that group leaders work to maintain a delicate balance between helping the group move beyond concrete cultural differences and yet being astutely aware of any cultural factors going on within the group process. Moving beyond obvious cultural differences involves emphasizing transcultural (or universal) reactions to human experiences, traumas, and events (Yalom & Leszcz, 2020). That is, the leader, while helping members to honor differences, can explore with them commonalities and similarities that are shared by all human beings.

Substance use is a complex behavior because of the intricate link with the cultural milieu in which it occurs (CSAT, 2005). Helping group members to reconnect with their cultural heritage and values, especially if these values discourage use, has the potential to be of significant therapeutic value in substance use group counseling. The importance of this reconnection was highlighted by Witherspoon and Richardson (2006), who offered a group counseling intervention to address culture-specific needs of African American women. The group, called Sisters in Support Together Against Substances (SISTAS), included topics relevant and important to African American women, such as "spirituality, self-esteem, racial identity, social support, and intimate relationships" (p. 51). These topics touch on the cultural heritage of African American women and serve as buffers against substance use.

There is some debate whether substance use group therapy should be homogenous in terms of culture, gender, or other sociodemographic characteristics. In many cases, such congruence among group participants may be difficult. In addition, homogeneous groups may miss learning about other customs and cultures that may enhance and broaden their recovery experiences. On the other hand, researchers have demonstrated that, at least among women, homogeneous groups provide superior results at 6-month follow-up compared to mixed-gender groups (Greenfield et al., 2007). The authors concluded, "A women-focused single-gender group treatment may enhance longer-term clinical outcomes among women with substance use disorders" (p. 39). When forming groups, the leader needs to balance the pros and cons of leading a culturally specific group, informed by research, client welfare, and leader experience.

Group leaders also need to be aware of the impact that racism, discrimination, poverty, and unemployment has on substance use behavior (CSAT, 2005). Culturally specific wellness groups include a variety of activities and interventions that incorporate a culture's healing practices to combat deleterious substance use. Such groups also structure therapy to be consistent with cultural values (CSAT, 2005). For example, in the Native American culture, group needs are generally considered more important than individual needs (Garrett, 2008). Effective substance use intervention respects this value and builds a treatment direction that incorporates both group and individual goals.

Clinicians should be open to learning about other belief systems, should not assume that every person from a group shares the same beliefs or characteristics, and should avoid conveying that a cultural perspective is wrong. In addition, generalizations about cultural values and behaviors should be kept in check due to within-group variability. That is, differences between members of a cultural group (within-group differences) can be greater than differences between cultures. The group member is the expert on self and what ethnicity, culture, and gender identity mean to them (CSAT, 2005).

Specific to substance use groups, group leaders should address the substance use issues in a way that is in line with the client's culture (CSAT, 2005). For example, in some cultures, substances may be used as a meditative enhancement, ritual, or other religious function. To absolutely demand that clients abstain from chemical use may disrespect a cultural interpretation of drug use. In some cases, it may be important to point out to clients that a return to use, even if done as a community ritual, may increase the risk of a return to heavy use. However, this information must be presented in a respectful manner with the understanding that it is the client's responsibility to balance personal behavior with cultural value and expectation. The client may indeed find that the risk of problematic use is too great and, although culturally sanctioned, decide to abstain from use.

Group leaders also need to be aware of the biases and prejudices related to diverse clients and substance use that often emerge in heterogeneous groups (CSAT, 2005). For example, the rampant use of cocaine in some inner-city neighborhoods may prompt members of the dominant culture to perceive African American group members as "hopeless" and "lost addicts." What members fail to realize is that many African American members may struggle with racism, poverty, and homelessness every day. The level of stress may become so unbearable that they seek out drugs to cope. The sensitive and culturally aware group leader acknowledges diversity in groups, recognizes that some members come with experiences of racism, discrimination, and oppression, and understand how members of different cultural groups communicate (Toseland & Rivas, 2001). Becoming culturally sensitive is an ongoing process, an obligation in which leaders continuously learn about the diversity of their members and how this impacts group participation (Toseland & Rivas, 2001).

DeLucia-Waack (1996) suggested that the integration of multiculturalism into group work requires attention to two key tasks: (a) the modification of theories and techniques of group work to different cultures such that the theories and techniques are consistent with, or do not run counter to, cultural beliefs and behaviors and (b) the further development of theories and strategies of group work so as explore and celebrate group differences in a way that leads to expansion and change. DeLucia-Waack's point is especially relevant for the substance use group counseling leader who relies on theoretical models and interventions to promote healing, growth, and change. All the theories presented in this text can be adopted for the group format. Given the likely heterogeneity of groups, it becomes imperative that group leaders adopt and adjust their theoretical leanings to account for diversity. For example, a group leader who follows Yalom's 11 curative factors may be adamant that group members engage in interpersonal disclosure and learning. In a diverse group comprised of Asian refugees, who may value directive counseling approaches and immediate resolution to problems (Kim & Park, 2008), such insistence on interpersonal learning disrespects the diversity present in the group. To address this issue, the group leader might downgrade the amount of interpersonal learning in the group or educate group members on why interpersonal learning can be beneficial for some, process what to expect, and honor their reactions. The following Diverse Perspective and Example illustrates how group leaders must constantly be aware of culture and its impact on beliefs, perceptions, and behaviors.

DIVERSE PERSPECTIVE AND EXAMPLE

◇◇◇◇◇◇◇◇

A 45-year-old Japanese American man was referred to a substance use group for alcohol and cocaine use disorder. After preparation through pre-group counseling, he joined the group with anticipation that it would help his substance use behavior. As the group progressed, however, he became increasingly aware of the intense emotion that was shown by group members. He grew increasingly uncomfortable with the intensity and level of emotion because he grew up in a culture that valued self-control and restraint. He began to worry that he would be "forced" to show such emotion, and subsequently lost interest and motivation in the direction of the group. The group leader, aware of his withdrawal and consternation in the group, approached him after a meeting. After sharing his concern, the leader stated that it was not a requirement to share such strong emotions and, if he was comfortable, they could discuss these cultural issues in the next group. It could be explained, for example, that self-restraint is a sign of strength for him and that he would prefer to rely on his own resources to help his cocaine use disorder. He could ask the group to help him discover his inner resources and power to resolve his substance problem. The client agreed to continue. During the next session, the other group members were very interested to learn about cultural differences and vowed to respect all differences that emerge in the group. The Japanese American client stayed in the group and successfully abstained from chemical use. He valued and respected the cultural competence of the leader.

CASE STUDY

Using Group Therapy in the Case of Michael

In the following case example, we revisit the case of Michael and ask ourselves the question of whether group therapy would be an appropriate format for him. In the case study, we learn that Michael not only struggles with alcohol and cocaine use, but also with bouts of depression and anger. He struggles in his interpersonal relationships (with his spouse and coworkers). It appears as if Michael would be a good candidate for substance use group therapy. Whereas substance use would be the primary focus, he also would benefit from numerous therapeutic factors that a therapy group offers.

In the following, I highlight three clinical examples in which the group leader (there is only one leader because the group is relatively small) demonstrates a skill-building group, a support group, and an interpersonal process group with Michael as a member. These examples are designed to give the reader a brief snapshot of what a particular group might look like in practice. Each group is comprised of five members: Al, a 45-year-old Caucasian struggling with alcohol use disorder; Tim, a 32-year-old African American who has heroin and alcohol use disorders; Brenda, a 31-year-old Caucasian with cocaine use disorder; Mia, a 29-year-old Chinese American who struggles with misuse of prescription pain medication and alcohol use disorder; and Michael. Assume that Michael and the other group members were in early recovery.

Skill-Building Group

A group leader working from a skill building mind-set would focus the group on building healthy life skills that could be incorporated into a recovery plan. All group members, including Michael, needed assistance in managing negative emotions and handling stress. Acknowledging this observation within the group, the leader proposed that they work on relaxation skills to help better negotiate stressful situations. A short introduction to the connection between stress and substance use was presented, followed by an exploration of key stressors that crop up for each group member. Michael acknowledged that his work situation gives him stress every day and that his anger makes things worse with his wife. The leader, using didactic instruction, pointed out how the foundation of relaxation was the breath. He then demonstrated a diaphragmatic breathing exercise, which he invited the group to participate in. The leader instructed the members to focus on the breath going in and out of their nose for 5 minutes. When they inhaled, they also were instructed to picture relaxation and calm (however they visualized it) coming into their bodies; when they exhaled, they were instructed to expel stressful experiences, emotions, and thoughts. After this exercise, the group members were invited to share their experiences. Michael and the other group members were pleasantly surprised at the effectiveness of focusing on their breath. He reported that he was better able to focus his mind and felt lighter. The leader noted that learning how to relax is a skill and needs practice; he encouraged members who found this exercise beneficial to practice daily for the next week and report any insights or experiences as a result.

Supportive Group

A group leader working from a supportive group mind-set would focus on helping members to be there for each other. In this example, the leader prefers to take a more nondirective, process-oriented approach. In the following sequence, assume that Michael is struggling with cravings and is living day to day trying to avoid relapse. Notice how all the group members and leader join in to provide support.

> **LEADER:** Michael, it sounds like you have been struggling with cravings as of late and it's keeping you up at night. (acknowledging difficulty)

> **MICHEAL:** Yeah, it's been tough lately, and I am not sure why. I mean, work seems to suck and my wife and I just argue. I feel like taking a hit [of cocaine].

> **AL:** Michael, I don't know if this would work for you or not, but I find removing myself from the situation, if possible, helps me calm down and gather my thoughts. Could that be something you could do? (offering a suggestion as a notion of support)

> **MIA:** Remove yourself but do something in addition, like the deep breathing we learned when we started this group. That might help—taking 5 minutes and just breathing. (building on previous suggestion as a notion of support)

> **MICHEAL:** All that sounds good, but when I am in an argument or am hot at work, I just kinda freeze. I just am not confident that any of the skills would work.

> **LEADER:** When stress overwhelms you, you tend to lose motivation and confidence to practice some of the skills we learned early on. What can the group do now to help provide support? (reflection followed by open question)

> **MICHAEL:** Well, I would like to know if any of you ever have similar problems. Do any of you lose motivation to practice skills when you are under stress? If so, what do you do to stay substance free?

> **TIM:** I know exactly what you are talking about. The other day I so much wanted a drink after I had a fight with my wife. I just forced myself to practice the breathing and other skills we learned, and over time it helped. That is what I always remember: It is difficult to do the skills in the moment, but if you can muster the will to do them, they will help, and you will feel better. But I'm not saying it's easy; I can definitely relate to your struggle. (conveys empathy and support and offers additional suggestion)

> **LEADER:** Michael, a lot has been offered for how to manage your craving to use. What thoughts are going through your mind right now? How can we further support you? (checking in with Michael to see what he makes of information; assessing if he feels supported)

It is important to note that this supportive stance in the group would be applied to each member at different times, depending on what issues were brought up in the moment.

Interpersonal Process Group

A group leader working from an IPG mind-set would focus on interpersonal dynamics as a mechanism for intrapersonal and interpersonal change among members. Indeed, all group members in this group example suffer from poor interpersonal relationships, and these dynamics tend to replay themselves in the group. In one instance, Michael really wanted to talk about a recent argument he had with an old buddy who uses in which his buddy owed him some money. The group generally agreed with Michael about the money but was taken aback that he met up with a using partner. Brenda had a vehement reaction to Michael contacting his old buddy and stated this was evidence that he was not working very hard in the group. Brenda was struggling with her own abstinence issues and was usually reserved in the group. The leader decided to direct the group's attention to what is going on between Michael and Brenda:

> **LEADER:** Brenda, I am aware that you seem really upset with Michael. I am wondering if you can tell Michael directly how his behavior makes you feel.
>
> **BRENDA:** I just don't understand it, Michael. It just seems like you are not trying in the group. I feel manipulated in a sense because I am trying like crazy to stay cocaine free, and here you are hanging out with the wrong crowd.
>
> **LEADER:** [turning to Michael] How do you feel about what Brenda just said?
>
> **MICHAEL:** I *am* trying in the group. I feel this is a bit of an unfair attack, Brenda. Since when have you been so concerned with who I hang out with? I feel defensive.
>
> **LEADER:** Michael, how could Brenda have expressed concern in a way that might make you feel less defensive?

In this brief exchange, both Michael and Brenda are beginning to relive their relationship styles outside of the group: Brenda's tendency to attack others, sometimes unfairly, based on a perceived injustice, and Michael's tendency to become defensive and respond with anger. In response to the leader's last question, Michael may suggest that Brenda soften her tone and express concern rather than attack. The leader could then have Brenda practice repeating her concern in a gentler fashion, followed by asking Michael how that was for him. As the intervention moves forward, the leader could help Michael respond to criticism with less defensiveness and anger, which apparently creates many problems in his real life. The other group members also could provide feedback to Michael and Brenda as they practice new ways of relating to one another.

Notice how in the case example that drug use was not the primary focus. However, relationship issues in Michael's and Brenda's lives serve as a major source of stress, which ultimately leads to substance use. Michael noted in individual therapy that he often drinks after an argument with his wife. Learning how to respond with less defensiveness and anger will go a long way toward minimizing stress and subsequently remaining free from alcohol.

Strengths, Limitations, and Ethical Issues Related to Group Therapy

As discussed throughout this chapter, group therapy for substance use has many strengths and is an effective, efficient, and cost-effective mode of substance use therapy. At the same time, we must acknowledge that group therapy is not for everyone. I recall seeing a client who had been in group therapy for 2 years because of narcotics use. When she came to see me, she stated that her previous treatment was exclusively a group format and, while she found it very helpful, was ready to focus on herself more than had been the case in the group. Clients who would benefit more from one-on-one attention may be better suited for individual counseling. Table 9.3 summarizes the strengths, limitations, and ethical issues related to group therapy for substance use.

TABLE 9.3   Summary of Strengths, Limitations, and Ethical Concerns
of Group Therapy in the Treatment of Substance Use Problems

Strengths	<ul><li>Group therapy is often as effective as individual therapy. It also is cost-effective given that one clinician can see many individuals in a relatively short span of time.</li><li>Group therapy rests on a solid theoretical and research base. Yalom's 11 factors operate across all therapy groups and are the driving force for change. Curative factors are not always realized in individual therapy formats.</li><li>Group therapy is considered standard care in many substance use treatment facilities.</li><li>Given the homogeneous nature of substance use problems, group therapy offers a unique setting from which individuals can share emotions, suggestions, and support.</li><li>There are a variety of format options from which group therapy can be delivered, including skills training, interpersonal process, and interpersonal process. What format the clinician decides depends on the nature and purpose of the group.</li><li>Group therapy is effective at treating problems often associated with substance use, such as depression, anxiety, and personality disorders.</li></ul>
Limitations	<ul><li>Group therapy may not be suitable for all clients. For example, some clients may value more one-on-one attention of individual therapy.</li><li>According to CSAT (2005), additional training and skill are needed to run more advanced substance use groups, such as interpersonal process groups. For busy clinicians, this may be difficult to fit in to their schedules. As a result, group leaders may be unprepared for the demands of certain groups.</li><li>Group therapy is more complex than individual therapy, from the standpoint of having to attend to several process and content-oriented variables at one time. Group leaders can become easily overwhelmed. To minimize this experience, coleader arrangements are recommended.</li></ul>
Ethical Issues	<ul><li>Despite its effectiveness in substance use counseling, group therapy takes considerable skill and understanding to use competently. There is potential risk that some clinicians' lack of skill and theoretical understanding, as well as confusion as to its application, could constitute unethical practice.</li><li>Group therapy can present a bevy of ethical issues for the group leader, including informed consent and confidentiality, psychological risks of groups, personal relationships with group members, misuses of group strategies, and group leader competence (Corey, 2016). Leaders of substance use groups must constantly be mindful of these issues and clarify their values as they apply to ethical practice. For an excellent overview of group therapy ethical issues, see Corey (2016).</li><li>Multicultural group counseling may pose ethical issues for leaders who do not consciously acknowledge the reality of our multifarious society. Given the diversity of individuals that may form a group, group leaders must maintain a stance of broad sensitivity to client differences.</li></ul>

References

Alcoholics Anonymous. (n.d.). A.A. at a glance. Retrieved July 23, 2012, from www.aa.org

Beck, A. T., Wright, F. D., Newman, C. F., & Liese, B. S. (1993). *Cognitive therapy of substance abuse.* Guilford.

Brooks, F., & McHenry, B. (2015). *A contemporary approach to substance abuse and addiction counseling* (2nd ed.). American Counseling Association.

Brown, S. (1995). A developmental model of alcoholism and recovery. In I. D. Yalom (General Ed.), *Treating alcoholism* (pp. 27–53). Jossey-Bass.

Burkey, M. D., Kim, Y. A., & Breakey, W. R. (2011). The role of social ties in recovery in a population of homeless substance abusers. *Addictive Disorders & Their Treatment, 10,* 14–20.

Cappuzi, D., & Gross, D. R. (1992). *Introduction to group counseling.* Love.

Center for Substance Abuse Treatment. (2005). *Substance abuse treatment: Group therapy.* Treatment Improvement Protocol (TIP) Series 41. SAMHSA.

Chi, F. W., Kaskutas, L. A., Sterling, S., Cambell, C. I., & Weisner, C. (2009). Twelve step affiliation and 3-year substance abuse outcomes among adolescents: Social support and religious service attendance as potential mediators. *Addiction, 104,* 927–939.

Corey, G. (2016). *Theory and practice of group counseling* (9th ed.). Cengage.

DeLucia-Waack, J. L. (1996). Multiculturalism is inherent in all group work. *Journal for Specialists in Group Work, 21,* 218–223.

Duncan, B. L., Miller, S. D., Wampold, B. E., & Hubble, M. A. (Eds.). (2010). *The heart and soul of change: Delivering what works in therapy* (2nd ed.). American Psychological Association.

Garrett, M. T. (2008). Native Americans. In G. McAuliffe & Associates (Eds.), *Culturally alert counseling: A comprehensive introduction* (pp. 220–254). SAGE.

Gladding, S. T. (2011). *Groups: A counseling specialty* (6th ed.). Prentice Hall.

Greenfield, S. F., Trucco, E. M., McHugh, R. K., Lincoln, M., & Gallop, R. J. (2007). The women's recovery group study: A stage I trial of women-focused group therapy for substance use disorders versus mixed-gender group drug counseling. *Drug and Alcohol Dependence, 90,* 39–47.

Kaskutas, L. A. (1994). What do women get out of self-help? Their reasons for attending Women for Sobriety and Alcoholics Anonymous. *Journal of Substance Abuse Treatment, 11,* 185–195.

Kim, B. S. K., & Park, Y. S. (2008). East and southeast Asian-Americans. In G. McAuliffe & Associates (Eds.), *Culturally alert counseling: A comprehensive introduction* (pp. 188–219). SAGE.

Kinney, J. (2003). *Loosening the grip.* McGraw-Hill.

Kuebrich, B. (2012). Top 10 most prescribed psychiatric drugs, top 10 overall, and the 10 we spend the most money on. *Neuroamer.* https://neuroamer.com/2012/07/06/top-10-most-prescribed-psychiatric-drugs-top-10-overall-and-the-10-we-spend-the-most-money-on/

Margolis, R. D., & Zweben, J. E. (1998). *Treating patients with alcohol and other drug problems: An integrated approach.* American Psychological Association.

Marques, A. C. P. R., & Formigoni, M. L. O. S. (2001). Comparison of individual and group cognitive-behavioral therapy for alcohol and/or drug-dependent patients. *Addiction, 96,* 835–846.

McHugh, R. K., & Greenfield, S. F. (2010). Psychiatric symptom improvement in women following group substance abuse treatment: Results from the women's recovery group study. *Journal of Cognitive Psychotherapy: An International Quarterly, 24*, 26–36.

Miller, G. (2021). *Learning the language of addiction counseling* (5th ed.). Wiley.

Miller, W. R., Forcehimes, A. A., & Zweben, A. (2019). *Treating addiction: A guide for professionals* (2nd ed.). Guilford.

Miller, W. R., & Rollnick, S. (2002). *Motivational interviewing: Preparing people for change.* Guilford.

Psychotherapy.net. (Producer). (1990). *Understanding group psychotherapy with Irvin Yalom, M. D.: Volume I Outpatients* [DVD]. Author: San Francisco, CA.

Rawson, R. A., McCann, M. J., Shoptaw, S. J., Miotto, K. A., Forsch, D. L., Obert, J. L., & Ling, W. (2001). Naltrexone for opioid dependence: Evaluation of a manualized psychosocial protocol to enhance treatment response. *Drug and Alcohol Review, 20*, 67–78.

Rosenblum, A., Magura, S., Kayman, D. J., & Fong, C. (2005). Motivationally enhanced group counseling for substance users in a soup kitchen: A randomized clinical trial. *Drug and Alcohol Dependence, 80*, 91–103.

Sharry, J. (2001). *Solution-focused groupwork.* SAGE.

Southern, S., & Thornton, B. (2013). Group treatment in the continuum of care. In P. Stevens & R. L. Smith (Eds.), *Substance abuse counseling: Theory & practice* (5th ed., pp. 203–239.). Pearson

Thombs, D. L., & Osborn, C. J. (2019). *Introduction to addictive behaviors* (5th ed.). Guilford.

Tonigan, J. S. (2001). Benefits of Alcoholics Anonymous attendance: Replication of findings between clinical research sites in project MATCH. *Alcoholism Treatment Quarterly, 19*, 67–77.

Toseland, R. W., & Rivas, R. F. (2001). *An introduction to group work and practice* (4th ed.). Allyn & Bacon.

Tuckman, B. W., & Jensen, M. A. C. (1977). Stages in small group development revisited. *Group and Organizational Studies, 2*, 419–427.

Vannicelli, M. (1996). Group psychotherapy with substance abusers and family members. In A. M. Washton (Ed.), *Psychotherapy and substance abuse: A practitioner's handbook* (pp. 337–356). Guilford.

Weiss, R. D., Griffin, M. L., Kolodziej, M. E., Greenfield, S. F., Najavits, L. M., Daley, D. C., Doreau, H. R., & Hennen, J. A. (2007). A randomized trial of integrated group therapy versus group drug counseling for patients with bipolar disorder and substance dependence. *The American Journal of Psychiatry, 164*, 100–107.

West, E. C. (2010). Solution focused group treatment with publicly funded alcohol/other drug abuse clients in rural settings. *Alcoholism Treatment Quarterly, 28*, 176–183.

Witherspoon, K. C., & Richardson, A. W. (2006). Sisters in Support Together Against Substances (SISTAS): An alcohol abuse prevention group for Black women. *Journal of Ethnicity in Substance Abuse, 5*, 49–60.

Yalom, I. (1998). *The Yalom reader: Selections from the works of a master therapist and storyteller.* Basic Books.

Yalom, I. (2005). *The Schopenhauer cure.* HarperCollins.

Yalom, I., & Leszcz, M. (2020). *The theory and practice of group psychotherapy* (6th ed.). Basic Books.

Zweben, J. E. (1995). Integrating psychotherapy and 12-step approaches. In A. M. Washton (Ed.), *Psychotherapy and substance abuse: A practitioner's handbook* (pp. 124–140). Guilford.

CHAPTER 10

Applying Family Therapy in the Treatment of Substance Use Disorders

Introduction

It is a rather common observation that individuals who engage in severe substance use often sacrifice connections with other human beings. This is one reason group therapy (discussed in Chapter 9) can be a powerful aspect of substance use treatment: Helping clients reconnect with fellow human beings and learn interpersonal skills along the way breaks the isolation that is the hallmark of substance use disorders. If the client has a strong relationship with alcohol and/or other drugs, one set of relationships will invariably suffer: the family. Indeed, the impact on family functioning and effects can be particularly damaging and intense (Fisher & Harrison, 2018).

Researchers have documented the myriad problems that children and the family system itself suffer because of members using substances. Substance use also can be a consequence of adverse family conditions. Other researchers have brought attention to the compromised parenting styles (e.g., harsh parenting) and communication patterns in families where drug and alcohol use are evident (Barrett & Turner, 2006; Bosk et al., 2021). Substance use problems play a prominent role in the abuse, neglect, and psychological/behavioral problems among children in the United States. For example, Famularo et al. (1992) found that excessive alcohol use was tied to physical maltreatment, whereas severe cocaine use was implicated in sexual maltreatment, among a sample of parents who mistreated their children. More recently, Capusan et al. (2021) found that child maltreatment was a considerable risk factor for substance use, even when familial factors were controlled. Children of substance-using parents were found to experience greater levels of depression and anxiety that resemble diagnostic conditions more frequently than children from families where substance use was not problematic (Bufferd et al., 2014; Earls et al., 1988). Clearly, the psychological, emotional, social, and monetary costs of substance use disorders in the family are far greater than the cost of treating these disorders.

Traditionally, substance use treatment has focused on the individual with the problem, without much regard for involving significant others in the treatment process. When clients stop using substances, however, they may be faced with many relationship problems that suddenly come to the surface. Unfortunately, the progress that is made from a short time living substance free cannot offset months or years of negative relationship consequences.

Substance use disorders impact all close relationships with significant others. As Miller et al. (2019) pointed out, effective therapy approaches to substance use disorders should not only address the client's substance use problem, but also the client's relationships with significant others to promote a strong, supportive recovery.

Substance use clinicians understand that substance use disorders have a negative impact not only for the user, but the entire familial and cultural systems as well. As clinicians become increasingly aware of the need to provide therapeutic services to the families of substance use clients, proficiency in family conceptualization and family therapy is relevant and needed. Indeed, researchers have found that family therapy is helpful in getting those with substance use disorders to enter treatment (Edwards & Steinglass, 1995), is favored over other modes of therapy (e.g., individual, psychoeducation, peer group therapy), and has higher retention rates than nonfamily modalities (Stanton & Stadish, 1997). More recently, among families with a relative who has a substance use disorder, Ulas and Eksi (2019) found that family therapy over a 2-year period promoted greater flexibility, structure, and connection and improved resilience, stress coping, and problem solving of family members who struggled with substance use. It is a model of therapy that substance use clinicians cannot ignore.

In this chapter, I explore the tenets of family therapy, primarily from a "systems" perspective. Specialized training in family therapy exists, and the interested reader is encouraged to seek such training. This is not meant to be an exhaustive review of family systems therapy. For general outpatient counseling, however, knowledge of family issues and treatment approaches is critically important. Addressing family issues reflects the obvious fact that if one family member has a substance use problem, the other members are going to be impacted. In addition, comprehensive substance use treatment programs usually contain family education and family therapy as part of their programs. My intention is to provide a basic overview of family theory and therapy and general guidelines for how to counsel families struggling with substance use problems.

Before we get into the major concepts and applications of family therapy, it is important to define what is meant by "family." In the traditional White, Anglo-Saxon Protestant tradition, family refers to the intact nuclear family (Fisher & Harrison, 2018), consisting of a couple, the parents, and their dependent children under one "household." However, the definition of "family" varies across cultures (Fisher & Harrison, 2018). For example, many families from different cultures expand the definition to include extended members such as aunts, uncles, grandparents, and cousins. In the West, psychological growth is measured by differentiation, a topic covered in depth later. For other families, such as those with an Asian background, growth may be measured in terms of collectivism, deference to authority, reciprocity, and self-control (Kim & Park, 2008). It is important to note that much of the research on family therapy assumes the traditional Anglo definition of family. Indeed, many of the concepts, terms, and applications in this chapter derive primarily from Western conceptualizations of family and will not fit all situations that clinicians encounter in their daily practice. It is incumbent upon the substance use clinician to ensure that any family therapy strategy is appropriate for their families they counsel and avoid the trap of forcing one cultural viewpoint onto clients from diverse backgrounds.

The Major Tenets of Family Therapy

To speak of "family therapy" as one overall clinical approach would be mistaken. Family therapy refers to a multitude of approaches depending on the theoretical perspective and philosophy of the practitioner. Family therapy has grown tremendously over the past several decades and comprises several different approaches the clinician can implement, including Bowenian family therapy, experiential family therapy, narrative family therapy, strategic family therapy, solution-oriented family therapy, and structural family therapy, to name a few (Gladding, 2019).

The purpose of this chapter is not to cover every family therapy approach as applied to substance use counseling. Rather, the approach taken in this chapter rests heavily on *systems theory*, which serves as the foundation for several family therapy approaches (Thombs & Osborn, 2019). Perhaps the most well-known systems theorist is Murray Bowen, and as such I draw many ideas in this chapter from Bowenian family systems theory. It is important to note that Bowen did not create a theory of addiction but rather a theory of family dysfunction, based on the concept of differentiation (discussed later in the chapter; Thombs & Osborn, 2019). However, many Bowenian and systems concepts have direct application to families struggling with substance use issues.

In systems theory, the family is seen as an organism with a focus on the relationship between members. Each member is thus impacted by the behaviors and actions of other family members. System is defined by Merriam Webster's Online Dictionary (n.d.) as "a regularly interacting or interdependent group of items forming a unified whole." Thus, from a systems perspective, the individual's behavior cannot be understood out of social context. The substance use clinician must emphasize the *whole interactions* and *patterns* that emerge between and among members (patterns that are maintaining substance use behaviors) rather than the specific content that the family brings to the session.

Boundaries

Families live by rules of interaction, called boundaries (Thombs & Osborn, 2019). Boundaries can be fixed and rigid at one end of a continuum and diffuse and loose at the other end. Optimal boundary development in a family is somewhere in the middle, what Thombs and Osborn called clear boundaries. Clear boundaries are characterized by mutual respect, clear communication, the ability of members to individuate *and* remain intimate and the ability to show genuineness, concern, and love. Clear boundaries mean that family members do not engage in "external control psychology" (Glasser, 1999). That is, they do not attempt to control or manipulate others, believe that others do not control them, and accept responsibility for their behavior, thoughts, and feelings.

An example of a boundary is a family who lives by the rule that emotions are not to be shared between members. If this is a rigid boundary, we can assume that relationships are characterized by little intimacy and much isolation (Thombs & Osborn, 2019). If emotions are displayed, the boundary has been crossed and the situation may get worse (e.g., fighting, violence). As one can imagine, families who struggle with problematic substance use can have a host of boundaries and rules within these boundaries. According to Lawson et al. (1983) families with problematic alcohol use have diffuse (i.e., disengaged) boundaries and certain rules of interaction. In such homes, families generally have three rules (a) "don't talk about the drinking"; (b) "don't confront the drinking behavior"; and (c) "protect and shelter the member consuming alcohol so that things don't become worse" (Lawson et al., 1983, p. 42). Notice how each one of these rules perpetuates silence about the problem. Unfortunately, such rules can lead to a vicious cycle where the member using substances embarrasses the family (e.g., by acting inappropriately), leading to family isolation, which leads to greater distance between family members, leading to more drinking to cope, and so on, all the while strengthening the substance use behavior (Lawson et al., 1983).

The substance use clinician must be cognizant of cultural expectations and norms surrounding family boundaries (Stevens, 2018). Most families fall somewhere between disengaged/rigid boundaries or enmeshed/diffuse boundaries. Substance use clinicians must guard against automatically adopting a Western view of what are considered "normal" boundaries. For example, "enmeshment" or closeness and emotional expression are valued among many Hispanic mothers (Lawson & Lawson, 1998). Such boundaries need to be respected as part of the family's cultural background and used to help understand the family's perspective on the substance use problem.

Homeostasis

Homeostasis refers to the tendency among families to maintain a sense of coherence, equilibrium, and structure in the face of change. Thus, change in one family member leads to changes in other family members (Lewis et al., 2014, as cited in Stevens, 2018). From a systems perspective, families resist change, even if it would benefit the system in the long run. It is important to note that families define their own homeostasis or balance points (i.e., there is no set point that is considered "normal"). There is a level of comfort in maintaining the status quo. For example, the family may want the drinking family member to keep consuming alcohol to keep the attention away from internal strife and dysfunction. It is "safer" to maintain the substance use behavior than to confront and address difficult feelings. The introduction of change, then, threatens to disrupt the delicate family balance and throw the system into chaos (Stevens, 2018). Homeostatic mechanisms serve as a natural resistance to change and chaos.

We normally think of homeostasis as something that is in balance or has equilibrium, and it serves as a regulatory mechanism that precludes change. In healthy families or systems, that is a good thing to have in place. However, in families struggling with substance use disorders, homeostasis can be a pathological equilibrium in which non-using members have an emotional, financial, or other investment in keeping the substance use disorder going (Thombs & Osborn, 2019). If the member with the substance use disorder stops using drugs, the family is then thrown out of balance, and the other members may consciously or unconsciously disrupt recovery to return the family to homeostasis. For example, members who do not use problematically may be cynical toward any recovery efforts by the member with the substance use disorder, offer little support, or even act out to "drive" the member back to drug use.

In general, alcohol and drug use can "stabilize" a family in several ways, including (a) diverting attention away from marital problems/family crises, (b) establishing emotional distance so that feelings go unexpressed, and (c) to avoid intimacy where members are ambivalent about feelings, marriage, love, and other family members (Thombs & Osborn, 2019).

It is important to note that many families that have substance use problems operate under rigid rules that make change very difficult. In any system, change is a natural part of life, especially in families: Kids get older, parents develop new interests, families move, and so on. Healthy families strike a balance between change and the status quo—not moving too fast to leave needs unmet, but not moving too slow to preclude growth. Rigid families cannot adapt when change is thrust upon them. They lack the fluidity to creatively adjust to new environmental demands and thus remain stuck in a pathological, albeit familiar and "comfortable" pattern.

Subsystems

Subsystems refer to smaller systems within the larger family system (Stevens, 2018). Multiple subsystems can exist, each with the goal of carrying out the family rules and maintaining boundaries. Within a typical family system, subsystems may include siblings, members who have similar interests, or those who are similar in age (Stevens, 2018). The most obvious subsystems are marital (or spousal), in which both partners assume roles in taking care of each other, financial management, communication patterns, social activities, and caregiver duties. The birth of the first child introduces another subsystem: the parental subsystem. Here, the parents are responsible for tending to the needs of the child, instilling the family rules, demonstrating affection, and establishing discipline. In healthy families, subsystems operate smoothly and serve to maintain appropriate family boundaries and rules. In families where one parent has a drug problem, the other parent often takes on most of the parental power—taking care of *everything* from washing the kids' clothes to discipline. The parent with the substance use problem usurps their power as part of the "bargain" (i.e., "I'll give up my power if you let me drink or drug"). The trouble with this scenario is that, over time, the parent without the substance use problem often becomes resentful and angry at having to take care of everything (Thombs & Osborn, 2019). This increased tension leads to greater stress, and the cycle of substance use continues. In some cases, a child/adolescent might take on a parenting role, precluding healthy developmental milestones and effectively clouding the subsystem boundaries (Thombs & Osborn, 2019).

Rules

According to Gladding (2011, as cited in Fisher and Harrison, 2018), "all culturally and ethnically diverse families as well as Euro-American families have overt and covert contracts between their members that operate as rules governing family interactions" (p. 207). This important point suggests that family rules are an endemic part of the human family. Rules can be spoken but often are unspoken codes that develop through interaction and reaction. For example, if a father gets angry every time he is asked about work, then through this interaction the rule "don't talk to dad about work" has been established. This rule may be part of the larger boundary of "leave dad alone." Barnard (as cited in Fisher & Harrison, 2018) stated that rules can manage when, what, and how to communicate experiences and who has permission to speak.

Bowen Systems Family Theory

Murray Bowen was among the first theorists to clarify systems thinking regarding family relationships. He argued that the complex family patterns people are born into necessitate that they assume certain roles within the family system (Corsini & Wedding, 1989). Bowen postulated that the family is an organic, living system (Kerr & Bowen, 1988). Therefore, individuals' emotional functioning can be understood through their relationship systems (i.e., the family), the subsystems within the family, and their relationship to nature. Indeed, Bowen conceptualized the family unit as a system, but the *modus operandi* of this system was rooted in natural, physical processes. As such, family behavioral patterns can be observed as reactions to the social environment (Kerr & Bowen, 1988). Bowen's theory of family therapy is based heavily on family systems. There are several core principles from which Bowen theory primarily operates. These principles are described next.

Differentiation of Self

The well-being of family members depends on one's level of "differentiation of self" and is the cornerstone of Bowenian theory. Differentiation refers to the ability of a person to separate their emotional and reactive self from their intellectual self. Bowen (1978) described a "differentiated self" as "one who can maintain emotional objectivity while during an emotional system in turmoil, yet at the same time actively relate to key people in the system" (p. 485)—in other words, one who can effectively separate emotion from intellect.

Bowen (1978) believed that all human beings fall somewhere between complete fusion (or undifferentiation) to complete differentiation. People who have a low level of differentiation lack the ability to distinguish their emotional processes from their intellectual processes and thus live in an emotionally saturated world; much of their energy is used seeking love and approval from others. Low differentiation does not always equate to psychological symptoms if their need for love, attention, and approval is met and their relational system intact (Bowen, 1978). However, when their needs are not met or their relational system is thrown in disarray, persons with low differentiation may manifest any number of clinical and psychological symptoms (Bowen, 1978).

Low differentiation is represented by a "fusion" of the emotional system with the intellectual system. Relationally, this fusion occurs when persons with low levels of differentiation have an overly strong bond to a particular family member/spouse. The fusion becomes problematic when one of the fused members wants distance, or when anxiety presents itself in the relationship. The fused person is unable to cope with the other's need for distance or the anxiety that the other may be experiencing. Symptoms emerge when the relationship undergoes a significant amount of stress.

A person with a high level of differentiation has a strong sense of self; they are "operationally clear about the difference between feeling and thinking" (Bowen, 1978, pp. 474–475). Highly differentiated people are less emotionally reactive, and they experience a healthy balance of individuality and closeness with others (Bowen, 1978).

Triads (or Triangles)

When two people are emotionally close, there is no place or person to transfer anxiety should it develop. Bowen (1978) suggested that within a two-person emotional system there will be constant fluctuation between closeness and distance. This fluctuation leads to an unstable dyad, especially when anxiety becomes overwhelming. To alleviate the anxiety of the dyadic system, dyads sometimes bring in a third member to create a triad (or triangle). The purpose of the triad is to shift the anxiety from the original dyad to one member of the dyad and the new member completing the triad. The other member of the original dyad, then, gets some relief from the anxiety (Brown, 1999). When anxiety begins to overwhelm a particular dyad, the triad will shift so that the other member from the original dyad can take a respite from anxiety. This pattern continues as the triangle gains momentum (Bowen, 1978).

It is important to note that outside individuals, such as teachers, friends, and clinicians, can sometimes serve as the third member of a triad. As such, families may bring outsiders into their conflict to ease tension within the family unit (Bowen, 1978). Understanding the triangulation patterns of the family is a significant aspect of substance use therapy and provides the client and clinician a lens from which to observe and understand the degree of fusion/differentiation or cutoff between and among family members (Bowen, 1978). For example, a family member who uses substances might form a dyad with another member. As the substance use inevitably creates more anxiety in the dyad, a third member may be brought in to ease some of the tension away from the original dyad. Family therapy, then, focuses on helping family members face tension and diffuse it in healthy ways.

Nuclear Family Emotional System

The nuclear family emotional system is "the pattern of emotional forces as they operate over the years in the nuclear family" (Bowen, 1978, p. 425). Several factors contribute to this pattern, such as family stress, differentiation levels, and degree of emotional cutoff between family members (Bowen, 1978). As these factors accumulate, Bowen (1978) theorized that "the emotional problem manifests as (a) emotional distance between the spouses; (b) dysfunction in one spouse which is manifested as physical illness, emotional illness, or social illness; (c) marital conflict; or (d) projection of the problem onto one or more of the children" (p. 425). Therefore, the substance use of a family member is conceptualized as a manifestation of family dysfunction and a result of distress on the emotional system over a span of time.

Family Projection Process

Bowen observed that parents can pass along levels of differentiation to their children. The family projection process occurs specifically when parents transfer their low differentiation onto one or more children (Bowen, 1978). Undifferentiated parents who are struggling with unresolved issues from their own family of origin repeat the process of projecting their unresolved emotional suffering onto their child/children. In families with more than one child, Bowen theorized that there may be one child who bears the brunt of this projection process: "The child who is the object of the projection is the one most emotionally attached to the parents, and the one who ends up with a lower level of differentiation of self" (Bowen, 1978, p. 477). The effects of the family projection process manifest as psychological and behavioral symptoms of the child or children.

Multigeneration Transmission Process

The multigenerational transmission process is progression of how differentiation increases or decreases over multiple generations in a family. The notion is that traits that are passed down from generation to generation is not just through genetics. According to Bowenian theory, families can and do pass down their relational patterns and differentiation levels across multiple generations. This process expands the single-family projection process by explaining how families "transmit" their own differentiation levels onto their children and how these children transmit them to their children and so on, creating multiple generations of similar family patterns and differentiation levels. Bowen (1978) theorized that the manifestation of the most severe clinical, behavioral, and emotional problems, such as schizophrenia, bipolar disorder, and substance use, is the result of multiple generations moving further and further away from differentiation.

Emotional Cutoff

Emotional cutoff is a psychological coping mechanism designed to block off or withdraw from intense emotions within family relationships (Brown, 1999). Cutoff can occur both physically and emotionally. It can resemble a sort of "checking out" of a family relationship emotionally; a member may decide to be completely different from their family of origin. Although moving toward autonomy from one's family of origin is a characteristic of differentiation, emotional cutoff is reactionary and indicative of *less* differentiation. Because the cutoff family member never truly resolves the emotional attachment issues, differentiation remains unchanged and family processes for that individual will repeat themselves consistent with the family of origin (Bowen, 1978).

Does Bowen's Theory Have Any Empirical Support?

Limited research has been conducted to validate many of Bowen's key theoretical tenets (Nelson, 2003). However, Bowen held that those who attempted to research his theory did not grasp it (Nelson, 2003). Indeed, researchers who have sought to operationalize and quantify Bowenian constructs admit that research lags regarding Bowenian theory because of the complexity of its constructs. In addition, many studies on Bowenian theory have utilized very small sample sizes that have not been representative across cultural groups. Nonetheless, several studies have supported some of the key Bowenian family concepts including differentiation (Calatrava et al., 2022; Miller et al., 2004; Murdock & Gore, 2004; Skowron, 2005), the family projection process (Tuason & Friedlander, 2000), and nuclear family emotional functioning (Klever, 2001). Calatrava et al. (2022) conducted an in-depth review of the available research on one of Bowen's core constructs: differentiation of self. The studies for their review ranged from when the construct was first formulated through 2020. Results suggested abundant evidence for differentiation as a predictor of mental health, physical health, marital happiness, and better intergenerational relationships. However, their results also suggest that more longitudinal and causal research is needed to better explore differentiation over time and across generations. In addition, more research is needed to assess the effectiveness of interventions that impact differentiation in a way that encourages better health (Calatrava et al., 2022).

Richard Charles (2001), after a review of the empirical research on Bowenian concepts, concluded that many were supported with empirical data. Miller et al. (2004) also conducted a synthesis of research on Bowenian theory and found that of all the theoretical constructs of Bowen, differentiation of self received the most empirical support. Some researchers believe that Bowen's theory serves as a systems framework for family-based research (Keller, 2020).

As noted, Bowen's theory is not a theory of substance addiction. However, it does provide a systems perspective on how problematic substance use, as well as other behavioral and psychological problems, develop in the context of the family. It also provides an intriguing explanation for how substance use and addiction often pass from generation to generation. Entrenched patterns of interaction, particularly those that reflect and promote undifferentiation, are at the heart of symptoms and pathology among family members. Many of the techniques and strategies discussed later are designed to undo these patterns, and based on Bowenian concepts.

Characteristics of the Family Struggling With Substance Use Disorders

Although many families can show dysfunctional patterns, families who struggle with substance use issues seem to have commonalities in form and function that may perpetuate substance use. In this section, we explore common family characteristics and behaviors, family roles, and issues related to enabling and codependency. The substance use clinician is encouraged to look for these characteristic patterns to promote awareness, assessment, and treatment.

Families and Substance Use Disorders

When substance use problems are in the family, there is a general belief that members with the substance use disorder acts out family problems. Another camp suggests that members turn to substances because of the problems inherent in the family (Fisher & Harrison, 2018).

In fact, systems theory and the substance use field have traditionally disagreed about the genesis of problematic substance use (Stevens, 2018). Much of this disagreement stems from whether substance use disorders are disorders with family or individual origins and causes (i.e., are substance use disorders primarily an individual issue or family issue?; Stevens, 2018). Both camps are probably correct (Fisher & Harrison, 2018) as families with substance use disorders engage in a never-ending circle of acting out, experiencing family discord, greater acting out, and so forth.

Clinical experience and research have shown that severe substance use within the family almost always has a negative impact on children, although some children display enough resilience to mitigate these effects (Fisher & Harrison, 2018). In addition, these families display common characteristics such as discouraging change or growth, discouraging conditional love and affection, and emotional withdrawal and detachment of members. Boundaries may be quite rigid. There typically is a distorted sense of responsibility for the substance use among the members who are not problematically using. The process of individuation and separation of children, and other "markers" of growth depending on the family's cultural background, is thwarted due to the problematic use of drugs.

Family Roles

It is probably evident by now that the family who struggles with substance use is a rigid system that tends to isolate itself, leading to increased tension (Thombs, 2006). This tension can be quite uncomfortable and must be managed. Families creatively adjust to this tension by adopting certain roles designed to divert attention from the family member with the substance use disorder, which eases stress and makes day-to-day life easier (Thombs, 2006).

The various roles that family members "play out" depend on their position in the family, personality, motivation, and reactions. Some time ago, the most common role classification scheme came from the work of Wegscheider (1981), who described children's roles in family addiction as the hero, scapegoat, lost child, mascot, and enabler. These roles are still used today by family therapists, with slight modifications that fit a particular family. Although these typologies were not generated from empirical research (Thombs & Osborn, 2019), they are clinically useful to share with families and provide perspective on how roles are adopted to maintain homeostasis and reduce tension. Families also become more aware of these patterns and, as a result, choose to interact in a more preferred way. Each role is briefly described:

- **The chemically dependent person.** The primary role of the chemically dependent member is to divert attention away from family dysfunction. They are usually emotionally distant from their spouse and give up their power to parent. In the typical process of substance use, the chemically dependent person begins substituting human relationships with substances. Alcohol or drugs become their "first love" (Thombs & Osborn, 2019, p. 209).

- **The family manager.**[1] The manager is usually the spouse without the substance use problem. They are the member whose role is to protect the person with the substance use disorder from natural and logical consequences of the substance use behavior (Wegscheider, 1981). This family member is seen as "sweeping things under the rug," "turning the other way," or otherwise taking care of any fallout from substance use to reduce tension (Thombs & Osborn, 2019; see section on enabling for a more detailed description).

- **The family hero.** The family hero is usually the oldest child and is highly responsible, accomplished, and self-motivated (Stevens, 2018). They try to work hard around the house by assuming responsibilities the parents have shirked (e.g., taking care of younger siblings; Thombs & Osborn, 2019). They will try to divert attention away from the substance use by achievement and accomplishment and hold very high self-imposed standards (Wegscheider, 1981). After all, because the hero brings positive recognition to the family, the problem can't be that bad.

- **The scapegoat.** The scapegoat, traditionally the second-born child, often has difficulty with authority figures across multiple settings (Wegscheider, 1981). Also referred to as the "problem child," the scapegoat acts out to divert attention away from family problems. They engage in opposite behaviors of the hero and enabler and may identify more with the member with the substance use disorder (Thombs & Osborn, 2019).

- **The lost child.** The lost child simply disappears. They may experience chronic loneliness and anxiety (Wegscheider, 1981). This child may be very quiet to not create any more problems with the family. Conflict is avoided. Although well behaved, the lost child may internalize much of the family tension created by the substance use.

- **The mascot.** The mascot is usually the baby of the family and likes to lighten the mood. They may be considered the class clown at school. Typically insecure, these children use humor to divert tension away from the substance use and break tension in the family (Wegscheider, 1981).

This typological system probably never happens as neatly as presented here. For example, a family member could be both a manager and a family hero, or a combination of feeling lost and being the mascot. In addition, roles may change over time as circumstances, personalities, and environmental factors change.

Enabling

When someone enables, as defined by Doweiko (2019), they are "knowingly behaving in such a manner as to make it possible for another person to continue to use chemicals, in a manner that

---

1   This role used to be called "the chief enabler." However, according to Van Wormer and Davis (2013, as cited in Thombs and Osborn, 2019), the term *enabler* may be seen as derogatory to some. Indeed, this has been the reaction of many students who first hear the term. I agree with Thombs and Osborn that *family manager* is a more appropriate term and will use it here.

protects the person misusing substances from having to suffer the natural consequences of his or her behavior" (p. 313). For whatever reason, some family members adopt certain behaviors that seem to let the member with the substance use disorder off the hook. Enabling behaviors are common among families struggling with substance use issues and include actions such as accepting lies, bailing the substance use member out of negative consequences, looking the other way, accepting blame for the problem, covering up the family member's use, and making excuses for the family member. The key element here is that the person knows they are engaging in these behaviors (Doweiko, 2019). As such, the enabling member may misinterpret their behavior as a sign of caretaking and affection that is the responsibility of any good spouse (or family member; Perkinson, 2012).

Doweiko (2019) made an important distinction between enabling behavior and codependency. Although the two can go hand in hand, a person might enable another's substance use but not be in a codependent relationship. Enabling refers to specific behaviors that a person carries out whereas codependency entails a relationship pattern with the family member who has the substance use disorder. We will turn to this concept next.

Codependency

Codependency is a relatively new term that emerged in the late 20th century and is based on the clinical experience of family therapists working with families struggling with substance use issues. Despite controversy surrounding the concept (Doweiko, 2019), it does seem to characterize certain dynamic patterns in dysfunctional homes where emotional needs are not met. Codependency generally refers to finding an identity in becoming a caregiver to those who appear to be in need, such as a family member with a substance use disorder. It is generally believed to be an unhealthy pattern of relating to others that results from being too closely involved with a family member using substances. Enabling behaviors or protecting the family member with the substance use disorder from consequences of use is often characteristic of those who are codependent. Codependents Anonymous (CoDA), a support group for those struggling with codependency issues, captures the essence of codependency in their welcome message to new members by acknowledging their use of others (friends, family, etc.) as their source of identity, worth, and mental health to make up for emotional deprivation in childhood (Codependents Anonymous, Inc., n.d.).

Although differing definitions and perspectives abound (Doweiko, 2019), codependency has certain core aspects, including (a) over-involvement with the family member with a substance use disorder; (b) compulsive attempts by the codependent member to control the person with the substance use disorder; (c) excessive tendency to turn to others for self-worth, for example, by seeking approval, even from those who treat the codependent poorly; and (d) making personal sacrifices in an attempt to mitigate the family member's damaging behavior due to substance use (Doweiko, 2019).

The "traditional" codependent relationship is between the non-using partner, usually the wife, and the substance-using partner, usually the husband. However, codependency is not defined by who comprises the dyad but rather the behavior that occurs between the two individuals. Thus, a codependent relationship can occur between a mother and son, a father and daughter, or between two individuals in a same-sex relationship. It can even be evident between close friendships.

Essentially, codependency is about the loss of self, in the service of protecting the person with the substance use disorder. Isolation is common to not avoid anyone finding out (Thombs, 2006). Psychologically, the codependent family member has a strong emotional need to be needed. They often display the "martyr syndrome" in which their willingness to suffer is seen as a badge of honor and to strive for superiority above one's spouse (Thombs, 2006). Codependent individuals have a strong need to change and control others, believing that they have this power (Thombs, 2006). Struggling with poor self-esteem, they also have an overdeveloped sense of responsibility for the consequences, care, and rehabilitation of the member with the substance use disorder (Thombs, 2006).

In clinical settings, spouses or significant others are often unaware of their codependent and enabling behavior. Resistance to change is strong as they see what they are doing as just helping. Not surprisingly, they fear change. After all, a substance-free loved one might become more assertive, no longer wanting their needs met in the same way. Abstinence might "upset the apple cart": disrupt the family system in such a way that problems hidden by the substance use suddenly rise to the surface. For example, rekindling of interest in sexual relations by the spouse with the substance use disorder may instill fear in the codependent spouse, who thus avoids sex altogether (Thombs, 2006).

Controversy

Despite clinical experience and observations, there is little empirical evidence to support the concept of codependency. In addition, controversy has surrounded the concept since it emerged on the scene in the late 20th century. Lewis (1994) noted that the self-corrective aspects of codependency are particularly biased against women, who now have the extra burden of concentrating on their own growth in addition to keeping the peace in the family. Indeed, behaviors such as caretaking, protecting, and loving, traditional motherly roles are considered dysfunctional according to the codependency concept (Walters, 1993). Whereas these traits are expected when raising healthy children, they are pathological in relations with men. In essence, women are caught in a double-bind (Walters, 1993).

Frank and Golden (1992) noted that any concept that includes more than 50% of the population must be viewed with skepticism. One of the problems with the concept of codependency is that it is a vague, poorly defined concept in which *everyone* has at least some its characteristics (Doweiko & Evans, 2019). Other criticisms have been raised by several other authors as well (Lewis, 1994; Webster, 1990). In general, these criticisms have been aimed at how codependency pathologizes traditional, socialized female behavior. In essence, codependency fails to take into consideration the social context of behavior and ignores the idea that many of these characteristics have been considered normal for millennia.

These criticisms of codependency are valid. It is somewhat remarkable that we, as a society, turn to the spouse without the substance use problem as the one with the dysfunction and in need of "correction" while the spouse with the substance use disorder continues drinking alcohol or using drugs. Yet, at the same time, used with appropriate caution I believe that frank and open discussions with clients about enabling and codependency can *potentially* lead to insights and ideas for behavior change. In my clinical experience, I am careful with the concept of codependency and typically take a "middle-way" approach. I educate families about how family systems operate, the roles that each member plays, and that the behavior of one impacts the behavior of others. Without using the term *codependent*, I explore communication patterns and relationships within the family. I explore with families how their relationships are and are not working for them. I might point out that calling in to work because one's spouse is too drunk precludes them from experiencing consequences of their behavior. Eventually, terms like *enabling* and *codependency* may surface and are explored to see if they fit for the particular family. Many spouses without substance use problems are quick to embrace these terms, whereas others are more resistant. The astute substance use clinician honors this resistance and realizes the trap of labeling normal, socialized behavior. The clinician avoids using language to disempower clients. Whether or not codependency becomes a clinical center of attention, *the emphasis of any substance use treatment needs to be on the person with the substance use disorder and how the family can assist in their recovery.*

Application of Family Therapy With Substance Use Disorders

Counseling the family experiencing substance use and addiction can look quite different from session to session depending on who is available to attend, motivation, and commitment by the family to address the substance use issues. In addition, substance use clinicians can see a variety of clinical issues that manifest during family counseling. Examples of clinical issues include a client with a partner, child, or sibling who uses substances; a child with a a parent who uses substances; an adult child of parents with substance use problems; or an adolescent client with substance use problems. Other factors that the substance use clinician must recognize when formulating an intervention include how the family defines itself, who the family leans on when in trouble, and what ethnic and cultural considerations need to be made. It also may be helpful to explore the differences in family behavior when substance use is present and when it is not present (Stevens, 2018). The extent and variety of issues can be quite complex!

From a family systems point of view, counseling a family with severe substance use issues involves determining the dysfunctional system that created and maintained the problem in the first place. For example, enabling, codependency, and denial may be the systemic factors that create and maintain a father's harmful drinking. Many families have little to no understanding of the addiction process, the effect of drugs, or how drug use sabotages family development (Curtis, 1999). Curtis (1999) argued that there is a common belief that if the substance use is stopped, then everything will be "normal." Unfortunately, many families fail to comprehend the processes of homeostasis and how members might feel uncomfortable with a substance-free family member. As such, psychoeducation on how substance use problems begin and develop, how change happens, and systems thinking becomes an important tool for the substance use clinician. The next section provides a brief overview of Bowen family therapy and how it can be applied to help families who struggle with substance use issues.

Bowen Systems Family Therapy

Bowen (1978) stated that the goal of any family therapy is to increase differentiation of self in clients. Keep in mind that healthy differentiation refers to developing autonomy *while at the same time* cultivating intimacy (Nelson, 2003). It is a balance between the two. Bowen (1978) wrote about the importance of orienting the family properly by establishing a working relationship, decreasing anxiety, making sure everyone is heard, and modeling emotional neutrality. After establishing a positive orientation and relationship with the family, the clinician then moves onto issues that feed the family projection process (Bowen, 1978). Discussion of the family projection process begins with psychoeducation: "The goal is to teach the family member about the functioning of emotional systems, to discover the part that [one]self plays in the system and especially towards the other spouse, and to modify the system by controlling the part that [one]self plays" (Bowen, 1978, p. 237).

When working with substance use clients individually, the clinician will want to informally conceptualize the differentiation level of the client. From a Bowenian systems perspective, this conceptualization will involve understanding the nature and degree of anxiety and disruption that occurred within the emotional system of the family of origin and how that disruption led to substance use to alleviate anxiety. In sessions with all or most family members present, Bowen (1978) believed that both parents are the primary focus of therapy; any symptomology the child or multiple children may exhibit, including substance use, is a direct result of the family projection process and unresolved differentiation issues with the parents.

In Bowen family therapy practice, the clinician begins by involving themselves in a communication triangle with the parents (or caregivers). Bowen (1978) stated, "Conflict between two people will resolve automatically if both remain in emotional contact with a third person who can relate actively to both without taking sides with either" (p. 224). He also contended that specific techniques for the therapist include encouraging the family to take ownership of the substance use problem and asking questions that imply it is the family's problem to solve (e.g., What are some ways that *you as a family* can solve *your* substance use problem?).

The clinician's goal is to help develop a healthier triangle with the family by encouraging family members to talk "to and through" the clinician rather than to each other in the initial stages and continue this communication pattern until family members can talk to each other without becoming overly emotional (Nelson, 2003, p. 269). The strategy behind this is to alleviate overly emotional entanglements between parents that hinder growth (and thus avoid cutoff and fusion) and encourage differentiation at a slow and steady pace. The clinician encourages the use of "I statements" and individual ownership of thoughts, behaviors, and emotions (Nelson, 2003).

The role of the clinician in the practice of family therapy forces an added triangulated dimension to the family system. Instead of allowing the family to continue the usual patterns of fusion/cutoff/triangulation, the family addresses the clinician and practices forming a "healthy" triangle. Through therapy, the parental (or caregiver) dyad stabilizes and moves toward greater differentiation. Problems, disagreement, and arguments are resolved with less reactivity than in the past. According to Nelson (2003), an important characteristic of the clinician is to resist being drawn into an unhealthy triangle by keeping a calm presence during intense, emotional discussions, stress, and anxiety. The ability to remain calm in these situation stems from the clinician's own degree of differentiation. As such, in Bowenian therapy, clinicians are encouraged to work at expanding their own differentiation (Nelson, 2003).

Conceptualizing family work in terms of triangles is particularly important for substance use clinicians who operate from the sociocultural model (see Chapter 2). The primary conceptualization from a systems theoretical orientation is that clients with substance use disorders are seeking relief from the family emotional system, which involves the triangulation patterns of family members, nuclear family emotional processes, and multigenerational transmission processes. Unraveling these facets of a person's differentiation requires intense exploration of family relationships with the substance using client. A clinician may want to know in what ways the client finds family relationships stressful and how they react when other family members become upset. The clinician then may wish to explore how the client reacted when their parents were upset or stressed when they were a child. If the patterns of emotional reactions when one was a child are like current reactions, then the family clinician helps the client explore ways to find greater differentiation (i.e., balancing autonomy with intimacy) to interrupt the family projection process.

When implementing Bowen and other systems theories into practice, the clinician needs to conduct a thorough assessment of family relationship history. An in-depth review of the multitude of assessment strategies is beyond the scope of this text; however, a few important concepts can be discussed here. Assessing family relationship history using Bowen and other systems approaches is usually done through family mapping or a family genogram. With a family genogram, clients can outline the relational patterns and traits in their family, both nuclear and extended, using lines, symbols, and pictures that denote relational aspects (see Juhnke & Hagedorn [2006] for an excellent review of genograms). The multigenerational transmission process with substance use clients can be examined through use of a family genogram. Clients can examine their family's relational patterns and symptoms over a period of at least three generations. Helping the client gain insight into family patterns encourages differentiation by allowing the client to "step back" from the family system and examine patterns without being emotionally embroiled in them. Examining the role that drugs or alcohol may play in multiple family generations can be particularly helpful for substance use clients and their families.

Another strategy to assess family relationships is the Adlerian lifestyle assessment, discussed at length in Chapter 12. Aside from assessing individual symptoms and problems, the Adlerian assessment goes in depth about family atmosphere, constellation, and early recollections. Family relationships are explored at length. Although not technically a "systems"-based assessment, the Adlerian lifestyle assessment has potential to provide a thorough evaluation of rigid family patterns and levels of differentiation among its members.

One of the strengths of a systems approach to substance use treatment is placing responsibility on the system rather than the individual client. Emotional suffering and clinical symptoms arise in individuals when the family experiences chronic anxiety, and the least differentiated family member begins to act in ways to alleviate this anxiety. Symptoms manifest in various ways, ranging from schizophrenia, depression, chronic illness, and alcohol and drug use. In counseling families with substance use problems, the family member with the substance use disorder is viewed as the "sick one," or the member with the least differentiation. However, it is important for the clinician to remain aware that the client's differentiation level reflects the differentiation of the family system, and *blame is irrelevant*.

Despite the differences in the way clinical symptoms manifest, they share one commonality: he purpose is to protect the homeostasis of the family system and the family's emotional processes against the anxiety that threatens to disrupt the family emotional system. If this information is conveyed appropriately, the client can begin to gain insight into the role substance use plays in protecting the nuclear family system and how this process may be projected onto their current and future family systems.

Family Therapy Techniques and Strategies

When substance use clinicians meet with families struggling with substance addiction for the first time, ground rules must be established. For example, who will meet with whom, when will sessions occur, confidentiality, examples of proper communication (e.g., the avoidance of argumentation and blaming), and group norms and expectations are common initial ground rules (Stevens, 2018). Families must understand that therapy time is for learning and education, practicing healthy communication, practicing new skills, expressing both positive and negative emotions, and setting boundaries (Stevens, 2018). There are several techniques at the clinician's disposal when conducting family therapy. The following strategies draw from a variety of family therapy approaches.

Joining

Joining refers to making a strong connection with the family and all its members. It entails establishing trust, showing empathy, building rapport, being supportive, and respecting the views of all members and the family (Edwards, 1990). Of course, there is nothing new about joining as its importance runs across all forms of therapy. However, it is even more important in family therapy because there is greater risk of alienating a member with so many potentially different viewpoints (Edwards, 1990). Edwards (1990) outlined several activities that constitute joining: (a) active listening, (b) supporting both individual and family strengths, (c) respecting family values, (d) using the family's own words, (e) expressing understanding, (f) gently challenging rigid viewpoints, and (g) providing hope.

The idea in joining is to build rapport and diffusing intense emotions that most likely are present. The strategies of MI would be quite applicable here, as part of the essence of MI is joining with clients.

Assigning Tasks

Assigning tasks refers to giving families homework to practice so they can apply what they are learning (Edwards, 1990). Assigned tasks can introduce new experiences, provide insight into family patterns, "test" out new behaviors and change, and keep families in tune from session to session (Edwards, 1990). One of my favorite assigned tasks for both couples and families is to encourage them to have a "miracle day." A miracle day is a time, preferably a whole day but can be part of day, in which the family does something together that all members enjoy: going to a movie, going out to eat, traveling, shopping, and so forth. The only "rules" for the miracle day are (a) to have fun and (b) engage in absolutely no talk about the problem in any way. The second goal cannot be stressed enough. The family is to avoid talking about dad's anger, or Billy's drug use, or sister Kerrie's depression. When the family returns to the next session, the miracle day can be explored—what happened? How was it? What were the interactions between everyone like? It is a miracle (no pun intended) that families often rave about how their miracle day was a success. The clinician's task is to help the family understand that during the miracle day there was most likely mutual respect, better communication, and no arguments. In other words, the blueprint for healthy interactions was created by the family.

Ideas for assigned tasks are numerous and are limited to the creativity of the clinician. However, Edwards (1990) noted that tasks should be kept simple, especially at first, specific, and involve all members, if possible. In addition, exploration of the proposed task should occur before it happens. For example, after the task is planned, the family can explore the questions "What are some barriers to this plan? How might it fail?" (Edwards, 1990).

Creating Enactments

It is generally true that clients who talk "to someone" rather than "about" someone have a more powerful experience that can catapult change. Many times, in family therapy individual members talk about another member to the clinician. Whereas this can be useful as an objective analysis of the problem, creating an enactment in which the member talks directly to the other member can be powerful. Usually, dysfunctional communication patterns will emerge in the session, and having members talk to each other as they typically do can provide useful information and feedback. Enactments can be formally set up by the clinician or emerge as a natural flow in the session. For example, if a member tells me how they feel about another member, I may gently encourage them to talk to the other member directly.

During the enactment, the clinician is not passive but an active observer (Edwards, 1990). They may stop the communication and point out observations, ask for clarification, or inquire about any reflections that emerged during the communication. I prefer to work within a Gestalt framework when helping families communicate with each other, especially difficult emotions. For example, an enactment exercise might look like this:

TFL: Instead of talking to me, tell what you just said directly to your husband.

Wife: Okay [turning to husband], I don't like it when you come home and ignore me, especially after the kids have gone to bed.

TFL: And when I say that I feel …

Wife: [to her husband] And, when I say that I feel … frustrated and sad.

TFL: [turning to husband] When I hear you say that I feel …

Husband: [speaking to wife] When I hear you say that I feel … lost, not sure what to do.

TFL: [to husband] I encourage you to tell her more how you feel and what your thoughts are about what she said.

In this example, the husband and wife were able to tune in to their feelings and communicate them in the safety of the therapeutic session. Family members are usually unaware how another member feels because communication has been so poor.

Enactments can be used in many other ways. For example, they can be used to help parents decide on measures of discipline, help parents encourage their children, and help teens negotiate rules in the home. Parents can be encouraged to talk with each other about how they will discipline their son should he use substances again while their son and the clinician listen. Then, their son can negotiate with both parents to set reasonable rules at home. If one parent is enabling their son's substance using behavior, they can listen to him talk with his father, resisting the temptation to "jump in and save him." Enactments keep the focus on the family and preclude putting the responsibility for change on the clinician (Edwards, 1990). Because enactments have the potential to involve intense emotional reactions, they should be considered in the later stages of family therapy, where members have learned healthier patterns of communication (see previous discussion on initial approaches with families).

Segmenting

Segmenting refers to dividing the family into smaller groups so that certain goals can be accomplished (Edwards, 1990). Segmenting helps to set boundaries among family members. For example, many adolescents of families who struggle with addiction set their own rules. Such families have dysfunctional structures where the parents have lost all authority over their children (Edwards, 1990). With segmenting, children may be asked to step outside while parents talk about how to better communicate and incorporate discipline. Segmenting can occur as preparation for the next session. Here, the clinician might ask only the parents to attend for the next session, provided that the family agrees with the strategy. Clinicians also can ask the parents to leave the session while they talk with children or adolescents. This might be needed to build rapport with the children and learn their side of things without the oversight of parents. Again, everyone should agree with this strategy, and it should be seen as advancing the goals of the family.

Other Strategies

There are many other strategies at the clinician's disposal to add flexibility and range in family therapy. A brief review of these is presented next.

Family Sculpting

Family sculpting is an effective way to get the family moving, to learn a lot, and, in some cases, have some fun. It starts off by having one family member "pretend" they are a sculptor and to position the other family members in frozen postures that resemble the day-to-day life of the family. Family members can come up with creative "sculptures" with this technique. For example, I once counseled a family in which the teenage daughter struggled with substance use and acting out. In session, I asked her to position the family, including herself, according to how she perceives family life day in and day out. The most remarkable scene from this experience was how she placed her father. He (the father) was leaning forward, arms above his head with a scowl on his face. The daughter was leaning back, with a scared look on her face, as if she wanted to run. I was reminded of the poor cat in the Pepe Le Pew cartoon, who is always leaning back trying to get out of Le Pew's grasp (although Le Pew doesn't typically have the scowl on his face)!

This exercise led to an important and insightful discussion among the family. The father was largely unaware of his dominant nature and impact on his daughter. He realized that he was too overbearing, and when he communicated with his daughter, she felt like she wanted to disappear. Future work with this family focused on better communication between father and daughter.

Drawing

Drawing can be an effective way to engage children and adolescents in therapy. It can be done with or without parents being present. With drawing, several options exist. Following are some possibilities:

- Draw the problem using lines, colors, and shapes.
- Draw a typical day in your home.
- Draw your relationship with your mother, father, sister, and so forth (Edwards, 1990).
- Draw how you would like the problem to change.

In any of these examples, clients can be asked to elaborate on their picture, tell a story related to their picture, or "become" a character in the picture. The idea is to help clients, especially children, express their feelings related to their family. Parents who are part of the process may become more aware of how they are perceived by their children.

The Solving Circle

The solving circle (Glasser, 1999) is a technique from Glasser's choice theory and is effective in eliminating blaming, criticizing, and demanding types of communication that can sabotage therapeutic progress. To start, the clinician draws an imaginary circle in the room (move tables and chairs) and suggests that the circle represents the family. Each member is invited to step into the circle *if* they agree that the family's needs are more important than individual needs. That is, the family relationships are more important than individual wants. Stepping or staying out of the circle suggests that, at the moment, individual needs are more important.

Most family members are willing to step in the circle and work toward the benefit of the family over their individual needs. Once in the circle, the first member states *what they will do to make the family better*. For example, a father with a substance use disorder may state that he will remain abstinent and work hard in his recovery for the benefit of the family. The next person then tells what they will do to make the family better, and so on until everyone has a chance to speak. The family can go through as many rounds of as needed. The solving circle eliminates blaming and arguing because family members are directed away from worrying about what others will do and instead focus on the self. It also sends the message that trying to control others is futile.

Techniques are an important part of any counseling modality. However, they should always be used within the context and framework of theory. Above all, there is no technique that is useful to all families or clients. Each family is unique and must be treated individually.

Sequential Family Addictions Model

Juhnke and Hagedorn (2006) created a unique synthesis of many theoretical concepts discussed in this (as well as other) chapters in this book to create the *sequential family addictions model*. For these authors, family therapy works best if it is organized in an orderly fashion where families begin with noninsight, here-and-now, briefer forms of counseling and sequentially move to more insightful, long-term, psychodynamic methods. The model includes seven stages, each with a specific focus for the family. If a family plateaus in a stage, or the intervention proves powerless against the family system, then the next stage of treatment is considered. However, families do not necessarily need to complete the entire seven-stage process. They and the clinician may perceive that they have improved greatly by stage 4 and no longer need counseling help. The strength of this model is that it provides a roadmap for clinicians beginning with the least intensive, most cost-effective approaches (Juhnke & Hagedorn, 2006). If these early approaches fail to resolve the family issues, then clinician and family move on to more intensive interventions. Let's take a closer look at stages 1–5. Stages 6 and 7 will only be given brief mention as they are more complex, and a thorough discussion is beyond the scope of this chapter.

Stage 1: MI

My general counseling approach is to always begin with MI, whether working with individuals, couples, or families. In the sequential addictions family model, the clinician begins with MI techniques rather than "diving right in" with other, more advanced approaches. This makes intuitive and clinical sense. After all, if a family is not ready to change, no amount of cognitive, behavioral, systems, or psychodynamic interventions are going to work. Many of the interventions in this stage were discussed in Chapter 6. According to Juhnke and Hagedorn (2006), this stage is completed in one to two sessions.

Stage 2: Solution-Focused Family Therapy

If the family appears motivated to change their problematic substance use and other dysfunctional patterns, then counseling moves on to solution-focused methods. Here, the emphasis is on examining how their lives would look different if substance use was absent (Juhnke & Hagedorn, 2006). Many of the techniques in Chapter 11, including searching for what is working, the miracle question, and envisioning change would apply here. This stage lasts from three to seven sessions (Juhnke & Hagedorn, 2006).

Stage 3: Cognitive Behavioral Family Therapy

By this stage we can assume that the family is (a) motivated to change their patterns and, specifically, the member with the substance use disorder is motivated to change their substance use and (b) the family understands what is working, is doing more of this, and can envision what a life without substance use problems would be like. In stage 3 of the sequential family addictions model, the focus turns to helping families understand the role of thoughts and behaviors in maintaining substance use behavior. In addition, families explore the various consequences of problematic substance use, both positive and negative, to get a sense of how these behaviors are reinforced. Finally, family members are taught cognitive restructuring methods to help substitute more adaptive thinking that runs counter to "addictive thinking" patterns (Juhnke & Hagedorn, 2006). Many elements of RP, which are based on CBT ideas, may be explored here as well. Once again, several of the techniques discussed in Chapter 7 would apply here. This stage typically lasts from 3–11 sessions (Juhnke & Hagedorn, 2006).

Stage 4: Structural Family Therapy

In stage 4, the focus moves to more formal types of family therapy, beginning with structural family therapy (Minuchin, 1974). Here, family structure, and its potential contribution to maintaining problematic substance use is given emphasis. The goal is to find a workable structure that creates stability and allows the members to address and work through the substance use behaviors (Juhnke & Hagedorn, 2006).

Structural family therapy is generally concerned with two overarching goals. First, the clinician strives to promote healthy relationships and communication patterns within the various subsystems of the family. For example, the marital subsystem may be strained due to the substance use, and the sibling subsystem may be fraught with argumentation. If these subsystems are strengthened, then the overall family system will work better (Juhnke & Hagedorn, 2006). The second goal is to assess the power hierarchy and restructure if needed. For example, in families with excessive alcohol consumption, a common dysfunctional structure is to have a hierarchy where only the drinking parent holds the "power" (usually through coercion) and is separated from the other parent and children. The non-drinking parent is united with the children as victims in the family (Taibbi, 2011). The goal would be to help the family return to an ideal structure that fits for them and that does not perpetuate the substance use. For example, the parents can be encouraged to keep a hierarchy in the family in which they are united but also both involved in the children's lives (Taibbi, 2011). That is, strengthening and empowering the marital subsystem becomes the foundation for improvement. This stage typically lasts 5–10 sessions (Juhnke & Hagedorn, 2006).

Stage 5: Extended Family Systems Therapy

In stage 5, the clinician and family move into more insight-oriented interventions. The focus in this stage relates to many of the Bowenian (systems) concepts discussed in this chapter. Thus, family members are encouraged to strengthen differentiation and converse without emotional entanglements. Triangulation strategies are important techniques for the clinician. Families, using genograms, are encouraged to look closely at multigenerational processes and how problematic substance use may have been passed down from generation to generation. This stage typically lasts 5–10 sessions (Juhnke & Hagedorn, 2006).

Stages 6 and 7: Deeper Family Therapy Processes

Stages 6 and 7 complete the sequential family addictions model. Stage 6, a modified intergenerational family-of-origin therapy approach, is an optional stage and may not fit with some clients or families (Juhnke & Hagedorn, 2006). The focus here is to help adult clients reconnect with their family of origin and their experiences with severe substance use while growing up. This reconnection may be an actual meeting with key family-of-origin members. In general, the goal of such meetings is for spouses to enhance differentiation (which is facilitated with adult, mature conversations) and effectively resolve their family-of-origin "baggage" to be more loving and affectionate toward their each other (Juhnke & Hagedorn, 2006). Stage 7 of the model is used when families have unsuccessfully resolved their problematic substance use via the earlier stages. This final stage, based on psychodynamic object relations principles, is long-term and usually lasts no less than 15 sessions (Juhnke & Hagedorn, 2006).

The sequential family addictions model incorporates many of the theoretical constructs presented throughout this text, but applied to family situations: MI, CBT, relapse prevention, solution-focused counseling, and family systems therapy. The sequential nature of the approach makes it a viable and cost-effective option for substance use clinicians working with families. It would be a mistake, for example, to jump right into psychodynamic work without the "prerequisite" work of motivation, envisioning change, and healthy thought patterns. It is interesting to note that family systems therapy is not until stage 5 of the model! Clearly, rushing too far ahead before families are ready can result in frustration for all parties involved.

There are other aspects of this model that need brief mention. First, after the seven stages of the model, individual counseling for the family member with the substance use disorder is encouraged. In addition, throughout the sequencing of therapy, certain family members may get more or less individual attention. Second, family members are encouraged to attend Al-Anon (a support a group for family members of individuals with substance use disorders) throughout therapy. Finally, the model accounts for the presence of domestic violence. As the authors noted, there is nothing more disruptive to the family therapy process than the trifecta of severe substance use, domestic violence, and family dysfunction. I could not agree more. In their model, the perpetrating partner, stereotypically the male spouse, is required to receive individual and group counseling as well as a 12-step batterer's support group separate from family therapy until family therapy is complete. At that time, provided sufficient rehabilitation, the perpetrating partner may reenter the family therapy process. (For a more detailed description of the sequential family addictions model, see Juhnke & Hagedorn, 2006.)

The sequential family addictions model provides a roadmap for how to integrate many ideas and concepts from the family therapy literature into a coherent, stage-by-stage process for working with families struggling with severe substance use issues. As a relatively new approach, it has not garnered empirical support to date, although many of its components (e.g., MI) have been studied extensively. Let's quickly look at other family-based therapy approaches that have been supported in the empirical literature.

Other Family Therapy Approaches

Several family therapy approaches have emerged to help adolescents and their families address a range of issues when the *teenager is the identified client with the substance use problem*. Although these approaches have considerable differences, there are a few commonalities. For example, they all rely on cognitive behavioral family therapy as a foundational theory, and all have some component of parental skills training. Another commonality and strength is that they have empirical support for their effectiveness (Miller et al., 2011; Robbins et al., 2011). My intention in this section is to provide a brief overview of these approaches, and the interested reader can consult the relevant literature for a more detailed description.

Brief strategic family therapy (BSFT; Szapocznik et al., 2003) is an evidence-based treatment approach with the overall goal of reducing adolescent behavior problems by strengthening family relationships and connecting the family to outside systems and resources to promote positive youth engagement (Robbins et al., 2011). BSFT targets children and adolescents who show signs of problematic behaviors, including substance use. BSFT is short-term and problem focused and includes four primary steps: (a) cultivating a strong therapeutic alliance with each family member; (b) identifying individual and family strengths and patterns of relating that impact the adolescent's behavior negatively or preclude the parents from correcting the behavior; (c) creating a change plan that is problem focused, direction oriented, and practical and that focuses on strengths and correcting problematic family relationships; and (d) implementing the change plan and reinforcing family interactions that promote abstinence and competence in communication (Fischer et al., 2007). Specific strategies include reframing the meaning of interactions, shifting family alliances, clarifying/strengthening interpersonal boundaries (Fischer et al., 2007; Taibbi, 2011), enhancing one's ability to handle and resolve conflict, and strengthening parenting skills via coaching (Fischer et al., 2007). BSFT is endorsed as an effective evidence-based approach by SAMHSA (2020) and the NIDA (Fischer et al., 2007).

Multidimensional family therapy (MDFT) is an evidenced-based outpatient family therapy approach designed to address adolescent substance use and delinquent behavior (Liddle, 1995, as cited in Fischer et al., 2007). Its orientation is toward enhancing the development of the adolescent as well as environmental systems in which they reside (Fischer et al., 2007). The term *multidimensional* is fitting for this approach as it is designed to strengthen protective processes and deter growth-inhibiting processes that may come from the family, community, and peers. Thus, MDFT focuses on addressing multiple pathways that contribute to the continuation of substance use and promotes healthier behaviors (Miller et al., 2019).

MDFT treatment objectives include shifting the developmental trajectory of the adolescent away from a substance-using lifestyle to normal developmental experiences. The resulting shift therefore improves functioning in several domains. Therapy includes promoting positive peer relations, cultivating a strong identity that does not involve drug use, developing healthy relations with institutions such as school, and respecting autonomy within the parent–teenager relationship (Fischer et al., 2007). The MDFT clinician also works with the parents. Here, the focus is on helping parents increase their commitment to their child's welfare, improve parent–adolescent communication, and increase parenting practices such as limit setting and striking a balance between granting autonomy and establishing control (Miller et al., 2019). Henderson et al. (2010) found that MDFT was more effective for adolescents with severe substance use problems concomitant with comorbid psychiatric difficulties compared to individually focused CBT. According to Fischer et al. (2007), MDFT is cost effective as well, with good results occurring at a substantially less cost of residential care.

Family Therapy in the Treatment of Diverse Populations

Family therapy and "systems" approaches are generally based on White, Anglo-Saxon, Protestant ideals, which define the family as a single, intact, intimate group (Fisher & Harrison, 2018). However, we must keep in mind that the definition of "family" varies from culture to culture (Fisher & Harrison, 2018). For example, the traditional African American culture defines family as a wider network of individuals beyond the nuclear family, such as aunts, uncles, and grandparents. Family may even expand beyond blood relatives to include intimate friendships that have lasted over the years (Fisher & Harrison, 2018). In addition to the immediate family members, other cultures may include ancestors, elders, and descendants as part of one's family (Fisher & Harrison, 2018). Thus, it is essential that substance use clinicians understand the dynamics of a particular family, especially if that family is from a different ethnic and cultural background. The substance-using adolescent from a Euro-American family may be encouraged to work on how to better differentiate from their family. On the other hand, the substance-using adolescent from an Asian American family may need to strive for other values important to the culture and family, such empathy, connection, and involvement.

Inclan and Hernandez (1992) criticized the concept of codependency, citing concerns with how it reflects White, Anglo-Saxon perspectives on what is "healthy" in a family. The codependence concept is based on the Bowenian, systems idea of separation and individuation. However, Incan and Hernandez make the point that individuation might look quite different depending on culture and society. The risk in family therapy, according to the authors, is that healthy recovery will be defined for the clients, and they may be forced to adopt cultural values that do not reflect their culture.

As an example, Inclan and Hernandez (1992) discussed the concept of familism that is central to Hispanic family culture. Familism refers to remaining loyal to the family and honoring family traditions and interdependence. As with many cultures around the world, "family" from the Hispanic perspective extends beyond the nuclear family to include extended family, especially in times of crisis. Elders are held with great respect. As the authors pointed out, the description of familism seems to match closely with the main concepts of codependency. The obvious concern is that a Hispanic family may be labeled as "codependent" when in reality they are expressing their deeply held cultural and societal values.

Inclan and Hernandez (1992) suggested that family therapy based on codependence as the organizing dysfunction may inadvertently pathologize normal cultural processes in the Hispanic family. The Western emphasis on differentiation, individuation, equality, and mastery run counter to the Hispanic notions of child-rearing and family roles. This is not to say that differentiation does not occur in Hispanic culture; it just may take a different form. In fact, differentiation occurs in most cultures (Corey, 2017). The culturally sensitive substance use clinician needs to be aware of these cultural family dynamics and issues surrounding relationships between members and work within the family's cultural lens.

There was considerable focus on Bowenian theory as an example of one systems theory earlier in the chapter and its potential to be a useful approach for substance use intervention. However, it must be acknowledged that there are significant gaps in the empirical evidence that support the effectiveness of Bowen theory in practice, particularly as it pertains to specific diagnoses and populations. For instance, there seem to be a scarcity investigations regarding Bowenian theory's effectiveness when used with minority clients as well as clients with a range of psychological issues.

Honoring and respecting the cultural differences of our clients is paramount to effective clinical work. In no therapeutic milieu is this more necessary than family therapy. This is because the parameters of "family" are defined differently depending on a multitude of cultural, ethnic, racial and gender factors. In their work with families from different cultural backgrounds, Breunlin et al. (1997) noted the importance of adopting a multicultural perspective that emphasized a range of cultural contexts of which families are a part. These contexts contribute to attitudes, perspectives, behaviors, and values (Breunlin et al., 1997). For example, one context might be religious practice and beliefs, whereas another might be the family's economic situation. Within each context, there are similarities and differences between clinician and client (e.g., clinician from privilege and client from poverty; Breunlin et al., 1997). Ultimately, the clinician strives to assess the degree of cultural fit between themselves and the client and the "relevance and salience" of these contexts in the clients' lives (Breulin et al., 1997, p. 208). Following are the cultural contexts, followed by sample questions to assess their relevance and salience, as outlined in Breulin et al. (1997).[2] These questions can be incorporated within the initial interview:

1. **Immigrant:** What is the fit between the clinician and the family regarding cultural context? Do some family members defend the old country's values? (p. 208)

2. **Economics:** What is the fit between clinician and the family regarding economic background? What do members of this family think about their current economic state? (p. 214)

3. **Education:** What is the fit between the clinician and the family regarding education? What are the educational aspirations of the members of the family? (p. 216)

   What is the highest level of education within the family? Barriers, if any, to education?

4. **Ethnicity:** What is the fit between the family and clinician regarding ethnicity? What is their ethnic diversity? (218)

5. **Religion:** What is the fit between the clinician and family regarding religion? How do religious beliefs enrich or estrange families? (p. 220)

6. **Gender:** What meaning do members of the family attribute to being a woman? A man? Who is in control of the relationship? (p. 221)

7. **Age:** How does age impact family process and functioning? Is there a hierarchical system based on age? (p. 223)

8. **Race:** What is the fit between the clinician and family regarding race? Is any member of the family experiencing racial oppression? (p. 225)

9. **Minority/Majority Status:** What meaning do the members of the family attribute to their being minority? Majority? If the family is minority, do any members experience and/or ethnocentrism? (p. 226)

These broad assessment contexts help the clinician understand the experiences that the family (as a whole, as well as individual members) has endured. It is important to note that even within families disagreements may occur. For example, parents of an African American family might speak of a particular religious belief system, yet their children may hold differing views on religion. This speaks to the importance of understanding each member's viewpoint across a range of important sociocultural variables.

Consider the Asian American family where the teenage son is experimenting with drugs. It is tempting to work with the son independently to enhance motivation, develop skills, and change self-defeating thoughts. Whereas these goals may be necessary and useful at some

---

2   Only two sample questions from Breulin et al. (1997) are provided under each area here, with relevant page numbers for interested readers. For a complete listing of possible questions related to each domain, see Breulin et al. (1997).

point, the substance use clinician must look at the cultural and family context that contributes to the substance use. Using the assessment guidelines of Breunlin et al. (1997), it was discovered that the family members are recent immigrants to the United States, they have not yet reached economic security, and the parents are struggling in a society in which individuation/differentiation are the prominent goals for children. Because of these significant contextual factors, the family is under considerable stress manifested by continual parental arguments, bouts of depression between mother and father, and limited time to enjoy life. The substance use seems to be a way for the son to cope with these difficult circumstances and maybe even "protect" the family by drawing attention away from these issues. The substance use clinician in this case must be sensitive to these cultural challenges and strive to build rapport, generate understanding, and brainstorm interventions that fit within the family's culture and circumstances.

Barón's integrative cross-cultural model (ICM; Barón, 2000) is a comprehensive meta-model designed to help clinicians integrate multifaceted personal, cultural, and familial factors that influence the cognitions and behaviors implicated in one's behavior. It is a particularly useful model to follow when making an initial assessment because of its comprehensiveness in determining both internal and external experiences that impact minority families. Barón (2000) proposed that four *domains of inquiry* can help clinicians understand the multitude of factors that contribute to behavioral problems within culturally diverse families:

- **Individual/systemic variables and dynamics.** In this domain, the clinician inquires about typical assessment items such as mental health issues, developmental history, childhood experiences, level of education, and so forth. Related to substance use, the clinician queries individual use patterns, quantity of use, frequency of use, presence of tolerance and/or withdrawal, age of first use, and so on.

- **Cultural and ethnic variables.** This domain includes cognitive mechanisms (beliefs, values, and thoughts) that have been influenced by one's native culture. Related to substance use, items such as cultural viewpoints on substance use behaviors, cultural norms regarding substance use, how one seeks help within one's cultural context, familial boundaries, gender roles, and parenting influences all comprise this domain.

- **Dominant group influences.** This domain includes how strongly a family incorporates the beliefs and values of the dominant culture. Related to substance use, the clinician assesses the correspondence between the client's cultural beliefs regarding alcohol and drug use and the dominant culture's beliefs. For example, does the family (or client) believe that abstinence is the only option in substance use treatment as espoused by proponents of the disease model of addiction? How do their conceptualizations of substance use differ from the dominant dialogue?

- **Minority group experiences.** In this domain, the clinician inquires about the minority family's experiences of how they are treated by the majority group. Differential treatment might include elements of discrimination, prejudice, and oppression, which can have a profound impact on personality development, beliefs, and the maintenance of the substance use problem. The clinician must avoid generalizations; each client is unique, and the effect of negative experiences with the dominant group differs for each person and family.

Bruenlin et al's. (1997) and Barón's (2000) assessment models provide a comprehensive outline for substance use clinicians to incorporate with minority clients. As one can see, there is far too much complexity for the substance use clinician to blindly adopt a certain therapy without thoroughly vetting the client's worldview, perceptions, experiences, and motivations.

Many ethnic and cultural groups place much emphasis on extended family. If a family from a diverse background respects aunts, uncles, grandparents, and cousins, then it would be worthwhile to incorporate them into therapy (Corey, 2017). With substance-using children and adolescents, I have noticed that several admire some extended family member, such as an aunt or grandparent. Even if extended family members cannot attend sessions, it is worthwhile to tap into their wisdom in an imaginary way. For example, I might ask a client, "What would your uncle say about how to better handle peer pressure?"

The job of the family clinician is not only to explore the unique culture of the family (i.e., rituals, rules, boundaries, celebrations, etc.) but the wider culture in which the family belongs and the dominant culture that impacts them every day (Corey, 2017). How does culture(s) both inform and mediate members' behaviors? Systems theory helps clinicians think about the processes and factors outside of the family (and within the family) that impact the substance use problem. However, techniques cannot be administered universally (Corey, 2017). Assessment and intervention must be individually tailored to each unique family.

CASE STUDY

Using Family Therapy in the Case of Michael

There are many possibilities and ways to work in family therapy. The case with Michael illustrates one possibility. At the initial intake with Michael, it becomes clear that he is experiencing significant issues related to his substance use, especially with alcohol. He noted several consequences that he could no longer ignore. He and his wife, Anita, were constantly arguing. Their son, Anthony, began acting out in school. Anthony and his sister, Monique, were arguing daily. The clinician, thinking that Michael's drinking might have systemic roots, proceeded to conduct a genogram.

Michael's genogram (see Figure 10.1) revealed several interesting insights that solidified the clinician's belief of a generational transmission process related to alcohol and substance use. It appears that alcohol problems have been an issue on his side of the family, especially the men. His father, Ed, struggled with alcoholism, as did his grandfather. Michael also grew up in a disruptive home, as evidenced by significant conflict between his mother (Candice) and father. Michael noted that these conflicts and arguments usually revolved around his father's drinking. Michael is still close to his sister Monique. It is interesting to note that there appears to be fusion between Michael and his mother, and this pattern seems to have emerged between him and Anita. Michael and Anita have some conflict, and he stated that it has escalated recently. He is afraid it is just going to get worse unless something is done.

Due to the probable projection process within Michael's family, as well as the systemic and relationship variables that seem to play into his drinking and substance use, the clinician suggested that Michael and his family attend the next session.

For the next several sessions, Michael, Anita, Monique, and Anthony were present. Ed and Candice could not attend counseling as they were out of town. The following excerpt is from a session in which the clinician discussed the various family roles with the members of the family and how these roles might change to improve relationships. This led to an insightful discussion among members through the clinician (i.e., using triangulation).

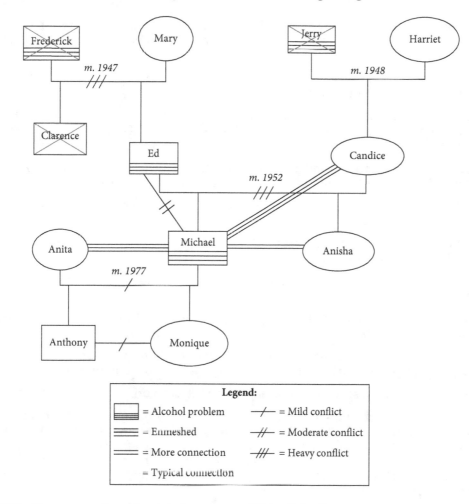

FIGURE 10.1   Three-generation abbreviated genogram of Michael's family.

CLINICIAN: Anthony, could it be that maybe you "act out" in order to move attention away from your mom and dad, or perhaps your dad's drinking? (assessing Anthony's role as the scapegoat)

ANTHONY: I guess ... I don't know. I mean, sometimes they are so stupid with rules and stuff, I just want to get away. But yeah, dad's drinking bothers me.

MICHAEL: (getting defensive and angry) That's the first time I've heard you say that, Anthony.

CLINICIAN: Michael, go ahead at this point and talk to me about how you feel and any other comments you want to make (creating a triad between Anthony and Michael to diffuse tension). Anthony, can you tell me specifically how your dad's drinking bothers you?

ANTHONY: I mean, it just does. He comes home late, yells at Mom. It's just uncomfortable. I feel like I want to get away. And then Mom just covers it up. I'm sick of it; she covers everything up and he treats her like crap.

CLINICIAN: Anita, what are your thoughts about what Anthony has to say? (ensuring all members have a voice)

ANITA: (becoming teary) I don't know. I might protect Michael a little bit. I wasn't aware that Anthony had such strong feelings about it. I just want to keep the peace. If I didn't, then who would?

CLINICIAN: Michael, what is it like, hearing this from Anthony and then Anita for the first time? (ensuring all members have a voice)

MICHAEL: I had no idea. But now I can see how Anthony has handled my drinking. He hasn't talked to me, but he has gotten into trouble as a way to talk to me. I love Anita. I don't want her to get hurt.

CLINCIAN: This is new to you and may take some time to digest. What about you Monique? What do you think of all this? (ensuring all members have a voice)

MONIQUE: I don't know. I just like to disappear. I don't cause as much trouble as Anthony; I'm a pretty good kid.

CLINICIAN: Do you think, Monique, that disappearing protects your family or you in some way? (assessing Monique's role as the lost child)

MONIQUE: I know if I keep shut then I can't get in trouble. But I feel scared walking around the house.

ANITA: I think Monique has slowly withdrawn from her friends and school; it has been more noticeable this year.

CLINICIAN: Michael, I'm hearing some feedback from Anthony and Monique that they want to distract everyone from the drinking. That seems to be the common denominator here.

MICHAEL: Yeah, maybe so. Look, I have said that I will stop drinking. Isn't that enough?

CLINICIAN: Well, as I said before, being alcohol free may bring about other changes that may be uncomfortable at first. For example, if you as a family continue to fight, even without alcohol, Anthony might continue to act out because the family still cannot communicate. (to the family) How can you all communicate in a more effective way—so that Anthony doesn't have to act out, Monique doesn't have to disappear, and Anita doesn't have to protect?

MICHAEL: We can start by practicing in here. (all nodding their heads)

CLINICIAN: Okay, how about if all of you pay attention to when you are acting out in the session, Anthony, or if you are disappearing, Monique, or if you are protecting, Anita, and then we can explore what you are really feeling, really trying to do? How does that sound? (ensuring ownership of the problem; all nod their heads)

ANTHONY: What a minute! Why do we have to do all this work, as if we are the reason Dad is drinking!

CLINICIAN: I hear you loud and clear, Anthony. You are concerned that you and the family are being blamed when the substance use is not your problem, so why should you change? There are two points I would like to make related to this: First, as we have discussed, the member who struggles with substance use, in this case your father, is responsible for his own treatment and care, and the family is invited to support him in his recovery. There is no place for blaming here. Second, as a family, you may be stuck in some patterns that are not as healthy as they could be. When communication and interactions between all of you improve, everyone benefits.

ANTHONY: (nodding in agreement) I just think living in our house has got to change!

CLINICIAN: For next session, I would like you all to notice what roles you are playing in the family and what purpose they serve to maintain the status quo in your family, including you, Michael. You don't have to change roles at this point, but just be aware. Just notice. (providing an assigned task)

This session was designed to help Michael's family think about the roles they play and the reasons they play them. There is nothing wrong with roles; however, if they are used in ways that sabotage growth or preclude awareness then they probably need changing. Notice how the clinician engaged in joining, encouraged the family to talk through them (forming triads/triangulation), and gave the family an assigned task. Also, Anthony presented some initial resistance to the idea that he needs to pay attention to his behavior when he is not the one with a substance use problem. This is a common sentiment among family members who do not use substances problematically. It is important for the clinician to validate these concerns and then educate the family on the systemic nature of substance use problems and the importance of support. At the same time, the clinician should emphasize that, when you boil it down, it is ultimately the member's choice to use or not use chemicals.

The sky is the limit in terms of where to go from here. Based on Michael's genogram, additional sessions might need to focus on strengthening the marital dyad, exploring Anita's enabling behaviors, and giving the children a chance to further express their emotions. Improving communication between family members also seems paramount.

Strengths, Limitations, and Ethical Issues Related to Family Therapy

Family therapy is an effective, viable treatment component when working with clients struggling with substance use issues. From a systems perspective, working on individual symptoms without considering the systemic variables that maintain the substance use problems may result in less than adequate treatment results. When possible, family work should be a part of every substance use client's recovery. This chapter reviewed the major tenets of family therapy, with systems theory serving as the foundation. Numerous family therapy strategies and interventions were offered for the substance use clinician to consider. Even if the primary mode of intervention is individual therapy, occasional focus on the family can provide a powerful adjunct to therapy.

TABLE 10.1 Summary of Strengths, Limitations, and Ethical Concerns of Family Therapy in the Treatment of Substance Use Problems

Strengths	• Family therapy is as effective, and in some cases more effective, than individual therapy. • Family therapy addresses the systemic factors that serve to create and maintain the symptom of substance use. • Much of family therapy rests on systems theory, which holds that psychological symptoms are a function of dysfunctional systems. Looking for and correcting faulty relationship patterns among family members can go a long way to alleviating substance use problems. • Family therapy offers a range of techniques to help families differentiate, communicate better, and develop mutual caring and respect. • In family systems therapy, neither the individual nor family is blamed for the family problems (Corey, 2017); rather, the focus is on learning and adjusting the system to live more happily.
Limitations	• Family therapy can be a complex process that requires attention to multiple processes, patterns, and content. Substance use clinicians can easily get confused without sufficient training and supervision. • Systems approaches do not focus exclusively on the substance use problem but rather on the patterns of relationships that maintain the problem. Some clients might view family interventions as addressing tangential issues rather than the main issue of substance use. • In systems thinking, the individual perspective within the system can sometimes get lost by overzealous family therapists who cling to systems terminology and concepts. The family is not a "car" that can be tweaked and adjusted. Clinicians should not forget to forge respectful and collaborative communications with all members in family clinical work (Corey, 2017).
Ethical Issues	• Despite its effectiveness in substance use counseling, family therapy takes considerable skill and understanding to use competently. There is potential risk that some clinicians' lack of skill and theoretical understanding, as well as confusion as to its application, could constitute unethical practice. • Family therapy can present several ethical issues for the clinician, including how confidentiality of the family is maintained, psychological risks of confronting family members, misuses of family strategies, and clinician competence. Substance use clinicians must constantly be mindful of these issues and clarify their values as they apply to ethical practice. • Multicultural family counseling may pose ethical issues for leaders who do not consciously acknowledge the reality of our multifarious society. Given the diversity of families that may enter treatment, clinicians must maintain a stance of broad sensitivity to client differences. Ethical issues arise if the clinician's perspective of what constitutes a healthy family is imposed on diverse clients.

Despite being an effective mode of therapy, skilled family work takes considerable training and supervision to apply competently as a sole form of therapy. However, substance use clinicians need not be licensed marriage and family therapists to provide basic family interventions. Still, care must be exercised in the provision of family-based assessment, interpretation, and intervention. In addition, whereas family therapy can occur with one member in attendance, it is ideal if more than one member attends and commits to change, which can be difficult in today's busy, fast-paced society. A summary of the strengths, limitations, and ethical issues related to family therapy is provided in Table 10.1.

References

Barón, M. (2000). Addiction treatment for Mexican American families. In J. Krestan (Ed.), *Bridges to recovery: Addiction, family therapy, and multicultural treatment* (pp. 219–252). The Free Press.

Barrett, A. E., & Turner, R. J. (2006). Family structure and substance use problems in adolescence and early adulthood: Examining explanations for the relationship. *Addiction, 101*, 109–120.

Bosk, E. A., Anthony, W. L., Folk, J. B., & Williams-Butler, A. (2021). All in the family: Parental substance misuse, harsh parenting, and youth substance misuse among juvenile justice-involved youth. *Addictive Behaviors, 119*, 106888.

Bowen, M. (1978). *Family therapy in clinical practice.* Jason Aronson.

Breunlin, Schwartz, & Mackune-Karrer (1997). *Metaframeworks: Transcending the models of family therapy* (rev. ed.). Jossey-Bass.

Brown, J. (1999). Bowen family systems theory and Practice. *The Australian and New Zealand Journal of Family Therapy, 20*(2), 99–103.

Bufferd, S. J., Dougherty, L. R., Olino, T., Dyson, M. W., Laptook, R. S., Carlson, G. A., & Klein, D. N. (2014). Predictors of the onset of depression in young children: A multi-method, multi-informant longitudinal study from ages 3–6. *Journal of Child Psychology and Psychiatry, 55*, 1279–1287.

Calatrava, M., Martins, M. V., Schweer-Collins, M., Duch-Ceballos, C., & Rodriguez-Gonzalez, M. (2022). Differentiation of self: A scoping review of Bowen family systems theory's core construct. *Clinical Psychology Review, 91*, 1–13.

Capusan, A. J., Gustafsson, P. A., Kuja-Halkola, R., Igelstrom, K., Mayo, L. M., & Heilig, M. (2021). Re-examining the link between childhood maltreatment and substance use disorder: A prospective, genetically informative study. *Molecular Psychiatry, 26*, 3201–3209.

Charles, R. (2001). Is there any empirical support for Bowen's concepts of differentiation of self, triangulation, and fusion? *American Journal of Family Therapy, 29*(4), 279–292.

Codependents Anonymous, Inc. (n.d.). *Home page.* www.coda.org.

Corey, G. (2009). *Theory and practice of counseling and psychotherapy* (8th ed.). Brooks/Cole.

Corsini, R. J., & Wedding, D. (1989). *Current psychotherapies* (4th ed.). F. E. Peacock.

Curtis, O. (1999). *Chemical dependency: A family affair.* Brooks/Cole.

Doweiko, H. E. (2019). *Concepts of chemical dependency* (10th ed.). Cengage.

Earls, F., Reich, W., Jung, K.G., & Cloninger, C.R. (1988). Psychopathology in children of alcoholic and antisocial parents. *Alcoholism: Clinical and Experimental Research, 12,* 481–487.

Edwards, J. T. (1990). *Treating chemically dependent families: A practical systems approach for professionals.* Johnson Institute.

Edwards, M. E., & Steinglass, P. (1995). Family therapy treatment outcomes for alcoholism. *Journal of Marital and Family Therapy, 21,* 475–509.

Famularo, R., Kinscherff, R., & Fenton, T. (1992). Parental substance abuse and the nature of child maltreatment. *Child Abuse and Neglect, 16,* 475–483.

Fischer, J. L., Pidcock, B. W., & Fletcher-Stephens, B. J. (2007). Family response to adolescence, youth, and alcohol. *Alcoholism Treatment Quarterly, 25,* 27–41.

Fisher, G. L., & Harrison, T. C. (2018). *Substance abuse: Information for school counselors, social workers, therapists, and counselors* (6th ed.). Pearson.

Frank, P. B., & Golden, G. K. (1992). Blaming by naming: Battered women and the epidemic of codependence. *Social Work, 37,* 5–6.

Gladding, S. T. (2019). *Family therapy: History, theory, and practice* (7th ed.). Pearson.

Glasser, W. (1999). *Choice theory: A new psychology of personal freedom.* HarperCollins.

Henderson, C. E., Dakof, G. A., Greenbaum, P. E., & Liddle, H. A. (2010). Effectiveness of multidimensional family therapy with higher severity substance-abusing adolescents: Report from two randomized controlled trials. *Journal of Consulting and Clinical Psychology, 78,* 885–897.

Inclan, J., & Hernandez, M. (1992). Cross-cultural perspectives and codependence: The case of poor Hispanics. *American Journal of Orthopsychiatry, 62,* 245–255.

Juhnke, G. A., & Hagedorn, W. B. (2006). *Counseling addicted families. An integrated assessment and treatment model.* Routledge.

Keller, M. N. (2020). Bowen theory: A systems model for family research. In M. N. Keller & R. J. Noone (Eds.), *Handbook of Bowen family systems theory and research methods: A systems model for family research* (pp. 49–61). Routledge.

Kerr, M. E., & Bowen, M. (1988). *Family evaluation. An approach based on Bowen theory.* Norton.

Kim, B. S. K., & Park, Y. S. (2008). East and southeast Asian-Americans. In G. McAuliffe & Associates (Eds.), *Culturally alert counseling: A comprehensive introduction* (pp. 188–219). SAGE.

Klever, P. (2001). The nuclear family functioning scale: Initial development and preliminary validation. *Families, Systems & Health: The Journal of Collaborative Family HealthCare, 19,* 397.

Lawson, A., & Lawson, G. (1998). *Alcoholism and the family: A guide to treatment and prevention* (2nd ed.). Pro-Ed.

Lawson, G., Peterson, J. S., & Lawson, A. (1983). *Alcoholism and the family: A guide to treatment and prevention.* Aspen.

Lewis, J. (1994). The codependence concept and the status quo. *The Family Journal, 2,* 238–240.

Merriam-Webster (n.d.). Systems. In *Merriam-Webster online dictionary.* August 18, 2022, https://tinyurl.com/yckpy35b

Miller, R. B., Anderson, S., & Keala, D. K. (2004). Is Bowen theory valid? A review of basic research. *Journal of Marital & Family Therapy, 30,* 453–466.

Miller, W. R., Forcehimes, A. A., & Zweben, A. (2011). *Treating addiction.* Guilford.

Miller, W. R., Forcehimes, A. A., & Zweben, A. (2019). *Treating addiction: A guide for professionals* (2nd ed.). Guilford.

Minuchin, S. (1974). *Families and family therapy.* Harvard University Press.

Murdock, N. L., & Gore, P. A. (2004). Stress, coping, and differentiation of self: A test of Bowen theory. *Contemporary Family Therapy: An International Journal, 26,* 319–335.

Nelson, T. S. (2003). Transgenerational family therapists. In L. L. Hecker & J. L. Wetchler (Eds.), *An introduction to marriage and family therapy* (pp. 255–293). Routledge.

Perkinson, R. R. (2012). *Chemical dependency counseling: A practical guide* (4th ed.). SAGE.

Robbins, M. S., Feaster, D. J., Horigian, V. E., Rohrbaugh, M., Shoham, V., Bachrach, K., Miller, M., Burlew, K. A., Hodgkins, C., Carrion, I., Vandermark, N., Schindler, E., Werstlein, R., & Szapocznik, J. (2011). Brief strategic family therapy versus treatment as usual: Results of a multisite randomized trial for substance abuse adolescents. *Journal of Consulting and Clinical Psychology, 79,* 713–727.

Ruben, D. H. (2001). *Treating adult children of alcoholics.* Academic Press.

Skowron, E. A. (2005). Parent differentiation of self and child competence in low-income, urban families. *Journal of Counseling Psychology, 13,* 337–342.

Stanton, M. D., & Standish, W. R. (1997). Outcome, attrition, and family-couples treatment for drug abuse: A meta-analysis and review of the controlled, comparative studies. *Psychological Bulletin, 122,* 170–190.

Stevens, P. A. (2018). Family therapy is substance abuse treatment. In P. Stevens & R. L. Smith (Eds.), *Substance abuse counseling: Theory and practice* (2nd ed., pp. 208–227). Pearson.

Substance Abuse and Mental Health Services Administration. (2020). *Treatment improvement protocol (TIP) 39: Substance use disorder treatment and family therapy.* https://tinyurl.com/5n82r6et

Szapocznik, J., Hervis, O., & Schwartz, S. (2003). *Brief strategic family therapy for adolescent drug abuse* (NIH Publication No. 03-4751). National Institute on Drug Abuse.

Taibbi, R. (2011). *Families in crisis: Strategies for defusing, defining, and problem-solving.* PESI Seminars.

Thombs, D. L. (2006). *Introduction to addictive behaviors* (3rd ed.). Guilford.

Thombs, D. L., & Osborn, C. J. (2019). *Introduction to addictive behaviors* (5th ed.). Guilford.

Tuason, M. T., & Friedlander, M. L. (2000). Do parents' differentiation levels predict those of their adult children and other tests of Bowen theory in a Philippine sample. *Journal of Counseling Psychology, 47,* 27–35.

Ulas, E., & Eksi, H. (2019). Inclusion of family therapy in rehabilitation program of substance abuse and its efficacious implementation. *The Family Journal, 27,* 443–451.

Walters, D. (1993). The codependent Cinderella and iron John. *The Family Networker, 17,* 60–65.

Webster, D. (1990). Women and depression (alias codependency). *Family and Community Health, 13,* 58–66.

Wegscheider, S. (1981). *Another chance: Hope and health for the alcoholic family.* Science and Behavior Books.

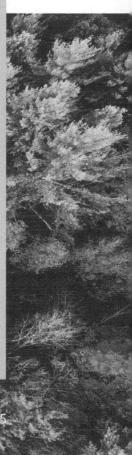

PART III

Theoretical Approaches With Less Empirical Support

Part III includes theoretical approaches that, in general, have less empirical support. In many ways, the very nature of some of these approaches, such as Gestalt counseling, do not lend themselves to positivistic, quantitative research that is the hallmark of traditional clinical trial outcome research. However, the lack of empirical support does *not* render these approaches any less effective: The concept of "evidence-based treatments" has been called into question (see Chapter 1 for a discussion of this particular point). Each theoretical model has a significant literature base from which conceptualizations, techniques, and approaches to substance use disorder counseling can be implemented into clinical practice. Part III begins with Chapter 11, which reviews solution-focused approaches to substance use disorder counseling. Solution-focused counseling offers a promising, positive alternative to the often "problem-saturated" narratives that plague many substance use treatment centers. In Chapter 12, I navigate Adlerian therapy and its application to substance use disorder treatment. Adlerian theory is a fascinating and comprehensive model that offers the clinician a complete approach for both conceptualizing substance use problems and intervention. In Chapter 13, I review Gestalt theory; as with Adlerian theory, Gestalt theory provides a viable model from which to help clients on the road to recovery. Chapter 14 covers existential theory. Existential crises often underlie many substance use problems, and the infusion of existential counseling can add meaning and depth to the therapy experience. Part III ends with a brief chapter (Chapter 15) on putting it all together and theoretical integration. This new chapter offers some final guidelines for clinicians to follow when counseling those struggling with substances.

CHAPTER 11

Applying Solution-Focused Therapy in the Treatment of Substance Use Disorders

Introduction

My first exposure to SFT occurred in graduate school while I was pursuing my doctoral degree. I had entered doctoral school just about the time that our department was going through a theoretical paradigm shift of sorts. Many of my professors were moving away from modernist theories (e.g., cognitive, CBT, psychoanalysis) and toward *postmodern* approaches to counseling such as constructivist, narrative, and solution-focused therapies, which have been shown to have widespread applicability.

The term *postmodern* refers to the underlying philosophy of these counseling approaches, namely that many social realities exist and that a particular reality is constructed through the medium of language. Meaning is relative to the individual and evolves and changes in conversation with others. In addition, postmodern thought rests on the assumption that reality is viewed as an individual construction of interactions with the environment, meanings made of life experiences, and personal interpretations (White & Epstein, 1990). Solution-focused clinicians seek to understand the client's constructions about a problem and then coconstruct alternative ways to view it so that solutions emerge naturally.

SFT is a growing, viable option for treating clients struggling with substance use disorders (Linton, 2005). Indeed, counseling models that promote a strength-based, what-is-working approach have made a significant impact on substance use counseling (McCollum et al., 2003). Pichot and Smock (2009), in their book, *Solution-Focused Substance Abuse Treatment*, argue how SFT methods *exceed* current standards of substance use disorder treatment. They effectively show how SFT can be used in substance use assessment, case management, and treatment. Many clinicians and programs across the world are implementing SFT to address substance use concerns (Smock et al., 2008). For example, Mott and Gysin (2003) transformed their TC (treatment community) model to a solution-focused model for clients with substance use disorders. Their original version of the TC model was deficit based and assumed that clients did not have the inner resources to heal. As will be discussed later, SFT focuses on what the client does right and honors the strengths the client brings to the counseling setting. Although Mott and Gysin did not provide empirical evidence, they reported greater success with their clients who became more motivated and positive. And, as an unexpected outcome, the more positive focus created greater satisfaction among personnel staff in their agency. More recently, Mullet et al. (2018) argued persuasively that brief therapy can be effective when incorporating family members; they proposed a solution-focused brief therapy (SFBT) model for families impacted by substance use.

SFT, in many ways, is a reaction to traditional forms of substance use treatment. For example, early substance use treatment was often based on Synanon, where clients were labeled as "addicts" and society needed to be protected from them. Furthermore, the only thing a "drug abuser" knew how to do was consume drugs (Mott & Gysin, 2003). The basis for intervention was pressure from the treatment community to change. Methods were often harsh, including ridicule, contempt, and sometimes hostile attack to "break down denial." Unfortunately, these methods are still in use today, if in attenuated form (Mott & Gysin, 2003). Much of chemical dependency treatment currently follows medical model philosophy, in which clients are viewed as having inherent weaknesses and the disease of addiction. This negative viewpoint, according to proponents of SFT, creates a self-fulfilling environment: If staff views clients as defensive, resistant, and weak, clients will as well (Mott & Gysin, 2003). Using this approach, clinicians seek to address deficits and create coping skills needed to manage the disease of addiction (Linton, 2005).

It should be acknowledged that many substance use clients have gone through treatment programs that rely on traditional or medical model philosophy and have come out free from substance use. However, substance use is an equal opportunity problem, affecting individuals and families from diverse backgrounds, cultures, and so forth. One model does not fit all. SFT offers an alternative approach that honors where the client stands relative to the possibility of behavior change and what resources and strengths can be called on to improve one's substance use patterns.

SFT is intended to be brief. de Shazer (1991) reported that on average SFT takes about five sessions. The demand for cost-effectiveness in substance use counseling makes this an ideal approach for working under time constraints (Nelle, 2005). Affordable, effective, and time-limited treatment for substance use is a vital need (Smock et al., 2008). Funding constraints across the mental health treatment spectrum dictate that substance use treatment is of limited duration. Although long-term care might be an option for some clients, most managed care establishments operate as if short-term treatment is the only practical and feasible option (West, 2010). SFT is a short-term therapy model that is designed to promote change in as few sessions as possible. There is evidence to suggest that brief interventions can be effective, and research has shown that short-term therapy is as effective as long-term therapy for problem drinkers (Berg & Miller, as cited in West, 2010; Miller & Hester, 1986).

As noted in Chapter 6, MI is a strength-based counseling approach that honors the client's own internal resources for change. SFT and MI are both considered competency-based treatments in the substance use treatment field, where the emphasis is on social support, modeling of success, and inspiring hope (McCollum et al., 2003). There are striking similarities between SFT and MI (Lewis & Osborn, 2004; McCollum et al., 2003); SFT is a promising strategy for engaging difficult clients, facilitating motivation in brief settings, and constructing solutions related to client problems (Matto et al., 2003). Given these similarities, and MI's solid research base, one could make a reasonable argument that SFT may be as effective as MI in treating clients with substance use problems. However, SFT researchers have yet to build the research base in substance use counseling that MI researchers have done in the past few decades. As with MI, SFT has been successfully adopted in substance use group formats (West, 2010). Using SFT in substance use counseling groups will be discussed later in this chapter.

In this chapter, I outline the major tenets of SFT, with a specific emphasis on its application to clients struggling with substance use disorders. I then cover the many techniques of SFT and its applicability in group counseling. The application of SFT with diverse clientele will be explored, followed by the application of the approach in the case of Michael.

The Major Tenets of SFT: Brief Overview

SFT has several underlying assumptions that guide the approach. These assumptions, along with the role of the clinician, SFT's theory of change, and criteria for effective outcomes are reviewed in the following sections. As you will see, SFT is presented as an alternative to more confrontational approaches to substance use counseling.

Underlying Assumptions

It has been my experience that clients struggling with substance use disorders present to counseling with *problem-saturated stories*. Their problems are inextricably linked to who they are, their core being. Simply put, they *are* the problems of drinking, drug use, addiction, or other problems that tend to co-occur with substance use. In addition, many clients come to counseling having been beaten up by the system (e.g., family, friends, society), and any success or progress has been ignored (Mott & Gysin, 2003). A key underlying assumption of SFT is that people are separate from their problems. In other words, a client is not the problem, but the problem (e.g., depression, anxiety, anger, drinking and drug use) is the problem (O'Hanlon & Weiner-Davis, 1989). This therapeutic stance is like *externalization* in narrative therapy. Externalization refers to a method of communication with clients that conveys that the problem is outside of them, exerting its devious influence, sometimes in unsuspecting ways. For example, a line of externalizing questions a clinician may ask a client include "Tell me when *alcoholism* tends to sneak up on you. What does *alcoholism* tell you? How does *alcoholism* trick you in to thinking you need to drink?" These questions could apply to any problem. The goal behind externalization is to create a social reality (via externalizing language) in which the problem is viewed as separate from the client.

Consistent with externalization, constructing solutions can occur separately from talking about problems. In counseling, "solution talk," or using language that focuses on how to resolve problems, is all that is needed for change to occur; focusing exclusively on the problem and pathology precludes development of solution construction (Walter & Peller, 1992). Statements of unhappiness are changed to statements of goals. Consider a client who struggles with alcohol use disorder and co-occurring mental health problems. From an SFT perspective, spending time too much time talking about these problems, what is wrong with the client, and how the client has a disease reinforces the client's problem dominated life script, or narrative. This is not to say that SFT clinicians never discuss problems with their clients. Rather, they do not *emphasize* them and always have an eye toward solutions. Understanding the problem is not necessary for change to happen (Linton, 2005). Focusing on the positives, strengths, solutions, goals, and the future promotes change in the desired direction.

A question that provides the thrust of SFT is "How do clinician and client construct solutions?" This question assumes that (a) solutions exit, (b) there are many solutions, (c) solutions can be built up and strengthened over time, (d) the clinician and client both coconstruct solutions, and (e) solutions are constructed (via language) rather than discovered (Walter & Peller, 1992). Solution-focused clinicians look for solutions by asking targeted questions, usually about when the problem is not happening (i.e., exceptions to the problem, discussed later). Given that clients are so often tangled in problem-saturated narratives, they often overlook experiences in which the problem was not happening or when they demonstrated healthy resistance to using drugs. Research in neuroscience has confirmed that human beings tend to have a negativity bias (Hanson, 2011) in which the brain is wired to focus much more energy on the negative events but overlook positive experiences (a similar concept to Beck's cognitive shift explained in Chapter 7). Solution-focused clinicians interrupt this bias by helping clients to coconstruct solutions by paying attention to what works in their lives. Indeed, clients have all they need within themselves to solve their problems; they just need to be made aware of these inner capacities and given encouragement to enact them.

Solution-focused clinicians believe that there are exceptions to every problem (Walter & Peller, 1992). For example, a client with a cocaine use disorder has most likely experienced times in their life in which they were able to resist cocaine or limit its use. These times refer to exceptions to the problem and are used to build solutions. Cooperation between clinician and client is necessary for solution generation (Walter & Peller, 1992). However, the burden lies on the clinician to discover exceptions in the client's story, even if the client has difficulty thinking of them. In SFT, clinicians insist that exceptions exist, no matter how trivial or small to the client.

Solution-focused clinicians assume that descriptions and actions are circular (Walter & Peller, 1992). In other words, the language one uses to describe some phenomenon will influence the actions that follow, how they interpret these actions, and what decisions will follow, and so on in a recursive loop (Walter & Peller, 1992). For example, if an individual with a substance use disorder tells themselves that they are a complete loser, and that heroin is the only way to feel better (action), they will most likely continue to take heroin, interpret this as giving them relief, which feeds back into their description of themselves as an "addict," leading to more substance use, and so on. Solution-focused clinicians use language and questioning in a way to shift client perspectives on the problem and encourage looking for solutions and expecting change (Berg & DeJong, 1996).

Solution-focused clinicians use verbs to indicate that behaviors (and problems) are change-able and temporary (Walter & Peller, 1992). For example, someone might be described as "showing" a substance use disorder rather than described as an "addictive" person. This idea is consistent with the "psychology of use" idea from Adlerian therapy. The implication of using language in this way is to convey that the client's substance use is not intransigent and unfix-able. A more subtle message is that clients have within themselves the strengths and abilities to overcome their substance use disorder.

Another assumption of SFT is that change is always occurring or constant (Linton, 2005; O'Hanlon & Weiner-Davis, 2003; Walter & Peller, 1992). The perspective that change is con-stantly occurring is critical from an SFT approach. Clients who perceive themselves in a "fixated" state of severe substance use fail to see the small successes that have been achieved in accomplishing their goals. For clients who continually relapse, SFT clinicians focus on helping clients build on small successes so that eventually they build their own solution to the relapse problem, one brick (or success) at a time.

Finally, in SFT the clinician is not viewed as the expert who diagnoses and implements treatment to account for deficits. Rather, clients are seen as experts on themselves, and it is the clinician's task to cultivate understanding of the client, focus on client strengths, and take a positive therapeutic stance.

These assumptions serve as the philosophical ground from which SFT operates. Let's exam-ine see how these assumptions manifest in the role of the SFT clinician.

Role of the Solution-Focused Clinician

SFT is considered a brief therapy in which the clinician focuses on essentially three ideas: "(a) find out what the client wants, (b) look for more of what is working and do more of that, and (c) do something different" (Walter & Peller, 1992, p. 6). Thus, clinicians look for what is working in the client's life and encourages more of it, rather than attempt to change what doesn't need changing. The SFT clinician believes that it is usually unnecessary to know much about the problem or even its cause (O'Hanlon & Weiner-Davis, 2003). Rather than looking for deep-seated etiologies for pathology, they keep in mind that clients are responsible for their actions and have the capability within to change their lives (Walter & Peller, 1992). This counseling stance, of course, is in the context of a collaborative relationship with the client.

The SFT clinician does not analyze the past; they are present and future oriented (Mott & Gysin, 2003). Again, this does not mean that clinicians do not care about the past, but that they simply believe that too much focus on the past misses opportunities to explore solutions in the present moment or future. Ultimately, SFC clinicians want to facilitate the evolution of new meaning of change in the present (or sometime in the future) moment (Walter & Peller, 1992), a coconstructed solution that the client will build into their life. "Failure" is not in the SFC lexicon as "there is no failure, only feedback" (Walter & Peller, 1992, p. 40).

The SFT clinician helps clients in clarifying and defining goals. Clinicians work with what clients want; goals and solutions are coconstructed, with the assumption that quick change is indeed possible (O'Hanlon & Weiner-Davis, 2003). A major role of the SFT clinician is to give positive feedback on what is going well in the client's life and how they are able to accomplish goals they set for themself in therapy. Even small tasks are recognized and observed as important steps in the right direction (O'Hanlon & Weiner-Davis, 2003). It is not uncommon for SFT clinicians to encourage clients in the form of affirmations, compliments, conveying positive language, and providing homework tasks to build success.

Theory of Change

Solution-focused clinicians observe change when clients become more flexible in their thinking and behaving and continue those behaviors that are consistent with what they want. Change also occurs when clients become aware of exceptions to the problem or times when the problem was not happening. Clients are encouraged to focus on what they were doing when the problem wasn't occurring and build on these positive behaviors over time. For example, if a client wants to be free of cocaine use disorder, they are encouraged to engage in activities that build on the exceptions to cocaine use, such as avoiding old "stomping grounds," obtaining employment, or incorporating a substitute activity such as exercise. By building on exceptions to the substance use disorder, clinicians coconstruct with clients positive, solution-oriented realities and meanings that can serve to guide clients outside of counseling. Changes counselors wish to facilitate also include opening new or different meanings for clients so they can act out these new, preferred ways of living.

Criteria for Effective Counseling Outcomes

The coconstruction and realization of a solution or goal is an important consideration in SFT. The solution (or change), however, is not conceptualized as a static concept but an active, moving phenomenon (O'Hanlon & Weiner-Davis, 1989). Through clinician–counselor dialogue, new realities, insights, and goals emerge as the client engages in a more preferred way of living. Critical here is the client's ability to act. Many clients believe that they must feel a certain way or that someone else must change before they can act. SFT inquires as to what the client will be *doing* to reach a solution, how they will be *doing it*, and what they have already *done* to accomplish it. Implicit in this expectation is that clients are expected to take responsibility for their own change. Solution-focused clinicians emphasize action and do not allow clients to place the onus of change on them.

Application of SFT With Substance Use Disorders

The SFT approach to substance use problems begins with focusing on what is going right in the client's life instead of focusing on what is wrong (Berg & Miller, 1992). The focus from the outset is on how clients can improve the quality of their lives through collaboration and utilization of client resources. According to Berg (Allyn & Bacon Professional, 2001), clinicians do not need to know the how, when, and where of drug use as the client already knows this. Instead, SFT clinicians ask:

- What does the client want?
- What has the client done to get what he wants?
- What does the client have to do to get more of what he wants?
- What are the client's goals?[1]

Berg and Miller (1992) outlined a solution-focused counseling approach for the problem drinker. (Although this approach is applied to problematic drinking, it could easily apply to other substance use disorders as well.) The first step in Berg and Miller's approach is to establish a cooperative clinician–client relationship. The SFT emphasis on building a strong clinician–client rapport is like most therapeutic approaches, especially that of MI. The SFT clinician understands that counseling is a shared responsibility. This contrasts with some traditional forms of therapy in which the approach is applied to all clients; resistance was seen as residing within the client rather than the clinician. In SFT, resistance indicates that a problem is occurring in the relationship *between* clinician and client (Berg & Miller, 1992). Duncan et al. (2003) noted that over 1,000 research findings indicate that a positive relationship is one of the best predictors of counseling outcome. SFT makes this critical variable a priority.

Berg and Miller (1992) discussed a useful strategy to use with "difficult" or "in-denial" clients that serves to bolster the therapeutic alliance. The strategy, called *finding the hidden customer*, is based on the idea that many clients who are precontemplative or who have been coerced to attend counseling will usually not be customers who are seeking help with substance use, but rather wish to deal with something else. The clinician's task is to cooperate with the client's view of the problem and goals, even if they do not immediately align with substance use. The idea is that this builds cooperation, thereby facilitating increased rapport. An example from my own practice illustrates.

I was counseling "William" (name disguised), a 34-year-old African American client who was sent to me because he was in danger of losing his job in middle management for a local company. William was slipping in his job and had become increasingly tardy at work mainly due to his increasing alcohol use. During our first visit, William was uncomfortable talking about alcohol and did not see it as a big problem; he only was there to please upper management. His goal was to get them, as well as his wife, off his back. When I inquired as to what he needed to do to get folks off his back, he sheepishly stated that he should probably stop using alcohol, which often led to arguments. By avoiding the natural tendency to lecture William on his alcohol use and impose immediate goals for abstinence, I was able to circumvent resistance. In addition, the problem of alcohol was inextricably linked to getting people of his back. William had no choice but to admit the obvious fact that his alcohol was getting in the way. This was *his* discovery, not mine, which makes it that much more powerful.

---

1 According to Berg (Allyn & Bacon Professional, 2001), wants and goals should be reasonable and healthy within society.

The next step outlined by Berg and Miller (1992) involves creating well-formed treatment goals. In SFT practice, formulating goals in a cooperative manner is a foundational technique. Berg and Miller outlined seven qualities of well-formulated goals:

- **Relevance to the client.** The counseling goal must create some passion and energy in the client or there will be little or no progress. Goals must fit into the clients' plans and motivations. Goals that are relevant to clients' lives increase the probability that they are accomplished. Again, goals do not always need to immediately address substance use, such as "abstain from cocaine" or "cut down on drinking." Many substance use counseling goals address the consequences of substance use such as "save my job," "get my license back," and "be a better father." These consequences are intimately tied to substance use, and it becomes obvious to the client what needs to change.

- **Goals must be small.** Small goals facilitate motivation and instill hope among clients who initially see an abstinent life daunting. As Berg and Miller (1992) pointed out, this idea is consistent with the AA slogan, "one day at a time."

- **Goals must be concrete, specific, and behavioral.** Aside from being good practice for treatment planning, goals that are well-formed provide the clinician and client a map from which to track progress. Vague, undefined goals often lead to counseling that is longer than needed (Berg & Miller, 1992) and make it difficult to determine if the client is improving. Well-formed goals help the client easily know when success has been achieved.

- **The presence rather than the absence of something.** An important contribution of the SFT approach to substance use counseling is the emphasis on what is working and using this to build solutions rather than focusing on what is wrong and getting bogged down with problem-saturated stories. This basic premise is reflected in creating positive goals for clients, *emphasizing what they will be doing differently* rather than what they will not be doing. For example, a client may recognize the need to completely stop alcohol, and their goal is that they will not drink. Setting goals up this way, however, may have the unintentional and paradoxical effect of obsessing more about alcohol; whenever we tell ourselves not to do something, especially something we enjoy, it is difficult to resist urges to do it (Berg & Miller, 1992). If the client were to extend their goal by adding something to their life, such as increased exercise, reaching out to others, and attending AA, they are able to easily see the fruits of what they are doing instead of drinking. In addition, clients seem to do better when they are asked to imagine their life a few months down the road with the presence of something positive as opposed to the absence of something negative (Mott & Gyrsin, 2003).

- **Start at the beginning rather than the end.** Many of my clients come to counseling with goals such as being "completely alcohol free" or "a better life." Whereas these are admirable goals, they also are vague and have the end in sight, without any plan to get there. Solution-focused clinicians help clients take the first step and subsequent small steps to reach the final goal. Envisioning a different life is important for clients with substance use disorders, and so is the process of how to get there.

- **Reasonable goals within the client's abilities and context.** It is well known in the substance use counseling field that clients often make sweeping promises about total abstinence only to fall off the wagon a couple weeks later. Nothing can be more frustrating for clinicians and clients. Keeping goals manageable for clients increases the chances for success and improves the possibility of attaining larger goals in the future. If a goal seems unrealistic given the circumstances, the SFT clinician acknowledges the client's desire to accomplish the goal and then works collaboratively to negotiate a more realistic goal (Berg & Miller, 1992). For example, a client may wish to have a "normal" life with their family after years of drinking and negative consequences. It may be better in such cases to help the client focus on smaller goals such as establishing a recovery plan and slowly building trust with their family as part of their journey toward a more normal life.

- **Goals should be perceived by clients as involving hard work.** Despite setting up small, achievable goals, clients should be reminded that *any* attempt at change is hard work. In SFT, the emphasis on hard work is done at the outset. Clients come to understand that it will take a lot of effort to overcome their substance use problem. The hard work reminder also respects how difficult it can be to stop something that has served as a crutch for so long. If the client fails to achieve their goals, it does not mean the client has failed, only that more hard work is needed. As Berg and Miller (1992) stated, emphasizing the hard work needed to accomplish goals is a win-win situation for clinician and client. Whatever the outcome, both can assess what hard work was done and what remains to be done.

It is important to note that negotiating and cooperating are two therapeutic imperatives from the SFT model. Berg and Miller (1992) stated that goals not only need to be well formulated but also fit within the clinician–client relationship. For example, negotiating goals with an involuntary client will look different than negotiating goals with a "visitor"-type client (i.e., one who wants to be told what to do but puts little effort in generating solutions). For the involuntary client, the clinician may need to assess what the referring person or agency needs to see for them to stop counseling. This may involve goals that do not have to do with substance use, at least initially. To minimize resistance, it is more therapeutically effective to begin where the client wants to begin, knowing that inevitably the discussion will turn to substance use. Pushing too hard for goals that do not fit the client may backfire and lead to more frustration and confusion on the part of the client. Another way to negotiate goals with the involuntary client is to agree to work on both what the client wants *and* look at their recent substance use patterns, because they appear to be tied to their legal, employment, or family problems.

The next step in Berg and Miller's (1992) model involves orienting the client toward a solution to problem drinking (or substance use). The SFT approach relies heavily on purposeful questioning designed to help clients think more about how to go about solving their problems. Thus, instead of asking questions about the problem, SFT clinicians turn the direction of the session toward client strengths and resources. Berg and Miller outlined several types of questions that can be used to create a solution-focused atmosphere. For example, questions about changes that have occurred before counseling started are useful to learn about what the client has already done. Usually, this type of questioning occurs when setting up the first meeting over the phone. The exchange might go something like this:

CLIENT: Hi, um, I am not sure want to do, but I was hoping I could set up a meeting to talk about my drug use. I think I have hit rock bottom.

CLINCIAN: I am sorry to learn that you have had such a struggle with drugs. Yes, I do have some time later this week, on Friday, from 2–4. Could you meet for an hour on that day?

CLIENT: Sure, whatever you have open. I just need to face this once and for all.

CLINCIAN: This is serious, and you are ready to make changes. I am wondering, *what changes to your substance use have you made already?*

CLIENT: Well, I've been drug free 1 day. Yesterday was the last straw. I am on the verge of losing my job and was told I needed to get help.

CLINCIAN: How were you able to stop? How were you able to stay drug free for the past day or so?

CLIENT: I just told myself that this is it. I *must* stop. I called a friend, and he has been a great support. In a fit of anger, I flushed all the drugs down the toilet.

CLINCIAN: That is great. It sounds like your friend is important to you and you are already taking important steps. If I may ask, do you think you could notice more of what you are doing already to stop using? Simply pay attention to what you are thinking, doing, and feeling to help you stop using drugs? I would like to talk about that a bit when you come in on Friday. Sound good?

CLIENT: Sure. Do I need to write this stuff down?

CLINCIAN: Many clients find that writing down notes helps, but it is not essential. I'll leave it up to you. See you Friday at 2:00!

We see in this exchange that the client has already (a) stopped using drugs, (b) became aware that their life was out of control, (c) demanded to themself that they stop, (d) called a friend, and (e) used their anger to get rid of drugs in their house. What is remarkable is that, unless the clinician asks, she may never know what positive changes are already taking place. This line of questioning can continue in the first session. For example, the clinician may ask the client, "So how have you continued to stay off of drugs since we talked on the phone?" Other strategic solution-focused questions include the miracle question, scaling questions, and asking for exceptions to the problem. These strategies are covered in more depth next.

SFT-Based Techniques

There are many SFT techniques at the clinician's disposal. Many of these involve the strategic and skillful use of questions (Linton, 2005).

Miracle Question

According to Berg and Miller (1992), the miracle question is one of the most important questions in the SFT model. It is designed to focus the client on the successes ahead without the problem. Here's how to ask it according to Berg and Miller (1992):

> I want to ask you a slightly different question now. You will have to use your imagination for this one. Suppose you go home and go to bed tonight after today's session. While you are sleeping a miracle happens and the problem that brought you here is solved, just like that (snapping a finger). Since you were sleeping, you didn't know that this miracle happened. What do you suppose will be the first small thing that will indicate to you tomorrow morning that there has been a miracle overnight and the problem that brought you here is solved? (p. 78).

The key idea behind the miracle question is that it helps clients imagine what life could be like without drugs, alcohol, and other problems. The client develops hope from their visualization of a better life. It is noteworthy that many clients simply recount rather ordinary daily activities as their "miracle" (getting up on time, taking a shower, leaving for work early; Berg & Miller, 1992). However, for clients who struggle with a substance use disorder, doing ordinary activities can indeed be miracle like and fits in with the client's desire to change.

Scaling Questions

Scaling questions provide an excellent way to check in with clients at the beginning and end of counseling sessions. Scaling questions are designed to ask clients to rate, on a scale of 1–10, where they think they are relative to their stated goal (Mott et al., 2003). For example, a clinician may ask, "On a scale of 1 to 10, with 1 being no progress on cutting down drinking to no more than three drinks per week, and 10 being goal accomplished, where do you fall at this point? Assume the client responds with a 3. The clinician then has several options from which to follow up. Because we are focusing on successes, asking the client "What makes it a 3 and not a 2 or 1?" acknowledges that at least *some* success occurred! The client may then state that their job or family keeps them from slipping to a 2 or 1. The clinician can explore this in more detail: "How is your family helping? What about your job keeps your progress from slipping?" Another follow-up question might be "What can you do to move from a 3 to a 4?" The client might say that they can start writing down positive thoughts and repeat them when they feel a need to go against their goal of controlled drinking. When asking clients how they might increase a number on the scale, clinicians should not create too much distance. For example, clinicians should avoid asking, "How can you move from a 3 to an 8?" This distance is too much for the client to handle in such a short time and might appear overwhelming. As a rule, I ask my clients how they might move their number up a half point to a full point, and then go from there.

As noted, scaling questions can be used at any time in the counseling process. Questions around the importance of changing substance use and having confidence in doing so also are good ways to use this technique (see Chapter 6 on MI).

Exception Questions

This key SFT strategy involves looking for times when the problem is not occurring and then using these instances to help the client build their own solution (Linton, 2005; McCollum et al., 2003). The purpose is to free the client from the belief that the problem is a fixed quality that is inherently unchangeable (Mott & Gysin, 2003). For example, a clinician may ask, "Tell me a time in the past month when you were not using cocaine." Clients may readily note that they had significant times within a month in which they were not using. These exceptions to substance use are the building blocks upon which solutions are generated. Examining exceptions helps clients build on preexisting knowledge and skill (Mott & Gysin, 2003). As O'Hanlon and Weiner-Davis (2003) stated, "If people want to experience more success, more happiness, and less stress in their lives, help them assess what is different about the times when they are already successful, happy, and stress-free" (p. 83).

When exceptions are provided, SFT clinicians amplify them by adopting a position of curiosity; follow-up questions such as "What was going on then? How were you able to do that? What was different? Who noticed the exception? What would _____ say you did differently? And how did you make that happen?" are asked to further "flesh out" the nonproblem experiences. Again, the idea is to help the client construct the roadmap to a solution.

When using exceptions, it is important that SFT clinicians honor the smallest of successes (Linton, 2005). One issue I continually run in to in my own practice is that many clients focus on the magnitude of change rather than the direction of change. I often tell clients that direction of change is important, no matter how small, and greater magnitude will come in time.

Presupposition Questions (aka Future-Oriented Questions)

Presupposition questions presuppose that change either has already happened or will happen down the road. In this technique, the clinician asks, "Six months down the road, *when you have kicked this substance use disorder problem*, what is the first thing that you will be doing differently?" The clinician presupposed that change will happen in 6 months (or any time frame that seems appropriate). Although subtle, the focus of such a question is clearly on the confidence that the client can accomplish their goals and has the resources to do so.

Relationship-Oriented Questions

Relationship-oriented questions are designed to help clients see how others might see them when they are living without the problem (Mott & Gysin, 2003). An example might be, "What will your coworkers say they notice something different about you when you are free from cocaine?"

Taking in the Good

Taking in the good (TIG) did not originate from SFT; however, the idea behind it is very much in line with SFT philosophy. I regularly use TIG with my clients who struggle with substance use because it counters what neuroscientists have come to call the *negativity bias* (Hanson, 2011). The negativity bias refers to our natural tendency to focus exclusively on the negative and ignore the good that happens to us every day. This bias is thought to have developed through evolutionary mechanisms, where avoiding pain and aggressors (i.e., sticks) had a greater impact on surviving than approaching "carrots" such as sex, sustenance, and protection (Hanson, 2011). In other words, we routinely overestimate threat danger and "failures" and underestimate strengths and opportunity. Positive experiences pass through the brain quickly without much notice while negative experiences are caught (Hanson, 2011).

To adjust for this bias, Hanson (2011) argued that clients need to *truly experience* positive activities to imprint them into the brain. There are generally three steps to the process of TIG:

1. Turn positive information and facts into affirming *experiences*. In other words, help clients become aware of all the positive events that do happen in their daily lives and solidify these as important experiences.
2. Take pleasure in the positive experiences, relish in them, and help them become a part of the client's being. Hanson (2011) suggested that clients "get in to" the positive experience for 10–30 seconds by consciously intending to feel it physically and emotionally.
3. Imagine bathing in the positive experience, penetrating one's physical self, including the brain. The goal is to help the experience connect profoundly in memory (Hanson, 2011).

Taking in the good is not a panacea, and the clinician needs to guard against the risk of minimizing the client's struggles. However, in my experience clients often are surprised at all that is going well in their life, despite their substance use patterns. These positive events are ignored, as clients are pulled to problem-saturated modes of thinking. Helping clients build on positive experiences can help set in motion additional experiences that are inconsistent with problematic substance use.

Exploration of Goals

In this technique, clients are asked to explore their goals. Specifically, they will explore what they want (goal), focus on how this goal is happening now or how the problem is not happening now, and how the goal will look in the future.

Taking a Break

Insoo Kim Berg (Allyn & Bacon Professional, 2001) advocated taking a break in the middle of the counseling session, about 5 minutes or so, to gather thoughts and reflect on what is working with the client. After the break, the clinician highlights strengths and summarizes these back to the client. This technique does not need to be done for every client; however, I have found it useful when there has been an impasse in counseling or when the client needs a little encouragement.

Solution-Focused Group Therapy

Many substance use clinicians have applied SFT principles to group counseling and treatment, called solution-focused *group* therapy (SFGT; Metcalf, 1998; McCollum et al., 2003; Smock et al., 2008; West, 2010;). Many of the tenets of SFGT are consonant with the curative factors espoused by Yalom, such as group support, vicarious learning, and instilling hope (Sharry, 2001). West

(2010) outlined the unique advantages of using a wellness-based approach when counseling groups in rural settings. Generally, there is little disagreement among clients when it comes to working on what they can do to improve the quality of their lives. The focus on wellness and health fits for clients in any stage of change and makes sense to many clients as a reasonable focus for counseling (West, 2010). For example, some group members may want to strengthen their recovery plan, whereas others desire to work on other areas of their lives. Goals among members may be different, and members are typically respectful of these differences (West, 2010). Above all, the therapeutic alliance with all members must be given priority—the SFGT approach places a premium on establishing a strong therapeutic bond.

In SFGT, exploring exceptions is a particularly effective technique (West, 2010). However, West argued that for clients with substance use disorders it is better to phrase exceptions as "periods of success" or "periods of being alcohol free" rather than as times the problem does not happen. Consistent with SFT philosophy, clients can assess their strengths and what has worked and are encouraged to do more of the same. In addition, the miracle question is an effective strategy that all group members can reflect on and process within the group format (West, 2010).

SFGT is an alternative to traditional substance use counseling groups. However, it is important to keep in mind that one approach may not work with all clients. Clinicians, especially in the substance use treatment field, must be flexible enough to change the focus of sessions quickly.

SFGT Strategies and Process

There is no one standard way to conduct SFGT. However, each session most likely involves several of the techniques already discussed. Smock et al. (2008) provide a useful outline for a typical SFGT session format. I have adapted this outline based on my own experiences using SFGT, presented in Table 11.1. Keep in mind that this is only one example of what a session

TABLE 11.1   A Possible Session in SFGT

1.	Asks group members to introduce themselves and identify who they are. Build community and rapport.
2.	The leader or leaders identify common themes stated by the group members and then create a main theme for the group.
3.	This theme is presented to the group as a springboard for discussion. Members are invited to discuss the theme or, if needed, share with the group another issue that they would like to work on.
4.	Leader's ask a future-oriented question based on the theme, such as the miracle question.
5.	The leader listens for exceptions in how the clients answer the future-oriented question. Once exceptions have been identified, the leader gets as much detail as possible (e.g., "Tell me how you were able to avoid drinking ... ?").

(continued)

TABLE 11.1   A Possible Session in SFGT (*Continued*)

6.	Scaling questions are asked to assess each group members' progress toward their goals: What makes the client at a certain level rather than a 0? What steps can the client take to increase from a certain point to a half point or point higher?
7.	Leaders take a break to compliment the members for their hard work and provide a summary of the discussion up to this point, highlighting themes of success.
8.	Have clients inquire how others might rate them on the scaling question and provide a rationale for their ratings.
9.	Inquire how the theme for the day fits in with the group members' miracles.
10.	Clients are invited to assign themselves tasks and homework for the upcoming week. These tasks fit with how they will accomplish their goals.

Note: Adapted from Smock et al. (2008).

might look like. During another session, for example, the focus might exclusively be on another SFT strategy, such as the miracle question.

McCollum et al. (2003) outlined their typical format for substance use SFGT. They start with asking group members about successful movement toward goals, elaborate on how they can better meet their goals, and explore homework as to what clients did to achieve their goals. The assumption that belief in change leads to change underlies how the authors approach group counseling with substance-using clients. Using the miracle question, group members are asked to imagine what change would look like and how their life would be different. Even if the "miracle" did not happen and the client relapsed, McCollum et al. (2003) explored how the relapse was limited and what the client can learn from this experience to move forward.

McCollum et al. (2003) espoused the importance of clients taking the lead in their own group therapy. Clients are invited to set their own goals, design their own strategies, and think about a future in which change is realized. Confrontation, unsolicited advice, and telling the client what they ought to do is inconsistent with SFGT. Clinicians communicate respect for clients and where they are in the process of changing their substance use patterns.

Outcome Research

Berg (Allyn & Bacon Professional, 2001) noted that SFT is an inductively developed model and a clinically derived approach. She acknowledged that a shortcoming of SFT is the limited empirical base. Few outcome studies examining SFT or SFGT exist, especially related to substance use, although it remains a "promising" approach from an empirical standpoint (McCollum et al., 2003). Outcome research is building slowly (Corcoran & Pillai, 2009), as interest in the solution-focused method as applied to substance use disorders has increased. Smock et al. (2008) found SFGT to be more effective than traditional problem-focused substance use group treatment for level 1 substance users (those who "require outpatient treatment services for no more than 9 hours per week" [p. 109]). The authors also found that SFGT was effective in treating concomitant depression as well, demonstrating similar and sometimes better results than traditional group therapy. The authors noted, however, that despite the widely held application of SFT to substance use issues, more quantitative research is needed to further examine its efficacy.

In a more recent randomized control trial examining the effectiveness of SFBT among clients struggling with substance use and trauma-related problems, Kim et al. (2018) found that the SFBT group decreased both substance-related and trauma symptoms, although SFBT was no more effective than the control. The authors noted, however, that SFBT provides a viable strengths-based alternative to working with substance use and trauma.

In another study examining the effectiveness of SFGT compared with control among at-risk adolescents, Newsome (2004) found that adolescents in the SFGT group increased their grade-point average compared to the control group. Although Newsome did not directly assess substance use among adolescents, many of the at-risk adolescents in this study struggled with substance-related issues.

In a review of the outcome research on SFT, Corcoran and Pillai (2009) concluded the effectiveness of SFT is equivocal at this time, and that more empirical research is needed to establish its efficacy. One must keep in mind, however, that much of traditional quantitative clinical trial research operates from a positivist perspective (i.e., definite reality exists, deductive reasoning), which runs counter to postmodern philosophy. This fact alone makes research on SFT challenging. Nonetheless, SFT is becoming more popular among clinicians as a viable approach in substance use counseling (Berg & Miller, 1992; Mollet et al., 2018; Mott & Gysin, 2003; Pichot & Smock, 2009).

SFT in the Treatment of Diverse Populations

SFT is applicable to a wide range of clientele because it is guided by an underlying philosophy of honoring what the client wants, the client's goals, and coconstructing solutions. This stance in counseling serves to honor what clients bring to the table, no matter the sociodemographic background. SFT is an approach that respects strengths, attributes, talents, and resources, something that many clients who have faced discrimination and racism in their life may find empowering (Archer & McCarthy, 2007).

Several authors have examined the applicability and appropriateness of SFT with African American, Latino, and Asian clients (Cheung, 2001; Corcoran, 2000; Yeung, 1999). Corcoran (2000) noted the value of SFT for African American and Mexican American families because of its focus on context, cooperation, client-generated goals, de-emphasis on feelings, and focusing ahead rather than in the past. The focus on finding pragmatic solutions rather than deep psychological discovery is consistent with some Asian cultures (Kim & Park, 2008). Archer and McCarthy (2007) warned, however, that solutions between two cultures as different as those from the East and West can look much different considering language and cultural factors. The substance use clinician must be cognizant that both they and the client are on the same page when coconstructing solutions to drug use.

Evans and George (2008) listed seven guidelines for counseling African American clients. Although these guidelines should be utilized no matter what theory one is using, they particularly resonate with SFT. For example, being genuine in verbal and nonverbal communications, engaging in advocacy, and utilizing nonpsychological methods are consistent with how SFT clinicians work with clients. In addition, Brooks and McHenry (2015) noted the need for African American clients struggling with substance use disorders to have allies and supports available, especially from family members and spiritual components, in their recovery process. In SFT, the clinician serves as an ally, encouraging the client, celebrating success with them, and helping them begin the process of building a new, preferred way of being free of substance use.

Solution-focused counseling has been applied successfully in the treatment of alcoholism in Germany (Nelle, 2005). The NIK-Ambulanz was created in response to pressures from German insurance companies for shorter therapies in the treatment of alcohol problems. In this model, SFT principles, such as exceptions and the miracle question, were successful in helping clients maintain controlled drinking patterns and abstinence. Indeed, SFT has gained notoriety among many in the international community, especially in the UK and Europe.

It may be argued that SFT focuses too much on the self to generate solutions to one's problems and therefore might ignore important cultural and racial issues that have negatively impacted clients. Although there is respect for the social context, SFT is ultimately about what the *client* is doing well, how the *client* can do more of it, and how these "successes" can be built on for the *client* to construct solutions. However, one may question how this helps the Korean American client who struggles with heroin use disorder, who struggles with depression, and who, because of inherent biases in some societal institutions, is facing constant legal issues and overt racism? Looking for what the client is doing well may be a start but, as Evans and George (2008) noted, clinicians should empower clients to work toward eliminating institutional racism by helping to document and report incidents. Ignoring issues around racism or other "isms" do our clients a great disservice.

Many African American, Native American, and Asian American clients hold collectivism as an essential component in any healing process. SFT does not emphasize the collective, unless it is woven into what the client wants. When working with clients who rely on members of their community for healing, SFT clinicians must be flexible enough to understand that solutions to problems may involve connecting and reaching out to others. The Diverse Perspectives and Examples presents an example of how an SFT clinician might honor the collective when counseling an African American client.

DIVERSE PERSPECTIVES AND EXAMPLES

◇◇◇◇◇◇◇◇

SFT is about helping clients cocreate and live out solutions to their problems. For some clients from different cultural backgrounds, however, focusing too much on the self ignores the value of collectivism and community in solving their problems.

Can a clinician use SFT with diverse clients given this apparent philosophical difference? The following is an example of a brief exchange between a Caucasian clinician and a Hispanic American client, Sierra, in which the clinician operates from a SFT approach. Notice how the clinician keeps close to SFT philosophy, while also honoring Sierra's need to connect with his community.

CLINCIAN: Hello, Sierra. How are you doing today?

SIERRA: Hi. I'm fine, thanks.

CLINCIAN: We've talked a lot about what you want related to your drug use, and we've set some goals for you, and it looks like you have had some success with these. How were you able to do that?

SIERRA: Yeah, I guess I have had some success. I like all this setting goals and focusing on what I'm doing right. But something seems missing ... (did not really answer the question as something else was on her mind)

CLINCIAN: (careful not to get defensive) I see. What do you think is missing from your treatment and recovery?

SIERRA: Well, I mean, my family is so important to me, and I get a lot out of my church group, but we never seem to talk about that.

CLINCIAN: I hear what you are saying. You wish there was more discussion or even involvement in your recovery from important people in your life [client nods]. Tell me, *what is it that you want* in terms of including more of your family and church group in your treatment. (keeping consistent with SFT while also honoring what the client wants)

SIERRA: I don't know. Maybe we can just talk about them more. I mean, some things I agree with and some I don't. Sometimes I just need to talk it out, but I'm not sure what to say.

CLINCIAN: We can definitely do that. How about every week we take some time to discuss what went on the week before related to your family and church group, or any other community group you would like to discuss.

SIERRA: That sounds good.

CLINCIAN: I also am wondering, since you are a little unsure about what to say, how you have been able to discuss family issues or your church group already, perhaps in group therapy or with others. (clinician begins to access what has worked before related to client's desire to talk more about her family and community)

As one can see in this brief exchange, the clinician honors the client's desire to talk more about her family and church group influence and keeps consistent with SFT by (a) asking what the client wants related to more family and church involvement, and (b) exploring ways that she already has been successful at doing so. Over time, Sierra may wish to include family members in her own counseling.

CASE STUDY

Using SFT in the Case of Michael

The following vignette is an example of what SFT might look when applied to the case of Michael. The example is one of the beginning sessions in which the clinician incorporates several SFT techniques to help Michael began to think about solutions instead of problems.

CLINCIAN: Michael, last week you told me about your use of alcohol and cocaine, and that your wife, Anita, gave you an ultimatum that if you don't turn things around, she will leave you. You mentioned that you don't want to lose her. I would like to take some time to see if we can clarify your goal for coming here. (helping Michael to construct a well-formulated goal)

MICHAEL: Yeah, sounds good. I think for me it is that I just don't want to lose Anita.

CLINCIAN: That is a goal in coming here: You do not want to lose Anita. Tell me, what does "not losing Anita" look like to you? (helping to create a more concrete, behavioral goal)

MICHAEL: What do you mean?

CLINCIAN: Well, how will I (or anybody) know that you are acting in a way to not lose Anita? (helping Michael be more concrete and behavioral in his goal)

MICHAEL: I guess the first thing is that I would be less irritable, less angry. I see where you are going with this; I guess would also cut down on my drinking and stop cocaine use. If I did these things, I think she would stay.

CLINCIAN: So "not losing Anita" would look different. You would be less irritable throughout the day, and your substance use would be under control in terms of alcohol and eliminated in terms of cocaine. That is a little more specific. What will you be doing instead of being irritable and using substances? (formulating the goal in terms of the presence of something instead of the absence of something)

MICHAEL: Well, I always wanted to take a martial art; I think that would help with some of my anger given their focus on being calm and all. I also think I would be exercising and just enjoying life.

CLINCIAN: You would be taking some martial arts class, exercising, and just reminding yourself to enjoy life a little bit. That sounds like some positive steps you can take and will involve some hard work. (emphasizing the hard work needed to begin these steps)

MICHAEL: Yeah, I know. And that is the main issue. I mean, do I have the energy and time to devote to this stuff?

CLINCIAN: Michael, let me ask you a question that I like to ask clients when they begin counseling. It is a slightly different question than what has probably been asked before and you will have to use a bit of your imagination. Suppose you go home and go to bed tonight after today's session. While you are sleeping a miracle happens and "not wanting to lose Anita" and "substance use" is solved. Because you were sleeping, you didn't know that this miracle happened. What do you suppose will be the first small thing you will notice tomorrow morning that there has been a miracle overnight and the problem that brought you here, not wanting to lose Anita and substance use, is solved? (miracle question)

MICHAEL: I don't know. I know I would have had a better sleep because I would not have gone to bed so late the night before. I think I would just try to catch my mood and remind myself to just relax and enjoy life. I would talk to Anita; we don't seem to communicate much anymore. I would try to get some weightlifting in, maybe read a little before work. It would be different from what I do now! Now, I stay in bed and don't even talk to Anita. I crave a hit as soon as I get up. Sometimes I have a drink as an eye-opener.

CLINCIAN: Those are some of the things you are doing now. If the miracle happened you would be relaxing, enjoying life, talking to Anita, exercising, and perhaps reading a bit. What else would be different? (expanding the miracle)

MICHAEL: I would be avoiding my using buddies. I know they are a bad influence and I have thought about leaving that group. If a miracle happened, that would be one thing different; my buddies would have no influence on me.

CLINCIAN: I am curious how much of this "miracle" is happening already? What aspects of your miracle are already happening? (looking for exceptions)

MICHAEL: I have thought about exercising more, and lately I have been thinking about cutting ties with my using buddies. I guess that is about it.

CLINCIAN: You have thought about making some key changes—that is great! What within you led you to consider making these changes? (reinforcing successes, no matter how small; tapping into strengths)

MICHAEL: I just am sick of how I am feeling, and this Anita thing has got me worried. I don't want to lose her! I just think of what I could lose from my drug use and drinking and began to think about making some changes.

CLINCIAN: So, on a scale of 1–10, with 1 being making no changes toward your goal and 10 being making significant changes to reach your goal, where would you fall? (scaling question)

MICHAEL: I would say about a 4. Yeah, that sounds about right.

CLINCIAN: Almost halfway. So, you have made some changes. What do you think makes it a 4 instead of a 3? (scaling follow-up question)

MICHAEL: I bought a workout book the other week, but it has been collecting dust (chuckles). I just have been giving things more thought. The ultimatum, how I feel, my irritability. I just want it to go away. The fact that I am coming to counseling also makes it a 4. At least I am trying to get help.

CLINCIAN: You have some definite things you are doing: thinking more seriously about your relationship, making changes, buying a book. Using the same scale, what might you do to increase your place from a 4 to a 5? (scaling question follow-up)

MICHAEL: Maybe I could start walking each day. I have not exercised since my early 20s. But I could do that to get the ball rolling. I have some family nearby, and friends, who would be willing to maybe start a walking group. I also think I could maybe do some relaxation stuff to help me stay a little calmer. Oh, and getting rid of the alcohol in my house, that would make Anita really happy. I think that would take some time, though. Not sure I am ready for that.

CLINCIAN: To tick up from a 4 to 5 you would make some small changes such as walking each day with family and/or friends and doing some relaxation exercises. However, something like removing alcohol seems a little overwhelming at this point; that would be like an 8 or 9 on the scale. (reflection)

MICHAEL: Yeah, I am not quite ready to go there yet. However, I have stopped cocaine use and haven't had a hit for 2 weeks. I think that would be easier to stop because it has more consequences, and I can just avoid being around it.

CLINCIAN: Stopping cocaine is something that you believe is more serious in the eyes of Anita and something that is worth stopping. Looking more closely at alcohol will take more time. I appreciate that you have concluded to take a serious look at your use. Michael, at this point I would like to take a 5-minute break to gather my thoughts. Would that be okay? Feel free to grab a drink of water, use the restroom, or have a quick stretch.

At this point, the clinician opted to take a break to gather their thoughts. Notice how a reflection was inserted before the break to ease into this phase of the session. The objective during the break is to summarize the positive changes and successes, no matter how small. After the 5 minutes, the session resumes:

CLINCIAN: I would like to summarize some things that I have observed in our meeting today. First, you have a lot of courage coming here today and recognize that counseling is a beginning step to make some changes in your life. You are already thinking about making some very important changes, which speaks to your resolve in figuring some of this out. You can clearly identify several changes that would occur if a "miracle" happened, such as talking more with Anita, exercising, and reading to relax. In fact, you are doing some of these activities already, placing you at a 4 on a scale of 1–10. You have a lot of strength to be able to resist your using buddies for the past 2 weeks and recognize that you just don't think continued use is worth it. Based on what we have discussed so far, I see courage, resolve, strength, and perspective.

MICHAEL: (lets out a chuckle) This is so different from what I was expecting today. I guess when you put it that way, I am doing some things already. I wasn't even aware of the steps I am taking, but I am taking some. Maybe I just need to build on these.

CLINCIAN: Well, you mentioned "taking steps"; I wonder, 6 months from now when you have kicked this substance use stuff and are on the mend with Anita, what will your other family members notice different about you? (presupposition/relationship-oriented question combination)

MICHAEL: My family, I think, would see a happier Michael, one who seems a little less "high-strung" and more at peace with himself.

As a follow-up to Michael's last comment, the clinician might continue the SFT line of questioning by asking Michael what specific steps he will take to be a little happier and at peace with himself. The goal is to help clients create their own solution as behaviorally clear as possible. There are two key points to make regarding this vignette. First, Michael is clearly doing more than he thinks to make changes in his life. However, because we live in a problem-dominated world and our negativity bias, Michael cannot see these changes nor give himself credit for them. It is the SFT clinician's task to point out these successes. Second, when using SFT, it is common for beginning clinicians to abandon the line of questioning too early. For example, when I have supervised counseling interns practicing SFT, many will ask the miracle question or scaling question and then move on without appropriate follow-up. If a client is at a 4, for example, what makes it a 4 and not a 3? What does the client need to do to get to a 5? What does a 4 mean to the client? There is no shortage of follow-up questions. Even "resistant" clients who state that they are at a 0 on a scale of 1–10 can be thrown a follow-up question: "Why are you not at a -1?" The SFT clinician refuses to believe there is nothing positive in a client's life to build upon.

Strengths, Limitations, and Ethical Issues Related to SFT

SFT offers an exciting alternative to more traditional forms of substance use counseling. It is brief, time limited, and strength based and offers a unique set of techniques that help the client construct solution-oriented life narratives. I find the techniques in SFT, especially the miracle question, very useful to start things off with clients. Clients with substance use disorders often come to counseling with problem-saturated stories that they have been living out every day. SFT shifts attention to what is working, which is often more than the client normally perceives. The focus on what is working, successes, and the "miracle" sets the stage for new solutions to emerge. The intriguing aspect about SFT is that even if the client continues to use substances, the SFT clinician is *always* looking for improvement; maybe the client used heroin, but they did not use as much as last time. If so, then how were they able to use less this time around? Every ounce of success, even if small, is honored and explored.

At the same time, SFT may come across as overly simplistic to address the complexities of substance use. Proponents of more traditional substance use counseling may argue that looking for solutions is fine, but it is not enough; there are physiological, disease-based mechanisms at play in substance use disorders that need medical care. In addition, clients may be a bit confused as to what solution-focused questions mean. For example, clients might be asked to put themselves in the shoes of another person (e.g., "What would you say about what steps you need to take?"). This may seem bizarre and pointless to some clients. In such cases, counselors may have to slow down and explain what they want from the client. Table 11.2 highlights the additional strengths, limitations, and possible ethical issues related to SFT and substance use counseling.

TABLE 11.2   Summary of Strengths, Limitations, and Ethical Concerns of SFT in the Treatment of Substance Use Problems

Strengths	<ul><li>SFT can operate as a standalone approach or in combination with more traditional forms of substance use treatment. This may appease traditional clinicians who like the SFT approach but aren't willing to adopt it wholesale into their established practice.</li><li>Respectful, strength-based approach in which client has significant say in their own substance use treatment.</li><li>Proponents of SFT do not see incompatibility with traditional models of substance use treatment.</li><li>SFT is flexible and seeks economical solutions that work for the client (Linton, 2005).</li><li>Emphasis on client strengths, resources, and abilities. Moves away from problem-dominated narratives to solutions.</li><li>Helps clients regain self-confidence and self-esteem to bolster change.</li><li>SFT is well suited for group therapy, a popular format for clients struggling with substance use.</li></ul>

(continued)

TABLE 11.2   Summary of Strengths, Limitations, and Ethical Concerns of SFT in the Treatment of Substance Use Problems (*Continued*)

Limitations	• Substance use problems can be complex, as many occur alongside psychological, social, cultural, and physiological issues. One might wonder if SFT is too simplistic to account for the multifaceted complexities of comorbidity. • It is sometimes difficult to know where to go after the first few sessions using SFT. Inherently a brief counseling approach, there may be a struggle using SFT with substance use clients who clearly need longer term care. • There is limited empirical support for SFT, although researchers are beginning to slowly study the approach across a spectrum of problems, including substance use. • SFT has not sufficiently addressed the physiological aspects of substance use disorders. The risk here is ignoring biologically based cravings and neurological damage that results from prolonged drug use. • Referral sources who were trained in traditional substance use treatment models may not understand or be familiar with the SFT paradigm and thus question the effectiveness or prematurely determine that treatment is not, or will not, be, effective (Linton, 2005).
Ethical Issues	• Despite being perceived as a simplistic approach, SFT takes considerable skill and understanding to use competently. There is potential risk that some clinicians' lack of skill and theoretical understanding, as well as confusion as to its application, could constitute unethical practice (Linton, 2005). • SFT clinicians who fail to consider the physiological aspects of addiction might miss crucial factors that need attention. Cooperation with other health professionals is essential. • SFT may seem like a hodgepodge of techniques. SFT clinicians must use technique responsibly and skillfully and stay firmly grounded in the theoretical assumptions of the approach and building the alliance.

References

Allyn & Bacon Professional (Director). (2001). *Solution-focused therapy for the addictions with Insoo Kim Berg* [VHS]. Author.

Archer, J., & McCarthy, C. J. (2007). *Theories of counseling and psychotherapy: Contemporary applications*. Pearson.

Berg, I. K., & DeJong, P. (1996). Solution-building conversations: Co-constructing a sense of competence with clients. *Families in Society, 77*, 376–391.

Berg, I. K., & Miller, S. D. (1992). *Working with the problem drinker: A solution-focused approach*. Norton.

Brooks, F., & McHenry, B. (2015). *A contemporary approach to substance abuse and addiction counseling*. Alexandria: American Counseling Association.

Cheung, E. S. (2001). Problem-solving and solution-focused therapy for Chinese: Recent developments. *Asian Journal of Counseling, 8*, 111–128.

Corcoran, J. (2000). Solution-focused family therapy with ethnic minority clients. *Crisis Intervention & Time-Limited Treatment, 6*, 5–12.

Corcoran, J., & Pillai, V. (2009). A review of the research on solution-focused therapy. *British Journal of Social Work, 39*, 234–242.

de Shazer, S. (1991). *Putting differences to work*. Norton.

Duncan, B. L., Miller, S. D., Sparks, J. A., Claud, D. A., Reynolds, L. R., Brown, J., & Johnson, L. D. (2003). The session rating scale: Preliminary psychometric properties of a "working" alliance measure. *Journal of Brief Therapy, 3*, 3–12.

Evans, K. M., & George, R. (2008). African Americans. In G. McAuliffe & Associates (Eds.), *Culturally alert counseling: A comprehensive introduction* (pp. 146–187). SAGE.

Hanson, R. (2011). *Buddha's brain: The practical neuroscience of happiness, love, and wisdom*. PESI Seminars.

Kim, B. S. K., & Park, Y. S. (2008). East and Southeast Asian Americans. In G. McAuliffe & Associates (Eds.), *Culturally alert counseling: A comprehensive introduction* (pp. 188–219). SAGE.

Kim, J., Brook, J., & Akin, B. A. (2018). Solution-focused brief therapy with substance-using individuals: A randomized controlled trial study. *Research on Social Work Practice, 28*, 452–462.

Lewis, T. F., & Osborn, C. J. (2004). Motivational interviewing and solution-focused counseling: A consideration of confluence. *Journal of Counseling and Development, 82*, 38–48.

Linton, J. (2005). Mental health counselors and substance abuse treatment: Advantages, difficulties, and practical issues to solution-focused interventions. *Journal of Mental Health Counseling, 27*, 297–310.

Matto, H., Corcoran, J., & Fassler, A. (2003). Integrating solution-focused and art therapies for substance abuse treatment: Guidelines for practice. *The Arts in Psychotherapy, 30*, 265–272.

McCollum, E. E., Trepper, T. S., & Smock, S. (2003). Solution-focused group therapy for substance abuse: Extending competency-based models. *Journal of Family Psychotherapy, 14*, 27–42.

Metcalf, L. (1998). *Solution-focused group therapy*. The Free Press.

Miller, W. R., & Hester, R. (1986). Inpatient alcoholism treatment: Who benefits? *American Psychologist, 41*, 794–805.

Mott, S., & Gysin, T. (2003). Post-modern ideas in substance abuse treatment. *Journal of Social Work Practice in the Addictions, 3*, 3–19.

Mullet, N., Zielinski, M., Jordan, S. S., & Brown, C. C. (2018). Solution-focused brief therapy for families: When a loved one struggles with substance abuse. *Journal of Systemic Therapies, 37*, 15–28.

Nelle, A. C. (2005). Solution and resource-oriented addiction treatment with choices of abstinence or controlled drinking. *Journal of Family Psychotherapy, 16*, 57–68.

Newsome, N. S. (2004). Solution-focused brief therapy groupwork with at-risk junior high school students: Enhancing the bottom line. *Research on Social Work Practice, 14*, 336–343.

O'Hanlon, W. H., & Weiner-Davis, M. (1989). *In search of solutions: A new direction in psychotherapy*. Norton.

O'Hanlon, W. H., & Weiner-Davis, M. (2003). *In search of solutions: A new direction in psychotherapy* (rev. ed.). Norton.

Pichot, T., & Smock, S. A. (2009). *Solution-focused substance abuse treatment*. Routledge.

Sharry, J. (2001). *Solution-focused groupwork*. SAGE.

Smock, S. A., Trepper, T. S., Wetchler, J. L., McCollum, E. E., Ray, R., & Pierce, K. (2008). Solution-focused group therapy for level 1 substance abusers. *Journal of Marital and Family Therapy, 34,* 107–120.

Walter, J. W., & Peller, J. E. (1992). *Becoming solution-focused in brief therapy.* Brunner/Mazel.

West, E. C. (2010). Solution focused group treatment with publicly funded alcohol/other drug abuse clients in rural settings. *Alcoholism Treatment Quarterly, 28,* 176–183.

White, M., & Epstein, D. (1990). *Narrative means to therapeutic ends.* Norton.

Yeung, F. K. C. (1999). The adaptation of solution-focused therapy in Chinese culture: A linguistic perspective. *Transcultural Psychiatry, 36,* 477–489.

CHAPTER 12

Applying Adlerian Therapy in the Treatment of Substance Use Disorders

Introduction

When I was pursuing my master's in counseling degree, I recall taking one theories class as part of my training program. In this class, we covered a theory per week, which was typical across counseling training programs at the time. In fact, this method of teaching theories (one class, one theory per week) is still quite common today, although some counseling training programs may divide theoretical training into two semesters (e.g., Theories I and Theories II across fall and spring). After taking my one and only theories class, I recalled that the theory I understood *least* was Adlerian.

Our instructor for this master's theory course was a passionate teacher and did a fine job navigating through the various theoretical models. Ultimately, I came to the conclusion that Adlerian theory is a comprehensive theory, incorporating elements of psychoanalysis, cognitive, behavioral, constructivist, and what we today call postmodern ideas. To truly do Adlerian theory justice, I was going to have to take more than one class in my master's program. Indeed, as I continued my education in doctoral school, I developed a greater interest in Adlerian theory and wanted to learn more. I was fortunate to take an Adlerian theory class and decided that it would serve as the theoretical foundation for my future research. The more I delved into Adler's ideas, the more I realized that Adlerian theory could serve as an effective and comprehensive intervention for clients struggling with substance addiction.

Adlerian therapy is well suited for the prevention, treatment, and education about substance use problems (Linkenbach, 1990). The characteristics of Adlerian therapy—brief and time limited, present and future oriented, directive, and eclectic—make it suitable for mental health and substance use clinicians in today's managed care environment (Carlson et al., 2006). Adlerians are technical eclectics (Carlson et al., 2006), making the approach flexible enough to be incorporated into more traditional forms of substance use counseling. Adlerian clinicians are integrative in that they adopt what is useful for a particular client, in a particular situation, under particular circumstances. For example, the "addiction as disease" concept runs counter to the Adlerian notion of "soft determinism" (behavior determined jointly by environment and biology); however, if the disease concept is something that "fits" for a client, the Adlerian clinician is flexible enough to incorporate that in therapy. I have found in my own work with clients that the Adlerian notion of social interest, or one's contribution to society and sense of community/belonging, is an exceptionally powerful idea for those on the path to recovery.

In this chapter, I discuss the major tenets of Adlerian theory, especially the lifestyle, and how it can provide a comprehensive assessment and intervention model for clients dealing with substance use disorders. The theory's comprehensiveness will be evident throughout the chapter, and my aim is to illuminate the clinical application of substance-related problems. I intend to make the argument that Adlerian theory has been underutilized and overlooked in the general substance use treatment literature yet can serve as a viable treatment option for clinicians working with these issues. Much has been written about Adlerian theory in the application of substance-related problems; however, empirical research supporting its effectiveness with substance use problems, or other populations, continues to be sparse. I have included what little empirical support there is and acknowledge upfront that more empirical research is needed.

I begin with an overview of Adlerian theory and its many terms and concepts. This is followed by an Adlerian explanation of how substance use develops, drawing primarily on Adler's original ideas. I then present Adlerian theory in the context of diversity and multicultural application. Finally, the chapter concludes with an example of how Adlerian theory might apply to the case of Michael.

The Major Tenets of Adlerian Therapy: Brief Overview

The individual psychology of Alfred Adler operates under the assumption that all behavior is purposive and goal directed (Mosak & Maniacci, 1999). Human beings strive toward goals that they create and perceive as necessary to find their place in the world (Mosak & Maniacci, 1999). Furthermore, Adlerian theorists assume that a basic dynamic force is behind all human activity (Ansbacher & Ansbacher, 1956). This force involves a striving from a *perceived* position of "less than" or inferiority to a position of "more than" or superiority and always moves toward their created lifestyle goals (Ansbacher & Ansbacher, 1956). Based on this idea, Adlerian theory has been suggested as a model for understanding personality, as well as maladjustment (Keene & Wheeler, 1994). Maladjustment occurs when one's personal goals are inconsistent with social interest (Adler, 1956); the person strives for personal superiority without regard for the welfare of others (Keene & Wheeler, 1994).

A person's lifestyle—or characteristic ways of perceiving self, others, and the world—largely determines how they strive toward goals in life (Mosak & Maniacci, 1999). In Adlerian terms, useful lifestyle patterns are those that involve movement toward others and endorsement of the common good. Conversely, useless lifestyles involve movement away from others in the pursuit of selfish interests (Manaster & Corsini, 1982). Let's take a closer look at the concept of lifestyle, which Mosak and Maniacci (1999) stated is "perhaps the crowning achievement of Adler's thinking as a clinician" (p. 46).

Lifestyle

According to Ansbacher and Ansbacher (1956), Adler equated lifestyle with terms such as *self, ego, individuality,* the whole attitude toward life and, most notably, *personality*. It refers to a series of conclusions that individuals create about themselves, others, and the world (Manaster & Corsini, 1982). Believing in the unity of the individual, Adler (1956) posed that the lifestyle was self-consistent, meaning that individuals express their thinking, feeling, and acting in consistent ways according to their life goals. It refers to the vague, subjective guidelines individuals create and use to "move" through life (Mosak & Maniacci, 1999).

One can conceptualize lifestyle as a movement toward certain activities, people, and environments that constitute perceived success, or as movement away from activities, people, and environments that constitute perceived danger (Slavik, 1995). Manaster and Corsini (1982) likened the lifestyle to a blueprint for human living. The lifestyle is a philosophy of life and represents someone's plan of action, their propensities and consistent way of being (Manaster & Corsini, 1982). It is the central part of humans, our essence. It guides our morality, tells us how to fit in, and what behavior accomplishes socially useful goals (Manaster & Corsini, 1982).

According to Adlerian theory, lifestyles develop and become relatively stable early in life. Understanding the influences on lifestyle development is important because it gives insight into how individuals create their current themes, convictions, and goals. How childhood experiences, in general, contribute to lifestyle development is considered next.

Development of the Lifestyle

Many schools of personality, including the Adlerian school, believe that early experiences within the family environment play a large role in personality development (Manaster & Corsini, 1982; Sweeney, 2019). Adlerians see lifestyle development as occurring in early childhood (between birth and 5 years; Adler, 1956) and as the convoluted interaction between (a) biological factors and heredity; (b) social experiences, especially early experiences within the family; and (c) creative interpretations of these biological and social factors (Manaster & Corsini, 1982). Sweeney (2019) further noted that children develop a lifestyle to make sense out of the plethora of data from the environment and their own physical selves. Information comes from internal and external sources; lifestyle has an important influence on how these data are processed and utilized.

Adler (1929) suggested that examining one's childhood is important to understand their lifestyle. Indeed, Adler (1956) proposed that by the time a child is 5 years old "his attitude to his environment is usually so fixed and mechanized that it proceeds in more or less the same direction the rest of his life" (p. 189). Thus, by this age children are believed to have attitudes and beliefs about self, world, and others that provide the foundation from which to interact in the environment. Certainly, fluctuations can occur in the way a person uses their lifestyle; however, Adlerians believe that core assumptions and convictions, established in early childhood, remain relatively stable throughout the life span.

Numerous psychosocial factors also play a role in the development of a lifestyle. Adler (1956) emphasized how parents affect children and how children affect parents through family interactions. Parents are usually the most notable models in the child's life, and children learn by the natural and social consequences of their behavior within the family (Sweeney, 2019). Indeed, the lifestyle is believed to surface via parent–child interactions in early childhood and is influenced by social contexts, most notably the family milieu (Watts, 1999). For example, a key psychosocial factor contributing to the development of the lifestyle is the *family atmosphere*, or the affective tone of the family and home life (Mosak & Maniacci, 1999; Sweeney, 2019). Any family member can set the affective tone of a family, although the parental relationship usually has the largest influence (Mosak & Maniacci, 1999). The style of interaction between parents can do much to set a tone for the family, thus impacting the child's perceptions of the world, others, and self. The relationship between parents and children also can impact lifestyle development. Parenting that is authoritarian, harsh, and suppressive may lead to an anxious, guarded lifestyle among the children. On the other hand, parents who are overprotective and pampering may lead to children who feel they are not capable and cannot make it on their own if parents are not around (Sweeney, 2019).

Although the family atmosphere is important, a child's perception of the atmosphere become equally, if not more, important (Mosak & Maniacci, 1999). For example, two children from the same family who grow up in the same household may or may not have very different perceptions of the family atmosphere. An important assumption of Adlerian theory is the *phenomenological perspective*, which emphasizes a person's unique, idiosyncratic perceptions of facts and events. In fact, Adler was often more interested in a client's perception of facts, their phenomenological reality, rather than the facts themselves (Mosak & Maniacci, 1999).

Another factor that influences the development of the lifestyle is the individual's family constellation, Adler's nomenclature for the primary influences of family structure, values, and dynamics (Seligman & Reichenberg, 2014; Watts, 1999). The family constellation includes such factors as the lifestyle of each parent, how the parents get along (or do not get along), perceived birth order of the siblings, other significant relatives such as grandparents living with the family, and the overall theme of the family (Manaster & Corsini, 1982). The theme can be thought of as a motto or code, which governs how family members relate to one another (Manaster & Corsini, 1982). Again, it is the child's perception of the family constellation plays a key role in lifestyle development (Dinkmeyer & Sperry, 2000).

Adler was one of the first to note how sibling relationships play an important role in psycho-social development, and this also is considered an important aspect of the family constellation (Mosak & Maniacci, 1999). Within the family constellation, children often strive to "carve out" a place within the family. Often, if one child takes a certain path in life, their sibling will pursue a different path. Each sibling finds a way to map out territories on their own. Within the family constellation, older family members socialize younger children, either formally or informally, on what is appropriate and inappropriate behavior (Manaster & Corsini, 1982).

Lifestyle development also is impacted by the birth order of children (Seligman & Reichenberg, 2014). Birth order refers to the sequential position of someone in the family; however, Adlerians believe that the psychological position of children is of greater significance than chronological order in lifestyle development (Manaster & Corsini, 1982). Thus, the oldest child might perceive themself as the "third parent" for their younger sibling. Another first-born might perceive their position as one of entitlement and strive to be the center of attention, behavior that generally describes the "only child." Many factors can influence how children perceive their position in the family—age spacing, expectations of gender behavior, and their own, unique way of thinking (Manaster & Corsini, 1982). Perceptions of their place within the family and the various roles they adopt influence how children view the world and interact with others. Whereas some scientific research has supported Adler's assumptions about the impact of birth order, other findings suggest drawing caution when making birth-order interpretations (Seligman & Reichenberg, 2014).

Another aspect of sibling relationships that can influence lifestyle development is sibling rivalries. Generally, sibling rivalry occurs when two or more siblings strive to attain a greater proportion of parental attention (Manaster & Corsini, 1982). Children will experiment with many behaviors to get this attention. For instance, a child who becomes "sweet" yet doesn't receive parental attention may turn to more extreme measures, such as substance use, which finally get them attention from parents, albeit negative attention; some children actually prefer negative attention to no attention at all (Manaster & Corsini, 1982). The significance of this to lifestyle development is that if children continue in their patterns to garner attention from parents, these patterns can harden into a permanent lifestyle of seeking similar forms of attention from others (Manaster & Corsini, 1982). Getting attention from parents by using substances, for example, may reinforce this "movement" outside of the family.

In summary, many factors are believed to play a role in the development of one's lifestyle (Sweeney, 2019). Through the specific influences of parenting styles, sibling relationships, the family atmosphere, the family constellation, and biological factors, the child develops specific ways of "moving" through life. Of course, this list is not all-inclusive; societal, cultural, and peer influences play a role as well. The lifestyle is an amalgamation of all these factors, the result of the individual's subjective perceptions of these factors, and the choices they make in reference to these factors (Dinkmeyer & Sperry, 2000; Mosak & Maniacci, 2000). During the development of the lifestyle, a person creates core convictions that are more or less the same throughout the life span. These convictions often revolve around themes, and knowledge of a person's lifestyle theme may give clues as to the typical core convictions (and vice versa). It may be that clients who use substances and experience several negative consequences have certain convictions and themes that undermine healthy adjustment. The realignment of these mistaken beliefs becomes a focus in Adlerian counseling. The next section describes lifestyle convictions in more detail.

Lifestyle Convictions

At the core of the lifestyle is the set of convictions one has about the self, others, and the world. These convictions can be thought of as a collection of strongly held beliefs, which assist one in finding a place in the world (Mosak & Maniacci, 1999). Humans develop in early childhood a fictional image of what is needed to be safe, to be superior, and to belong, which forms the central goal of one's lifestyle (Dinkmeyer & Sperry, 2000). Indeed, Adlerians believe that all individuals strive to belong (Mosak & Maniacci, 1999), as many of our strongly held beliefs revolve around how best to fit in. Lifestyle convictions develop in early childhood via the immediate social network (i.e., the family environment).

From an Adlerian perspective, individuals are both passive recipients of information from the environment and active creators of the meaning of that information. Adler (1956) noted, "Every individual represents both a unity of personality and the individual fashioning of that unity. The individual is thus both the picture and the artist" (p. 177). As such, children actively construct what they believe to be necessary to fit in with their families (Mosak & Maniacci, 1999).

As children mature and develop lifestyle convictions (about self, others, and the world), they begin to create their own rules and assumptions that are specific to the individual and that form their underlying lifestyle philosophy (Manaster & Corsini, 1982). These rules and assumptions are what Adler termed "private logic." Children who rely exclusively on private logic begin to assume that the truths about life they have created are true for everyone else (Mosak & Maniacci, 1999). With broader experiences, however, children become exposed to the perceptions and views of others. Thus, they incorporate others' views into their own schemata of the world and begin to develop what Adler called "common sense." Common sense refers to the ability to think in common with others and experience a consensual perception of life (Mosak & Maniacci, 1999). Whereas all individuals create private logic, they also have some measure of common sense. Healthy adjustment occurs when one's private logic is connected to common sense and social interest (Seligman & Reichenberg, 2014). Dysfunctional lifestyles occur when problem solving is based on self-protective, private logic rather than more socially useful common sense. Such lifestyles become inflexible and incapable of productively coping with the tasks of life: work, love, and friendship (Dinkmeyer & Sperry, 2000). Lifestyles that balance private logic with common sense are believed to be more successful at adapting (Mosak & Maniacci, 1999).

The cognitive activities related to private logic, which take place below the threshold of consciousness, largely determine one's actions and are a significant influence on the lifestyle (Dinkmeyer & Sperry, 2000). According to Manaster and Corsini (1982), convictions from one's private logic are often inconsistent with common sense. These mistaken convictions are called *basic mistakes*. Basic mistakes are analogous to cognitive distortions, such as the tendency to overgeneralize, and can be so subtle that people do not even realize they are using them (Manaster & Corsini, 1982). A lifestyle analysis is an Adlerian counseling technique designed to assist one in becoming aware of and modifying these mistaken convictions (Sweeney, 2019).

One strategy Adlerians use to get at the heart of private logic, convictions, and basic mistakes is to complete the following syllogism: "I am ..."; "The world is ..."; "Therefore. ..."[1] (R. E. Watts, personal communication, August 1999; Sweeney, 2019). Relating the basic mistake idea to substance use, assume that a client struggling with an alcohol use disorder problem

---

[1] There are several variations on this syllogism, but in general the client is asked to make conclusions about self, and others, with the "therefore" providing a concluding overall lifestyle conviction that can be explored (Sweeney, 2019).

believes the following: "I am not accepted," "The world only accepts those who have fun and drink," "Therefore, I must party and drink to fit in." The critical mistake in this example is the demand this person places on themself that they must absolutely fit in to every social situation or they are a social failure. Acting on this conviction, they engage in inappropriate drinking to reach the mistaken goal of "I must have complete acceptance by everyone." Mistakes such as this assist a person's movement through life and may be at the heart of certain lifestyle themes. According to Mosak and Maniacci (2000), lifestyle convictions either enhance or restrict individual behaviors. If a person believes that, for example, "I must drink excessively to belong," they will seek behaviors that reinforce that conviction and restrict behaviors that run counter to it.

Another important component of the lifestyle is goals. As with convictions, within each lifestyle theme one can determine the typical goals a person is striving toward. This topic is considered next.

The Importance of Goals

Adler (1956), in discussing the impact of goals on lifestyle, stated:

> A child, being weak, feels inferior and finds himself in a situation which he cannot bear. Hence, he strives to develop, and he strives to develop along a line of direction fixed by the goal which he chooses for himself. The material used for development at this stage is less important than the goal which decides the line of direction. It is difficult to say how this goal is fixed, but it is obvious that such a goal exists and that it dominates the child's every movement. (p. 187)

A key assumption underlying Adlerian theory is that all behavior is *teleological*; that is, it is purposive or goal directed. Therefore, goals play an important role in the direction and path one takes to progress through life. Adler (1929) stated, "The dynamic value of mental, emotional, and attitudinal movements consists of their direction toward, or determination by, a goal which has for the individual the meaning of securing for him what he regards as his position in life" (p. 180). These goal-directed movements involve an individual's efforts to move from a perceived minus situation to a perceived plus situation (Adler, 1956). Goals are intimately tied to one's lifestyle: "the style of life is ... the individual's opinion of himself and the world and his unique way of striving for the goal in his particular situation" (Ansbacher & Ansbacher, 1956, p. 172). The connection between goals and lifestyle lies in the convictions we hold: If individuals understand the goal of their behavior, they can understand the convictions that move them toward that goal.

However, sometimes humans engage in inappropriate behavior or, in Adlerian terms, behavior that is useless and inconsistent with social interest to accomplish goals. Dreikurs and Soltz (1964), for example, identified four goals of misbehavior for children: attention, power, revenge, and display of inadequacy. These four goals of misbehavior are observed in adulthood as well (Manaster & Corsini, 1982). One can see how problematic substance use might develop based on these goals. For example, a client who is in a tumultuous relationship may try various tactics to garner more attention from their spouse. When attention is still lacking after these efforts they may demand it by turning to more extreme measures such as heavy drinking. The goal in this instance might be to obtain a measure of power over their spouse, for whom they hold resentment (e.g., "I'll show them who is in charge; I can do whatever I want!!). When these efforts fail, they may seek revenge over feelings of being hurt and as if they are being treated unfairly. They are no longer seeking attention or power; rather, they feel ostracized and disliked, believing that the only way to be "successful" in the family is to make everyone hate them. They seek revenge by engaging in further heavy drinking, performing high-risk behaviors, and making their spouse and family suffer the fallout. Once they discover that drinking and associated consequences make them miserable, the goal of helplessness may emerge, in which they convey through behavior that "I cannot be successful, so what is the use of trying to live in a useful way?" (Manaster & Corsini, 1982). This helpless stance may lead to a depressive episode, in which case they engage in further alcohol consumption to self-medicate.

All humans seek attention, power, and revenge to varying degrees, but if one's goal were to "seek power over others no matter what the cost," for example, then this person is striving against the welfare of others. From an Adlerian perspective, this misguided goal is what is important, although misguided attempts to accomplish goals have also been emphasized by followers of Adler (Kopp, 1986; Mosak, 1991). Generally, much information can be gleaned from behavior once we understand the goals behind it (Sweeney, 2019): "If we know the goal of a person, we can undertake to explain and to understand what the psychological phenomena want to tell us" (Adler, 1956, p. 196).

The Tasks of Life

Adler (1929) stated that a healthy person creates enough energy and courage to adequately meet these tasks of life (also referred to as work, friendship, and love). The attitudes that one holds to these tasks are an important component of one's lifestyle (Adler, 1956). Adler (1931/1998) believed that how a person responds to the three life tasks reveals their perspective of the meaning of life. Suppose an individual is a diligent worker, has a satisfactory intimate relationship, and enjoys the company of many friends. Adler would say that such an individual would have sufficient courage to face the tasks of life. Meaning to this person might center on working hard and contributing to the common good.

In summary, development of the lifestyle, lifestyle convictions, goals, and how individuals approach the tasks of life all contribute and play an important role in the lifestyle. As we will see, understanding one's lifestyle aids the substance use clinician in formulating interventions.

Social Interest: The Heart of Healthy Human Functioning

Adler (1929) stated that the healthy human is one who lives in society and whose life movement is such that society garners an advantage from their work. Such a person would be said to have social interest. Social interest is *the* major key to healthy human functioning (Rareshide & Kern, 1991). Indeed, Adler (1979) stated that social interest is a critical factor for mental health. Although many definitions and perspectives exist, it can generally be defined as a genuine concern for others, a cooperative approach toward life, and striving for a healthy community (Adler, 1979). Individuals who display social interest function according to values that move a person toward the socially useful side of life (Ansbacher, 1991). Their choices allow them to meet life's demands, as they are responsible, creative, and cooperative members of society (Sweeney, 2019). Successfully completing the Adlerian life tasks depend, according to Adler, on high levels of social interest (Ansbacher, 1991). Destructive behaviors, including substance use disorders, are theorized to stem from a lack of social interest.

An important component of social interest is empathy toward others (Ansbacher, 1991). Empathy, in this context, refers to seeing situations as others see them and identifying with the struggles and joys of fellow humans. Empathy is contrasted with what Ansbacher calls "private intelligence" (analogous to private logic, discussed earlier) or idiosyncratic, selfish ways to handle the tasks of life. Such private intelligence implies a lack of common sense and is a key contributing factor to "all failures in life" (Ansbacher, 1991, p. 38) and mental disturbance. Empathy encourages one's self-concept to grow in a healthy, cooperative manner, which contributes to the development of their social interest (Mosak & Maniacci, 1999).

According to Ansbacher (1991), high social interest implies a connection with all of life and is equated with a positive attitude toward fellow human beings, nature, objects in the environment, and even the self. Indeed, those who exude high social interest not only show concern for the common good but also contemplate their own feelings of dignity, worth, courage, and optimism (Ansbacher, 1991; Kopp, 1986; Sweeney, 2019). This suggests that social interest includes coalescing one's interests with the interests of others to promote "essential harmony with and affirmation of mankind. This is at the basis of mental health and happiness" (Ansbacher, 1991, p. 37).

Mosak (1991) suggested that those with social interest have courage. Courage refers to having the will to meet life's tasks, even if there is a chance to be imperfect. Thus, when individuals have the *courage to be imperfect,* they do not feel a need to elevate themselves, put others down, or withdraw from life. Adler (1956) considered the person who lacks courage as one who has "mistaken answers to the tasks of life" (p. 299). Lack of courage, or discouragement, is believed to be a common component to all psychological problems (Dinkmeyer & Sperry, 2000). Importantly, the Adlerian perspective toward psychological problems is nonpathological, preferring to view clients as discouraged rather than "sick" (Watts, 1999). Courage is considered an important element of social interest (Mosak, 1991), and those who lack courage may find it difficult to strive for superiority in healthy and useful ways.

Although many individuals use substances to enhance group cohesion and bonding, substance use is thought to hinder the growth of a genuine connection among members of a group, thus facilitating the path to a "pseudo-community" (Dreikurs, 1990). A likely explanation for destructive substance use patterns is that the interests of those with substance use problems are not consistent with those of the larger community. The behaviors are more individual and selfish, such as drinking or using to "get high," forget about problems, or simply escape. Some support for the idea that lower levels of social interest are associated with greater alcohol consumption was provided by Wechsler et al. (1995), who found that a risk factor for binge drinking among college students was the belief that community service was *not* important.

Kopp (1986) noted that goals such as appearing attractive and sociable are not undesirable per se; rather, it is the method for accomplishing these goals that is considered socially useful or useless. Kopp further emphasized Adler's notion that all humans strive for significance in their lives to overcome inevitable inferiorities. However, striving for significance without social interest represents a failure to meet life tasks. Compensation for inferiority feelings is healthy only if it contributes to others and oneself.

Dreikurs (1990), a contemporary of Adler's, explained the emergence of substance-related behaviors based on Adler's view of lifestyle maladjustment. Dreikurs believed that individuals with substance use disorders possess a deficiency in social interest that develops when children are not properly prepared for the tasks of life. They begin to exhibit a proclivity toward self-interests without regard for others. Dreikurs believed that individuals with alcohol use disorder often formulate their personalities in a situation of excessive pampering, one common reason leading to lifestyle maladjustment. Such individuals become so accustomed to having their way that they become dependent on others and may exploit them for their own advancement (Dreikurs, 1990).

Dreikurs (1990) further noted that individuals who fail to develop social interest as children become impatient and do not feel capable and mature enough to handle the tasks of life. These individuals are believed to strive toward pleasure without social interest, and this represents the foundation for the development of substance use problems.

Application of Adlerian Therapy With Substance Use Disorders

The process of Adlerian therapy for substance use disorders follows a similar format for other presenting problems. The following overview highlights key theoretical principles in substance use treatment, Adlerian group therapy, the goals of Adlerian therapy, as well as numerous techniques that are at the substance use clinician's disposal when working from an Adlerian perspective. In this overview I emphasize individual treatment; however, many of the techniques and strategies could apply to group formats as well.

Many Adlerians find traditional concepts of substance addiction, such as the disease model concept, incompatible with Adler's notion of self-determination and the importance of client choice (Prinz, 1993). Indeed, Adlerian theory is a *psychology of use*, meaning that individuals are believed to choose symptoms to support their faulty lifestyle goals. Some Adlerians, however, regard the disease concept as a helpful "fiction" that individuals adopt to reassure them that they are not "moral degenerates." These contrasting views suggest that Adlerian therapy has some flexibility in how clinicians work with clients.

Based on his interview of 16 prominent Adlerians, Prinz (1993) summarized several theoretical principles that this group thought was especially applicable to the treatment of alcoholism.

These include fostering social interest, living with inferiority feelings without guilt, identifying the purpose of drinking, following the four goals of Adlerian therapy (explained later), examining basic mistakes, and using encouragement. Although these principles apply to alcohol, it is reasonable to assume that many, if not most, could also apply to other substance use problems. Several of the principles based on Prinz's (1993) work are listed, followed by a brief explanation (for a full list and discussion of each principle, see Prinz, 1993).

- **Social interest.** A key Adlerian principle in which clinician helps clients create and pursue positive, socially useful goals.

- **Teleology.** All symptoms, including substance-related behaviors, have a purpose. The idea is to help clients explore this purpose and find healthier ways to satisfy needs.

- **Holism.** Clients are viewed as whole beings rather than as labels such as "addict" or "alcoholic."

- **Self-determination.** It all comes down to choice. Clients can choose how they want to live their lives, including how much they wish to be involved in their own recovery.

- **Phenomenology.** All clients who use substances are unique individuals with unique causes of, and influences on, their substance use disorders.

- **Understanding the client.** The lifestyle assessment is a key strategy in Adlerian theory. Much more on this will be discussed later in the chapter.

- **Goal alignment versus denial.** Adlerian clinicians establish and maintain a mutually cooperative therapeutic relationship, where goals, interventions, and outcomes are discussed between clinician and client.

- **Life task emphasis.** Prinz (1993) outlined this beautifully. He argued that most drug and alcohol treatment programs focus on the substance, what it does, and the problems it causes. He further stated, and I wholeheartedly agree, that most clients know this information and can be as knowledgeable as the agency staff. What clients are missing, according to Prinz, are the courage, inspiration, and skills in meeting Adler's life tasks.

With this insight in mind, treatment focuses on helping clients function better in the areas of work, friendship, and love, areas previously shirked due to drug use (Prinz, 1993). Clinicians should levy the client's relationship to work and determine if it expands their life in healthy ways or creates more stress. Encouraging the client to be a part of a treatment group can be an important way for them to establish genuine connections with others, practice social skills, and gain interpersonal feedback. The family can be a critical foundation of support and encouragement and assessing this aspect of the client's life also is vital (Prinz, 1993). It is understandable that many forces in the client's life, such as poverty, racism, or other forms of discrimination, may preclude fully realizing these tasks of life. The astute Adlerian clinician is aware of these sociocultural issues and works with the client for how best to solve their substance use problems.

- **Self.** Individuals with substance use disorders have not only hurt others but hurt themselves in terms of self-loathing and neglect of healthy lifestyle pursuits and hobbies. Diet, exercise, and overall physical and mental health are ignored. An Adlerian approach focuses on helping the client cultivate self-respect and build on strengths that lead a healthy lifestyle.

- **Cosmos.** Spirituality has been included as an additional task of life, beyond Adler's original three. "It is important for problem drinkers who have lost faith in self others, and the world to deal with issues of spirituality" (Prinz, 1993, p. 102).

Adlerian Group Therapy

Dreikurs was one of the first Adlerians to recommend group psychotherapy for drinkers, based on the group format's ability to be a vehicle for social interest development (Prinz & Arkin, 1994). Indeed, the Adlerian substance use literature hosts a bevy of group-based strategies and techniques for the Adlerian clinician (Linkenbach, 1990; Mansager et al., 1995; Prinz & Arkin, 1994). Prinz and Arkin highlighted a successful alcoholism treatment program that incorporated Adlerian principles as their primary clinical approach. The program was almost exclusively group based. In this program, perspectives such as "powerlessness over alcohol" were replaced with discussions about choice and self-determination. The groups were educative in nature, consistent with the general view that Adlerian therapy is essentially an educative process.

Goals of Adlerian Therapy

The process of traditional Adlerian therapy generally includes four key components: building the relationship, understanding and investigation, interpretation, and reorientation and change. Each component builds on the previous one, providing structure to the therapeutic process.

Building the Relationship

As with many therapeutic approaches, Adlerian clinicians place a premium on the counseling relationship. Empathy and encouragement are the main engines that drive the development of rapport.

Understanding and Investigation

The second component of Adlerian counseling corresponds to psychological assessment. A major task of the Adlerian clinician is to comprehend what drives the client and how they move through life. Does the client move toward others or away from others? Does the client appear to show social interest? What private logic appears to be behind their substance use? What is the client's lifestyle like and how does it get in the way of healthy human functioning? What is the purpose of the substance-related symptoms? Adler believed that understanding early childhood experiences, particularly related to one's family, was critical to understanding the client's dynamics (Ansbacher & Ansbacher, 1956). A thorough exploration of childhood experiences provides understanding as to lifestyle patterns. Basic mistakes, low social interest, poor striving, and private logic often form early. Through the Adlerian assessment process, negative lifestyle patterns can be identified, which heightens awareness and opens possibilities for corrective action.

The primary tool the Adlerian clinician uses to help understand the client's lifestyle and how it connects to psychological and behavioral problems is the *lifestyle assessment*. The lifestyle assessment generally comes in one of two varieties: objective measures or the semi-structured clinical interview. An example of an objective lifestyle assessment is the Basic Adlerian Scales for Interpersonal Success (BASIS-A; Wheeler et al., 1994). The BASIS-A is a 65-item measure that assesses five general lifestyle themes: Belonging-Social Interest, Going Along, Taking Charge, Wanting Recognition, and Being Cautious. The measure takes 10–15 minutes to administer, which is attractive to busy clinicians who may not have time for lengthier assessments. The interpretation of the BASIS-A provides a lifestyle profile for the client and clinician to use as a foundation for further counseling.

In my professional practice, I prefer to use the lengthier clinical lifestyle interview to capture the client's movement and personality qualities. Although more time-consuming, the clinical lifestyle interview allows for a richer portrayal of the client's life. There are a bevy of resources one can consult that provide guidelines for how to conduct a lifestyle interview (Manaster & Corsini, 1982; Maniacci, 1999; Sweeney, 2019). In general, however, the Adlerian lifestyle interview should include at least three components: questions to assess the family atmosphere, questions to assess the family constellation, and questions that target early recollections. Let's look at each in turn.

Family Atmosphere

Family atmosphere refers to the "emotional tone" of the family while the client was a child. In general, the clinician is looking for emotional words that describe what it was like growing up in a particular family environment. Examples include happy, sad, "like walking on eggshells," chaotic, nerve-racking, anxious, blue, depressed, paranoia, abusive, and so forth. Clients can report as many words to describe their upbringing as they wish. It is remarkable how the emotional tone clients describe mirrors their current emotional problems. For example, I counseled James (name disguised), a 44-year-old African American male who struggled with alcoholism. Growing up, James reported that the primary emotion displayed in his family was anger, rage, and chaos. In addition to alcohol problems, part of James's counseling included themes of intense anger that he often displayed toward his family. An important piece of his counseling was discovering what purpose the anger served in his family and how that parallels his struggle with anger today.

There are several questions that can assess for one's family atmosphere. Following are typical questions that I use in an Adlerian lifestyle assessment:

- Describe your family environment growing up as a child.
- If you were to describe your family environment growing up, what words would you use? Focus your answers particularly on emotions.
- What was it like growing up in your home, emotionally?

Family Constellation

As noted earlier, family constellation refers to the family structure, values, and dynamics while the client was a child (Sweeney, 2019). It includes such factors as parental relationship, sibling–parent relationships, client–sibling relationships, and so forth. As one can imagine, the larger the family, the greater potential for complex interactions that influence and shape one's lifestyle.

There are several questions one can ask to comprehend the client's family constellation. In addition, because family constellation comprises many elements, there is a broader line of questioning compared to family atmosphere. Following are some examples of questions that assess family constellation:

- How did your parents get along? Was their marriage happy or unhappy?
- Who received the most attention from your parents? The least?
- Which child did your parents favor most?

Early Recollections

Early recollections (ERs) are an important aspect of the lifestyle assessment. Adler (1929) called early memories "old remembrances" and believed that individuals do not select memories accidentally; rather, early memories were seen as invented, selected, or revised by the individual to reflect current lifestyle patterns (Ansbacher & Ansbacher, 1956). ERs give clues as to the client's basic attitudes and approach for meeting the tasks of life, which illuminates the motives and purposes of current behavior (Sweeney, 2019).

Adler considered early recollections about childhood events one of the most useful ways to explore personality (Ansbacher & Ansbacher, 1956). He was fascinated that out of the plethora of memories we hold, the client chooses a particular one to share. He suggested that individuals select remembrances that correspond with how they currently feel and what they currently believe, while overlooking others.

The process of collecting early recollections begins with the question "Think back a long time ago when you were little, and try to recall one of your earliest memories, one of the first things that you can remember" (Clark, 2002, p. 92). Ideally, ERs are before the age of 8 and include one, single incident. After the ER is provided, three additional questions are used as follow-up (a) "Is there anything else you can recall in the memory?" (b) "What is the most vivid part of the memory that stands out for you?" (c) "What feelings or emotions did you have at that time?" (Clark, 2002).

The number of ERs can range from 1 to 10 and depends on several factors, including client comfort level with providing recollections, the number and depth of recollections, and how useful they are in interpreting the client's life. Clark (2002) stated that three recollections are often sufficient for clinical interpretation. However, I usually aim for five to six recollections, which provide enough information while at the same time avoids overwhelming clients. Some clients move through this process of the assessment quickly, whereas others tend to move more slowly, sometimes struggling to remember anything from childhood (which may also provide clinical insights).

There are many ways to interpret early recollections (Clark, 2002, 2013; Manaster & Corsini 1982; Mosak, 1958; Sweeney, 2019). According to Mosak (1958), early recollections may provide themes in the person's life, and these should generally be examined first before specific elements. Individuals (e.g., mother, father, friends, and siblings) who appear in early recollections should not be thought of as literal figures, but rather prototypes of authority or having other significant relational qualities (Mosak, 1958). Other elements of the early recollection can be explored: the client's general direction of movement (toward or away from others), the degree of client social interest, the level of activity versus passivity, the method of striving for superiority, how they deal with feelings of inferiority, and whether the client is an observer/participant in life.

The Adlerian clinician must be careful to secure recollections rather than reports (Mosak, 1958). The distinction is important because recollections are projections that serve as metaphors related to the client's inner dynamics whereas reports are vague, value laden, and lack detail (Clark, 2000). Thus, recollections are of greater clinical value and utility. For example, a client might report that they remember going to the farmer's market every Saturday morning as a kid. This vague report does not offer the insights and interpretive value that early recollections do. Early recollections involve clear, distinct single experiences and are discussed as if happening in the moment. Adler (1931/1998) noted,

> The first memory will show the individual's fundamental view of life, her first satisfactory expression of her attitude. It allows us to see at one glance what she has taken as the starting point for her development. I would never investigate a personality without asking for the first memory. (p. 60)

Adler (1931/1998) suggested that as clients progress through counseling and improve their current outlook and circumstances, their early recollections may change accordingly. For example, a client struggling with a substance use disorder may recall memories with themes of anger, fear, and pain. After a period of abstinence, their recollections may reveal brighter moments in their childhood, reflecting their new life perspective without substances. Indeed, one way to gauge client progress is to secure early recollections at different points throughout the counseling process. Clear changes in thematic content, emotions, and early relationships may suggest that the client has a more positive outlook.

A complete and thorough overview and examination of the interpretive process of early recollections is beyond the scope of this book. The reader is referred to several excellent resources for how to utilize and interpret early recollections within the counseling process (Carlson et al., 2006; Clark, 2000, 2013; Manaster & Corsini, 1982; Mosak, 1958; Olson, 1979; Powers & Griffith, 1987; Shulman & Mosak, 1988, as cited in Clark, 2000; Sweeney, 2019).

Mansager et al. (1995) incorporated early recollections into their group work with adolescents who problematically used substances. Their creative technique, called *interactive discussion of early recollections*, was designed to help adolescents gain greater insights into how their lifestyles play a role in their using substances. There are five general steps to this technique:

1. **Introducing ERs.** Clients are introduced to the concept of ERs and how they are different from reports.

2. **Gathering ERs.** ERs are written down and gathered by the clinician.

3. **Clients guess about generic ERs.** Here clients are read generic ERs and are then asked what is going on in these cases that might connect to substance use. Another method is for the clinicians to read a series of characteristics and then match these with the various generic cases.

4. **Clients guess about each other's ERs.** The previous step prepares clients for this step. Group members' ERs are shared. The group member whose ER is being read is to listen quietly as the group responds to counselor queries and offers comments and feedback. Emphasis is placed on positive aspects of the client's lifestyle (as reflected in the ER).

5. **Giving/receiving feedback about the accuracy of peer guessing.** The group member who offered their ER has a chance to discuss with peers the accuracy of any interpretations provided. This feedback to the group allows the group member to correct any misperceptions that have arisen and perhaps explore how misperceptions started in the first place.

Making Sense of the Lifestyle Assessment

Family atmosphere, family constellation, and early recollection data can provide a wealth of insight and information into the client's typical lifestyle patterns. From this assessment, the Adlerian clinician looks for significant themes, methods of striving, levels of social interest, approaches to accomplish the tasks of life, purposes of behaviors, and, if possible, one overarching goal on which the lifestyle is based. Basic mistakes and private logic also can be gleaned from such an assessment. Clinicians can create a "clinical summary"[2] based on the following questions:

1. What is the primary origin of the problem—physical, psychological, or both (Maniacci, 1999)?
2. How does the person move related to others and goals (away from them, toward them, with resistance) (Maniacci, 1999)?
3. Can the purpose of the symptoms(s) be determined (Maniacci, 1999)?
4. Based on the person's lifestyle and early recollections, how would you answer the syllogism "I am … ; the world is … ; therefore … " ?
5. Does the client harbor any "unfinished business" based on past experiences?

---

2   The clinical summary, especially the first three questions listed, is based on Maniacci (1999).

6. What was this person's family atmosphere like? Family constellation? How do these influence their current symptoms?
7. What is this person's level of social interest? Is it evident in the data or absent? How do they resist social interest, if at all?
8. What is the client's private logic on how to be somebody, how to have a place, how to be important?
9. What patterns of similarities and differences were there among siblings?
10. What was the client's sense of belonging, security, and being cared about in the family?
11. What are the client's strengths and how can they be used in counseling?
12. What was the experience of completing the assessment like for the client? What was it like to recount childhood like this? What insights emerged for the client?

The clinical summary also can include further insights, observations, or information that the clinician believes important to share. Whether to provide the client with the written summary is up to the clinician. In my practice, I often write a summary report, guided by the questions and present a copy for the client to have as we go through the assessment results and feedback.

It has been notable in my clinical experience how many clients simply appreciate the process of the lifestyle assessment, even when childhood experiences were negative. There is something about "telling their story" that is cathartic, and most find the process surprisingly fulfilling. The lifestyle assessment interview not only allows the clinician to gather important information but is a way to build rapport.

Interpretation

Once the Adlerian clinician gathers information via objective and/or subjective lifestyle assessment methods, they then interpret the findings within an Adlerian theoretical framework. For Adler (1956), there are many "meanings" (beliefs or opinions) that can be gleaned from client data, with each meaning an approximation of the truth. Adler was always fond of saying "everything could be different" when making an interpretation (Sweeney, 2019). Because several meanings can emanate from client experiences, clinician interpretations should be offered in a tentative manner, as if hypothesizing what might be leading to the client's distress. Adlerians call this stance *hypothesis interpretation*. Clinicians can determine if an interpretation is on the mark by noting the client reaction. If an interpretation does not fit the client's experiences, they will usually inform the clinician and subsequently the interpretation can be revised.

Reorientation and Change

The final stage of Adlerian counseling involves education, reorientation, and strategies to promote change. Adlerian therapy has a strong educational component, and it is in this final stage that clients are taught the likely reasons for their current struggles and methods to overcome them. Reorientation and change involve selecting a new attitude and approach to life. Adler believed insight was necessary but not sufficient for behavior change; clients must become familiar with and practice a new way of being in the world. Changing behavior often leads to new levels of insight. For example, a client with alcohol and cocaine use disorders may come to understand that their substance use developed as a reaction to a chaotic home life in which their mother and father were constantly fighting and where they were never taught appropriate boundaries. Reorientation might focus on challenging their convictions that "anything goes" and that "the fast and easy life is the only way to accomplish my goals." Their faulty lifestyle goal of "revenge and power" at the expense of others could be confronted, with the introduction and encouragement of social interest. A fundamental shift in thinking, behaving, and feeling, in essence a new approach to the world, is a key criterion for successful Adlerian counseling.

Adlerian-Based Techniques

Adlerian therapy is not a technique-laden approach. Techniques are of secondary importance to understanding, empathy, and compassion. Adlerians are free to use what works, if the strategy is respectful and will serve a useful purpose. Mosak and Maniacci (1999) noted that Adlerian therapy is based on an analytic–cognitive behavioral psychology. Thus, analytic techniques, such as the assessment of early childhood experiences, as well as cognitive and behavioral techniques, fit well within an Adlerian philosophy. In addition, Watts (1999) pointed out the remarkable similarities between postmodern approaches (constructivist and social constructionist thinking) and Adlerian psychology. Sweeney (2019) connected developmental counseling and therapy approaches to assist with the interpretation of lifestyle assessments. Adler was the forerunner for many contemporary counseling approaches. A brief description of each technique typically unique to Adlerian therapy is provided, followed by an example.

Lifestyle Assessment

Lifestyle assessment is a key technique/strategy in Adlerian therapy. Much of the learning about the client and ideas for interventions emanate from the lifestyle assessment.

Miracle Question

Adler often asked his patients, "If a miracle happened and you no longer had your symptoms, how would your life be different?" If the client stated, "I would be able to hold a job and wouldn't be so angry toward everyone," the problem (severe substance use) most likely has psychological roots, especially in terms of how the client is *evading the tasks of life* (Carlson et al., 2006). Treatment would then focus on encouraging the client to meet the tasks of life in a healthy and socially interested way. Sometimes clients might respond in a way that suggests their life would be different by relieving physiological complications from exessively consuming alcohol or drugs. Indeed, clients could respond suggesting the presenting problem has both physiological and psychological components (as would be the case with many substance use disorders). In this case, the client would be encouraged to seek medical assistance to assist with the physical aspects of substance use concomitant with psychotherapy.

Increase Social Interest

The central role of social interest in Adlerian theory was explained earlier. Related to substance use, the clinician may encourage a client who struggles with a substance use disorder to become a sponsor in his NA group or strive to consider how they might give more to the community.

Encouragement

Sweeney (2019) devoted an entire chapter to this foundational skill, encouragement, which is at the heart of Adlerian counseling. Primarily a growth/wellness model, Adlerian counseling emphasizes optimism, hope, and growth. The client brings many talents, skills, and abilities to the table, including creativity, competence, and resilience (Watts et al., 2008). These abilities are honored and used as resources in the counseling process. Adlerians believe a growth/wellness model more clinically useful, respectful, and positive compared to a *sickness* model; they conceptualize clients as discouraged rather than sick (Watts et al., 2008).

Adlerians consider encouragement the cornerstone behind healthy human development, and it is the primary and critical counseling "stance" in sessions (Watts et al., 2008). Dreikurs (1967, as cited in Watts et al., 2008) stated that presenting problems are "based on discouragement" and without "encouragement, without having faith in himself restored, [the client] cannot see the possibility of doing or functioning better" (p. 62). Adler's (1956) counseling and consulting work confirmed for him the critical nature of encouragement and came to believe that all psychotherapy is a process of encouragement.

Watts et al. (2008) identified several methods for incorporating encouragement into the counseling process. These include (a) honoring client's strengths and abilities, focusing on successes rather than failures, and building on these successes; (b) exploring the client's identity by helping them define who they are rather than being defined by others; (c) focusing on what is working, clients' efforts (even if not successful), and progress no matter how small; (d) helping clients reframe unhelpful perceptions or beliefs; and (e) appreciating clients' efforts and affirming their positive internal qualities.

Catching Oneself

Catching oneself encourages clients to be mindful of when symptoms occur and to "catch themselves" in the act of *performing* their symptom. All too often, clients fall into old patterns of behavior before they are even aware of what they are doing. Consider the craving symptom of someone with heroin use disorder. Various physiological, cognitive, and behavioral factors serve to intensify cravings, which seem to happen automatically. Ultimately, the self-defeating patterns lead to intense craving that eludes conscious awareness, leaving clients in a vulnerable position and unable to control them (Watts et al., 2008).

Catching oneself teaches clients to "spy" on the troubling symptom (Watts et al., 2008). Related to substance use counseling, clinicians can help clients (a) identify triggers associated with their substance use, (b) recognize when thoughts and perceptions sabotage recovery efforts, (c) modify their thinking and behavior, and (d) encourage them to "catch themselves" in the act of using drugs (Watts et al., 2008). Clients are encouraged to practice this sequence so as to generate and complete a menu of healthy choices *instead* of using drugs.

Assume a client struggling to manage on pain medication starts to feel the urge to use. They begin thinking about calling a friend and asking for some pills to get them through the next couple of days. They start to feel anxious as they approaches the phone to give their friend a call. Suddenly, they "catch themself" in the act, and immediately become mindful of what they are thinking, feeling, and doing. They may be encouraged to journal these instances in a notebook and bring them in to counseling. They may catch themself by pulling out 3 × 5 cards that have statements of encouragement written on them as they work through the urge to use. Catching oneself is a technique that can stop clients in their tracks of performing their symptom. The client may have chosen to catch themself as soon as they began to feel the urge. This can manifest by doing something else, such as calling a sponsor, exercising, or any healthy, alternative activity.

Acting "As If"

Adlerian clinicians see value in the distinctly human quality of acting *as if* something were the case (Watts et al., 2008). Adler's theory was strongly influenced by Hans Vaihinger, who developed the notion of "mental fictions" or subjective ideas that humans hold on to but do not have any basis in reality. Human beings, according to Vaihinger, have a proclivity toward behaviors that correspond to mental fictions as if these mental fictions were truth. For example, many individuals with substance use problems believe that "one more hit" won't hurt them, yet the person is clearly perpetuating a serious substance use disorder. These fictions hold a tremendous impact on thoughts, feelings, and behaviors.

Acting as if encourages clients to consider possibilities for alternative behaviors to narrate positive, more preferred ways of living (Watts et al., 2008). The technique begins with the clinician asking clients to act "as if" they were already the individuals they would like to be. For example, a client struggling with a substance use disorder may be encouraged to act as if they could resist urges and cravings to use. The low-risk nature of this technique makes it appealing to clients and may lower initial resistance—after all, they are only told to act. For example, a client who struggles with urges to use may see there is little risk in pretending that they are confident in the face of cravings. However, it is the clinician's responsibility to examine what being confident against cravings *looks like*. One can imagine that a client acting "as if" confident would avoid old buddies who use, participate fully in 12-step group activities, and practice relaxation strategies. *The purpose for this strategy is that as someone begins to act differently, they begin to feel differently, behave differently, think differently, gain confidence, and become a different, person who acts in a more preferred way* (Watts et al., 2008). Adlerians believe that one does not need to change emotions before behavior can be changed. Sometimes clients must behave a certain way and the emotions and motivation will follow. If the client's experience with this technique was negative or unsuccessful, then the clinician explores any barriers that got in the way (Watts et al., 2008). The technique may need to be "graded down" or tweaked.

Watts (2003) expanded the acting as if technique by developing a reflective approach in which the clinician asks the client to reflect on what acting as if would look like *before* engaging in the exercise. This process encourages clients to slow the process down and think through how they would be different if acting in a way that is consistent with their goals (e.g., substance free). Reflective questions posed before the acting as if exercise allows clients to think through specific actions, barriers, and goals related to their new, preferred behavior. The "Acting As If Reflective Process" technique (Watts et al., 2009) bridges Adlerian and constructivist ideas and can be a powerful intervention in counseling contexts. Whereas the application of this strategy could be applied to many different client problems and situations, it can be especially relevant and effective for clients struggling with substance use disorders.

The "Acting As If Reflective Process" includes three phases:

1. Phase 1: Clinician uses reflective questions to access the creativity of the client in terms of what a change in behavior would look like.
2. Phase 2: Client and clinician coconstruct a list of *as if* behaviors that reflect preferred actions the client will engage in consistent with his goal(s). These actions are then ranked from least challenging to most challenging (Watts et al., 2008).
3. Phase 3: Client and clinician select the least challenging behavior for the client to try out. More difficult behaviors from the list are explored over time.

In follow-up counseling sessions, the clinician processes client experiences with trying out new behaviors. Let's examine how the "Acting As If Reflective Process" works in the case of Roberto (Watts et al., 2008, 2009).

CASE STUDY

Mini Case Study

Roberto was a 19-year-old Latino American male who had come to counseling after a series of events that placed him in personal and legal trouble. Roberto's mother also was very concerned and told him that he needed help. Roberto came to the first session readily admitting that he struggled with controlling his alcohol. He did not show much resistance, as if recent events broke down any previous denial. He labeled his problem a "drinking problem" as evidenced by a recent display of public intoxication, physical fight, and subsequently passing out. Roberto was aware that his drinking had gotten out of control, and sure enough the police arrested him for underage consumption and assault. This was Roberto's second run-in with the law, so going to jail was a definite possibility unless he sought help. When pressed in the intake interview, he admitted that he had lost control of his drinking.

Using the three phases of the "Acting As If Reflective Process" technique, Roberto and the clinician proceeded as follows:

Phase 1: Roberto was asked the following questions for reflection: "If you were acting as if you were the person you wanted to be, how would you be acting differently? Thinking down the road a bit *after you make* changes in your life, what will your mother see you doing differently?" (Watts et al., 2005, p. 382).

Regarding the first question, Roberto stated that he would be able to better control his drinking and not be as influenced by his friends. He appeared very aware of the negative impact that drinking has on his life. He also would have some strategies to cope when he feels like drinking a lot. (Note: The italicized words presuppose that change has already occurred, consistent with constructivist type interventions [see West et al., 2001 for additional examples]).

Phase 2: In this phase, the clinician and Roberto attempted to get more specific by coconstructing a list of specific behaviors (Watts et al., 2005) that would indicate he has "controlled" his drinking behavior and given this greater attention. Roberto and the counselor generated the following list:

- Enlisting others to give him feedback on his drinking and behavior.
- Pace his drinking to one drink per hour and no more than four drinks per party/night.
- Stay away from people who have a negative influence on his life.
- Attend a party without drinking any alcohol.
- Remove alcohol completely from his life (Watts et al., 2009).

Phase 3: From the list, Roberto thought #1 and #2 were doable. The clinician then explained the concept of "acting as if" and encouraged Roberto to put #1 and #2 into action the next time he went out. For example, he encouraged Roberto to act "as if" he was getting feedback from others and "as if" he paced his drinking in a controlled manner. The clinician and Roberto also discussed what these behaviors might "look like" when put into use. (The clinician also has the option of helping the client visualize and imagine these changes through imagery exercises.) The other three behaviors on the list were a little more difficult. Although they were goals that Roberto wanted to accomplish, they also were more long-term in Roberto's mind. For example, the goal of completely eliminating alcohol from his life was unrealistic in the early stages of counseling, where confidence to make such a change was low. Pushing ahead too hard may set him up for discouragement. Over time, Roberto would need to face these more challenging goals, and clinician encouragement for small, positive directions of change becomes important.

Note: Adapted from Watts et al. (2009).

Pushbutton Technique

Adler believed that humans could control their emotions by the way they think, an idea that served as a precursor to modern cognitive and constructivist ideas (Carlson et al., 2006). The pushbutton technique was originally designed to help clients better manage difficult emotions, such as depression; however, this technique can also be useful in working with substance use because difficult emotions are often concomitant with substance use problems. When reorienting to life's challenges, clients may benefit from the awareness that they have control over their emotions, that no one can "make" them feel a certain way, and that they cannot have control over other people or situations they encounter (Watts et al., 2008).

There are three phases to the pushbutton technique. In the first phase, clients are asked to get in a relaxed position, close their eyes, and recall a pleasant memory in which they felt content, successful, or confident. Clients can choose any memory as long as it reminds them of being relaxed and content. Clients are encouraged to visualize the image in as much detail as possible, deepen the experience, and really connect with the imagery and positive feelings generated by the memory. After reliving the memory and connecting with the positive feelings, clients can indicate they are finished (Watts et al., 2008).

In phase 2, clients are asked to close their eyes and bring up an unpleasant memory, or a time when they felt negative feelings such as sadness, depression, or anger. For example, a client might choose to recall a recent relapse in which they felt guilty, shameful, and depressed. Again, clients are encouraged to "get in to" the imagery, to really experience and feel the negative emotions. Clients are then asked to indicate when they are finished recalling the memory and associated feelings.

Phase 3 has two components. First, clients are asked to again recall a pleasant memory with associated positive feelings. Once again, they are asked to remember the positive emotions in as much specific detail as possible. When they are finished, they are to open their eyes. In the second component, the clinician and client process the experience. Clients may be asked to share what insights they gained from the exercise, what surprised them, and what knowledge they can take with them. Watts et al. (2008) suggested that clinicians can help clients understand that (a) they are controlled by feelings, and they can become more aware of how their thoughts and feelings are related; (b) they ultimately create and maintain their own emotional misery; and (c) they can, as demonstrated in this technique, interrupt the cognitive processes leading to negative emotions, gain more control, and reexperience more positive emotions.

The pushbutton technique can be an effective way to help clients with substance use problems gain better control over their often chaotic emotions (which can be a key contributor to relapse). To use this technique in a creative way, clinicians can give clients two pretend *push-button props* that can be used in the office or taken home (Watts et al., 2008). For example, two big buttons, one red (or any other color for negative experiences) and one green (or any different color for positive experiences), cut out of construction paper can be a fun way to incorporate this technique. Clients are told that the pretend pushbuttons control the images clients create (Carlson et al., 2006). When they create negative, unpleasant, and unconstructive thoughts that negatively impact their emotions, they are pressing the "negative pushbutton." When they create positive, pleasant, and enjoyable images that lead to positive emotions, they are pushing the "positive pushbutton." These pushbuttons affirm the Adlerian notion that clients typically *use* symptoms to accomplish goals. The pushbutton technique reinforces that feelings and/ or behaviors are typically a *choice*. Clinicians can challenge clients to assess which buttons they have been pushing and why. If clients are pushing the negative button, they can come to understand that they also have the ability to press the positive button (Carlson et al., 2006).

Finding the Purpose of the Symptom

The teleological point of view refers to exploring and helping clients find the purpose behind the substance use disorder. This exploration includes assessing what is gained and what is avoided (primarily in terms of the tasks of life). Although this information most likely can come from the lifestyle assessment, it also can be a standalone technique to help the client gain some insights into the substance behavior payoff. For example, a client with alcohol use disorder may discover that their drinking is a way to get attention from others at social gatherings. Exploring the purpose of the drinking and other, more healthy ways to get needs met can be a worthwhile endeavor in substance use counseling.

Empirical Evidence

Although a full review of the Adlerian empirical literature is beyond the scope of this chapter, it is important to note that many researchers have found Adlerian methods associated with and useful for those struggling with substance use disorders (Boynton, 1989; Chaplin & Orlofsky, 1991; Curlette et al., 1997; Keene & Wheeler; 1994; Monakes et al., 2011; Mozdzierz & Semyck, 1980). In general, these studies confirmed positive associations between social interest and mental health and negative associations between social interest and severe alcohol and other drug use. Lifestyle themes that were strong in social interest emerged as significant predictors of substance use. For example, Boynton's (1989) findings indicated that the individuals who severely used substances scored significantly higher on lifestyle themes that emphasized immediate gratification and satisfying personal need for significance. They also were inclined to use exploitative, antisocial behaviors to a greater degree and scored significantly lower on the social interest theme. Research seems to confirm Adler's and Dreikurs's notion that enhanced social interest plays a key buffer against the problematic use of drugs. Other lifestyle themes that contribute to severe substance use problems include a desire to escape from reality, display of deep-seated denial patterns, and engaging in an everlasting struggle for fulfillment (Prinz, 1993).

Recall that from the Adlerian perspective early childhood influences play a large role how we "move" through life. Indeed, Adler was one of the first theorists to propose how early childhood experiences, family atmosphere, and family constellation influence the development of alcohol problems (Barry & Blane, 1977). Research has illuminated the connection between negative early family influences and substance use behavior (Laird & Shelton, 2006) and how protective and supportive parenting (i.e., parenting that involves lots of encouragement and development of social interest) could be a crucial objective to prevent substance use problems (Gerra et al., 2021). In general, researchers have found relationships between family functioning, birth order, and alcohol use problems (Barry & Blane, 1977). The Adlerian clinician is aware of the importance that early childhood experiences have on current behavior. In some cases, therapy entails providing the client with corrective emotional experiences, either through group or individual counseling, which can undo damage caused from toxic family relationships.

Research on early recollections and substance use has shown how useful they can be in interpreting personal dynamics behind substance use. Dimino (2003) found that the intensity of positive emotions within participants' happiest memories corresponded to their tendency to refrain from substance use activity. In an innovative study in which researchers examined the relationship between early recollections and willingness/unwillingness to continue with treatment, Chesney et al. (1986) found that participants without alcohol problems reported more visual content in their early recollections compared to alcohol-dependent participants. In addition, they offered many early memories that involved being in the home and participating in family activities compared to alcohol-dependent participants. The researchers speculated that memories of alcohol-dependent participants occurring outside of the home may suggest strained family relationships while growing up. Alcohol-dependent participants unwilling to continue treatment reported significantly more death content in their early recollections compared to alcohol-dependent participants willing to continue treatment and participants without alcohol problems. The authors suggested that more death themes among alcohol-dependent participants unwilling to continue treatment might suggest unconscious conflicts regarding persistent problems associated with alcoholism. Early memories can provide a significant source of information to help the clinician better understand personal dynamics behind substance use.

Adlerian Therapy in the Treatment of Diverse Populations

For any substance use counseling approach to be successful in contemporary society, it must successfully address issues of diversity and multiculturalism (Watts, 2000). This general statement is especially true in the substance use counseling field: Problematic substance use is an "equal opportunity" problem that does not discriminate among socioeconomic status, gender, race, or religious belief. Adler was considered ahead of his time in terms of respect for diversity in the therapeutic process. He addressed social equality issues and the social context of human behavior and suffering long before multiculturalism became the "third force" in professional counseling (Carlson et al., 2006). Watts (1999) pointed out how Adler was one of the first major theorists to campaign for social equality of women, and he stood against discrimination of minority groups.

Numerous authors have pointed out the clear relevance of Adlerian theory in working with a culturally diverse clientele (Seligman & Reichenberg, 2014; Watts, 2000). Adlerian therapy is not designed to tell clients what to do or how they should proceed, which would disrespect their own values, goals, ambitions, and the sociocultural context in which they live. Instead, Adlerian practitioners stress collaboration between clinician and client in the formation of goals. They also emphasize social interest and strength in community feeling, flexibility to explore personal problems within the client's sociocultural context, and the importance of the collective above individual needs, characteristics that are consistent with many cultural groups (Arciniega & Newlon, 2003, as cited in Corey, 2017). For these reasons, Adler's approach appears to fit well with Asian, Native American, Mexican American, and African American values of social group identity along with individual growth within social context (Archer & McCarthy, 2007).

One area that is often neglected in other theoretical approaches is that of spirituality and religion (Carlson et al, 2006). Adlerian therapy, however, has traditionally been open to issues of spirituality and religion and honors these as important components of one's social and cultural background. Spirituality is now considered a key "task of life" (Mosak & Maniacci, 1999), expanding on the original three espoused by Adler. Adler's general position toward religion was positive, believing that religion manifests as social interest (Carlson et al., 2006). Indeed, the value of social interest appears consistent with many religious perspectives that emphasizes gratitude and doing for others. One might see that the Adlerian stance toward spirituality and religious belief is in line with and respects many 12-step mutual help groups (e.g., AA) that are part of numerous substance use recovery programs.

Adlerian theory, despite being called *individual psychology*, focuses on the person in their social community and context (Corey, 2017; Seligman & Reichenberg, 2014). The counseling process is grounded in the client's culture and world perspective, giving these issues attention during both the assessment and treatment process (Corey, 2017); in fact, the Adlerian practitioner actively engages with clients to address problems of marginalization and discrimination (Seligman & Reichenberg, 2014). Clients do not fit into a convenient psychological model; rather, counseling is grounded in the cultural and social environment from where the client resides. Two key Adlerian constructs speak to this idea of understanding person in context. The first construct is the *phenomenological perspective* (Mosak & Maniacci, 1999). Adlerian theory emphasizes the phenomenology of the person, stressing the client's perceptions of their environment and how they make meaning of their cultural experiences. Adlerians do not assume that because a client is from a particular cultural group that the client will assume all the cultural values, perspectives, and tendencies of that group. The second (and related) construct, *idiographic orientation*, is the idea that everyone is unique, and clinicians should tailor their treatment with this uniqueness in mind. Adlerians do not see value in labeling or categorizing, as within-group differences can sometimes be greater than between-group differences. These two constructs serve as a philosophical foundation for Adlerian therapy and are responsible for why many theorists regard Adlerian therapy as well suited for a complex and multifarious society (Carlson et al., 2006).

One reason Adlerian therapy holds promise as a method that respects diversity is its emphasis on belonging and contribution, the common good, and social context (Arciniega & Newton, 2003, as cited in Corey, 2017). This collaborative stance allows clients to generate and fulfill their own goals based on their own values and norms. The Adlerian clinician is a guide in many respects, supporting clients in their quest for a better life as they define it without telling them what to do. The Adlerian clinician is not wed to any group of techniques but is flexible in their approach depending on what fits for the client based on their diverse background.

As with any approach grounded in Western thought, Adlerian theory may not be suitable for all clients from diverse backgrounds. Adler's theory of change places responsibility squarely on the self (Corey, 2017). Other cultures that hold alternative theories of change may find so much emphasis on the self as problematic. A key technique in Adlerian therapy is the lifestyle assessment, which is designed to inquire about early childhood experiences based on traditional Western family notions. Clients from diverse backgrounds may have different definitions of what constitutes "family" or family values, interests, and norms (Archer & McCarthy, 2007). Finally, Corey (2017) pointed out that the Adlerian emphasis on the egalitarian relationship between clinician and client may annoy clients from cultural backgrounds who view the clinician as the expert and hold expectations that they will provide advice, solutions, or information to help them solve their problems.

The flexibility of the Adlerian approach, however, is a strength that can often overcome some of the aforementioned concerns. For example, in working with African American clients, the culturally aware Adlerian clinician may need to take a broader view of what constitutes family, as extended family (aunts, uncles, grandparents, cousins) often live close by and have a large influence on the client (McCarthy & Archer, 2007). The Adlerian emphasis on contributing to the common good fits well with Native American cultural values of working together and sharing (McCarthy & Archer, 2007), and these values may need to be emphasized with Native American clients. Related to Asian American clients, the Adlerian clinician needs to be aware of the potential conflict between the Western value of striving for independence from the family and the Eastern view of remaining connected to and honoring the family. Overall, Adler's approach seems to have built in flexibility to address some of the theoretical drawbacks when it comes to multicultural counseling.

The emphasis that Adlerian theory places on community, support, cooperation, and connection seems to fit well with African American clients struggling with substance use disorders. African American clients who struggle with substance use problems have traditionally faced issues of racism, have not felt welcome in 12-step recovery meetings, and have limited role models in substance recovery (Brooks & McHenry, 2015). As Brooks and McHenry noted, clinicians need to be aware of the need for African American clients to have "allies, supports, and community resources available throughout the treatment and recovery process" (p. 20). The role of spirituality and the church, the role of women in the family, and collectivism are important factors when working with African American clients struggling with substance use disorders (Castro et al., 1999, as cited in Brooks & McHenry, 2015). As noted, Adlerian theory espouses spirituality as an important task of life and supports the growth of social interest.

Whereas the literature is replete with commentary on the applicability and clinical utility of Adlerian therapy with a diverse clientele, researchers have not yet tested the approach with diverse clients struggling with substance use disorders. Laird and Shelton (2006), however, found that the main tenets of Adlerian theory were identified as major explanatory mechanisms for heavy drinking among a sample of college students attending a historically Black university. Clinical experience also suggests that Adlerian therapy has a lot to offer the substance use treatment community and is indeed well suited to address the unique needs of clients from diverse communities and backgrounds.

CASE STUDY

Using Adlerian Therapy in the Case of Michael

In the following demonstration, I describe a lifestyle assessment with Michael using Adlerian therapy (see Chapter 1 for the full case study). This demonstration is designed to highlight the Adlerian philosophy and various techniques the counselor can use consistent with the Adlerian approach. Based on this assessment, the clinician provides inferences about Michael's lifestyle, method of striving, degree of social interest, basic mistakes, and private logic. After this interpretation, a brief outline of Michael's subsequent counseling is provided.

Family Atmosphere and Constellation

Several questions from the lifestyle assessment were geared toward clarifying Michael's family atmosphere and constellation while growing up. Recall that family atmosphere generally refers to the emotional tone of the family when the client was a child, and family constellation refers to relationships between family members and perceived position in the family. The lifestyle questions (in italics) present an example of how these family dynamics can be assessed via a lifestyle assessment. Michael's response follows each question. Note how he incorporates extended family as having influence on his upbringing.

> **CLINICIAN:** Hello, Michael. Good to see you today. As we discussed during our initial consultation, we agreed to begin the lifestyle assessment, and I introduced to you its components and the general process. Do you have any questions at this point? (starting the session and checking for understanding of the process)

> **MICHAEL:** Nope. Let's get it done.

> **CLINICIAN:** Okay. Great. Let me first start with the first question. *How would you perceive your role in the family while you were growing up? What role(s) did your siblings perform?*

> **MICHAEL:** My role in the family was the peacemaker and the one who caused little trouble. I would resort to humor to ease things around the house ... you know ... keep the peace sort of, especially between mom and dad. Anisha [his youngest sister] did not really take any role. I mean, I love my sister but remember her as sort of disappearing when we were kids. I think that her way to handle the chaos in the home was to simply retreat or hide.

> **CLINICIAN:** *Were there any nicknames associated with your physical appearance as a child?*

> **MICHAEL:** (Chuckles) ... I was a very "skinny" kid, barely pushing 100 pounds by high school. I seemed to be the target of many nicknames and jokes from my dad and people at school. I recall my father always called me "stick," which annoyed the hell out of me. My uncles would chime in, too. They were always teasing me, but it was good-hearted. Even though I would laugh along with him, I developed some insecurity about my physical appearance. My dad would sometimes compare me to other boys in the neighborhood who were more developed and would ask me why I wasn't as big as they were.

> **CLINICIAN:** Yeah, it was difficult hearing your dad always on your case about that and then comparing you to others, as if you weren't good enough. (reflection designed to convey empathy)

> **MICHAEL:** And my uncles, too, although they also would encourage me to go out for sports.

> **CLINICIAN:** *What were some typical childhood fears you had, if any? How did your family respond to these?*

> **MICHAEL:** I had a lot of fears growing up, with many probably becoming more noticeable by age 10 or 12. I was never really brought up in a religious home; my dad was the furthest thing from a religious person, yet I developed somewhat strange rituals in which I would have to pray the "correct" way. I know this sounds weird, but if during prayer I noticed a bad thought, I would fear that something bad would happen to me or my family. Yeah, I had this fear that something would happen to Mom and Dad when they went out. I would have to do every prayer perfectly; but if I didn't do it perfectly, I would force myself to do it again until I got it right or something bad would happen. Man, I think back about these rituals I developed and can see why I scared myself! I felt an urge to pray for forgiveness every time I said a swear word (chuckles) and would try to hide my rituals, usually by leaning forward, so that no one else could see me. I mean, I am not even that religious,

but there were a lot of religious families in my town, so maybe I picked up some of that behavior by being in that environment. I was eventually involved in sports and a good athlete, but I always feared failure or getting injured. It was just weird. I mean, sometimes my fears or religious hang-ups would cause me to be late to school. Thankfully (said with a large sigh relief), most of those fears are a thing of the past, although new ones pop up now and then. Fear has always played a big role in my life. Fear, fear, fear!! *It's who I am.* No wonder I am depressed!

CLINICIAN: I hear you loud and clear. You are not sure how some of these developed, but one thing you are clear about is that fear has been running your life. (reflection)

CLINICIAN: *Describe your family climate growing up.*

MICHAEL: Oh, that is easy! Let's see (somewhat sarcastically but serious): stormy, alcoholic, chaotic, angry, abusive, unpredictable, and sad. I mean, there were some bright moments, but most of my childhood was negative. I can't remember a time when there wasn't some crisis or dad wasn't running his mouth due to his drinking! On the other hand, when we would get together as a larger family, with my aunts, uncles, cousins, neighbors, things were pretty good. My dad would bang around with my uncles; the kids would have fun playing in the yard. Those were some fun summer nights!

To assess family constellation, the clinician asked several questions about siblings, sibling relationships, parents and their relationship with each other, and parental relationships with each sibling. Following is a sample of questions typically used to assess family constellation. Note that these questions were geared toward Michael having only one sibling; questions would need to be tweaked in cases where there is more than one sibling. Each question is italicized, and a summary of Michael's responses are after each question.

CLINICIAN: *List all siblings in descending order (including yourself). Place your age next to your name and then indicate the years difference in age with a + or − for each of your brothers or sisters* (Sweeney, 2019).[3]

MICHAEL: One sister, Anisha, age 29, 3 years my junior.

CLINICIAN: *How did you get along with Anisha?*

MICHAEL: Typical sibling arguments growing up, but overall got along pretty well with Anisha. I was sad to see her withdraw so much when our parents would argue. I felt like I had to protect her, especially when our dad left.

CLINICIAN: *Who fought with whom?*

MICHAEL: I rarely fought with my sister.

CLINICIAN: *Did you play together?*

MICHAEL: We played together when very young but went separate ways when we reached our teens. I was into sports and she was into music and band.

CLINICIAN: *Who cared for and protected whom?*

MICHAEL: I was the protector, both at home and at school.

---

3   One family constellation generally refers to siblings within 6–8 years of age (Sweeney, 2019). Siblings outside this range would have a different constellation. For example, if Michael had a younger brother of 10 years, the younger brother would most likely display traits of an only child given the separation between siblings.

CLINICIAN: *Who was most like who (sibling)? In what respect? How were you two different? In what respect?*

MICHAEL: Anisha and I are more different than similar. I am more of a motivator and go-getter, and probably more impulsive, whereas Anisha tended to withdraw and keep to herself.

CLINICIAN: *Rate self and sibling on each of the attributes by indicating who you believed was highest or most, and who was lowest or least, and if you were neither one, indicate to which sibling you were most similar* (Note: This last part was not applicable in Michael's case).

		Highest	Most like	Lowest
1.	**Intelligence**	Anisha		Michael
2.	**Hardest worker**	Michael		Anisha
3.	**Best grades in school**	Michael/Anisha		
4.	**Helped at home**	Michael		Anisha
5.	**Conforming**	Anisha		Michael
6.	**Rebellious**	Michael		Anisha
7.	**Tried to please**	Michael		Anisha
8.	**Got own way**	Michael		Anisha
9.	**Sense of humor**	Anisha		Michael
10.	**High standards**	Michael		Anisha

(For a full listing of attributes, see Sweeney, 2019).

CLINICIAN: *I know that you noted some problems with your parents' relationship before. How did your parents get along? Was their marriage happy or unhappy?*

MICHAEL: Their marriage was terrible. I mean just terrible. I can't remember a time when Mom and Dad weren't fighting. It was a very unhappy experience.

CLINICIAN: *How did your parents relate to their children?*

MICHAEL: Dad was kind of in and out of my life. I always felt he was kind of a "mystery man"—showing up here and there but never consistent. He would beat me occasionally, especially when he was drunk or high. He didn't seem to touch Anisha. He took all his anger out on me. He would often throw these vague threats my way. I never really connected with him. Mom was always there for me, and I love her. I felt sad that she was in such an abusive relationship—physical early on, and then more verbal.

Dad tended to ignore Anisha. They really didn't have much of a relationship or anything to talk about. Mom treated Anisha the same way she treated me.

CLINICIAN: *Who received the most attention from your parents? The least?*

MICHAEL: I received the most from Dad, but it was usually in the form of yelling. Mom treated us about evenly in terms of attention.

CLINICIAN: *Describe your mother and father.*

MICHAEL: Dad was a welder for a local construction company. He was an alcoholic and angry person. I am not 100% sure, but I think he was into some other shit as well, you know, like cocaine, heroin. He played around on Mom quite a bit too. Early on, a lot of their arguments were about that, but then later they turned to money issues. What is probably most hurtful to me now is that he seemed to like people outside of his family better than his own family. He treated others like gold, so that no one from the outside would suspect a problem.

Mom was, and still is, a very kind person. It is hard to see how the two got together. Mom was the glue that held the family together, until Dad a left. There was no way she was going to leave. She tends to worry a little bit, and can sometimes nag or be overbearing, but she has a kind heart and I love her dearly.

CLINICIAN: *Which child liked your father most? Your mother the most? In what ways?*

MICHAEL: Anisha and I felt the same about our father; we just did not like him. As much as I wanted a connection with him, we grew to hate him.

CLINICIAN: *Who was more ambitious for the children, Mom or Dad? In what ways?*

MICHAEL: Mom, definitely. But she did not really know what was going on with Dad; was he getting drunk? High? Cheating on her? So much of her energy was used up in covering up his mess that I think she consequently fell into a depression.

CLINICIAN: *Okay, Michael. Last question. If a miracle happened and this problem with substance use went away, how would your life be different?*

MICHAEL: Well, I would definitely be getting along better with Anita, no question there. I also think I would be a little more motivated at work. I mean, I do like my job but lately I have been feeling kind of blah about work. I wouldn't be so angry, and perhaps my health would be better. I guess a lot would be different.

Early Recollections

Michael was asked the question, "Think back a long time ago when you were little, and try to recall one of your earliest memories, one of the first things that you can remember." This was followed by three follow-up questions:

1. "Is there anything else you can recall in the memory?"
2. "What is the most vivid part of the memory that stands out for you?"
3. "What feelings or emotions did you have at that time?"

Michael reported the following four ERs:

- ER #1: Age 7. I am at home and I am crawling on the riding mower in our garage. It is cold outside, so all the oil and gas were out of the engine. I turned the key and heard a "pop" in the engine. Emotion: PANIC/FEAR at my how my dad would respond. Most vivid part: the popping noise.
- ER #2: Age 3. I am standing on a curb in our hometown holding my babysitter's hand. We just left a department store. My babysitter makes a motion to walk across the street but then steps back on the curb. I follow her but continue to walk into the street. A car slowly backs over me. I am under the car holding onto a pipe, gritting my teeth. Emotion: FEAR. Most vivid part: gritting my teeth.
- ER #3: Age 8: My mom and dad are yelling at each other. My dad grabs her by the neck and says he will kill her. I start yelling at Dad to let her go. He lets her go but then grabs me by the arm and throws me on the couch. He tells me that he "ought to beat the shit out of me." He was drunk. Emotion: FEAR and HATE. Most vivid part: My dad grabbing my arm.
- ER #4: Age 6: It is late at night and I can't sleep. I hear my dad downstairs fumbling around in the kitchen. I go down to see what he is doing. I peak around the corner and see him

passed out at the kitchen table with beer and liquor bottles all over the place. Emotion: SADNESS. Most vivid part: Seeing my dad passed out.

Lifestyle Interpretation

As one can see, the lifestyle assessment can produce a bevy of information. Using the questions outlined, the clinician created a clinical summary based on Michael's responses. The clinical summary questions are italicized, and the clinician's interpretation is provided after each question.

1. *Is this a medical or psychological problem(s) or both?*

Michael's substance use problem appears to be both. Based on his response to the miracle question, Michael is evading the tasks of love and working through his use of alcohol and cocaine. Subsequent treatment should focus on encouraging Michael to better meet these tasks. Michael's suggestion that his health would be better if he stopped using suggests a biological basis to his substance use problem. A referral to a medical specialist to help Michael with his physical symptoms and substance use disorders would be worthwhile.

2. *What is the person's style of movement (away, toward, and against people/goals)?*

Michael's movement in life appears to be away from others. His early recollections are mostly moments of fear and sadness. Metaphorically, fear is an emotion in which one usually retreats from life and others. Michael has so much energy tied up in some of these feelings and experiences toward his father that he moves away from others, even though he would like to make deeper connections.

3. *What is/are the purpose(s) of the symptoms?*

Michael's substance use may be a type of "revenge" against his father and life. He harbors hatred toward his dad, who figured prominently in his early recollections. Michael is acting out his anger and indifference to life via substance use. His depressed feelings are a way for Michael to momentarily withdrawal from life but also to make a cry for help. He knows something is not quite right and has lost his way. He is hanging on to his symptoms as a way to communicate to others something is amiss, and he needs help.

4. *Based on the person's lifestyle and early recollections, how would you answer the syllogism: I am ... The world is ..., therefore, I ...?* (R. E. Watts, personal communication, August 2000).

I am ... a scared, angry person, but I shouldn't be so. I should be a real man and own up to my responsibilities.
The world is ... sometimes nice, sometimes cruel ... therefore, I ... must use substance to help me cope with all this unpredictability, sadness, and fear!

5. *Does the client harbor any "unfinished business" based on past experiences?*

Probably. Given Michael's comments regarding his early experiences, particularly related to his father, he is probably holding internal psychological wounds that are manifesting as substance use and depression.

6. *What was this person's family atmosphere like? Family constellation? How do these influence their current symptoms?*

The emotional tone of Michael's family growing up was anger and chaos. He and his sister were walking on eggshells, with lots of inconsistency. Michael was peacekeeper in the family and was thrust into a fatherly role early in his life. He harbors a lot of anger because he was not able to experience some of the normal developmental tasks that his peers were able to experience. Michael described himself as *most/highest* hard working, got good grades, helped at home, was rebellious, was a pleaser, and that he got his way. He was the *lowest/least* in terms of intelligence, conforming, and sense of humor. Attention received in the family from father was largely negative. Attention from mother was positive but somewhat absent as her energy was tied up in worrying about her husband. On the other hand, Michael does speak positively about his extended family—aunts, uncles, and cousins. They seemed provide a buffer to some of the negativity within the immediate family.

Michael's chaotic family upbringing largely stems from his angry, abusive father. Michael probably never got much encouragement as a child growing up. He learned how to handle stress by observing his father (note the ER in which he saw his father passed out) escape through drinking. The only way he learned to deal with relationship problems was to drink and withdraw, which inevitably made the situation worse. On the positive end, Michael viewed himself as a hard worker and was good at getting his way. In addition, he had positive relationships with his sister, mother, and extended family, people he can rely on to this day.

7. *What is this person's level of social interest? Is it evident in the data or absent? How do they resist social interest, if at all?*

Michael is low on activity and social interest. His unresolved anger seems to be getting in the way of making genuine relationships with others. He has little connection to the community or world, as this was never modeled as a child growing up. Instead of reaching out for help, Michael turns his feelings inward. He may resist the world because the world has resisted him, from his perspective.

8. *What is the client's private logic on how to be somebody, how to have a place, how to be important?*

Mosak and Maniacci (1999) provided a template for how to conceptualize private logic. It is in the form of (a) the overall lifestyle goal; (b) the more immediate, smaller lifestyle goals; and (c) the hidden reasons behind the goals. The hidden reasons and, to some extent, the immediate goals, constitute one's private logic. Private logic is usually out of the person's awareness. Here is an analysis of Michael's private logic related to substance use.

Lifestyle goal:
    To have revenge against the world
Immediate goals:
    To get back at my father, manifest my resentment
    To create chaos through my drinking
    To numb out, not feel
Hidden reasons:
    I can't handle my fear!
    I can't stand not having a drink!
    I've gotten screwed in life!

Notice how the hidden reasons provide fuel for the immediate and lifestyle goals. Michael's movement in life is largely controlled by his overall goal for revenge.

9. *What patterns of similarities and differences were there among siblings?*

Michael and Anisha are more different than similar. Michael may have felt inferior to Anisha's intelligence, but this probably did not have a significant effect in him considering all the other issues he was dealing with, like serving in a protector role.

10. *What was the client's sense of belonging, security, and being cared about in the family?*

Michael and Anisha rarely felt secure in their family. They felt rejected by their father and cared for by their mother. Extended family helped buffer this somewhat, as many relatives lived close by.

11. *What are the client's strengths and how can they be used in counseling?*

Michael is a survivor. He is a hard worker and did what he had to do to survive. It is no wonder he feels fear and anger. Given that he did not have a very positive male role model growing up, it is remarkable that he was able to establish a loving relationship and find gainful employment. His taking on the fatherly role with his sister is admirable and cost him much of his adolescence. Despite growing up in a chaotic household, he was able to overcome many of his fears and keep focused on the tasks of life. Uncles nearby provided some role-model values. All of this, and more, should be pointed out to Michael in counseling. It is true that he has lost his way a bit via substance use and withdrawal; however, through gentle encouragement there appear to be several strengths he can fall back on as he begins his recovery.

The previous lifestyle analysis would be shared with Michael in subsequent sessions. In most cases, a formal write-up is not necessary (Sweeney, 2019). However, in my own practice, I usually write a brief overview of the findings and provide the client with a copy. Recall that in any Adlerian assessment, the information is offered tentatively, as if stating a hypothesis. If the clinician is off base on something, the client should be given an opportunity to correct anything that does not fit.

In subsequent counseling, the clinician and Michael would proceed along a collaborative path to help Michael live more effectively. A heavy dose of encouragement combined with reminding Michael of his strengths would be essential. Breaking down Michael's private logic would be important for him to see how his overall goal of revenge is getting in his way of meeting two of the three tasks of life (work, love). Assessing the purpose of his substance use (what is gained, what is avoided) may clarify the reasons for use; healthier methods for dealing effectively with his feelings of revenge and anger could be explored. Cognitive and behavior-based strategies, such as the pushbutton technique, could help Michael address his persistent angry and fearful emotions. The clinician should emphasize cultural factors as well, bringing in (either in vivo or by imagination) his extended family for encouragement and support. Finally, the clinician could encourage Michael to strengthen his social interest by exploring blocks to reaching out to others. Volunteer activities, methods of giving to others, or simply encouraging him to say one nice complement to someone else could help to loosen these blocks. Adlerian couples counseling with Anita also may be warranted.

Strengths, Limitations, and Ethical Issues Related to Adlerian Therapy

Adlerian therapy has many strengths and is one that I often use as a foundation in my own substance use counseling practice. In general, the more complex the client issues, the more I rely on Adlerian therapy given its comprehensiveness and holistic stance. I have found Adlerian therapy to be respectful of client differences based on race, gender, and ethnicity. The concept of social interest, lifestyle analysis, and methods of striving have been insightful for clients trying to get a handle on their substance use behavior. However, there are some occasions when Adlerian therapy is not appropriate. Some clients simply do not want their lifestyles analyzed and see no relevance in going back in time to try and understand their substance use disorder. Others may benefit from a more process-oriented approach. Whereas many Adlerian concepts have been validated via empirical research, there is unfortunately a dearth of clinical trial research using Adlerian therapy with clients who have substance use disorders or who struggle with other mental health disorders. At the same time, clinical experience suggests that Adlerian therapy is a comprehensive, effective approach for working with substance use problems; Carlson et al. (2006) noted that Adlerian therapy is consistent with recent trends in psychotherapy across several clinical problems.

As with any counseling approach, there are limitations to its use and scope. Table 12.1 provides a summary of the strengths, limitations, and potential ethical issues that might arise when using Adlerian therapy in the treatment of substance use problems.

TABLE 12.1 Summary of Strengths, Limitations, and Ethical Concerns of Adlerian Therapy in the Treatment of Substance Use Problems

Strengths	· Adlerian therapy is a flexible approach that allows for integration by drawing on behavioral, cognitive, analytic, and postmodern ideas. Its comprehensiveness makes it well suited for the complexities of substance use issues and treatment. · The lifestyle assessment is a comprehensive evaluation procedure that provides a wealth of information based on childhood upbringing. Complex interpretive methods, as in traditional psychoanalytic therapy, are not needed. Many clients find the process of reviewing their life in this manner therapeutic. This information can be invaluable for complex situations in which clients have coexisting problems. · Adlerian therapy has promise for working with a diverse clientele. · Adlerian therapy is well suited to brief, time-limited counseling (Carlson et al., 2006), meeting the demands of managed care. The brief format may be useful for some brief inpatient substance use programs as well as outpatient counseling. · Adlerian therapy views individuals as purposive, self-determining, and striving for growth. It is a positive approach that focuses on encouragement and strengths, something that runs counter to the often unhelpful negative stereotypes that many individuals struggling with substance use disorders face. · Education is a strong component of Adlerian therapy; clients struggling with substance use disorders can benefit from a combined educational/therapeutic model such as Adlerian.
Limitations	· Initially, Adlerian theory may be difficult to follow or understand. Corey (2017) noted that Adler did not have time to present a well-defined and systematic theory. Hence, his writings are somewhat difficult to follow. · Some in the substance use treatment field may have difficulty with the idea that early childhood years are so important. Sometimes people do things because they are reinforced. · A thorough lifestyle assessment can take up to three counseling sessions and so one may ask, how practical is this approach, especially if many clients with substance use problems do not come back after the first session? · More research is needed in the application of Adlerian therapy with diverse populations as well as its application to substance use problems.

(continued)

TABLE 12.1   Summary of Strengths, Limitations, and Ethical Concerns of Adlerian Therapy in the Treatment of Substance Use Problems (*Continued*)

Ethical Issues	• Some components of Adlerian therapy may seem irrelevant to clients struggling with substance use disorders, and thus not be very helpful. For example, clients who simply cannot meet their basic needs probably do not want to be told about choices and goals. Those who have been traumatized may have a hard time volunteering or reaching out to others.
	• Many aspects of problematic substance use, such as denial, rationalization, physical addiction, and so on would theoretically not be addressed by the Adlerian approach. This does not mean that these aspects *could not* be addressed; Adlerian clinicians must be aware of these issues and incorporate how they fit into the client's lifestyle. The physical mechanisms of substance use disorders are best addressed via medical professionals.
	• Adlerian therapists may hold differing goals for clients than what clients want. Ethical issues may arise when there is a discrepancy between what the clinician wants and what the client wants.

References

Adler, A. (1929). *The science of living.* Garden City.

Adler, A. (1956). Fictionalism and finalism. In H. L. Ansbacher & R. R. Ansbacher (Eds.), *The individual psychology of Alfred Adler: A systematic presentation in selections from his writings* (pp. 76–100). Harper Perennial.

Adler, A. (1979). Brief comments on reason, intelligence, and feeble-mindedness (1928). In H. L. Ansbacher & R. R. Ansbacher (Eds.), *Superiority and Social Interest: A Collection of Later Writings* (pp. 41–49). Norton & Company.

Adler, A. (1998). *What life could mean to you* (C. Brett, Trans.). Hazelden. (Original work published 1931)

Ansbacher, H. L. (1991). The concept of social interest. *Individual Psychology: Journal of Adlerian Theory, Research, & Practice, 47,* 28–46.

Ansbacher, H. L., & Ansbacher, R. R. (Eds.). (1956). *The individual psychology of Alfred Adler: A systematic presentation in selections from his writings.* Harper & Row.

Archer, J., & McCarthy, C. J. (2007). *Theories of counseling and psychotherapy: Contemporary applications.* Pearson.

Barry, H. III, & Blane, H. (1977). Birth positions of alcoholics. *Journal of Individual Psychology, 33,* 62–69.

Boynton, R. D. (1989). Drug addiction, lifestyle personality factors and psychopathology. *Dissertation Abstracts International, 50,* 647.

Brooks, F., & McHenry, B. (2015). *A contemporary approach to substance abuse and addiction counseling* (2nd ed.). American Counseling Association.

Carlson, J., Watts, R. E., & Maniacci, M. (2006). *Adlerian therapy: Theory and practice.* American Psychological Association.

Chaplin, M. P., & Orlofsky, J. L. (1991). Personality characteristics of male alcoholics as revealed in their early recollections. *Individual Psychology: Journal of Adlerian Theory, Research, & Practice, 47,* 356–371.

Chesney, S. M., Fakouri, M. E., & Hafner, J. L. (1986). The relationship between early recollections and willingness/unwillingness of alcoholics to continue treatment. *Individual Psychology: Journal of Adlerian Theory, Research, & Practice, 42*, 395–403.

Clark, A. J. (2002). *Early recollections: Theory and practice in counseling and psychotherapy.* Brunner-Routledge.

Clark, A. J. (2013). *Dawn of memories: The meaning of early memories in life.* Brunner-Routledge.

Corey, G. (2017). *Theory and practice of counseling and psychotherapy* (10th ed.). Cengage.

Curlette, W. L., Wheeler, M. S., & Kern, R. M. (1997). *BASIS-A inventory technical manual.* TRT Associates.

Dimino, R. A. (2003). Early memories, attachment style, the role of peers, and adolescent substance use. *Dissertation Abstracts International: Section B: The Sciences and Engineering, 63*, 6091.

Dinkmeyer, D., & Sperry, L. (2000). *Counseling and psychotherapy: An integrated, individual psychology approach.* Prentice Hall.

Dreikurs, R. (1990). Drug addiction and its individual psychological treatment. *Individual Psychology, 46*, 208–216.

Dreikurs, R., & Soltz, V. (1964). *Children: The challenge.* Hawthorn Books.

Gerra, M. L., Gerra, M. C., Tadonio, L., Pellegrini, P., Marchesi, C., Mattfield, E., Gerra, G., & Ossola, P. (2021). Early parent-child interactions and substance use disorder: An attachment perspective on a biopsychosocial entanglement. *Neuroscience and Biobehavioral Reviews, 31*, 560–580.

Keene, K. K., & Wheeler, M. S. (1994). Substance use in college freshman and Adlerian lifestyle themes. *Individual Psychology: Journal of Adlerian Theory, Research, & Practice, 50*, 97–109.

Kopp, R. R. (1986). Styles of striving for significance with and without social interest: An Adlerian typology. *Individual Psychology: Journal of Adlerian Theory, Research, and Practice, 42*, 17–25.

Laird, G. T., & Shelton, A. J. (2006). From an Adlerian perspective: Birth order, dependency, and binge drinking on a historically black university campus. *The Journal of Individual Psychology, 62*, 18–35.

Linkenbach, J. (1990). An Adlerian technique for substance-abuse prevention and intervention. *Individual Psychology, 46*, 203–207.

Manaster, G. J., & Corsini, R. J. (1982). *Individual psychology: Theory and practice.* Adler School.

Maniacci, M. P. (1999). Clinical Therapy. In R. E. Watts, & J. Carlson (Eds.), *Interventions and strategies in counseling and psychotherapy* (pp. 63–65). Accelerated Development.

Mansager, E., Barnes, M., Boyce, B., Brewster, J. D., Lertora, H. J., Marais, F., Santos, J., & Thompson, D. (1995). Interactive discussion of early recollections: A group technique with adolescent alcohol substance abusers. *Individual Psychology, 51*, 413–421.

Monakes, S., Garza, Y., Weisner, V, & Watts, R. E. (2011). Implementing Adlerian sand tray therapy with adult male substance abuse offenders: A phenomenological inquiry. *Journal of Addictions and Offender Counseling, 31*, 94–107.

Mosak, H. H. (1958). Early recollections as a projective technique. *Journal of Projective Techniques, 22*, 302–311.

Mosak, H. H. (1991). I don't have social interest: Social interest as construct. *Individual Psychology: Journal of Adlerian Theory, Research, and Practice, 47*, 309–320.

Mosak, H., & Maniacci, M. (1999). *A primer of Adlerian psychology: The analytic, behavioral, cognitive psychology of Alfred Adler.* Brunner/Mazel.

Mozdzierz, G. J., & Semyck, R. W. (1980). The social interest index: A study of construct validity. *Journal of Clinical Psychology, 36,* 417–422.

Olson, H. A. (Ed.). (1979). *Early recollections: Their use in diagnosis and psychotherapy.* Charles C. Thomas.

Powers, R. L., & Griffith, J. (1987). *Understanding lifestyle: The psycho-clarity process.* Adler Institute.

Prinz, J. (1993). Alcoholics and their treatment: Current Adlerian thinking. *Individual Psychology, 49,* 94–105.

Prinz, J., & Arkin, S. (1994). Adlerian group therapy with substance abusers. *Individual Psychology, 50,* 349–358.

Rareshide, M., & Kern, R. (1991). Social interest: The haves and have nots. *Individual Psychology: Journal of Adlerian Theory, Research, & Practice, 47,* 464–476.

Seligman, L., & Reichenberg, L. W. (2014). *Theories of counseling and psychotherapy: Systems, strategies, and skills.* Pearson.

Sharf, R. S. (2004). *Theories of psychotherapy and counseling: Concepts and cases* (3rd ed.). Brooks/Cole.

Slavik, S. (1995). Presenting social interest to different life-styles. *Individual Psychology: Journal of Adlerian Theory, Research, & Practice, 51,* 166–177.

Sweeney, T. J. (2019). *Adlerian counseling and psychotherapy: A practitioner's approach* (6th ed.). Routledge.

Watts, R. E. (1999). The vision of Adler: An introduction. In R. E. Watts & J. Carlson, (Eds.), *Interventions and strategies in counseling and psychotherapy* (pp. 1–14). Accelerated Development.

Watts, R. E. (2000). Entering the new millennium: Is individual psychology still relevant? *Journal of Individual Psychology, 56,* 21–30.

Watts, R. E. (2003). Reflecting "as if": An integrative process in couples counseling. *The Family Journal, 11,* 73–75.

Watts, R. E., Lewis, T. F., & Peluso, P. (2008, March). *Using and applying Adlerian-based counseling techniques* [Paper presentation]. Annual American Counseling Association Convention, Honolulu, HI.

Watts, R. E., Peluso, P. R., & Lewis, T. F. (2005). Expanding the acting "as if" technique: An Adlerian/constructive integration. *Journal of Individual Psychology, 61,* 380–387.

Watts, R. E., Peluso, P., & Lewis, T. F. (2009, October). *Expanding the acting as if technique: An Adlerian/constructivist integration* [Paper presentation]. ACES Conference, San Diego, CA.

Wechsler, H., Dowdall, G. W., Davenport, A., & Castillo, S. (1995). Correlates of college student binge drinking. *American Journal of Public Health, 85,* 921–926.

West, J. D, Watts, R. E., Trepal, H. C., Wester, K. L., & Lewis, T. F. (2001). Opening space for client reflection: A postmodern consideration. *The Family Journal, 9,* 431–437.

Wheeler, M. S., Curlette, W. L., & Kern, R. M. (1994). *BASIS—A interpretive guide.* TRT Associates.

CHAPTER 13

Applying Gestalt Therapy in the Treatment of Substance Use Disorders

Introduction

In my experience, clients with substance use disorders struggle with staying present, focused, and aware of who they are, what they want, and, in particular, what they feel. Gestalt therapy offers a unique and exciting perspective related to substance use and holds promise as a model that can help clients live with greater awareness, connection, and happiness, all substance free! This is not an approach that lends itself well to scientific scrutiny, mainly because there is no one way to "do" Gestalt therapy. The clinician usually adopts a "creative stance" in which they work with the present moment and whatever emerges, or becomes *figural*, in the here and now. As such, it is difficult to operationalize many Gestalt concepts and study them through a traditional quantitative research lens.

That empirical research is limited, however, does not diminish the richness and history of Gestalt therapy (for an excellent review on the outcome literature related to Gestalt therapy, see Corey, 2017). Gestalt ideas are now incorporated into businesses, community agencies, university systems, and substance use treatment centers. As with the other theories in this text, a compelling case can be made for the usefulness and effectiveness of Gestalt therapy in the treatment of substance use issues. Gestalt theory and techniques can be used either as a standalone approach or infused with other approaches. Gestalt therapy's emphasis on integration, awareness, and growth are a welcome breath of fresh air in a population that all too often swims in a sea of negativity.

Gestalt therapy is an approach that cuts through facades and gets right to the matter at hand. For example, a client may say what the clinician wants to hear, but it is extremely difficult to hide true feelings in the body. Gestalt's emphasis on holism allows clinicians to pay attention to the whole person and thus point out inconsistencies between what is spoken and what is nonverbal. A client might say, for example, "My recovery is fine, and I had a good week" yet be holding their breath, wringing their hands, and shifting about in their seat. Clearly, this client is saying one thing but feeling something else; Gestalt therapists see this discrepancy as important information to explore in the here and now.

Traditional forms of substance use interventions and CBT-based strategies are helpful, but I often come across clients who either (a) already know a lot about substance use, relapse, and the effects of drugs, or (b) do not find CBT based strategies helpful. Consider this quote by Kappeler (2004), who struggled with an eating disorder and substance-related problems:

> In my case, at the beginning of treatment, I did not have any alternatives that I knew and trusted would work. A traditional-style coercive attempt to teach new coping and living skills failed utterly. In contrast, the Gestalt approach helped me to become aware of my self-defeating patterns and to start to take responsibility for my actions and choices. (p. 2)

Gestalt therapists avoid lecturing, advice giving, and interpretation. Clients may know a lot about their substance use behavior but may be inadequate in knowing and understanding *themselves*. The theoretical stance and practical techniques of Gestalt therapy offer the clinician a unique, novel approach to working with clients struggling with substance use disorders. When clients have been medically withdrawn from the substance, Gestalt ideas can provide a structure for recovery (Buchbinder, 1986).

It is appropriate, however, to emphasize a cautionary note: Gestalt therapy is not an "easy" approach to master and, unfortunately, can be harmful if used carelessly or inappropriately. It has a powerful ability to bring to the surface difficult emotions where they can be processed in the here and now. Staying present centered is surprisingly difficult. With that being said, some of the Gestalt-based approaches and techniques in this chapter require advanced training and continual supervision and/or consultation, especially with clients struggling with substance use disorders. Approaches and techniques that require more oversight are indicated in the chapter.

In this chapter, the major tenets of Gestalt are provided, which include numerous key concepts and terms. The application of Gestalt therapy to those struggling with substance use problems is considered next. Numerous techniques from the Gestalt approach, as applicable to substance use counseling, are provided. The applicability of Gestalt with diverse clientele is considered, followed by an examination of Gestalt therapy in the case of Michael.

The Major Tenets of Gestalt Therapy: Brief Overview

Gestalt therapy was founded by Fritz and Laura Perls in the mid-20th century. The major goals of Gestalt therapy include growth and maturation and integration of feelings, perceptions, thoughts, and behaviors (Luellen, 1998). This integration is based on the assumption that a person functions optimally as a systematic whole (Luellen, 1998; Polster & Polster, 1973). Indeed, the Gestalt clinician conceptualizes intrapersonal and interpersonal behavior as efforts to maintain personality organization (Luellen, 1998). Fragmented existence means that individuals live with internal conflict and dissonance, as when an individual with a substance use disorder feels love for their family but destroys their home life by continuing to take drugs. Change is not forced on clients; however, space is provided in the therapeutic setting to allow for client exploration, experimentation, and growth. This space sets the stage for enhanced awareness, which is considered the precursor to change (Luellen, 1998). Several tenets of Gestalt therapy are considered next. Where appropriate, examples are provided within the realm of addiction problems.

Figure/Ground

The concept of figure/ground is central to Gestalt theory. Figure refers to what stands out in the moment upon which our focus is placed (Zinker, 1977). Gestalt clinicians often assess what is becoming "figural" in the clinical session. In other words, what is emerging from the client (e.g., emotions, thoughts, urges, sensations) that needs clinical attention? Ground represents the backdrop that surrounds the figure and is a constant spring of new figure formations (Polster & Polster, 1973). The ground is made up of context, environment, past experiences, and relationships. All of us have a ground of experience that we bring to the table. What becomes figural emerges from a background of experiences and the surrounding environment. Perhaps a clinical example may clarify.

I recently counseled a client with alcohol use disorder who was in early stages of recovery. During one, slow-progressing session, the client started talking about his relationship with his wife and how frustrated he was with her apparent lack of motivation. He was in recovery and, not unlike many who begin living drug free, was trying to make sense of his newfound energy and freedom (from drug use). His wife, however, did not share the same enthusiasm. She was trying to negotiate the changes in her husband—positive changes, yes—but changes nonetheless. This relationship became strongly figural for him, meaning it was at the forefront of his mind and something from which he felt a lot of energy. It became the focus of our entire session. Once the figure was identified, the client seemed to gain momentum and energy, and we cocreated a productive session developing his awareness of what he was experiencing emotionally and how he could support himself, and of the unique dynamics that occur whenever a partner experiences the recovery process.

Contact

I recently took a vacation on Lake Michigan and spent several evenings watching the beautiful sunset across the beach. The light hit the water perfectly as the shimmering blue lake rippled slightly across miles and miles of horizon. I was contacting nature, taking it in, understanding it, and fully enjoying the experience. This short example is what Gestalt therapists refer to as contacting one's environment. Contact is a central component of Gestalt therapy. It happens between two separate beings, "always requiring independence and always risking capture in the union" (Polster & Polster, 1973, p. 99). Contact (or lack thereof) can occur between two people, a person and an object, or a person and different aspects of themself. All of life is in cycles of contact with others followed by rest and assimilation (Crocker, 1999). Healthy contact is when the client strikes a balance between contact with themself and contact with others (Buchbinder, 1986). As we will see, disruptions in contact usually entail too much focus on the self, on others, or on both.

I-Boundaries

We all set boundaries in life related our relationships with self, others, and the world. For example, a self-boundary might be a college student who will only drink alcohol but not "cross the boundary" to using marijuana. A person with a substance use disorder may have very rigid, or, perhaps more commonly, too loose boundaries with their environment. "I-boundaries are determined by the whole range of experiences in life and by built in capacities for assimilating new experiences" (Polster & Polster, 1973, p. 108). A primary goal of general Gestalt counseling is to expand the client's (often rigid) I-boundaries.

I believe many clients with substance use disorders struggle with boundary issues. When I was counseling Sam (name disguised), a client who used a range of substances, it became clear through an early assessment that he did not learn *any* boundaries in his life, a consequence of growing up in a chaotic, discouraging, violent household with parents who excessively consumed alcohol. His carefree, destructive, and "anything goes" lifestyle emerged as a confluence between self and drugs; that is, he did not understand the boundary between self and object. Developing healthy boundaries sets the stage for healthy and appropriate contact.

Contact Functions

Contact is achieved through seven functions, including (a) looking/seeing, (b) listening, (c) touching, (d) talking, (e) moving, (f) smelling, and (g) tasting (the taste function is important for Gestalt therapists because of Fritz Perls's analogy of this function being like how the individual assimilates and takes in what the environment throws at him; Perls, 1969; Polster & Polster, 1973). If these functions are interrupted or otherwise compromised, contact is blocked or avoided, leading to psychological disturbance. As we will see, many Gestalt strategies involve the expansion of the contact functions so individuals can live with greater awareness, acuity, and choice.

Interruptions to Healthy Contact

Because contact is so critical to human life, Gestalt therapists focus on how contact is blocked, disrupted, or somehow goes awry, which results in problems in living (Crocker, 1999). Disruptions of contact most often result from cognitive distortions or inconsistencies between internal wants, desires, and needs and outward expression (Crocker, 1999). Gestalt therapists focus on how individuals distort their own contact processes, leading to distortions in how they interact with others and perceive their world. As Crocker noted, the process of Gestalt therapy is not to rid the client of all cognitive distortions or internal/external inconsistencies, which would be impossible, but rather to enhance awareness and restore the client's range of choice. If clients are aware of how they distort contact, then they can make choices to minimize these distortions and live with greater authenticity and clarity. It is important to keep in mind that contact distortions are often performed to help individuals better manage complex situations and otherwise survive in an emotionally charged environment. Used in a healthy way, they facilitate human teaching or help humans manage their emotional life (Crocker, 1999). However, if contact distortions are prevalent, they block awareness, decision-making, and effective problem solving. Clients end up ill-prepared to face reality; whereas their anxiety may lessen as a result diminished contact, their intrapersonal and interpersonal problems remain. Let's take a moment to review several contact distortions. Where appropriate, examples of how clients with substance use problems engage in these distortions are presented.

Introjection

Fritz Perls (1969) often used the analogy of eating and digestion for how we take in our experiences from the world. If someone, for example, gobbles down their food, barely noticing the texture or taste, they probably approach life in the same manner: taking in experiences at a furious pace, unable to truly "taste" what is going on in their life. In a similar vein, introjection involves taking in messages from others wholesale (Buchbinder, 1986), without truly tasting or digesting them to see if they can or should be assimilated. As a result, the person fails to convey what they need or prefer (Polster & Polster, 1973). Introjections often have roots in childhood when individuals are vulnerable to adult messages. Unfortunately, many children hear messages such as "You are such a loser" or "I wish you were never born" that they end up carrying around well into their adult life, impacting their self-concept, self-esteem, confidence, and so forth. Of course, introjects can be positive, too. Encouraging statements can equally stay with someone into adulthood and have a positive influence on work ethic.

Introjection does not only occur in childhood. As a normal human ability, introjection helps us learn new ideas and skills that aid in our getting along with others and survival. The ability to learn unquestionably from others is essential in life as it is impossible to know everything there is to know by one's own efforts (Crocker, 1999). When I learned how to drive a car, I took what my teacher said as great pieces of wisdom; it would have been much more difficult (and dangerous) if I had rejected their teachings and decided to learn on my own!

Introjects that lead to distortions of contact blind us to our own experience and the choices we have in life (Crocker, 1999). Individuals who distort contact through introjects are unable to critically examine their beliefs about how to conduct their lives. It is as if the person says, "That is how I have always been, and it is just the way it is." In Gestalt therapy, introjects that appear to be holding a person back need to be explored, a process like challenging negative beliefs in CBT-based approaches. Undoing distorted introjections involves the client becoming more aware of choices available to them and heightening awareness of self (Polster & Polster, 1973).

I recently counseled a client, Stu (name disguised), who came from an abusive and problem-saturated early childhood. His parents struggled with substance use issues of their own. Stu clearly learned early on that the way to solve problems was to medicate them away. His mother, who suffered from bouts of chronic pain, consumed opiate medication "like it was going out of style." Even when her pain was better, she continued to use medication for their psychological effect. His father was an angry man who always seemed to be under stress. When he would come home, he would drown himself in alcohol to escape mounting pressures at home and work. Stu remembers his father telling him, "Ah, it's nothing that a good beer couldn't solve" when he faced some stressor in his life. Stu's introjections from childhood seemed to have a profound impact on his current behavior. He had specific beliefs about how to be a husband, father, and employee. He had a very narrow view of how to handle stress (by turning to alcohol). Stu's counseling work included increasing his awareness of these introjects and exploring his notions of being a man, husband, father, and employee to see if there was room for expansion. It also involved broadening his ideas for how to handle stress by calling into question his current process for doing so.

Projection

Projection involves attributing a negative characteristic of oneself onto another person when in fact that characteristic is primarily true for oneself (Buchbinder, 1986). When people find it difficult to face their own characteristics, behaviors, or emotions, they will try to reduce anxiety by projecting them onto someone else and then react to that person as if they really had that trait (Crocker, 1999). Projection serves a denial function; it is a way of avoiding unpleasant traits about oneself that a person does not want to deal with (Crocker, 1999).

As a normal human distortion, projection aids in human development by helping a person understand others based on what they know about themself (Crocker, 1999). In essence, the ability to project helps us live in others' shoes and thus develop empathy. Empathy is the foundation for moral behavior. Projection becomes a problem when individuals fail to distinguish between their own characteristics and behavior and that of others. It is one thing to be able to use our own experiences as a guide to understand others, but quite another to assume others have negative traits that are really based on our own.

Projection can manifest in substance use counseling in many ways. I often see projection in couples counseling work where one or both individuals are struggling with substance-related problems. For example, a husband may project negative feelings, such as anger, shame, and guilt, onto his children and spouse, which leads to constant fights and arguments. Projection serves to protect him from facing these negative feelings; rather than taking ownership and distinguishing between his feelings and that of others, he avoids them and places them onto his family. Gestalt therapy is designed to help clients increase their awareness of this contact disturbance and explore healthier ways to handle difficult emotions. The task with distorted projection is to restore and take ownership of the client's identity that they have projected on others (Polster & Polster, 1973).

Confluence

Confluence is essentially a loss of self. The person tends to go along with others, making few choices of their own, to interrupt disturbing feelings of separateness and novelty (Polster & Polster, 1973). Stated differently, it involves an identification of person Y with person or group Z, such that person Y loses their identity (Crocker, 1999). As an extreme example, consider a cult group in which members identify so strongly with the group that they "lose themselves" to the group's values, norms, and behaviors. As a normal ability, confluence aids in connecting with another on an intimate level and forming close bonds to the community at large (Crocker, 1999). Dysfunctional confluence occurs when a person fails to separate from another person (e.g., parent, teacher, or spouse) or group (e.g., church) such that they have difficulty forming their own thoughts, emotions, and identity. It also can manifest as a refusal to tolerate differences (Buchbinder, 1986).

In substance use counseling, confluence may emerge when clients are members of gangs or other social groups that use substances. Failing to forge enough differentiation to create separate values and identities, the individual lets the group make decisions for them. For some individuals, it is easier to adopt another person or group's ideas than to expend the energy or creativity to shape one's values and goals. To address distorted confluence, the person must learn to make contact, differentiate, and articulate identity and values (Polster & Polster, 1973). Therapeutic questions such as "What do you feel now? What do you want now? or What are you doing now?" (Polster & Polster, 1973, p. 95) allow clients to strengthen their sense of self-direction.

Confluence is most likely operating when we observe traditionally viewed codependency within a couple or family dyad. Although controversial in the substance use treatment field (Miller, 2005), traditional codependency refers to a person who focuses on an another person's needs to the exclusion of their own. Often, the codependent person in a family is the non-using spouse, who depends on the spouse with the substance use problem for fulfillment. For example, a spouse without a substance use problem may have an extreme need to care for and please others, and therefore completely dedicates their life to the spouse with the substance use disorder. This need fits perfectly within addiction because of the care that is needed to "hide the family secret." These dynamics certainly reflect confluence and the subsequent loss of self. Codependency was addressed in Chapter 10.

Retroflection

Retroflection refers to turning energy that one would like to direct at another person back onto oneself (Buckbinder, 1986). For example, I may get angry at a colleague, but because expression of my anger may be misinterpreted, or worse come out aggressively, I turn the angry energy back onto myself. Polster and Polster (1973) defined retroflection as occurring when the client blocks attempts to influence the environment by becoming exceedingly self-sufficient (i.e., doing *everything* themselves/not asking for help). As a normal process, retroflection helps us keep our impulses in check, so we don't hurt ourselves or others (Crocker, 1999). Dysfunctional retroflection, on the other hand, can be destructive to the individual. Constantly checking and turning impulses and emotions onto oneself may show up as physical symptoms, such as hypertension, and psychological problems, such as depression (Crocker, 1999). Individuals who retroflect often hide their disappointment and anger in intimate relationships only to explode at their partner later.

Substance use behavior can be an ultimate form of retroflection. Indeed, Perls (1969) noted that to alleviate severe alcohol problems, one must cure the retroflection of self-destruction. Individuals who harbor angry, destructive feelings toward the world may turn this energy inward by destroying themselves with alcohol or drugs. The stress that can build internally from unexpressed emotions may become unbearable, thus leading to substance use. In my experience, many substance use clients who retroflect developed this pattern of disrupted contact at an early age. For whatever reason, expression of their emotions, thoughts, and beliefs were never encouraged. They may learn to drink or use drugs to deal with the buildup of feelings. The Gestalt therapists' job is to help clients redirect energy away from the self toward other people (Buchbinder, 1986; Polster & Polster, 1973). Doing to others what you do to yourself needs to be followed to undo retroflection (Boylin, 1975).

Egotism

Perls et al. (1951) asserted that egotism is when someone remains a bit skeptical, somewhat aloof, and noncommittal. Healthy egotism prevents persons from jumping right in without sufficiently vetting the process and consequences. It allows individuals to prepare goals and maintain interest in them, develop the strength to overcome obstacles, and have the courage to stand up and fight for values that are important to them (Crocker, 1999). Egotism helps humans avoid indifference and is the foundation for respect and care for self and others. Dysfunctional egotism occurs when a person persistently and incessantly wants their own way no matter the cost to self or others (Crocker, 1999). A key factor here is control; the egotistical person wants to control everything and everyone around them, creating too much differentiation with others (and thus avoiding healthy contact). What drives this behavior is often insecurity and doubt about how to handle situations (Crocker, 1999).

Dysfunctional egotism can manifest as persistent use of alcohol and drugs despite the havoc created on self and others. Especially in the later stages of substance use disorders, the client will attempt to control a narrower and narrower range of events, all in the service of securing the drug. In fact, one might argue that substance use and addiction is egotism run amok. Indifference sets in as the person cares less and less about their life, friends, and work, and more about the next high. Of course, in substance use behaviors it might work the other way as well: The person may have limited ego strength before problems begin, and thus fail to negotiate and plan for difficult obstacles ahead. Gestalt counseling, then, strives to help clients become aware of the strength of their egotism and how it impedes healthy contact. With awareness, clients then decide if they need to pull back and bring others into their lives or enhance their ego strength to stand up for themselves and others.

Deflection

Deflection is turning away from, or avoiding, direct contact with another person or the environment (Buchbinder, 1986; Polster & Polster, 1973). Deflection primarily occurs in the interpersonal context. It happens when one person wants to communicate something important to another person, usually with intense emotions, but the receiving person refuses to engage in the communication or overture (Crocker, 1999). Healthy deflection allows us to hold off dealing with a situation until we feel confident that we can address it in an appropriate manner (Crocker, 1999). If a spouse is angry or sad about their partner's behavior, their partner may walk out of the room to "gather their thoughts" or "sleep on it" until they feel ready to address the situation. Deflection is an important contact disruption because it allows some breathing room when faced with intense emotional experiences. When learning of the loss of a loved one, individuals may be in shock and simply need time to process what happened. Dysfunctional deflection occurs when the person develops a persistent pattern of avoidance and refuses to engage others, thus precluding healthy contact.

Substance use clients might deflect in a dysfunctional way by avoiding facing the consequences of their use. When confronted with potential negative consequences, they may deflect away the severity of their use and refuse to engage in serious conversations with concerned others. Deflection is about avoidance; it is easier to turn away from arguments or the truth about consequences than to face the harsh reality of how their behavior has hurt themselves and others.

Deflection is a common theme among couples who struggle in their relationship because of substance use. When the nondependent spouse confronts the dependent spouse, usually with intense emotions, the dependent spouse will leave the room, become sarcastic, change the subject, or ignore the other, all characteristics of deflection. In Gestalt counseling, the clinician works to point out deflection processes, help individuals meet people clearly, and make contact rather than engage in typical avoidance patterns (Polster & Polster, 1973).

These contact processes help individuals negotiate their world successfully. Without them, we could not empathize (projection), hold ourselves back (retroflection), develop a sense of connection and community (confluence), and take in the wisdom and authority of others (introjection). We could not retreat from an emotionally discharged situation before we had a chance to reflect on it (deflection) or exert our own power and conviction in terms of what we believe (egotism; Crocker, 1999). The trouble occurs when these contact processes become distortions and preclude growth and maturation. Crocker noted that much of the therapeutic work in Gestalt therapy is working with these distortions of contact; to understand the client's experiences of contact, however, the clinician must understand the *ground*, or context, from which they emerge. For example, if an individual's retroflection is such that they turn their destructive feelings and tendencies back on themself by using drugs, what is the context from which this distortion emerged? It may be, for example, that they grew up in a household that discouraged any expression of emotion and never learned to communicate what they wanted out of life. Therapy then focuses on learning how to express their wants and desires in an appropriate manner.

Gestalt Cycle of Experience

Gestalt therapy is predicated on the assumption that individuals consistently respond to internal sensations and the environment (field) in which they live (Clemmens, 2005b). Clemmens (2005b) and Woldt and Toman (2005) proposed a Gestalt cycle of experience that visually captures the main processes involved between the person-environment contact (see Figure 13.1), in addition to resistance processes that preclude healthy contact. As one can see in Figure 13.1, a healthy contact cycle begins when an experience emerges from the ground (left-hand side of the continuum) and becomes figural. The flow of experience starts with sensation/perception, leading to greater awareness. At this point, energy is rising as the person becomes excited and begins to mobilize toward an encounter or action with the experience. Energy is at its peak when the person acts, followed by full contact with the experience. After contact, energy will lower, and the person will integrate/assimilate the experience through rest and reflection. This is then followed by closure and withdrawal as the experience fades into the background as part of the cadre of experiences from which new figures will emerge. This entire process is referred to as "organismic self-regulation" in which the person moves form sensation to withdrawal in a smooth, uninterrupted fashion.

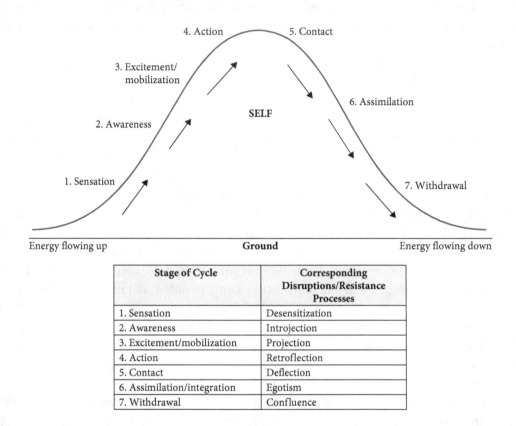

Stage of Cycle	Corresponding Disruptions/Resistance Processes
1. Sensation	Desensitization
2. Awareness	Introjection
3. Excitement/mobilization	Projection
4. Action	Retroflection
5. Contact	Deflection
6. Assimilation/integration	Egotism
7. Withdrawal	Confluence

FIGURE 13.1   The contact cycle of experience.

As an example, consider my recent experience with hunger the other night. Before I went to bed, I noticed that I was hungry (sensation) and then quickly became aware that I wanted something to eat to satisfy my hunger (awareness). I remembered that we had some leftovers in the refrigerator, and I became excited and mobilized (excitement/mobilization) about the prospect of enjoying a snack. I decided to go downstairs to the kitchen, open the refrigerator door, and pull out the leftover snack (encounter/action). I ate the snack, making sure I enjoyed every bite (interaction/full contact). After the snack was gone, I took a few minutes to watch some TV and rest (assimilation/integration) before I went to bed (closure/withdrawal). What became initially became figural (I'm hungry and want something to eat) was now fully in the background of my experience.

In Figure 13.1, it is easy to observe how we resist contact through interruptions. Using the previous example, I might have resisted making contact with my hunger if I remembered a message that came up earlier in the day about it being unhealthy to eat right before bedtime (introjections). If I would have followed that message, I would have disrupted the contact experience, leading to a "damming up" of energy. Indeed, resisting the cycle of contact can be quite common among human beings and manifest as physical, emotional, and behavioral problems.

The Gestalt term for incomplete contact experiences is *unfinished business* and becomes an important component of the therapy work. Unfinished business occurs when people ignore incomplete events by forcing them into the background. If powerful enough, these events continually seek completion and may manifest as psychological problems if not addressed (Polster & Polster, 1973). All our experience seems to hang around and "knock on the door" until a person is finished with it. One powerful technique to address unfinished business is through the experiment (discussed later). Examples include talking to an empty chair, role-playing disparate parts of the self, or fantasizing the completion in the present moment.

Awareness

Awareness is a key therapeutic goal of Gestalt therapy and refers to the uninterrupted process for "keeping up to date with oneself"—thoughts, feelings, and actions (Polster & Polster, 1973, p. 211). Perls believed awareness was essential for growth and maturation (Buchbinder, 1986). The idea is that, with greater awareness, individuals have greater choice. Gestalt clinicians prefer to allow the client to become aware of their own self-defeating behavior (Boylin, 1975). If a client is aware that their substance use is partly a consequence of how they deflect contact, then they have a greater range of choices for how to stop these distortions. The client struggling with a substance use disorder is chronically unaware, fearing their experience of feelings, values, and thoughts. Using substances, they deaden themself to life, precluding greater awareness and expression (Buchbinder, 1986).

Polster and Polster (1973) stated that before an individual can change behavior, they must take in the sensations and feelings that are part of it. That is, the person *must get in touch with how they feel and what they sense about their behavior and then decide if they wish to continue.* Substance use behavior can be so automatic, so mechanical, and habitual that clients are ultimately cut off from the awareness of what they are doing, how they are feeling about what they are doing, and the negative impact that drugs have on their bodies and minds. When clients hit rock bottom, they have usually made a commitment to avoid using substances. However, this commitment is often short-lived because they have not fully experienced the feelings and sensations that are part of the behavior. I will have much more to say about this topic in a later section.

Polster and Polster (1973) argued that human beings can enhance their lives by focusing awareness on four main elements: (a) sensations and actions, (b) feelings, (c) wants, and (d) values. Before action occurs, one must become aware of the building sensations and excitement (Polster & Polster, 1973). For example, the awareness of excitement that an athlete experiences while they play a game represents a healthy experience defined by the union of sensation and expression. Problems occur when there is a cutoff between sensation and doing, which may lead to self-alienation (Polster & Polster, 1973). Indeed, this split is exactly what can happen in the case of substance use. The substance-using client jumps from sensation to action without any reflection or awareness of their experience. The disrupted contact cycle will be discussed in a later section.

Awareness of feelings refers to "sitting with" feelings (rather than avoiding them) and using them to provide guidance and integration in one's life (Polster & Polster, 1973). Awareness of wants, feelings, and values promotes greater clarity and paves the way for greater expansion, growth, and health.

Here and Now

Gestalt clinicians place a premium on the present moment, referred to as the "here and now." The here and now refers to taking a keen interest in how clients emerge, grow, and develop in the immediacy of the therapeutic endeavor (Zinker, 1977). A well-known maxim in Gestalt therapy, emphasized by my Gestalt teacher, is that people do not change in the past or in the future, but *now*. Clients prevent themselves from living in the moment by obsessing about the past or fearing some future event. Keeping one's attention on what might happen or what has already happened can be a recipe for anxiety (Buchbinder, 1986). This is not to say that the past is unimportant to the Gestalt clinician. The client's context and ground from which figures emerge provide significant understanding of their struggles. However, awareness and change can only be achieved in the now, and that is what is worked within the counseling setting (Luellen, 1998). Gestalt clinicians *attend to the obvious* in the here and now, where thoughts, feelings, and behaviors *together* provide a picture of the whole person. Attending to the obvious might mean noticing the client is not talkative on a particular day, that they are more nervous than usual, or that they are avoiding eye contact. Gestalt clinicians meet the client where they are; they illuminate what exists in the moment to invigorate the client toward change (Buchbinder, 1986).

Gestalt clinicians focus on the "what" and "how" of behavior rather than the "why." Using what and how keeps the conversation in the present moment, such as "What are you experiencing when you say that?" or "How are you upsetting yourself now?" Using why questions keep clients too cerebral and focuses them on causes, explanations, or intellectualizing. Whereas understanding the causes of deleterious behavior or troubling emotions is helpful, it does relatively little to enhance awareness and create change. Becoming aware of how the client contributes to the cause of a problem is usually more powerful that simply knowing the cause. As Boylin (1975) noted, "The Gestalt therapist is not interested in 'why' a person began drinking, but in allowing that person to become aware of how he now chooses to continue that behavior" (p. 524).

The Creative Stance and the Role of the Gestalt Clinician

Joseph Zinker (1977) described Gestalt therapy as a creative process in which clinician and client venture to invent and improvise methods to help the client live a more productive life.

This stance, of course, is in stark contrast to other theories that are more mechanical and governed by fixed rules and principles. According to Zinker, the creative process is what gives zest to life (and therapy, for that matter). The foundation of the creative process is change—transforming from one form of being, feeling, or thinking into another.

Taking a creative stance requires that the clinician be open to possibilities in the moment. It also refers to being one's own best assessment instrument. That is, Gestalt clinicians pay attention to their own responses and feelings that arise in the moment, using these reactions as guideposts for creative responses, ideas, and feedback (Polster & Polster, 1973).

Gestalt clinicians generally avoid interpretation, diagnosing, and intellectualizing. Although these functions may be necessary in some clinical settings (e.g., diagnosing), they are not emphasized in the therapy hour. From the Gestalt perspective, such activities preclude the creative process by keeping clients (and clinicians) in their head, a convenient way to distance oneself from one's own experiences and emotions. Clients are encouraged to interpret their own behavior, thoughts, and feelings based on their awareness of moment-to-moment experiences (Joyce & Sills, 2001).

Gestalt therapists help clients rely less on external support and more on internal support. In substance use, this is an ideal strategy as clients have perpetually turned to external supports (i.e., drugs) to address internal states, such as depression, anxiety, isolation, or social discomfort. Helping clients to strengthen self-confidence, self-esteem, and other indicators of intrinsic motivation can build their internal mechanisms of support. This is not to say that external supports are discouraged; however, they need to be in the best interests of the client and relied on as secondary to internal supports. In Gestalt therapy, clients cultivate internal support by correcting disruptions in contact, enhancing awareness, and learning to accept what is as a precursor to change.

Paradoxical Principle of Change

The paradoxical principle of change (Beisser, 1970) is based on the idea that nothing changes until it is first accepted (Polster & Polster, 1973). The paradox is this: The more one tries to be who one is not, the more one stays the same (Beisser, 1970). In other words, change does not take place when clients force themselves or are coerced to change, but rather when they take the time and effort to accept and be what is—to make full contact with one's experiences, behaviors, and emotions, no matter how difficult. By relaxing the need to change, we create space for wholeness and growth (Yontef, 2005). Gestalt therapists encourage clients to accentuate that which exists rather than simply trying to change it. This concept plays a key role in how Gestalt clinicians address resistance (like MI). Joining with a person's resistance transforms that resistance to assistance (Buchbinder, 1986; Kappeler, 2004).

The paradoxical principle of change may be helpful to recovering clients struggling with cravings or urges to use substances. Clients struggle to resist cravings, trying desperately to make them go away. According to the paradoxical principle of change, these clients will only strengthen their cravings because they have failed to accept what is and are trying to force change. Teaching clients to make full contact with their cravings and accepting them leads to the paradox of diminished of cravings. If craving emerges as a figure, the client needs to take the experience through the cycle of contact where it will eventually fade into the ground. This strategy, however, is not for the inexperienced clinician and must be done with clients who have some established recovery and who have strong internal and external support systems.

Criteria for Effective Counseling Outcomes

Gestalt clinicians look for several client outcomes that indicate progress and growth:

- Completion of unfinished business
- Greater awareness of resistance to contact and restoration of healthy contact
- Greater awareness of sensations, actions, feelings, wants, and values
- Integration of disparate parts of the self
- Increased ability to experiment with new behaviors in the counseling session and generalize them to other areas of their life. Creative experimentation with new behaviors allows clients to realize that they have alternative choices to problematic behavior patterns
- Reaching a new realization about themselves as capable individuals who can influence their environments (Corey, 2017)

Application of Gestalt Therapy With Substance Use Disorders

According to Buchbinder (1986), Gestalt therapy has both the knowledge base and techniques to promote change among substance-using clients. Gestalt theory views substance use as encompassing several elements: (a) distorted retroflection and other contact processes; (b) disruptions in the contact cycle manifesting as diminished sensation, diminishing new figures, and unfinished business; and (c) limited self-awareness and inability to engage in the natural flow of figure/ground processes. With clients who struggle with substance use disorders, the Gestalt clinician's task is to help them get in touch with their own experiences, especially at the sensation level of the cycle of experience. This increased awareness slows down the flow of experience so they can be able to make better choices rather than act impulsively.

Clemmens (2005b) proposed substance use may be a type of *creative adjustment*. College students attend a party and engage in binge drinking to moderate their social fears and inhibitions. An individual with cocaine use disorder smokes crack to numb an emotionally draining and disappointing day. Rather than making contact and trying to understand their experiences or emotions, individuals will use drugs to creatively adjust and modulate how they feel. The pattern may begin with relatively harmless creative adjustments, as when a person has one beer to "loosen up" at a party. However, if this pattern intensifies, the creative adjustment begins to work against the person.

Clemmens's Addictive Cycle Model

From a Gestalt therapy perspective, individuals struggling with substance use disorders develop an impaired cycle of experience. Specifically, the flow of the cycle is modified, and parts are compromised and/or skipped. To illustrate, Clemmens (2005b) created the "addiction cycle," which represents how an individual's contact processes become dysfunctional when using substances. Figure 13.2 outlines the addiction cycle.

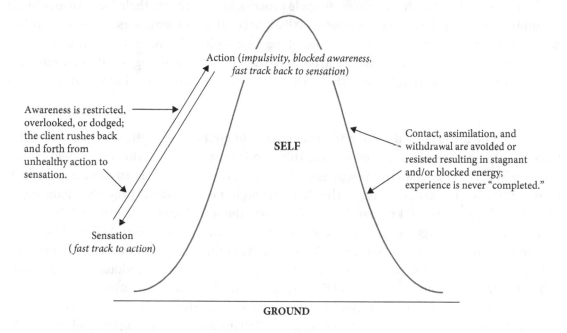

Action (*impulsivity, blocked awareness, fast track back to sensation*)

Awareness is restricted, overlooked, or dodged; the client rushes back and forth from unhealthy action to sensation.

SELF

Contact, assimilation, and withdrawal are avoided or resisted resulting in stagnant and/or blocked energy; experience is never "completed."

Sensation (*fast track to action*)

GROUND

FIGURE 13.2 The addicted cycle of experience.

There are several important observations worth mentioning regarding Figure 13.2. First, notice how the cycle is much narrower and taller than the "normal" cycle in Figure 13.1. This represents a shorter amount of time dedicated to developing one's experience through sensation, followed by awareness and so forth (Clemmens, 2005a). For the individual with a substance use disorder, dysfunction begins at the first point of the cycle, sensation. Sensation is experienced as discomfort or a desire for the drug (Clemmens, 2005a); however, the next two steps in the contact process are rushed through straight to action. As Figure 13.2 shows, once the sensation related to drug use begins, it becomes "hot-wired" directly to action, without any awareness or mobilization/excitement for alternative behaviors. Once action (i.e., seeking drug, taking drug) is established, the individual fails to make healthy contact, assimilation, and withdrawal of the experience, hence the cycle never completes itself. Instead, the individual jumps down to sensation and the shortened, narrower contact cycle perpetually continues. As Clemmens (2005a) noted, the individual develops a sensation-action loop. They can certainly feel sensation, but there is no effort or awareness to understand it, experience it, or intervene consistent with pledges to remain abstinent. Notice also that the individual stays almost exclusively on the first half of the cycle, failing to properly integrate and close the experience. Figure 13.2 illustrates what is meant by a "fixed figure"; the figure of substance craving and use remains fixed in the experience of the client, never completing itself to free up energy for alternative pursuits and interests. In essence, individuals who become substance dependent learn to interrupt other emerging needs, figures, and sensations as they hold on to the dominant figure of intoxication (Clemmens, 2005b).

The individual, through the addiction cycle process, has narrowed their focus to an almost singular interest in the drug (Clemmens, 2005a). According to Clemmens, recovery involves helping the client to broaden contact outside of the drug itself and to reestablish a healthier flow of contact experiences. Clemmens (2005a) outlined three development stages with corresponding "tasks of recovery"; the overall goal is the "progressive restoration of contact functioning" (p. 37).

Stage 1: Early Recovery

In stage 1, the focus is on the self and development of boundaries, with the primary goal of helping the client to maintain abstinence. This may involve detoxification or residential programs where the client can live in a drug-free environment before seriously working on their recovery. It also may entail assisting the client through the withdrawal process, encouraging understanding and insight rather than avoidance of the withdrawal (Clemmens, 2005a).

A second task of stage 1 is learning how to retroflect (Clemmens, 2005a). At first glance, this task may seem counterintuitive given Perls's assertion that the person with an alcohol use disorder must "undo destructive retroflection." Indeed, one reason individuals struggle with substance use problems is the retroflective process of turning self-destructive feelings back on the self in the form of substance use. However, retroflection also can be utilized strategically to help clients in the early stages of recovery. The skill involves developing the ability to resist or inhibit the desire for the substance. In other words, instead of reaching for the drink or drug, the client learns to inhibit this process, fully experience the urge or craving, understand the feelings (instead of avoiding them), and move on with alternative interests and pursuits (Clemmens, 2005a).

One way to help clients retroflect their drug-using desires is to encourage persistent awareness of negative consequences. Keeping negative associations and experiences in the foreground of awareness may help clients pull back from drugs and move on to other experiences. The clinician, for example, could help a client work through the cycle of experience via imaginative techniques. The client could slowly picture himself at a tempting location where drugs are available, remember the negative consequences of using, and imagine resisting drug use despite having urges to use. Emphasis can be given to the back half of the cycle, where the client contacts, assimilates, and then withdrawals for a complete experience (Clemmens, 2005a).

The third task in stage 1 is to assist clients in turning sensations into awareness. This process gets at the heart of the problem with individuals who struggle with substance use. In essence, clients are taught to slow down the process so that when sensations arise, they can label them, feel them, and develop awareness. A common Gestalt phrase is to "lose your mind and come to your senses," highlighting the importance of addressing direct sensory experiences and sensation rather than remaining in a cerebral, intellectualizing stance (Boylin, 1975). Here is an example focusing on direct experience and sensation with a client:

Client: Man, I used to love taking that hit ... took my problems away!

Clinician: Can you say, "I love taking a hit?" (keeping the language in the here and now)

Client: I love taking a hit.

Clinician: Say it one more time, this time with emphasis.

Client: [with emphasis] I LOVE taking a hit!

Clinician: What's happening now? What are you experiencing?

Client: I don't believe myself. I don't love taking a hit. I hate what drug use has done to me.

Clinician: Stay with your experience. What is happening now?

Client: I feel very sad—sad that I have wasted so much time.

Clinician: How do you experience your sadness?

Client: It eats me up. I want to cry. I want to stop.

In this vignette, the clinician takes a comment from the client and brings it into the moment by asking about the "what" and "how" of the experience. If the client continued talking about his love of getting a hit, he would have remained in the safe and comfortable cognitive realm, unaware of his experience or sensations. This short vignette demonstrates the potential of Gestalt therapy: getting to the heart of the matter by staying present and working in the here and now, where change happens. Asking the client to "stay with" feelings also is a way to help them avoid moving too fast through their emotions.

Stage 2: Middle Recovery

In stage 2, the focus for the client becomes differentiation *and* relatedness, or put differently, self and others (Clemmens, 2005a). Here, the goal is for the client to establish a balance between contact with self and contact with others. Tasks include helping the client to develop a complementary, rather than competitive, relationship with the world, redefine self–other boundaries that are more flexible, and develop interpersonal skills and competence (Clemmens, 2005a).

In middle recovery, the individual is better prepared to broaden their experiences and contact with others. Engagement in groups, organizations, community activities, or family events moves the client toward greater contact balance. The efforts of 12-step groups can greatly facilitate the process as clients learn to "make amends to them all," "take a moral inventory," and become sponsors as way *to give back to others*. The focus in stage 2 is to move away from self toward others but to remain flexible at the self–other boundary.

Stage 3: Later Recovery

In stage 3, the focus is reaching beyond the self and observing self in relation to all systems, including nature and the environment. The tasks include reflection, contemplation, and transcendence (Clemmens, 2005a); there is a spiritual quality to this step in that individuals in recovery develop a deeper meaning and purpose in their lives. The clinician's task is to support this burgeoning development by helping the client move beyond self or to transcend self. Of course, this process takes great courage on the part of the client, who has habitually relied on self-management (Clemmens, 2005a). Can they trust the world to support them if needed? Can they let go of the need to control everything? Letting others support the client involves cultivating the belief that there is help beyond themselves and that they don't have to do it all.

Clemmens's (2005a) model of addiction, and subsequent stages of intervention, provides a Gestalt framework for working with substance-using clients. Its strength is in identifying disrupted contact processes and reestablishing healthy ways of relating to self, others, and experiencing the world.

Working With the Person–Drug Relationship

White (1999) outlined a Gestalt model of substance use based on contact boundary disturbances, fixed figures, and unfinished business that impairs healthy movement through the cycle of experience. According to White (1999), the most direct way to help individuals with substance use disorders involves "re-formation, destruction, and/or integration of the figure of the drug effect itself" (p. 147). In other words, the client needs to make full, satisfying contact with the drug experience in the safety of the therapeutic session to assimilate it into the ground, allowing them to move forward. White's model is stage based and corresponds to the *transtheoretical stages of change model.*

Stage 1: Sensing and Building Ground (Precontemplation)

Clients in this stage usually have limited or poor awareness. Drug use is a "fixed figure" that immediately emerges from the ground. Nothing in the environment captures the client's attention other than the drug itself. The client may actively try to avoid this current relationship with the drug, which only makes the figure stronger. At the same time, they are unaware of the possibility of creating a new person–drug relationship, one that establishes drug use as a past behavior. The key interventions at this point include (a) clinician–client rapport and (b) *somatic sensitization* through gentle experimentation, that is, helping the client to make direct contact[1] with the drug using behavior, which is often avoided but remembered somatically (White, 1999).

For example, in this stage a clinician may ask a client to talk about the drug-using experience and then process what the client is experiencing in the moment. A clinician–client exchange might look something like this:

CLINICIAN: Talk about your experiences using cocaine.

---

1 Making "direct contact" understandably sounds a bit vague, but the process is rather simple. Contact means connecting to the environment with one or more of the five senses, either in vivo or through imagination. For example, making direct contact with drug behavior could include having the client imagine the sight or smell of a drug and "sitting with" that experience as it progresses through the contact cycle.

CLIENT: It was great. I mean, I could never get a high like I did with coke.

CLINICIAN: Can you feel the experience now?

CLIENT: Somewhat. Yeah, talking about it makes me want it, but I know I can't do that.

CLINICIAN: Sit with the experience of wanting the drug. Tell me what is happening now, *especially in your body.*

Stage 2: Clarifying the Figure (Contemplation)

According to White (1999), the sticking point with many individuals with substance use disorders is their old (or current) relationship with the drug. This relationship may metaphorically play out with the drug acting as an old, reliable friend, or perhaps as the only way to escape reality. Whatever the dynamics, the dominant experience of the individual is the old (or current) relationship. However, the individual with a substance use disorder typically has little understanding or direct experience of this relationship. Old (or current) relationships with drugs can be transformed into new relationships and experiences, but only if the old substance use relationship is explored and clarified. White argued that the treatment community's insistence on using terms like *abstinence* or *recovery* are meaningless to someone who has a fixed, current relationship with a substance.

Following the previous example, here is a brief clinical exchange to illustrate the point:

CLIENT: I feel a surge of feeling in my gut, and my heart is beginning to beat faster.

CLINICIAN: Good, stay with this. Anything else?

CLIENT: Hmmm. I guess I somewhat have this sick feeling, too. And anxiety, which I think is related. I can't seem to relax.

CLINICIAN: If you could speak as this anxiety to your old relationship with drugs, what would it say? Give the anxiety a voice.

CLIENT: (speaking as anxiety) This relationship is not good for him! I am trying to communicate with him, but I can't—he puts up defenses all the time. I exist because part of him wants to use and part of him doesn't.

CLINICIAN: (to client) What are you experiencing now?

CLIENT: I see more clearly what I am doing. Whereas I want to quit, part of me likes my relationship with cocaine.

Stage 3: Encouraging Awareness (Decision)

Stage 3 in White's (1999) model includes exploring ambivalence by shifting the inner conflict between urges to use and resistance to use into open awareness. Enhanced awareness of this ambivalence allows for integration and then dissolution of thoughts, feelings, and beliefs about the old (or current) person–drug relationship. That is, through awareness the client is actively exploring competing feelings about drug use instead of avoiding them.

Following from the clinical excerpts, the client clearly stated their ambivalence about using cocaine. Instead of avoiding these competing feelings, the client is encouraged to embrace and explore them. Techniques used here might be like the decisional balance exercise discussed in Chapter 6.

Stage 4: Mobilizing Energy (Action)

In this stage, the clinician's task is to keep the client moving by prompting and encouraging awareness of drug-related experiences (thoughts, cravings) that appear spontaneously (White, 1999). The client may experience a pull to reestablish their old relationship with the drug. However, it becomes important for the clinician to help the client "sit with" and "work through" experiences related to relapse *or* recovery. It would be counterproductive, for example, for the clinician to attack intentions to relapse and reinforce intentions toward recovery instead of letting the client fully explore these two polarities on their own. In the meantime, the clinician can introduce the client to alternative tasks, relationships, and behaviors that compete with cravings to use (White, 1999).

Again, in White's (1999) model avoidance from feelings, both positive and negative, are discouraged. The client has most likely built up a lifetime of avoidance behaviors. This only serves to create more confusion and inner turmoil as the client becomes more unaware of self. The notion of "sitting through" or "working through" experiences and emotions help clients build up tolerance to these feelings and, because they are contacted, will recede into the background just like a wave crashing on shore recedes back into the ocean.

Stage 5: Contacting and Withdrawing (Maintenance)

If the client works through the cycle from sensation to assimilation, making full and satisfying contact with the old drug experiences, space is opened for new relationships to emerge. White (1999) suggested that clients contact all relevant drug experiences, including the part of the experience that is most satisfying. This can be done several ways but is primarily accomplished through imagery and imagination. Although many clinicians may fear the possibility of reactivating drug use in this step of the process, White argued that clinicians need to trust that the client will, in the safety of the therapy office, work through such feelings and eventually come to significant insight and understanding. In essence, White's model involves (a) reactivating the drug experience, (b) working through it, and (c) creating gestalt. Creating a closed gestalt refers to completing the drug experience for it to fade into the background and free up space toward growth and maturity.

White's (1999) perspective and approach certainly runs counter to traditional forms of substance use treatment. Yet, one wonders if traditional approaches that ignore the client's experiences are missing a vital component in the client's recovery. White's point, although not explicitly stated, is that clinicians need to shed the fear of reactivating drug use by exploring drug experiences. Nonetheless, White's model is, in my opinion, for more experienced clinicians, preferably who have had some training in Gestalt methods. Continual supervision when using this method is recommended as well.

Multiphasic Transformation Process

Helga Matzko (1997) created a treatment approach for substance use disorders based on Gestalt principles. According to Matzko, traditional treatments for substance use fail to address the complexities of how substance use impacts all aspects of the person's functioning.

She developed the *multiphasic transformation process* (MPTP), which, like Clemmens's (2005a and 2005b) model, examines the cycle of experience as it relates to growth and change, and how this process becomes dysfunctional leading to an impaired addiction cycle.

Matzko (1997) believed that problematic substance use behaviors are only one aspect of the person's total functioning and that labels ("addict," "abuser") are limiting and should be avoided. Substance use and addiction, from this perspective, is the dogged, persistent use of creative adjustments with the intent to make experience more bearable but that outlived their usefulness. For example, a person might retroflect so much that they become depressed and creatively adjust to this by using substances.

The MPTP is phasic, overlapping, and gender neutral (Matzko, 1997). It is relationship oriented and focuses on empowerment to transform one's life in a preferred path. The integrity of the individual is exemplified as it aims to generate awareness of one's personal responsibility in creating deleterious habits and self-defeating behaviors (Matzko, 1997). Consistent with the Gestalt perspective, MPTP enables the client to amplify behaviors, thoughts, and emotions in the here and now so they can be fully experienced. The entire MPTP includes 11 phases of treatment. These phases, along with key objectives are outlined in Figure 13.3.

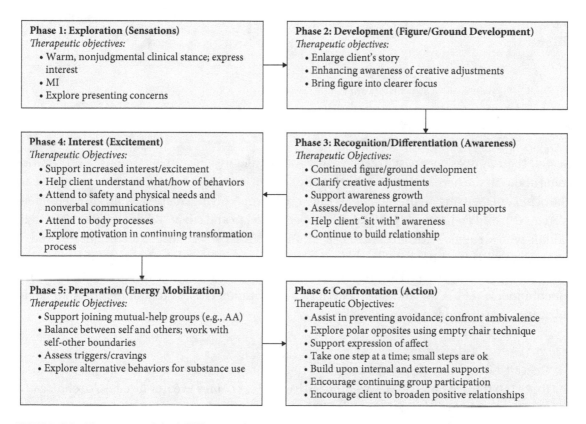

FIGURE 13.3   The phases of the MPTP.

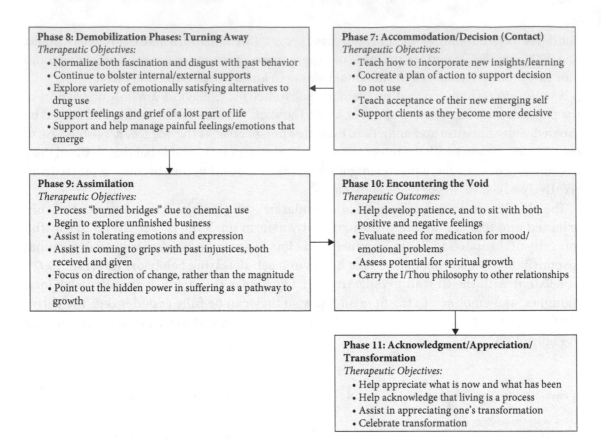

Phase 8: Demobilization Phases: Turning Away
Therapeutic Objectives:
- Normalize both fascination and disgust with past behavior
- Continue to bolster internal/external supports
- Explore variety of emotionally satisfying alternatives to drug use
- Support feelings and grief of a lost part of life
- Support and help manage painful feelings/emotions that emerge

Phase 7: Accommodation/Decision (Contact)
Therapeutic Objectives:
- Teach how to incorporate new insights/learning
- Cocreate a plan of action to support decision to not use
- Teach acceptance of their new emerging self
- Support clients as they become more decisive

Phase 9: Assimilation
Therapeutic Objectives:
- Process "burned bridges" due to chemical use
- Begin to explore unfinished business
- Assist in tolerating emotions and expression
- Assist in coming to grips with past injustices, both received and given
- Focus on direction of change, rather than the magnitude
- Point out the hidden power in suffering as a pathway to growth

Phase 10: Encountering the Void
Therapeutic Outcomes:
- Help develop patience, and to sit with both positive and negative feelings
- Evaluate need for medication for mood/emotional problems
- Assess potential for spiritual growth
- Carry the I/Thou philosophy to other relationships

Phase 11: Acknowledgment/Appreciation/Transformation
Therapeutic Objectives:
- Help appreciate what is now and what has been
- Help acknowledge that living is a process
- Assist in appreciating one's transformation
- Celebrate transformation

FIGURE 13.3   The phases of the MPTP. (*Continued*)

Gestalt-Based Techniques

Gestalt therapy does not boast a treasure trove of techniques; however, numerous opportunities come about in the here and now of the therapy session from which the clinician can intervene. The beauty of focusing on the moment is that a rich supply of information emerges. Excitement is created around what becomes figural between clinician and client. When working with individuals who struggle with substance use (or any client for that matter), techniques in and of themselves will offer little help (Buchbinder, 1986). To apply Gestalt techniques effectively, the clinician must comprehend the theoretical and philosophical undergirding of Gestalt therapy (Buchbinder, 1986). A list and brief description of common Gestalt techniques (as applied to substance use disorders) are provided next.

Heightening Awareness

All Gestalt-based techniques are designed to heighten awareness. Awareness, as stated, is the first step toward change. With enhanced awareness comes greater freedom of choice. If a client becomes aware of how their thinking, feeling, and behavioral patterns sabotage their recovery efforts, they will be in a better position to make choices to avoid entanglements with drugs. To varying degrees, the rest of the techniques discussed serve to heighten awareness.

Empty Chair

Probably the best-known Gestalt technique is the empty chair. Contrary to popular opinion, the empty chair originated from Adlerian theory but was greatly popularized by Fritz Perls and the Gestalt movement. In this technique, the clinician asks the client to dialogue with some identified other—such as a person, polarity, or characteristic of the self—whom they imagine sitting in an "empty chair" in the therapy office. For example, a client who is afraid to start conversations during social gatherings might practice doing so to an empty chair. Or a client who harbors ill feelings toward their father might talk to "him" using an empty chair.

This technique can be used in a variety of ways and offers many possibilities for the substance use client. For example, a client might dialogue between that part of the self that wants to stop and the part that wants to continue using. I have encouraged clients to speak as their "new" self (i.e., in recovery) to their "old" self (i.e., before treatment), and vice versa. After clients speak to an empty chair as one part of a dichotomy, it is a good idea to have them physically get up and sit in the other chair to play the opposite role. This dialogue back and forth should be closely monitored by the clinician, periodically stopping the role play to "check in" with the client with questions such as "What are you experiencing now? What just happened when you said that?" and "What insights came up for you after this exercise?"

In my experience, clients often become aware of how much stronger one voice or side is compared to the other. In some cases, the differences in physical posture between two polarities are striking. For example, I counseled a client who struggled with two polarities—one that wanted to stop drinking and the other that wanted to continue. When playing the "not wanting to stop drinking" voice the client assumed a more aggressive posture, made eye contact, and sat up straight. When playing the "wanting to stop drinking" voice, he slouched, lowered his voice, and spoke with hesitation. The client became aware of this difference and realized one reason it was so difficult for him to stay away from drinking. The remainder of the session focused on how he might strengthen his "wanting to change" voice.

Focusing on the Body

Gestalt therapy takes a holistic stance when working with clients, in that mind and body are seen as one entity instead of separate parts ("the whole is greater than the sum of its parts"). As such, the body and physical awareness are important components in the therapy process. Emphasis is placed on the client's posture, tone of voice, facial and other expressions, movements, and breathing (Boylin, 1975). Before those who struggle with substance use can journey into emotional expression, they must be aware of how they physically stop this process from occurring (Buchbinder, 1986). For example, I counseled a client who persistently sat at the edge of the couch in my office, huddled up like she was going to be attacked. Making this observation allowed her to experiment with relaxing her body and getting in touch with how she carries himself. Interventions related to the body might include asking the client to exaggerate a certain movement or posture (Buchbinder, 1986), to notice her breathing, or to "try out" a new movement. The importance placed on the body is especially important for substance-using clients, who often develop tendencies to say one thing but mean another (Boylin, 1975). As my Gestalt supervisor once said, the body does not lie.

I counseled a client with cocaine use disorder who had made a strong commitment to abstain. During one session, we engaged in a discussion about what was holding him back from finding peace in his life after cocaine. The client was having trouble coming up with emotions or experiences to explore, so I encouraged him to get in touch with his body. I asked him if he noticed anything physically that caught his attention. He became aware of some pressure in his chest and diaphragm. I encouraged him to place his hand on his chest and to give the sensation a voice. The client noticed immediately that he was holding his breath, and the message he received from his body was to breathe! We followed this experiment up with a few breathing exercises that seemed to relax him in the moment and free up some energy that he could now place toward his recovery.

Dreamwork

Gestalt therapy dreamwork is a unique and fascinating way to process client dreams. True to Gestalt philosophy, all aspects of the dream are considered representations of the client. In this technique, the client is asked to live out the dream as if it is happening now. (Polster & Polster, 1973). A. Woldt (personal communication, April 9, 2009) outlined five steps in experiential Gestalt dreamwork:

1. Encourage client to *tell* the dream in the present tense.
2. Encourage clients to *identify* what is figural or most interesting about the dream.
3. Encourage clients to *become* various parts of the dream.
4. Encourage clients to *dialogue* between parts of the dream.
5. Help clients find closure to the dream experience by giving it a name or creating some existential statement about the dream.

Through this process, clients may become more aware of what is getting in the way of change or clues as to what needs to happen to strengthen recovery. Van (name disguised) was one of my clients who struggled with opiate use disorder. During one counseling session, he volunteered a vivid dream experience in which he was in a large, empty house looking out the window. He was in a back room in the house in which a large chest sat in the middle. In the dream, he stated that he felt extreme loneliness and sadness and, when he woke up, the sadness became almost unbearable. He identified the large house as most figural in the dream. I asked him to speak as if he were the house. He stated (as the house) that he was "very large and provided protection for Van. I also am very lonely; I feel safe but lonely." Van came to the realization that he was indeed lonely in his life, something he simply brushed off before this session. He also remarked on his extreme sadness in the dream, which he tied to a close relative's recent death. The empty house represented his safe, childhood home, but he felt extreme loneliness and sadness without his trusted relative (or anyone else) around. This led to a productive discussion about how Van might reach out more to others and how his unresolved grief about the loss of his relative may be holding his recovery back. This work had the benefit of addressing a key issue related to substance use and relapse: isolation.

The reader should note that any aspect of Van's dream could have been explored further in the therapy session. In fact, it is impossible to explore the entire dream in one session! I could have encouraged Van to speak as the chest in the back room, dialogue between the house and the chest, or enact a closing of the dream that he would wish for, such as the chest opening and some secret to life coming out to provide wisdom. The possibilities are endless. The important point is that, based on Gestalt theory, every aspect of the dream represents some aspect of the person's life.

Creating Experiments

A unique quality of Gestalt therapy is working on behavior change in the here and now of the therapy hour (Zinker, 1977). When behavior modification or adjustment comes directly out of the client's experience, it is called an experiment (Zinker, 1977). The philosophy behind experiments is that action in the here and now is more fruitful therapeutically than simply ruminating or talking about past concerns or troubles (Polster & Polster, 1973). The experiment is designed to transform talking about (i.e., "aboutism") theorizing into being fully present with one's thoughts, feelings, and actions (Zinker, 1977).

The range and possibilities for experiments are limitless. The key, however, is for the client to pay attention to how they move from present awareness to action (Polster & Polster, 1973). For example, the client may have negative feelings toward their mother (present awareness), and then be asked to experimentally "talk" to her in an empty chair (experimental action). The client may be presently aware of any number of things—past relationship issues, future projects, difficult emotions, and intransigent thoughts. Thus, the client may speak to someone from the past or present, role-play an upcoming social event, talk to two opposing emotions, or "become" their thought. The only requirement is that the client experiments from present, here-and-now awareness, as if the event were occurring in the moment rather than in the past or future.

Polster and Polster (1973) identified several forms of experiment:

- **Enactment.** Experiments that require action seem to have the best effect. For example, instead of talking about a dream, clients can be encouraged to act out the dream in the here and now.

- **Directed behavior.** This refers to directing clients to do something with greater emphasis or passion, or something they avoid or fear in the moment, such as being assertive.

- **Fantasy.** Using one's imagination can be a powerful way to help clients act "as if" they were who they wanted to be.

- **Dreams.** As noted, Gestalt dream work is a unique and fascinating way for clients to explore their lives.

- **Homework.** It is always good to encourage clients to practice new insights outside of the counseling office.

No matter which format is used, it is important to stress the need to process with the client the insights that emerge from the experiment. What does the experiment say about the client? What is the "take away" for the client?

Integration of Polar Opposites

Many individuals have opposing thoughts and feelings that keep them stuck in a situation. In MI, the term that describes this is *ambivalence*, and it plays a strong role in why substance use problems can be so difficult to change. When an individual is aware of one aspect themself, a duality is assumed. Usually, one side of the polarity is figural, while the opposite is in the background (Luellen, 1998). The key to resolving polarities is to help clients get in touch with each polarity, giving them a voice, and then contacting each side (Polster & Polster, 1973). One of the most well-known polarities among humans is the top dog/bottom dog split. In this polarity, one aspect of the person dominates (top dog) the opposite (bottom dog). For example, a client might have a self-defeating side of their personality that dominates the more positive, encouraging side. Gestalt clinicians may ask clients to "try out" the bottom dog voice in a more confident manner, while at the same time making contact and acknowledging the top dog voice.

In substance use counseling, ambivalence is prevalent as clients struggle with a side of themselves that wants to quit using drugs and a side that wants to continue. I have asked clients to create a dialogue between these two polarities using the empty chair technique. One goal of Gestalt therapy is integration of the personality, and this growth partly depends on rekindling contact between disconnected sides of the individual (Polster & Polster, 1973).

Another method for exploring polarities is through completion of sentence fragments, outlined by Passons (1975). The purpose behind the technique is to help clients become free from rigid, "locked in" feelings, behaviors, thoughts, and identities. The client is asked to complete sentence fragments with as many words as are true for them (Luellen, 1998). Some examples include the following (Luellen, 1998, p. 10):

> A reason I choose to drink (or use) is ... A reason I might not drink (or use) is ...

> If I continue to drink (or use) ... If I choose not to drink (or use) ...

> My life with alcohol (or drugs) is ... Without alcohol I ...

The reader should note that each initial sentence fragment is followed by its polarity. This exercise helps clients become aware of their attitudes toward drinking or using, reasons for drinking or using, and potential obstructions to recovery (Luellen, 1998). Clients expand their thinking and feeling about using, which enhances responsibility and promotes better choices.

Elusive Client Language

Part of the creative stance in Gestalt therapy is tending to clients' own awareness of what is happening in the moment. Gestalt clinicians pay close attention to elusive client language designed to distance themselves from painful feelings. Examples include using the words *it* or *you*. For example, a client might say, "This situation is horrible. It is just pathetic." Gestalt clinicians might encourage this client to change the "it" to an "I." So, "It is pathetic" becomes "I am pathetic." Similarly, a client might change "You are all against me" to "I am against me." Such changes often have significant impact on the client and can open the door for further exploration (Boylin, 1975).

Other examples include reframing questions into statements and changing phrases such as "I can't" to "I won't." Reframing questions into statements avoids the "why-because" discussion that leads to endless rationalizations and excuses (Boylin, 1975), unfortunately common among substance-using clients. As an example of turning questions into statements, consider the following exchange:

CLIENT: Do you think I should seek intensive care?

CLINICIAN: See if you can put that question into a statement.

CLIENT: I want to seek intensive care but am unsure and anxious about how it will help.

CLINICIAN: Stay with your "unsureness" a minute. How do you make yourself unsure?

Changing phrases from "I can't" to "I won't" is a good example for how clients who use substances can assume greater responsibility for their substance problems ("I can't quit" is much different than "I won't' quit," which implies having a choice).

Gestalt Therapy in the Treatment of Diverse Populations

Despite limited empirical research with a diverse clientele, most experts in counseling theory agree that Gestalt therapy has great potential to be effective in working with culturally diverse populations. Frew (2013, as cited in Corey, 2017) cited Gestalt therapy as a sensitive and friendly diverse counseling approach. The emphasis on client phenomenology and unique experiences underscores the promise of Gestalt as a culturally relevant modality. The focus on the present moment, awareness, and experiment can help individuals understand and perceive their own cultural background. The figure/ground concept in Gestalt therapy is a reminder that clients come to counseling with unique backgrounds, including cultural upbringing that provides context to their presenting problems. Such a perspective can help clinicians comprehend the demands, barriers, and stressors that minority clients confront living within a dominant culture (Archer & McCarthy, 2007). Gestalt therapists understand the importance of assessing and working with contextual issues (i.e., the ground) as clients address immediate struggles in their lives.

Gestalt therapy may be especially applicable to bicultural clients who sometimes struggle with pressures from two cultures (Corey, 2017). Gestalt therapy's emphasis on integration and wholeness may allow bicultural clients to assess and process their experiences from two cultures as they integrate traits and characteristics from both. For example, a client might dialogue between their two cultural polarities via an empty chair technique. Experiments can be tailored to fit clients' unique circumstances and background.

Regarding substance use disorders, the adage "all addicts are the same" appears to be relatively common across treatment centers and 12-step mutual group meetings (Clemmens, 2005a). This perspective presumably exits because individuals with substance use disorders do indeed share a small group of similarities such as compulsive drug use, guilt, and insecurity (Clemmens, 2005a). However, individuals struggling with substance use are not the same, and their personalities, cultural backgrounds and gender experiences are many and varied. Clemmens (2005a) pointed out that ethnic systems influence many facets of drug use, including the drug used, social behavior, and the meaning of drug use. Clemmens's stance is one that affirms cultural background and experience while exploring the person.

As with all theories, Gestalt therapy also may create problems with clients from different cultural backgrounds (Corey, 2017). As noted earlier, Gestalt therapy is a powerful approach for bringing up and expressing deep-seated emotions. Whereas this might be acceptable for clients from primarily Western cultural backgrounds, it can be a concern for clients from traditions where emotional expression is seen as a sign of weakness or is discouraged. For example, in many Asian cultures, expressing negative feelings toward one's parents goes against the cultural value of showing honor, respect, and deference to one's elders. To express anger or disappointment, even though an imaginary experiment, would be difficult and potentially harmful to the client (Corey, 2017). Archer and McCarthy (2007) pointed out that Gestalt's emphasis on individualism and personal responsibility may contradict cultural values from more collectivistic cultures. Thus, care would need to be taken for clients where cultural, familial, and social influences share some of the responsibility for substance-using behavior and its treatment.

Gestalt therapy's emphasis on emotional expression may find resistance in males (Sharf, 2004), even from the Western societies, who are socialized to keep a "stiff upper lip" and show a limited range of emotions lest they be called "sissies." The lack of emphasis on intellectualizing, cognitive exploration, and rational thinking may turn off clients who prefer these activities in the therapy session.

Corey (2017) warned that jumping ahead too quickly using powerful Gestalt techniques may at the least cause clients to not come back to counseling and at the worst cause serious emotional harm. This advice is especially true for clients from diverse backgrounds, who may recoil at the thought of talking to their father in the counselor's office. In my own Gestalt training, instructors consistently stressed that a strong rapport is needed before diving in to experiment and other techniques. I also would add that clinicians can apply Gestalt theory in a gentler, flexible manner, such as "grading down" an experiment (e.g., instead of having a client talk to their father in an empty chair, explore what they might feel comfortable saying to him given their cultural background and upbringing). Corey (2017) expressed it well when he commented that Gestalt clinicians who fully understand their approach find the flexibility and sensitivity to be effective practitioners with all clients.

The entire process of developing awareness can be influenced by culture. Gestalt therapists need to be mindful of how cultural factors impact awareness and insight of self, others, and the world—striving to help clients fully experience themselves in the moment (Corey, 2017). This may especially be true for clients from diverse backgrounds who have substance use disorders; different cultural backgrounds may have unique values, beliefs, and norms related to substance use, influencing one's awareness of the behavior.

Fernbacher (2005) provided an excellent overview of cultural influences and considerations in Gestalt therapy. She stressed that the wholeness and availability of the clinician is what is crucial to healing during the therapy hour. In addition, she recommended that to undertake work with different cultures, Gestalt clinicians must explore their own cultural selves. Awareness of one's own cultural influences helps to support others in making contact and developing awareness of themselves and important others in their lives. Gestalt therapy, when used with sensitivity and flexibility, can be an effective approach when used with clients across cultures.

CASE STUDY

Using Gestalt Therapy in the Case of Michael

Michael and the clinician have had some time to build rapport, as he has been attending counseling for several months. The clinician has slowly incorporated more Gestalt-based principles into the sessions, preferring to ease into Gestalt experimentation and techniques. The clinician's goal in this vignette is to help Michael get in touch with and understand his angry feelings, which seem to fuel his substance use. This goal is accomplished through staying in the present moment, working on unfinished business, and developing awareness. As the reader will see, Gestalt therapy also can lead to unexpected explorations.

CLINICIAN: Good morning, Michael. Thanks for coming in today.

MICHEAL: Sure thing. No problem.

CLINICIAN: So, what would be most helpful to talk about today? (clarify figure)

MICHAEL: I don't know. Everything seems to be going okay. I had a pretty good week. (wringing hands and becoming a bit uncomfortable)

CLINICIAN: I am aware of your hands and shifting around in your seat. What are you experiencing now? (points out contrast between verbal and behavior, keeping in the present moment)

MICHAEL: Man, you don't miss a thing! I guess I am a little anxious for some reason. I mean, I think I know why I am rattled; Anita and I got into it last night. It was explosive.

CLINICIAN: Can you change the "it" to an "I"? (addressing vague language)

MICHAEL: "I was pretty explosive." (clinician asks to repeat it again a few times) "I was pretty explosive." "I was pretty explosive."

CLINICIAN: What do you notice when you say that? (keeping focus on client's experience in the now)

MICHAEL: Yeah, I think it is true. I am explosive. I just can't understand why I am so angry all the time. I mean, I know we talked about how drug use probably contributes, but I have been substance free for several months now.

CLINICIAN: Do you feel angry now? (keeping the focus on the present)

MICHAEL: Yes, I do. I feel angry—not like last night, but I just seem on edge.

CLINCIAN: Okay, stay with that feeling for a moment; where do you feel it in your body if at all? (staying with a feeling and body process work to enhance awareness)

MICHAEL: Hmmm, I do notice my chest feels somewhat tight. The anger seems to be right here (gesturing to his mid-chest)

CLINCIAN: Place your hand on your chest for a moment. What might your chest say to you about this angry feeling? How might it speak to you? (body process and simple experiment)

MICHAEL: It would say that I just need to relax and breathe! I can't seem to get a deep breath.

CLINCIAN: Okay. Well, let's try what your chest is telling you. How about we take a few deep breaths together?

At this point, the clinician instructs Michael on diaphragmatic breathing and slowly practices a few deep breaths with him. To Michael's surprise, he begins to feel a little better. He has loosened up considerably and noted a slightly "free" feeling. This new, emerging feeling was given full attention; however, the clinician sensed that Michael had not made full contact with his anger. Indeed, it was quite possible that Michael harbored unfinished business that keeps his anger as a fixed figure. The session proceeds with greater attention to anger.

CLINCIAN: Michael, is there anyone in your life who reminds you of your own anger process or how you get angry? (trying to assess for possible unfinished business)

MICHAEL: Well, I guess my father. My father was a drunk, angry man. The way he would mistreat my mother. The way he left our family. I lost some of my teen years because I had to care for my sister and mother. I have a lot of resentment toward him (talking louder, getting angry). And now, I am scared to death of becoming him!

CLINCIAN: I notice that when you talk about your father, your voice rises, and you *seem* angry. Do you notice this? (heightening awareness)

MICHAEL: Yeah, I also notice me tightening up—that feeling in my chest is back. (Michael is starting to demonstrate increased awareness of his body.)

CLINICIAN: I would like to try a brief experiment with what is happening now if you are okay with it. (Michael nods.) Take a moment and picture your father right here (motioning to the empty chair in the office). Assuming he is sitting right here, I encourage you to speak to him about how you feel. (introducing empty chair technique)

MICHAEL: Okay, this seems a little weird, but I'll give it a try. Dad, why did you leave us? I don't think you realize the pain you caused me and Anisha, both when you were living with us and when you left. Part of me hates you and part of me loves you (to the surprise of Michael, he starts to tear up). I feel so angry because of you ... and now I fear becoming you.

CLINCIAN: What is happening now? (keeping the process in the present moment)

MICHAEL: Wow, I wasn't expecting that! I didn't realize how much sadness is there. I also realize that I feel two ways about him—love and hate—I always thought it was hate. (Michael developing and clarifying greater awareness of his feelings)

The empty chair exercise continued, with the clinician periodically stopping Michael to process what was happening, how he was feeling, and any insights that emerged. He had an opportunity to play his father in the empty chair exercise and, to his surprise, spoke (as his father) in caring terms and apologized for all that he had done. More tears followed.

Michael's unfinished business with his father was a sticking point in his recovery. The task at this juncture was to help Michael complete the cycle of experience with anger, particularly the back half of contact: assimilation and withdrawal.

CLINICIAN: (after the empty chair) Where is your anger now?

MICHAEL: It is still here, but less. My chest feels a little lighter.

CLINCIAN: Stay with the experience now. Get into the anger and feel it fully if you can. (staying in present moment)

MICHAEL: Okay. Takes a deep breath. Yeah, I feel it, but it is diminished.

CLINCIAN: Now, reflect on the empty chair experience and what is happening now. What insights have come your way, if any? (encouraging assimilation and withdrawal)

MICHAEL: I feel lighter now. I realize that my anger toward my father may be more about sadness. I also understand that he probably does feel bad for what happened when we were younger, whether he would ever say it or not. The apology from him (in the empty chair) seemed genuine. Yeah, I feel better and more aware of where my anger has come from and how I hold on to it.

CLINICIAN: How might this new insight help you remain substance free right now? (tie in session to substance use)

MICHAEL: Well, first, I can understand that when I feel angry it is more about feeling sad about my past. If I get angry again, I can just ask myself, what am I sad about? I think this will take some work with Anita, but for some reason I think that this will give me pause when I feel like using. And I can, as you say, stay with angry feelings until they pass over rather than drink them away. I learned today that I can tolerate them and move on from them.

This vignette demonstrates the power of Gestalt therapy. Michael had no intention of "talking to" his father today, let alone crying in the session. Had the clinician stayed in the cognitive, intellectual realm, he and Michael could potentially have gone on and on endlessly "talking about" how he had been wronged in the past. Michael would have left the session with little awareness and insight into *his* experience. Staying in the present moment allowed Michael to understand where his anger came from, how he created it, and how he can "stay with" it through the cycle of experience.

This session could have gone down many avenues; the potential opportunities in the here and now are endless. Notice also how the focus of the session was not on substance use per se, but on angry feelings. However, the connection between Michael's anger and substance use was quite clear. Experiencing his anger and bridging the connection to substance use at the end may help Michael reduce his "need" for substances to assuage his angry feelings.

Strengths, Limitations, and Ethical Issues Related to Gestalt Therapy

Gestalt therapy is an alternative model to traditional forms of substance use treatment. Based largely on the disease concept of addiction, traditional treatment approaches may inadvertently interfere with the client assuming responsibility for their drug-using behavior. Gestalt therapy places choice, contact, meaning making, and personal responsibility back into the equation. Too much emphasis away from these processes may lead to muddled and unproductive sessions in which the client walks away understanding little about themself. The cycle of experience is a useful metaphor related to how clients develop rigid substance use patterns. Gestalt therapy for the substance use disorders is a different approach and a breath of fresh air.

Gestalt therapy is not for everyone. Clients who are overly cognitive oriented or who thrive on practical, how-to advice might find Gestalt sessions difficult. Encouraging clients to contact previous drug experiences might turn some clinicians off who fear such activities might reactivate drug use. Of course, one does not have to implement every aspect of Gestalt therapy in their practice; indeed, in my own practice I incorporate Gestalt principles as an approach in and of itself or integrated with other approaches as needed. Table 13.1 lists the strengths, limitations, and ethical issues related to Gestalt therapy as applied to substance use counseling.

TABLE 13.1 Summary of Strengths, Limitations, and Ethical Concerns of Gestalt Therapy in the Treatment of Substance Use Problems

Strengths	• Gestalt therapy can be used effectively in individual and group therapy formats, making it applicable to substance use counseling. • Gestalt therapy focuses energy on personal responsibility, awareness, contact, and choice, items that are often ignored or de-emphasized among traditional substance use treatment approaches. Clients who successfully complete Gestalt therapy feel more integrated, whole, and aware. • Gestalt therapy has a solid theoretical base and a cadre of therapeutic strategies to be effective with clients struggling with substance use disorders. • The focus on the here and now avoids nonproductive discussions about the past or worry about the future. In Gestalt therapy, individuals learn to work with and accept what is, allowing them to create new possibilities for themselves. • Gestalt therapy greatly assists with affective expression, a notable difficulty among individuals struggling with substance use problems. Negative emotions lead to high risk for relapse; Gestalt therapy helps clients experience these emotions, understand them, learn how to tolerate their energy, and work through them as a complete experience.
Limitations	• Gestalt therapy may not be suitable for all clients. Clients who are cognitively oriented or who prefer traditional models of substance use treatment might have difficulty with Gestalt methods. • Gestalt therapy takes practice and training. It is a potentially powerful approach. Neophyte clinicians should strive to receive supervision and/or training if considering adopting Gestalt into their practice. • It is difficult to argue against the notion that some clients with substance use disorders need to examine their thought processes and learn life skills. Focus on emotion and contact is important, but is it enough? Some may argue that Gestalt is limited in that sense. • Gestalt therapy does not have a well-developed empirical base with clients using substances. This, however, is mostly a feature of the technique; Gestalt therapy, because of its focus on what emerges in the present moment, is more creative and intuitive than empirical.

TABLE 13.1   Summary of Strengths, Limitations, and Ethical Concerns of Gestalt Therapy in the Treatment of Substance Use Problems (*Continued*)

Ethical Issues	
	• Despite its application to substance use counseling, Gestalt therapy takes considerable skill and understanding to use competently. There is potential risk that some clinicians' lack of skill and theoretical understanding, as well as confusion as to its application, could constitute unethical practice.
	• In addition, encouraging clients to mentally reexperience their drug-using behavior, without competent and proper oversight, could be cause for ethical concern. This practice would be a slippery slope for neophyte clinicians who are not properly trained in Gestalt methods or who ignore supervision.
	• Gestalt therapy rejects many of the traditional addiction concepts and applications, which have some empirical support. Using Gestalt methods to the full exclusion of evidenced-based addictions practice may be grounds for ethical concern.

References

Archer, J., & McCarthy, C. J. (2007). *Theories of counseling and psychotherapy: Contemporary applications*. Pearson.

Beisser, A. (1970). The paradoxical theory of change. In J. Fagan & I. L. Shepard (Eds.), *Gestalt therapy now: Theory, techniques, applications* (pp. 77–80). Science and Behavior Books.

Boylin, E. R. (1975). Gestalt encounter in the treatment of hospitalized alcoholic patients. *American Journal of Psychotherapy, 29*, 524–534.

Buchbinder, J. (1986). Gestalt therapy and its application to alcoholism treatment. *Alcoholism Treatment Quarterly, 3*, 49–67.

Clemmens, M. C. (2005a). *Getting beyond sobriety: Clinical approaches to long-term recovery*. Gestalt Press.

Clemmens, M. C. (2005b). Gestalt approaches to substance use/abuse/dependency: Theory and practice. In A. Woldt & S. Toman (Eds.), *Gestalt therapy: History, theory, and practice* (pp. 279–300). SAGE.

Corey, G. (2017). *Theory and practice of counseling and psychotherapy* (10th ed.). Cengage.

Crocker, S. F. (1999). *A well-lived life: Essays in Gestalt therapy*. Taylor & Francis.

Fernbacher, S. (2005). Cultural influences and considerations in Gestalt therapy. In A. Woldt & S. Toman (Eds.), *Gestalt therapy: History, theory, and practice* (pp. 117–132). SAGE.

Joyce, P., & Sills, C. (2001). *Skills in Gestalt counselling and psychotherapy*. SAGE.

Kappeler, F. (2004). A Gestalt approach to treating alcoholism and eating disorders. *Gestalt!, 8*, 1–6.

Luellen, R. (1998). The use of Gestalt interventions in the treatment of resistant alcohol-dependent client. *Journal of Mental Health Counseling, 20*, 202–215.

Matzko, H. M. G. (1997). A Gestalt therapy treatment approach for addictions: Multiphasic transformation process. *Gestalt Review, 1*, 34–56.

Miller, G. (2005). *Learning the language of addiction counseling* (2nd ed.). Wiley.

Passons, W. (1975). *Gestalt approaches to counseling*. Holt, Rinehart, & Winston.

Perls, F. (1969). *Ego, hunger, and aggression.* Vintage.

Perls, F., Hefferline, R., & Goodman, P. (1951). *Gestalt therapy: Excitement and growth in human personality.* The Gestalt Journal Press.

Polster, E., & Polster, M. (1973). *Gestalt therapy integrated.* Vintage.

Sharf, R. S. (2004). *Theories of psychotherapy and counseling: Concepts and cases* (3rd ed.). Brooks/Cole.

White, R. J. (1999). A Gestalt approach to working with the person-drug relationship. *Gestalt Review, 3,* 147–156.

Woldt, A., & Toman, S. (2005). Prologue-foreword. In A. Woldt & S. Toman (Eds.), *Gestalt therapy: History, theory, and practice* (pp. ix–xiv). SAGE.

Yontef, G. M. (2005). Gestalt therapy theory of change. In A. Woldt & S. Toman (Eds.), *Gestalt therapy: History, theory, and practice* (pp. 81–101). SAGE.

Zinker, J. (1977). *The creative process in Gestalt therapy.* Brunner/Mazel.

Figure Credits

CHAPTER 14

Applying Existential Therapy in the Treatment of Substance Use Disorders

Everything can be taken from a man but one thing: the last of the human freedoms—to choose one's attitude in any given set of circumstances, to choose one's own way

(Frankl, 1992, p. 75)

Introduction

I've always had an interest in philosophy. In undergraduate school, I recall taking an introductory philosophy class and was encouraged by the professor to consider philosophy as a major (the philosophy department, at the time, needed majors!). Despite my interest in the subject, it was difficult envisioning my parents accepting a switch in majors from business administration to philosophy. I ended up sticking with business administration and psychology, which has certainly served me well. However, when I reflect on my education, there is part of me that secretly wishes I had taken my professor's encouragement to heart. Philosophy would have provided a solid foundation for the work that I do today as a counselor and counselor educator. Indeed, many of the major counseling theories, including the ones presented in this text, have philosophical roots. This philosophical grounding is no more evident than with existential psychotherapy and counseling.

My introduction to, and exploration of, existential philosophy has had a direct and indirect impact on my own counseling practice. To understand existential philosophy (and the therapeutic approach based on this philosophy), it is important to realize that it was born out of and reflected the times—world wars, industrialization, and an existential angst that was not felt before among human society. Existential philosophy began with several influential figures who were influenced by the situation in the world in which they lived and who turned attention to matters of existence itself, what it means to *be* human, how to create meaning in a supposedly meaningless world, and what it means to have total responsibility for our actions and thoughts. Unfortunately, we do not have the space to take a full survey of existential philosophy, as interesting as that would be. However, it is important to have some philosophical understanding from which existential psychotherapy emerged. Indeed, philosophical elements that have direct implications for psychotherapy will be infused throughout this chapter.

Existential therapy and counseling draw from philosophy, but the therapeutic approach was expanded and developed by several other prominent individuals in professional psychiatric circles. The first major publication on existential therapy was Yalom's (1980) seminal text *Existential Psychotherapy.* Other psychotherapists and authors, including Rollo May, Viktor Frankl, and James Bugental, emphasized existential therapy as more of a therapeutic attitude and philosophy rather than a structured treatment system. As such, it can serve as an approach in and of itself, or as the "ground" from which other approaches can operate. An existential stance can provide depth to the therapeutic hour. Forays into such topics as death, meaning, and responsibility cut to the core of one's existence and, if left unattended, often percolate to the surface in the form of psychological and behavior symptoms. Indeed, my attraction to existential philosophy and psychotherapy was, interestingly enough, related to some of my own existential struggles—how to create a meaningful life, connecting anxiety to deeper existential issues, and face the fear of my own mortality.

According to Ford (1996), many substance use clients fail to progress through the stages of change because inadequate attention has been given to resolving existential issues that hinder deeper levels of progress. Substance use programs that promote "action-oriented" therapies are inadequate for many clients who struggle with the concept of change (i.e., who are not ready for acting). Ford noted that the traditional disease concept is ultimately confusing for many clients with substance use disorders. This is because the disease concept is based on the idea that addiction is a lifelong, incurable disease. Yet, substance use programs utilize cognitive and behavioral strategies and self-help approaches designed to help clients stay off drugs. If the disease of addiction is ultimately incurable and people are incapable of change, then why use behavioral interventions? Ford's response to this question is that the disease model has been misinterpreted by many individuals with substance use disorders in a way that absolves responsibility and choice (i.e., the "addiction" made me do it) and that the focus in rehabilitation must always be on the choices faced now and in the future, ideas consistent with existential thought.

Existential therapy rejects the Freudian, deterministic view of human nature and instead focuses on freedom, human choice, and living authentically (Fernando, 2007). A major goal of existential therapy is for clients to live in accordance with their wants and needs instead of living based on someone else's standards. Existential therapy acknowledges individual victories as well as difficulties in the context of the human situation (Hart & Singh, 2009). As such, it offers the substance use clinician a more comprehensive, balanced, and realistic model compared to other approaches that may only superficially address client difficulties and struggles (Hart & Singh, 2009).

In this chapter, the major tenets of existential therapy are explored. Emphasis will be given to the four "ultimate concerns" (also known as the "givens" of existence) and how they manifest among substance use clients. Attention will then turn to applications of existential therapy with clients, focusing on techniques and strategies. The applicability of existential therapy with diverse clientele who struggle with severe substance use will be explored. The chapter concludes with the application of existential therapy with the case of Michael and a list of strengths, limitations, and ethical issues.

The Major Tenets of Existential Therapy: Brief Overview

Existential therapy has several underlying assumptions that guide the approach. These assumptions include self-awareness, self-transcendence, authenticity, unique views of human nature, the four ultimate concerns of existence, and existential psychodynamics. The following discussion touches on each of these important areas.

Self-Awareness

Self-awareness encompasses having a presence in the world, with freedom, choice, and responsibility as the foundation (Corey, 2017). The person who has reached self-awareness opens possibilities for freedom and strikes a balance between caring for self and transcending the self by reaching out and caring for others. Self-awareness allows human beings to reflect on circumstances and cultivate the meaning of events.

May (1977) suggested that our presence in the world can be phrased as "I-am" or the person who can make mature choices and recognizes their own responsibility for existence. Human beings all too often put up pretenses or engage in behaviors, such as substance use, that preclude knowing the self. If people were to strip away how they conventionally define themselves (e.g., as a doctor, mother, teacher), like peeling back an onion, all that would be left is the onion core, or "I-am." May (1958) noted that connection with and acceptance of "I-am" is a necessary step in helping the client to heal. When a person becomes aware that they can know themself without interference of the ego, they can begin to change their life toward a more authentic existence.

Self-Transcendence

Self-transcendence refers to the ability to transcend the immediate situation and strive for something above or beyond the self. Human beings are unique in the sense that they care about their uniqueness and personal integrity and at the same time strive to connect to others and nature (Corey, 2017). Indeed, the spiritual nature of human beings is to rise above themselves and to search for something greater (Yalom, 1980), whether that be in their relationships or with the natural world. According to existential theory, only when individuals transcend the self can they rise above loneliness and alienation, forming healthy connections with others and their environment.

The ability to transcend self is an important step in one's ability to self-realize (Frankl, 1992). Frankl likened self-transcendence to a spiritual process in which a person strives for values and meaning by rising above their biological and psychological self. The process of "getting out of oneself" is like Adler's notion of social interest. Individuals who concern themselves with the welfare of others and creating a healthy community are not bothered by everyday trivialities, which can bog us down and create unnecessary stress.

Authenticity

What does it mean to be an authentic person? Some might argue that authenticity means being "real" or not acting "fake" or as if you are someone that you are not. Someone who is authentic doesn't exacerbate problems and, at the same time, is not a Pollyanna. They hold a realistic perspective on themselves, others, and the world. Helping clients become more authentic is a significant therapeutic goal in existential therapy.

Bugental (1981) suggested that authenticity is "central genuineness and awareness of being" (p. 102). Authentic individuals know the limitations of human existence and, at the same time, develop their own sense of values, struggle with moral choices, cultivate meaning and purpose, and explore what it means to be human. They engage in activities that are meaningful and have some relevance beyond themselves as they strive to reach their full potential. In contrast, inauthentic individuals are seen as superficial in their relationships and are less concerned with the welfare of others or society. They may avoid taking responsibility for their choices or miss opportunities to be fully present with others (Seligman & Reichenberg, 2014).

One of the struggles among clients in recovery is establishing an authentic life. Many clients with substance use disorders find their intimate relationships in ruins, grapple with meaninglessness, and live with a distorted sense of morality. These inauthentic patterns of relating to self, others, and the world exist beyond abstinence, and thus can (and should) become important topics in recovery. I recall counseling a client who worked very hard at remaining alcohol free (he was diagnosed with alcohol use disorder) and reached the 7-month mark without taking a drink. Whereas this was cause for celebration, the client continued to struggle in interpersonal relationships, acting toward others the same way as when he was drinking: aggressive, arrogant, and indifferent. The description of being abstinent but acting the same as when drinking is called the *dry drunk*. A significant part of counseling was helping the client become more genuine and authentic with himself and others.

View of Human Nature

Existential clinicians place a premium on responsibility. Each human is responsible for who they are and become. When clients complain that someone "made me feel this way" or "made me do it," existential clinicians gently challenge this viewpoint and suggest that, at the end of the day, we are responsible for our existence and all that this entails. As such, existential clinicians reject the notion that our behaviors are conditioned or determined by outside sources.

The Four Givens of Existence

The four givens of existence, or ultimate concerns, death, freedom, isolation, and meaning, represent the key existential issues that all human beings confront and face daily. Each given, or ultimate concern, is a fact of life and is rooted in the complex and inescapable part of human existence (Yalom, 1980). Indeed, recovery from drug and alcohol use requires acceptance of the possible fatality of addiction, the ability to accept responsibility for choices, the capacity to connect with others yet understand our ultimate isolation, and to infuse life with meaning rather than chaos and absurdity (Johnson et al., 1987).

Death

Probably the most recognizable and obvious given is death. Of course, our death isn't news to us: We all know we are going to die. It is an inevitable existential truth. Throughout history, human beings have sought to prolong long life, and we see today significant energy directed toward extending life and escaping the grasp of death (Fernando, 2007). Death manifests as a core existential conflict resulting in tension between the unavoidability of death and the wish to continue to be in existence (Yalom, 1980). As such, the fear of death plays a major role in our inner perspective and experience.

Yalom (1980, 2008) and May (1977) wrote extensively about death's role in anxiety. Indeed, death anxiety may be the "hidden problem" that underlies much of the everyday anxieties we experience. From an existential perspective, full awareness of one's finality can be so over-whelming that individuals will "create" smaller anxieties to have some measure of control in their lives. For example, a client who compulsively cleans and organizes may indeed be acting out unconscious anxiety about their own death. As humans it is difficult for us to get our minds around the concept of dying; however, what we can control is avoiding snakes, elevators, or the cleanliness of our living quarters. Smaller, more trivial anxieties serve to distract us from the broad, overwhelming idea that someday our existence will end.

Although this tension between being and nonbeing is a major source of anxiety for all humans, from an existential perspective it is the understanding of death that allows a person to live an authentic and purposeful life (Yalom, 1998). This point is reflected in Yalom's (1980, 2008) often cited maxim: Whereas the idea of death strikes terror in us, it is the reality of death that saves us. Confrontation with and acceptance of our finality puts life into perspective. We learn to shed the trivial, petty concerns that plague and push us into inauthentic living. Yalom (1980) recounted several clinical examples in which cancer patients, in advanced stages of the disease, rearranged life priorities, had a stronger sense of freedom, lived in the present moment, and formed an enhanced appreciation of nature and life. Many of these patients experienced anger—not because they felt betrayed by life, although that certainly happened—but because they wished they had this insight at an earlier stage of their lives. They reflected on their lives and were saddened at the missed opportunities, trivial concerns, and poor choices. When we come to grips with our own death, we are potentially transformed into more genuine human beings.

It does not have to take a cancer diagnosis to experience life in a deeper fashion; however, living through a *boundary experience* (Yalom, 1980) may set in motion a shift in life priorities. A boundary experience is an event that throws individuals into a crisis, such that they are transformed by the process. Examples include being diagnosed with an illness, observing a close relative or friend become ill, or experiencing a "close call." Less extreme experiences might include simply thinking more about one's death, reaching a milestone birthday, watching a movie that touches one emotionally, or a change in life circumstances (e.g., getting a new job, new house, moving). Such experiences help us reflect on our lives and our brief moment of existence.

The denial system surrounding death can manifest as several psychological problems, including anxiety, personality disorders, aggression, and substance use disorders. Johnson et al. (1987) believed that the individual with a substance use disorder lives their life in "a state of primitive, almost psychotic, denial against the reality of death and its very real immediacy for [them]" (p. 17). The failure of the individual with a substance use disorder to confront the reality of their death places in them in a precarious situation. Denying the reality of death, they may live as if they have forever, harming themself and others along the way. Life then loses its immediacy, passion, and urgency and ultimately is experienced as boring and meaningless (Johnson et al., 1987). This less-than-optimal existence then perpetuates more substance use to self-medicate the boredom.

Substance use may become a means to manage unbearable death anxiety. It is interesting that when clients finally do come into treatment, they often speak of a "rock-bottom" moment (boundary experience) in which they may have totaled their car, got in a fight in which they were seriously hurt, or experienced a severe consequence, such as passing out for several hours. Regardless, their rock-bottom stories often entail a close call with death. Reality increases their awareness that they may be on the fast track to nonexistence and thus become committed to turning their lives around. Keeping these consequences in the forefront of clients' minds becomes a powerful tool in RP and recovery work.

There is no better portrayal of death anxiety and its potential to heal than one of my favorite holiday stories, "A Christmas Carol" by Charles Dickens. In the story, Ebenezer Scrooge, a miserly old man who could learn a thing or two about human relationships (my favorite movie version of this story is the 1984 adaptation with George C. Scott as Scrooge), is confronted by three spirits who intervene to teach him the true meaning of Christmas. The third apparition, the Spirit of Christmas Yet to Come, boldly confronts Scrooge on his mean, miserly ways and ends up showing him his own gravestone. When Scrooge observes this (as well as other events), a rush of anxiety and panic enter his mind as he contemplates and *fully knows* death is on the horizon for him if he does not change. This confrontation with death, as the story goes, made him a changed and better man. He became more caring, more giving, and a greater man than ever before and used his remaining time to enjoy life to the fullest.

Freedom

Freedom is typically viewed as a positive concept instead of a "concern." However, from an existential perspective freedom is closely aligned with taking responsibility for shaping one's life and creating a future in a universe without an obvious design or meaning (Yalom, 1980). Existential freedom refers to the absence of structure, which leads to a sense of what Yalom (1980) called "groundlessness." The implication is that a person is responsible fort—that is, the author of—their own world, life design, and choices. This situation taps into our responsibility for self-creation, choice, will, and action. Once this existential reality sets in, people realize that they are alone in these choices; there is no "ground" or support, creating existential anxiety. Many individuals with substance use disorders have perpetually denied responsibility for their lives in part to escape or avoid the intrinsic and unavoidable anxiety of free choice (Johnson et al., 1987).

It is a paradox that people always ask for more freedom, but when issues related to freedom, such as responsibility, surface into consciousness they complain they have *too much* freedom (Johnson et al., 1987). Barring societies that severely restrict human liberties, freedom has given mankind the blessing of innumerable choices but also cursed mankind because of innumerable choices. What should one do with their life? How should one live? Creating a life takes responsibility, choice, and will, existential realities (and anxieties) that are often shirked by those with substance use disorders. The key dynamic in existential freedom is the conflict between our confrontation with groundlessness and our desire for ground and structure. Failure to acknowledge our existential freedom might manifest as one who remains too indecisive, displaces responsibility, acts compulsively (Johnson et al., 1987), and prefers others to make difficult decisions.

In substance use counseling, existential freedom is an important concept for clinicians to keep in mind. If human beings are the architects and authors of their lives, one wonders how clients with substance use disorders might create their own story of recovery moving forward. A focus on freedom precludes traps such as blaming others, shirking responsibility, and letting others decide their fate. At the end of the day, the person with a substance use disorder is responsible for their own will, choices, and action. At a surface level, such a realization may be liberating for clients who are resistant to change; nobody is telling them what to do as it is up to them to decide. At deeper, existential levels, responsibility becomes more anxiety provoking. If they are indeed solely responsible for their lives, then they are responsible whether they succeed or fail in recovery. For some, it may be better not to try than to try and fail. A common existential theme among clients with substance use disorders is failure to take responsibility for their behavior and choices (Sharf, 2004).

Another important aspect of freedom is taking action. One can understand cognitively that one is responsible but be unwilling to act. Knowing without acting is the same as not knowing (Johnson et al., 1987). In existential therapy, action occurs through focusing on the client's will. Will "is the mental agency that transforms awareness and knowledge into action" (Johnson et al., 1987, p. 19). It bridges desire (or the assumption of responsibility to act) and action, thus moving a step beyond simple awareness. As many substance use clinicians can attest, transforming responsibility into action represents a major hurdle in substance use recovery. Understanding can only take one so far and, without action, corresponds to treatment failure (Johnson et al., 1987).

Isolation

Existential isolation refers to the idea that, no matter how close we may get to another human being, there is still a gulf between people. We are born into the world alone and leave the world alone (Fernando, 2007). The key existential conflict is tension between awareness of absolute isolation and wish for contact, warmth, and protection from others (Yalom, 1980).

It is well known in substance use treatment that interpersonal isolation becomes more pronounced as the drug use literally takes over the individual's life. However, interpersonal isolation is not the same as existential isolation (Yalom, 1980). Interpersonal isolation is like loneliness in that the individual is not around other people. Many factors contribute to interpersonal isolation such as a judgmental personality, poor social skills, or geographical location (Yalom, 1980). Existential isolation, on the other hand, is a more profound, fundamental separation between people that underlies human existence. Death and freedom are two ultimate concerns that shine a bright light on our existential isolation: We all die alone, and we are responsible for our own life.

There is no "magic bullet" to cure existential isolation. However, individuals can learn to live with it and integrate this awareness into their lives. Although interpersonal and existential isolation are not the same thing, healthy, mature interpersonal relationships, what Yalom (1980) calls "need-less" love, represents a mode of relating in the world that leads to fulfillment and happiness despite one's existential isolation. If individuals learn to accept the fundamental premise that we are ultimately alone in this universe, they are in a better position to move on with their lives and attend to important life matters.

Many individuals with substance use disorders have difficulties and conflicts with love, intimacy, and isolation (Johnson et al., 1987). Compulsive substance use may indeed be a response to problems in these areas as it leads to a powerful but temporary respite from intense isolation. As a person becomes more aware of their ultimate separation from others, they may grow increasingly anxious and powerless. They may assuage these feelings by turning to drugs or creating relationships with others who use drugs, all in the service of creating the illusion of connection (Johnson et al., 1987). However, others often are hurt in the addiction process—family members, friends, colleagues. The individual with a substance use disorder learns to use others for selfish gains, as if they were objects to be discarded after their usefulness has run out. With severe substance use, caring and relatedness are the antithesis to drug-taking behavior, as the individual, left unchecked, never goes on to fully know or engage with others. Others' growth and happiness is of no concern. As we will see, addressing isolation involves a two-part process in which the client (a) learns to fully accept and confront existential isolation and (b) develop relationships of mutual sharing and caring.

Meaninglessness

The fourth and final ultimate concern is meaninglessness. Yalom (1980) asks rhetorically, "If we must die, if we constitute our own world, if each is ultimately alone in an indifferent universe, then what meaning does life have? Why do we live? How shall we live?" (p. 9). Frankl (1992) believed that the most fundamental drive for individuals is to find and understand their meaning or purpose in life. He theorized that a sense of meaning and purpose in life contributes to physical and psychological adjustment and, alternatively, a lack of meaning causes deviant behavior and psychopathology (Frankl, 1988). A concern is that, more so than at any other time in our history, we are bogged down with information (or misinformation), social media, family, and work responsibilities, and so forth that finding the time to forge a purposeful and meaningful life is elusive. Frankl, back in 1978, observed that the impersonal nature of society, largely forged by technology and industrialization, contributes to a profound sense of loneliness and problems in finding meaning. (With the advent of the internet, social networking sites, and computerized gadgets, imagine what Frankl might think of our situation today if he were alive.) To cope with these demands, many individuals turn to quick fixes, such as problematic substance use.

The lack of meaning and purpose has a profound impact on one's life. I am struck by the number of clients with substance use disorders who reveal that their life feels meaningless. Frankl (1992) likened lack of meaning to a feeling of emptiness, or what he called an *existential vacuum*. The existential vacuum is the result of human beings' frustration when their resolve to find meaning is diffuse or otherwise blocked. When this occurs, they become filled with emptiness, despair, alienation, boredom, and loss of meaning. It doesn't take much of a leap to suggest that this situation may propel someone to drug use. Such widespread phenomena as violence, depression, anxiety, and severe substance use are understandable, according to Frankl (1992), given the existential vacuum that confronts many people.

Through informal discussions with colleagues, as well as conversations with clients, I believe that substance use becomes a way for individuals to address their existential anxieties, especially the meaninglessness they experience. It may be that individuals use substances as a misguided attempt to create meaning. However, Olive (1990) suggested that substances provide an artificial meaning to life compared to an authentic life. Instead of experiencing their anxiety, pain, and meaninglessness and forging the will to create a better life, individuals with substance use disorders live inauthentically by avoiding these issues through the numbing effect of alcohol and drugs.

There is a silver lining, however, regarding the connection between hitting rock bottom and meaning: suffering. Indeed, suffering can be meaningful, as one only has to read Frankl's (1992) account of his experiences in concentration camps to appreciate how meaning can emerge even in the direst of circumstances. Many clients come to counseling experiencing a great deal of suffering. Despite their intense pain, suffering has given them resolve to take a closer look at their substance use behavior, make changes, and forge ahead with a more meaningful existence. This is not to say that suffering always leads to such a turnaround, as we must acknowledge how it also can be painful, overwhelming, and depressing (Fernando, 2007). However, Frankl stressed that suffering can be a catalyst for greater fulfillment if individuals see meaning through their suffering (Hart & Singh, 2009). The point to stress here is that individuals become resilient *if* they can create a meaning *because* of their hardship and efforts to overcome it. The implications for counseling substance use clients are for clinicians to help clients explore perspective and purpose related to the hard times they have faced due to drug use. Frankl's form of existential psychotherapy is that value, virtue, and worth can emanate from disease, illness, and hardship *and* in the process of healing from these circumstances (Hart & Singh, 2009).

If meaning provides an important ingredient to a more fulfilling life, let's explore its definition. Seligman and Reichenberg (2014) stated that "meaning is the purpose and logic of our lives and often is reflected in the choices we make" (p. 185). Corey (2017) posed common existential questions related to meaning that clients bring: "Why am I here? "What do I want from life?" and "What gives my life purpose?" (p. 143). Yalom (1980) made the distinction between cosmic meaning, referring to whether human life fits into some grand cosmic plan, and terrestrial meaning, referring to experiencing life as having some purpose to be fulfilled, some overriding direction or goal from which to direct one's resources. Usually, one who establishes a cosmic meaning also has terrestrial meaning; however, it is possible to have terrestrial meaning in the absence of cosmic meaning. Whatever form of meaning a person establishes, it will most likely infuse the individual with a renewed sense of vigor and zest.

In the substance use treatment field, clients often find meaning in their recovery process. They become energized at the prospect of a new, more fulfilling life free from substance use. In my experience, substance use clients first must answer the question "What do I have to get substance free for?" Once this has been answered, meaning can be explored through a bevy of pursuits such as being a better person (e.g., mother, father), living with greater integrity, working through the 12 steps, starting a hobby they are passionate about, finding work, engagement, or attending classes. Kellogg and Triffleman (1998) noted that meaning can come from understanding the context of events, exploring meaning within stories of trauma or disappointment, clarifying and connecting to values, establishing an identity that is active, and rejecting one's past choices to affirm life. Martin et al. (2011) concluded from their empirical study that purpose in life is a worthy focus in substance use disorder treatment.

Frankl pointed out that the direct pursuit of meaning often makes it elusive. In other words, the more one consciously tries to force meaning into their life, the more difficult it is to experience. I am reminded of the old phrase that if one were to chase a butterfly, the more it eludes you, but if you turn your attention to other things, it will come and sit softly on your shoulder. The butterfly in this metaphor refers to meaning. When I work with clients, I try to find what gives them energy and passion and use this as a conduit toward a more rewarding, meaningful life, encouraging activities consistent with this goal.

Empirical research appears to support the notion that absent or low meaning in life is related to substance use (Martin et al., 2011). Copeland et al. (2020) found that the presence of meaning in life had a negative correlation with indices related to alcohol consumption, whereas the *search* for meaning in life was positively associated with drinking. The implications are the clients who are searching for meaning have not yet settled these issues in their lives and thus may consume more alcohol a method to cope. In a study of alcohol and drug use among college students, Nam et al. (1994) found that low purpose in life and high existential anxiety were significant predictors of alcohol and drug use. Hart and Singh (2009) found that clients with alcohol use disorders in recovery significantly improved their quality of life if they perceived a sense of meaning and purpose in their lives at a 2-year follow-up from the study. The authors also found that for a sizable sub-sample of participants, greater meaning was associated with increased personal well-being, interpersonal well-being, and increased contributions to the community. Purpose in life, along with positive affect and cognitive well-being, was found to relate negatively to substance use among 602 community volunteers (Ciarrocchi & Brelsford, 2009). Kim et al. (2020) found that participants who were not misusing drugs at baseline and were in the highest quartile of purpose in life had a lower likelihood of substance misuse 9 to 10 years later. These studies suggest that meaning is inconsistent with a life of heavy substance use.

Indeed, a growing empirical base has been established supporting the notion that meaning in one's life can strengthen resilience in the face of difficult circumstances (Hart & Singh,

2009), including substance use. Evidence suggests that attendance in community-based support groups, such as AA, may be associated with greater meaning (Junior, 2006), and that long-term recovery in AA is beneficial in helping clients find a purpose in life (McInerney et al., 2022). Robinson et al. (2007) found preliminary evidence that alcohol-dependent individuals in remission found their life of recovery meaningful and thus had better drinking outcomes. These outcome studies suggest that substance use clinicians should, at the very least, supplement their established protocols with an emphasis on helping clients find meaning and purpose (Hart & Singh, 2009).

Existential Psychodynamics

Freudian psychodynamics places primacy on instinctive drives, resulting from id impulses, inadequate coping mechanisms, anxiety, and the use of ego-defense mechanisms (Yalom, 1980). Defense mechanisms are a normal part of our psychology. However, if anxiety reaches a point where our coping resources are taxed, we may overuse defense mechanisms to the point that we distort reality and subsequently develop neurotic and/or psychotic symptoms. According to existential theory, anxiety is not caused by instinctive impulses; rather, it is caused by greater awareness of the ultimate concerns, leading to the use of defense mechanisms (Yalom, 1980). Existential anxiety is the tension and worry that emerge when we become aware of the ultimate concerns. It also is the reaction to our awareness that we are ultimately responsible for living our lives (Fernando, 2007).

Psychological and behavioral problems result when we try to ignore or evade existential anxiety or experience so much of it that it narrows our growth (Fernando, 2007). Yalom (1980) identified two existential defense mechanisms that we incorporate to try to deal with existential anxiety. First is the idea that one is *special and unique*, and thus will not succumb to the natural laws of the universe. When I first read about this defense mechanism, I was reminded of the *invincibility fable* that is common among adolescents, many who believe that they are invincible and immortal, leading to risk-taking and dangerous behavior (e.g., driving fast). Whereas thinking one is special can be helpful to bolster self-esteem and self-worth, at distorted levels it leads to the inability to confront the ultimate concern of death (Yalom, 1980). The second defense mechanism is the idea of the *ultimate rescuer*, or belief in a personal, omnipresent entity who watches over us to protect our welfare (Yalom, 1980).

Clients with substance use disorders may engage in indiscriminate use of drugs because they believe that they are special (i.e., nothing will happen to *me*) and, if something does go wrong, that they will be rescued (by their spouse, sponsor, religious leader). Many clients manifest one or both dynamics, and it usually takes facing the ultimate concerns, self-awareness, and responsibility to undo their grip on the individual.

Process of Existential Therapy

The process of existential therapy flows directly from its underlying assumptions and major tenets. Three areas are discussed below, including the function of the existential clinician, the three phases of existential therapy, and types of existential therapy. From here, I will extend these key ideas to the application of existential methods to substance use disorders.

Function of Existential Clinician

Existential philosophy and therapy were heavily influenced by Martin Buber (1970) and his concept of the I-thou relationship. I-thou relationships are the most thoughtful, meaningful, and empowering type and have had a large impact on existential dialogue (Seligman & Reichenberg, 2014) and are the main stance of the clinician in the therapy room. According to Buber, the bedrock of healthy relationships involves an *I* and a *thou*, where individuals in relationship are treated as human beings and with mutual respect. If one in the relationship manipulates the other, or treats them as an object, the relationship turns to *I-it*. Buber pointed out the enormous negative toll that I-it relationships exert on human life and called for greater sensitivity, awareness, and compassion to transform our world into I-thou.

The I-thou concept has not only influenced existential therapy, but also Gestalt and other approaches. Clients who encounter an I-thou relationship experience the clinician as an equal partner in the counseling relationship and as someone who encourages genuine interaction without pretense. The clinician relates to the client in a genuine, authentic manner and tries to be as human as possible (Fernando, 2007), avoiding the pretense of degrees and status. Irvin Yalom (2009), heavily influenced by existential thought, preferred to conceptualize the therapeutic relationship as *fellow travelers* on the road of life, a term that eliminates artificial distinctions between us (counselors, therapists, healers) and them (clients). Yalom's (2009) message is this: "We are all in this together and there is no therapist and no person immune to the inherent tragedies of existence" (p. 8).

The role of the existential clinician is to infuse the ultimate concerns in whatever topic is being discussed between client and counselor (Fernando, 2007). Instead of alleviating suffering, the clinician helps the client turn their suffering into productive avenues and pursuits. This is accomplished by tackling the deeper meaning and issues related to presenting symptoms and problems (Fernando, 2007). The existential clinician is on the same life journey as the client (in terms of the ultimate concerns) and is therefore seen as a co-traveler on life's path. Problems are discovered and solutions are coconstructed, and the clinician works with the totality of the client's life rather than separate parts like thoughts or feelings. The existential clinician operates in the here and now and focuses on the client's immediate experience and feelings (Fernando, 2007).

Three Phases in Existential Therapy

Archer and McCarthy (2007) outlined three phases of existential therapy. In the *initial phase*, the clinician explores with clients their assumptions about the world. This involves both identifying and clarifying these assumptions, which often emerge out of the client's immediate awareness. In the *middle phase*, clients are challenged to examine their value system more fully. Specifically, clients are asked to explore the source and authority of their value system. In the final phase, the clinician helps clients develop their will to act, that is, to take what they have learned in counseling and put it to action. From an existential perspective, mental and behavioral problems represent a failure of one's potential.

Types of Existential Therapy

The existential approach has been criticized for its lack of structure in the therapy hour. However, the essence of the approach is to focus on one's whole existence, which is ever changing and thus may look different from week to week. Nonetheless, without therapeutic structure, there is risk that clinician and client may travel down unproductive paths and waste precious therapeutic time. Although variations and nuance in existential counseling exist, two approaches have offered the clinician more guidance and structure.

Yalom (1980) is generally credited with providing clinicians a solid roadmap in applying existential psychotherapy to their practice. In Yalom's approach, personal reflection is encouraged, and clients need to recognize their responsibility and ability to shape their own lives, their freedom to choose and act, and the need to confront death and loneliness. The existential themes of death, responsibility, isolation, and meaninglessness are important discussion points, not techniques. The most important intervention is being aware of the client's existential issues and proceeding to explore these in depth. Yalom was trained in psychoanalysis and thus incorporates some analytic strategies into his existential therapy, such as dream interpretation.

The second type of existential counseling was created by Viktor Frankl and is based on his experiences in concentration camps during World War II. Frankl's (1988) approach, called *logotherapy*, is designed to help clients discover meaning, especially when faced with difficult life circumstances. In this "therapy through meaning," Frankl emphasized not what makes us sick, but what keep us healthy. A discussion of key techniques based on logotherapy is provided in a later section.

Application of Existential Therapy With Substance Use Disorders

A primary criticism of traditional approaches to substance use treatment is that they focus too much on the behavioral and physiological mechanisms to the exclusion of underlying intentions, subjective experiences, and meaning making of substance use (Paul & Lucas, 2005). Certainly, physiological dependence plays a role in addiction, but does not fully explain why a person would choose a potentially deleterious behavior. Counseling clients with substance use disorders through an existential lens shifts the focus to how subjective experiences play a large role in maintaining one's substance use behavior. Indeed, the focus on subjective experiences is supported by a wealth of substance use literature that suggests subjective and emotional correlates of substance use (Paul & Lucas, 2005). Importantly, integration of subjective experiences into the treatment process re-interprets compulsive substance use as a psychological process rather than simply a behavioral problem with physiological aspects (Paul & Lucas, 2005).

From the existential perspective, an exclusive focus on objective behaviors and symptoms dehumanizes individuals. As such, human experience in the form of values, beliefs, assumptions, and choices are given primary importance (Seligman & Reichenberg, 2014). Substance use disorders, rather than being conceptualized as only behavioral or physiological, may reflect how the person is choosing to manifest internal experiences and how they may be denying deeper existential issues of which they are unaware (Paul & Lucas, 2005). Problematic substance use says something about the way person is living, primarily related to intentions, judgments, choices, and expression of feelings. Being faced with the harsh realities of life, the person may turn to drugs to escape or cope.

Research has demonstrated that existential well-being, defined as a sociopsychological concept representing one's positive attitudes and beliefs toward purpose, meaning, and life experiences, is inversely associated with indices of alcohol use and positively related to several measures related to alcohol prevention (vonDras et al., 2007). Specifically, existential well-being was found to be associated with attributing personal responsibility to one's actions, a possible cognitive mechanism to alcohol prevention (vonDras et al., 2007). This research suggests that an existential perspective and spiritual practices may enhance prevention and shape behaviors that deter heavy drinking.

Development of Maladaptive Behavior

In general, maladaptive behavior results from a clumsy, ineffective manner of coping with anxiety that emanates from confrontation with the four ultimate existential concerns (Yalom, 1980). For example, misplaced confrontation with death anxiety can lead to compulsiveness, narcissism, aggression, depression, masochism, and phobic anxiety (Yalom, 1980). A life devoid of meaning might manifest as crusadism, nihilism, vegetativeness, and living in an existential vacuum. Confrontation with freedom may lead to indecisiveness and displacement. Finally, failure to come to grips with one's existential isolation leads to depression and interpersonal struggles (Yalom, 1980).

Of course, substance use can be secondary to many of these psychological experiences. The compulsive client may grab a drink of alcohol to assuage underlying death anxiety. The depressed client might turn to amphetamines as a pick-me-up, but the underlying issue is an intense dread of isolation. Freedom and taking responsibility for one's choices can create feelings of anxiety and fear (Seligman & Reichenberg, 2014). The existential clinician may need to address the overarching issue of responsibility before diving into other existential roots of problematic substance use behavior.

Goals of Existential Therapy With Substance Use Disorders

Many substance use clinicians may not use existential theory as a standalone approach but infuse it within other methods as the need arises. For clinicians who incorporate existential theory as their main approach, the goal is not to alleviate anxiety but to help clients live constructively with it (Fernando, 2007). Existential clinicians help clients become aware of avoidance strategies (through substance use) and explore their ultimate concerns. Therapy is centered on helping clients reach their full potential and acting on this enhanced awareness (Fernando, 2007).

The goals outlined by Fernando (2007) may sound vague. After all, what does "reaching their full potential" mean? As with any therapeutic goal, it is helpful to think in terms of behavior. For example, if a client wants to improve their self-esteem, the clinician can ask them what that looks like or what people will see the client doing differently that indicates their self-esteem has improved. The assumption here is that a change in an observable behavior indicates an internal shift in attitude, mental outlook, and emotional state. Let's take a closer look at Fernando's goals. The italic parts show how the goals might manifest in a client struggling with a substance use disorder:

> Goal 1: Help clients constructively live with anxiety. *The client acknowledges their anxiety when it arises and does NOT turn to drugs and alcohol to deal with it. Rather, they practice yoga as way to dissipate the anxious energy.*
>
> Goal 2: Become aware of avoidance strategies. *The client stops themself when they have the urge to use drugs to escape and instead practices deep breathing exercises.*
>
> Goal 3: Explore the ultimate concerns. *The client is instructed to take time outside of the counseling session to reflect and journal on one or more ultimate concerns.*
>
> Goal 4: Reaching one's full potential. *This must be defined by the client! For example, reaching one's full potential might be staying alcohol free for a year, securing a job, and making amends for past misdeeds.*

There are many other ways to construct goals beyond these examples. As with any client, goals must be individualized and fit with what clients want for themselves. Notice, too, that the behavioral-based goals represents an infusion of behavioral therapy with existential therapy. In fact, existential therapy can be incorporated with almost any approach, and thus add depth to the therapeutic experience. Several techniques to achieve the aims of existential therapy within substance use counseling are discussed next.

Existential Techniques

Existential theory is not a technique-laden approach. In fact, the existential clinician may find the use of techniques artificial and contrived, relying instead on a strong therapeutic relationship to cultivate meaning and authenticity. At the same time, existential clinicians are free to incorporate techniques from other approaches, so long as techniques are consistent with their underlying philosophy of change (Corey, 2017). Their emphasis is to deepen therapy by infusing some of the ultimate concerns in their work. Interventions are based on philosophical views about the nature of human existence, targeted to the client's issues (Corey, 2017). The clinician adopts more of a philosophical stance compared to other approaches, pushing clients to face the harsh reality of life to experience its splendid beauty, love, and meaning (Yalom, 1980).

According to Fernando (2007) the critical issues for the client to understand are freedom and responsibility. The clinician must be cognizant of how the client does or does not assume responsibility for their predicament, find out what role the client plays in their own misery, and communicate these insights to back to the client (Yalom, 1980). All techniques designed to facilitate change, whether based on cognitive, behavioral, or emotional methods, should be predicated on clients' recognizing and accepting their responsibility for their substance use and treatment outcome (Ford, 1996). Once clients recognize and assume greater responsibility, motivation is enhanced, and they are better prepared to address problems.

One of the ways that individuals avoid taking responsibility for their lives is consuming drugs. Drug use is the ultimate escape, an evasion tactic that is extraordinarily effective in the short run but diminishes in effectiveness as time passes. Clients with substance use disorders may have a limited sense of their own responsibility because they have avoided it for so long. Once substance free, reality sets in as they begin to rebuild their lives. Relapse becomes a serious concern during the early stages of recovery because clients are facing reality for the first time, with diminished skills for how to successfully negotiate life.

One existential approach that relies more on technique is Frankl's (1988) logotherapy, an approach that helps clients cultivate spiritual meaning. Let's look at some of the main techniques from this approach and how it applies to substance use counseling.

Logotherapy Techniques

Frankl (1988) developed a system of psychotherapy called logotherapy, in which the primary focus is helping individuals discover and cultivate meaning in their lives. Sharf (2004) noted that logotherapy may be particularly well suited for those with substance use disorders. It is important to note that techniques in logotherapy are not used in a mechanistic, reductionist manner in the same way that some techniques of behavior therapy might be utilized (Logogroup, 2010). Rather, underlying these techniques is the assumption that problems take away our own humanity (Logogroup, 2010); we become immobilized, and energy is taken away from our experience of the world. The heart of logotherapy is to equip people to find meaning in their lives through self-transcendence (Nam et al., 1994). According to Frankl (1988), self-transcendence is a distinctly human ability and is the foundation of our personal power. Three key logotherapy techniques are considered next: dereflection, paradoxical intention, and Socratic dialogue.

Dereflection

A common problem that Frankl (1988) encountered in his clinical work was clients trying too hard to succeed or find purpose (hyperintention) or who were too self-absorbed and self-focused. Dereflection occurs when one directs energy and focus away from oneself and redirects it toward other people or some value such as love (Logogroup, 2010). For example, if a client is struggling with remaining alcohol free, a logotherapist might encourage them to identify the meaning and purpose of their suffering so that they might transform it into human achievement (Logogroup, 2010). The process behind this transformation is the *will to meaning*—what Frankl (1988) referred to as a deep motivation to help others and cultivate important values.

Paradoxical Intention

Paradoxical intention involves asking for the very thing we fear. It is particularly effective in addressing phobic anxieties and obsessive behavior (Logogroup, 2010). The paradox is that if one tries hard to make the symptom happen, laughs at it, and adopts a position of "detached amusement" related to it, the symptom loses its power. This technique speaks to Frankl's notion of will; we, as human beings, have the will to change our circumstances by the attitudes we take toward those circumstances. Whereas events in our lives may indeed be dire, one thing we still have control over is how we think about these events.

Paradoxical intention is contraindicated for its direct application to drug use. As Miller (1998) noted, there is something ethically concerning about asking a client to go out and use more drugs as a paradoxical way to limit or stop drug use. However, paradoxical intention may be quite effective for addressing other psychological issues that may be at the heart of someone's problematic substance use behavior. For example, a client whose substance use results from unbearable anxiety might be asked, in the safety of the therapy office, to experience the anxiety fully (instead of running from it) to defuse its power over the individual. Alternative methods for addressing anxiety could be taught to the client to help them adopt a different perspective on their symptoms and strengthen coping resources.

Socratic Dialogue

Socratic dialogue is by no means exclusive to logotherapy. Some forms of cognitive therapy, for example, use Socratic-style questioning to assess the veracity of irrational thoughts. Socractic dialogue, as a logotherapy technique, refers to listening intently to the client and asking provocative questions or pointing out clues to meaning based on the client's words (Logogroup, 2010). Because logotherapy helps clients discover their own meaning, clinicians listen deeply and ask questions to clarify any themes in meaning that might emerge. In Socratic dialogue, the clinician's line of questioning parallels questions that life itself is posing to the client (Logogroup, 2010). The technique is designed to encourage the client to think more deeply about the meaning of life. According to Frankl (1992), meaning is discovered by the individual through the process of Socratic dialogue rather than provided from outside sources. To demonstrate what Socratic dialogue from a logotherapy perspective might look like, consider the follow excerpt with a client trying to stay cocaine free. In this example, the client is quite familiar with pat phrases and slogans from Narcotics Anonymous (NA) attendance, and often relies on these and other empty statements to make a point. Through Socratic dialogue, the clinician attempts to extract greater meaning from the client as a process of self-discovery.

> **CLIENT:** (speaking with little emotion or conviction) Well, as they say in NA, happiness is appreciating what you have, not getting what you want.
>
> **CLINCIAN:** When might one be unhappy even when appreciating what they have?
>
> **CLIENT:** Hmmm. I guess that can happen. I admit that I appreciate what I have but am still unhappy. But maybe I don't appreciate what I have fully enough.

CLINCIAN: It seems that now it is possible to appreciate all that one has, but to still be unhappy. Can you think of how you might modify your original statement in a way that fits your own truth?

CLIENT: Well, how about happiness is appreciating what you have *and* getting what you want.

CLINICIAN: How does that statement fit for you?

CLIENT: It feels okay. I mean when I get what I want I do feel better. But I just feel that getting what I want is selfish and against all this NA stuff I have learned.

CLINCIAN: Let's clarify what you mean by getting what you want. Are there ways to do this without using drugs?

CLIENT: Sure, I want to get shared custody of the children. That doesn't involve drugs.

CLINCIAN: Tell me more about what you want and how these fit with your life purpose.

Notice how the clinician in this excerpt began challenging the client's basic premise that "happiness is appreciating what you have, not getting what you want." Clearly, this statement did not fit the client's experience. Through Socratic dialogue, the client refined their definition of happiness and became aware that wanting something is not always a bad thing. They *want* shared custody of their children, and this desire can serve as a motivator to straighten their life out.

Death-Awareness Techniques

Yalom (2008) discussed several methods for helping clients overcome death anxiety. He encouraged clinicians to talk directly about death with their clients. Death is an ever-present reality that can lie under the surface of consciousness. Many anxieties, fears, and maladaptive behaviors (including substance use) may result from unexplored death anxiety. Confronting the fear of death can help clients live a more authentic life (Corey, 2017) by letting go of more petty and trivial concerns.

Connection to Others

Yalom (2008) believed that a powerful antidote to death anxiety is healthy human contact or connection to others. He stated, "It is the synergy between ideas and intimate connection with other people that is most effective both in diminishing death anxiety and in harnessing the awakening experience to effect personal change" (p. 119). It is interesting to note that substance use disorders, especially in their advanced stages, are behaviors of isolation, where individuals slowly withdraw from the human community. Indeed, it is well known in treatment communities that connection to others is an extremely important variable in successful substance use recovery. This is the reason 12-step programs, such as AA, built on community and sharing, are helpful for so many clients. An interesting, albeit unproven, hypothesis is that substance use may be a way in which individuals avoid the reality of death and, through renewed human connection, mitigate death anxiety and by proxy discontinue substance use.

Clinicians can help clients develop greater connection by demonstrating empathy and simply being a presence in the face of death terror. Yalom (2008) argued that there is no greater gift than simply being present with someone who is experiencing a literal confrontation with death (e.g., a serious medical diagnosis due to heavy drinking), or who fears death due to a recent accident. Empathy is a critical factor in forging healthy human connections. Clinicians who demonstrate empathy provide a model for clients; teaching clients how to be empathetic provides a foundational skill for their interpersonal relationships. Teaching empathic skills is especially important for aggressive, substance-using adolescents who struggle to place themselves in other people's shoes. In family counseling, I have often found the lack of empathy to be central to families' struggles.

Self-Disclosure

Mental health counselors are taught about the importance of self-disclosure, if it is used appropriately (i.e., the clinician does not over-disclose to the point where their needs are more important than the client's). Self-disclosure can be a delicate balancing act; indeed, I have found times where I probably disclosed more than I should have and other times where I did not disclose enough. Yalom (2008) noted that self-disclosure and being transparent are strategies that can help alleviate death anxiety. Clinicians who are appropriately transparent convey the message "we are in this [life] together, and I have experienced similar fears myself." Clients who hear this message realize that they are not alone in their struggle and that everyone on earth must face their own mortality.

I recall seeing a client, Megan (name disguised), who was literally drinking herself to death. Alcohol was the ultimate form of escape from her intense anxiety. She experienced panic-level symptoms that created tremendous strain at work. When we discussed the nature of her anxiety, Megan focused on macabre topics such as dying in her sleep or fear of being brutally attacked, despite no obvious reasons for such fears. It was proposed that Megan had a fear of dying and death and that her other anxieties and alcohol use stem, in part, from an unconscious terror of death. Megan acknowledged that her struggle with death anxiety may have stemmed from learning about a friend who was killed in a car accident when she was in high school. "After I lost my friend, I developed some strange rituals, thinking I could protect myself." I disclosed my own journey and confrontation with death anxiety and spoke about how fears of death manifested for me in other forms of anxiety. I found this transparency surprisingly effective for Megan; rather than present a stoic presence for her (which would have been disingenuous and inauthentic), I opted to share my experience, which improved our relationship and helped Megan realize that she is not alone in her struggles. We began to work through her death anxiety as a path to reduced drinking.

Rippling

Rippling refers to the belief that, although one's physical presence may be no more, values and actions can ripple through generation after generation. This idea can be comforting to those gripped by death anxiety (Yalom, 2008). If one becomes aware of how they have influenced the world through good deeds and works, they come to the realization that their legacy will live on, that they influenced others for the better, and that even small amounts of caring and giving ripple through life like small waves in a pond. There is probably no better example of rippling than parents passing down their values, beliefs, and actions onto their children.

I believe rippling has tremendous benefit for those struggling with substance use disorders. Beyond its help with death anxiety, rippling forces clients to ask a key question moving forward in recovery: "What values and actions can you do now to influence the world for the better?" It is important to stress to clients the ripple effect of good deeds, which continue beyond one's physical existence. Unfortunately, many clients struggling with substance use disorders come to counseling thinking they have nothing to give, nothing of value to offer. When they realize that giving, no matter how small, impacts others in a positive way *and* ripples through the lives of (potentially) many, they begin building self-esteem as a foundation for recovery.

Discovering Wisdom and Leading a Fulfilling Life

Yalom (2008) stressed the importance of living the examined life. I agree with the notion, as I am sure do most clinicians, that truth discovered by oneself is far more powerful than truth handed down from another person. This is not to say that others do not *influence* clients, but it is ultimately clients' responsibility to incorporate wisdom from others and find how it fits or doesn't fit with their own being. I have been amazed at how much clients know about their substance use disorders. They hold much knowledge in this area because they have experienced it firsthand. I sometimes find psychoeducation is not the best use of a client's time (although, for some clients who have limited insight into their substance use patterns, this approach can be helpful). However, knowledge is not the same as wisdom, and what clients may be lacking is more about awareness and understanding of the process of addiction rather than facts. Discovering one's own wisdom, like how Socrates questions a student, might evoke from the client the insight that, for example, having a substance use disorder is living a life with empty promises and unfulfilled goals.

Leading a fulfilling life is another buffer against death anxiety (Yalom, 2008). Individuals who live with a sense of purpose and meaning, who are otherwise fulfilled, are psychologically healthier and are, frankly, too busy to worry about death. Again, this notion can be quite helpful with clients who struggle with substance use issues, many of whom struggle with finding a meaningful, fulfilling life on the road to recovery. Drug use may be a misguided attempt to find meaning, or to fill the existential void created by feeling unfulfilled. In my work with clients, I like to talk about what gives clients passion and encourage them to explore these possibilities. I also attempt to help clients define what a fulfilled life looks like for them. Sometimes issues may surface that preclude fulfillment, such as past resentments and other unfinished business. These new issues then need clinical attention as the client begins to construct a more meaningful existence.

Additional Techniques

Yalom (1980) stated that existential psychotherapy is effective in as much as it helps the client alter their future. Clients with substance use disorders may have past experiences of which they are not proud and that produce much guilt and remorse. A powerful way to atone for their past misdeeds is to focus on building their life now and in the future (Yalom, 1980).

Establishing clarity and structure and promoting action are important factors in building a new, more preferred existence (Kellogg & Triffleman, 1998).

How is one to build a life that challenges the old identity and self-definition that is connected to the substance use? According to Kellogg and Triffleman (1998) the first step is to clarify clients' values to assess what gives them purpose and passion. This step cannot be emphasized enough because of the connection between values and action (Yalom (1980). The suffering caused by their substance use may renew a sense of importance and connection to values such as family and friends, a deeper spirituality, and a sense of generativity toward the younger population (Kellogg & Triffleman, 1998). Clinicians should encourage clients to visualize a picture of their new, emergent self, consistent with their clarified values. Values clarification is part of living an examined life, which takes awareness, intention, and purpose (Paul & Lucas, 2005). The examined life requires analyzing values, choice, and insights, assessing alternative choices, exploring limitations of choices, and gauging risks of certain paths toward self-reflection and growth (vonDeurzen-Smith, 2000).

In existential therapy, there is no improvement without action. Clients who clarify and visualize living their values must take action to realize a new life. The next step in the process, then, is to help clients formulate life goals (Kellogg & Triffleman, 1998). If a client wants to be a better husband to his wife, then he might set the goal of spending quality time with her for 20 minutes every day. Goals become plans of action and thus should be formulated specifically as to what the client will do. The final step is that of acting (Kellogg & Triffleman, 1998). It is important to note, however, that sometimes the appropriate action is to *not* act (Yalom, 1980). This premise has clear relevance to substance use clients, as their defining action is to avoid substance use as a part of their recovery.

Paul and Lucas (2005) outlined a model of treatment for nicotine use disorder that rests largely on existential ideas. The model, based on Bugental's (1978, as cited in Paul and Lucas, 2005) existential approach, views nicotine use disorder (and other substance-related disorders as well) as primarily psychological and existential, with behavioral and physiological components. Nicotine use disorder is an expression of being and reveals much about how one characteristically lives life (Paul & Lucas, 2005). The Bugental approach consists of six steps, although only the first five are described:

1. **Development of an alliance.** As with many approaches, the therapeutic relationship takes precedence in existential psychotherapy. Here, the clinician explores the client's life, operates in the here and now, and encourages the I-thou encounter.

2. **Focusing the client's motivation to have a centered awareness of being.** The idea here is to encourage self-observation to enhance awareness. For example, a clinician may encourage the client to notice what happens when they are about to use drugs. What is going on? Who is with them? What are they experiencing in their body? This self-observation process may clarify choices through enhanced awareness (Paul & Lucas, 2005).

3. **Pointing out and working through resistance.** Resistance, in this sense, refers to stumbling blocks toward greater self-observation and awareness. It also refers to the

client's resistance to experience life to the fullest—not in terms of taking drugs but in relation to experiencing a full range of emotions, thoughts, and actions, both pleasurable and difficult. The clinician's task is to discover these resistances and then strive to determine their function. Essentially, clients need to face the question "What aspect of your life are you avoiding now?"

4. **Confronting existential anxiety.** Working through resistances will inevitably expose the client to the existential anxiety that defenses were covering up. Confronting and working through this anxiety help the client move toward greater authenticity and freedom.

5. **Supporting new learning and new ways of being.** Clinicians support new client insights and behaviors that emerge through their work together.

Existential Therapy in the Treatment of Diverse Populations

In general, existential therapy has wide applicability and appeal across a broad spectrum of cultures (Seligman & Reichenberg, 2014). The emphasis on the human condition and concerns that beset all people, regardless of cultural background, makes existential therapy a relevant and culturally sensitive approach. The human experiences of love, anxiety, death, suffering, and meaning (Vontress et al., 1999, as cited in Corey, 2017) transcend cultural differences and are thus universal (Corey, 2017).

A part of being authentic is living in according to one's own values and goals rather than living up to some other value system. Existential therapy encourages individuals to examine how they are conditioned by social and cultural factors and if this conditioning is what they want (Archer & McCarthy, 2007; Corey, 2017). Choice and responsibility, as already discussed, play a big role in existential therapy. Existential therapists do not judge client choices, but rather help them examine the consequences of their choices.

Corey (2017) pointed out the wide appeal of existential therapy as several existential societies have emerged in Europe, Scandinavia, Mexico, and South America. Online training also is available in the UK, Israel, and several other countries. This evidence suggests that existential therapy strikes a universal chord with diverse societies across the globe.

Viktor Frankl's personal account of cultural oppression and rampant discrimination led to the development of logotherapy. Logotherapy, as noted earlier, focuses on the development of meaning even when life becomes unbearable. Persons from cultural and ethnic groups who have experienced widespread discrimination and racism may benefit from such an approach (Archer & McCarthy, 2007). Indeed, Laudet et al. (2006) found a significant correlation between greater meaning and greater subjective ratings of life satisfaction among 353 ethnic minorities who lived in the inner city and struggled with alcoholism. Frankl, who was Jewish, relied heavily on his religious faith and spirituality to construe the basic parameters of logotherapy (Archer & McCarthy, 2007). The search for meaning is universal and, no matter one's background, plays an important role in healthy psychological functioning.

I have been amazed at how much clients from all walks of life connect with the concept of meaning. My personal observation is supported by Krentzman et al. (2010), who found race moderates the relationship between purpose in life and alcohol use. Specifically, African American participants who had higher levels of purpose in life were more likely to remain abstinent from alcohol compared to Caucasian participants. In a study by Martin et al. (2011), purpose in life was positively related to substance use treatment outcomes for cocaine and alcohol use among individuals with cocaine use disorder. Their sample included a sizable percentage of minority participants (31%).

Existential therapy's emphasis on individualism, however, has prompted some critics, particularly within feminist theory, to note that social factors and causes of behavior are overlooked (Corey, 2017; Sharf, 2004). Rushing to point out one's personal responsibility for a client who has faced years of oppression, racism, and other cultural problems disrespects the clients' social experiences of which they may have limited choice to influence (Corey, 2017). For example, an African American client with a substance use disordrer may come from a ghetto environment where drugs, poverty and violence are daily concerns. It is difficult, if not impossible, to self-actualize when one is confronted with these troubling issues. The client would likely see the clinician as insensitive and feel misunderstood. In these instances, existential clinicians need to incorporate a sensitivity of the client's background into their approach: What choices does the client have, *within the context of their environment?* In addition, the relatively new "existential-integrative" model of practice (Schneider, 2011, as cited in Corey, 2017) promotes engaging in social advocacy and action to help change oppressive factors in addition to individual transformation. Both should be a part of the cross-cultural, existential approach.

Existential theory was influenced primarily by Western thought, and thus clients from Eastern cultural backgrounds may not fit with such a strong emphasis on self-determination. Clients from Asian backgrounds, for example, may desire more direction and intervention from their clinician. The astute existential clinician attempts to balance providing direction without taking responsibility away from the client (Corey, 2017).

CASE STUDY

Using Existential Therapy in the Case of Michael

We will now consider the application of existential therapy to the case of Michael. As with many who experience substance use disorders, Michael struggles with the ultimate concerns, especially taking responsibility and finding meaning. In these brief clinical vignettes, several existential concepts are demonstrated: establishing a genuine I-thou counseling relationship, encouraging Michael to assume responsibility, exploring the ultimate concerns through a consideration of Michael's values, and transforming meaning into action. Assume that Michael has been mandated for treatment by his employer. Continuing to struggle with abstaining from alcohol and cocaine use, and on the verge of violating the stipulations of his parole and near losing his marriage, Michael is skeptical about the counseling process, but willing to give it a try. Although Michael is in the early stages of recovery, existential themes are infused to establish groundwork for therapy (strong alliance, taking responsibility for recovery), with greater attention to these issues as recovery strengthens. The clinician combines reflective listening while being alert for existential themes throughout.

Genuine Relationship

The ability to form a strong alliance is an asset to any practitioner, as the therapeutic relationship has consistently shown to be a primary influence on outcome variance (Norcross, 2010). Existential therapy is built on the premise that the relational dimension of the therapeutic process is of utmost importance, paving the way for an empathic, collaborative, and authentic client–counselor relationship. The following example demonstrates an existential approach with Michael that begins to build a collaborative relationship with greater depth. Notice how reflective listening is infused throughout the process.

> **CLINICIAN:** Thanks for coming in today, Michael. Your probation officer tells me you hit a rough patch recently. And I'm guessing this is not your favorite place to be today. (expresses appreciation and acknowledges client affect)

> **MICHAEL:** I still can't believe I have to be here. (angrily)

> **CLINICIAN:** You are angry that you are forced into doing something. You're not even sure what this is all about. Tell me your thoughts about what has been going on. (reflection; expresses empathy and begins to establish a collaborative relationship by asking for the client's perspective)

> **MICHAEL:** Well, I've admitted that maybe my use is a problem. It is probably why Anita and I can't get along. But I have made good decisions before. In fact, I'm pretty good at that.

> **CLINICIAN:** You're an able person and have made healthy decisions before. Your drug use isn't as bad as others think, yet at the same time you acknowledge some negative effects with your wife and kids (affirms client's unique identity while using a strategic reflection)

> **MICHAEL:** I'm not stupid; I have already said things need to change. But I get angry when people pick at me and pressure me against my will.

> **CLINICIAN:** Like coming to counseling, that being against your will.

> **MICHAEL:** Yes, coming here is against my will, but I am warming up to it. I kind of like getting things off my chest. But it has got to come from me; I'm the one that needs to make the choices!

> **CLINICIAN:** I hear you loud and clear. I want you to know that you are an expert on you and the one in charge of your life. No one can change for you. I respect your thoughts, feelings, attitudes, and perspectives, even if I may not necessarily agree. That is what is important to me: relating to you as a whole person and one who has the capability of making choices about your life. In counseling, only you can decide how you want to make use of our time together. I also hope that you feel you can be real with me in here and trust it won't leave this room [with noted exceptions] (affirms client; emphasizes I-thou encounter; encourages client to be genuine in the therapeutic relationship)

Confronting and Promoting Responsibility

The process of confronting and assuming the ultimate concern of responsibility is a key goal in existential therapy. Promoting responsibility can involve pointing out the client's role in his predicament, exploring what responsibility looks like, exploring feelings associated with this existential reality, and assessing a range of possible choices and the will to act on these choices. The clinician supports the client in considering the steps that need to be taken to establish change.

As clients assume responsibility and consider alternative life paths, the will to act and make changes strengthens. The following exchange with Michael illustrates this point.

MICHAEL: Things need to be different. That's the bottom line. My wife and I haven't been getting along, and I get angry a lot. Also, I don't want to go to jail because of my drug use.

CLINICIAN: The prospect of jail scares you and has you thinking that the status quo is unacceptable. It sounds like, Michael, that you are beginning to take responsibility for what has happened, but you're just not exactly sure what needs to change. (reflection followed by introduction of responsibility as ultimate concern)

MICHAEL: I think realizing my own responsibility has been a slow process. I mean when I was high, I basically had the attitude that everyone can "f— off." I was so angry and didn't want to face my own role in the matter.

CLINICIAN: And what is your role in your predicament? (enhancing awareness of responsibility)

MICHAEL: Funny, a few months ago I would have blamed everyone else. But attending AA and hitting rock bottom has helped me realize I need help and I am the one who is responsible for getting it. It was a scary realization when I realized I cannot blame anyone else but me. (Here, Michael uses a boundary experience that thrust him into a confrontation with responsibility.)

CLINICIAN: I see you are a bit upset now; I would imagine you were a bit uncomfortable coming to the realization that you and you alone are responsible for your life. (carrying on the dialogue about responsibility)

MICHAEL: Right. It was like, wow! I have been feeling anxious and guilty lately about my role in things.

CLINICIAN: And that's a big insight of all this: knowing that you're in charge of your own destiny. Confrontation, awareness, and acceptance of your responsibility are the first steps in realizing that you have choices in how to live. You have been giving this some serious thought. I wonder where you lean now in terms of choices; for example, how might you strengthen your responsibility for your own recovery? (deepening discussion of responsibility by pointing out choices)

MICHAEL: Oh, I want to stop using. I take responsibility for what I have done in the past, but I guess I never thought about what that would look like in my recovery. I know I want to stop; I guess I could attend AA more regularly and come up with a treatment plan and stick with it.

CLINICIAN: Taking responsibility means more AA, and a stepped-up treatment plan. (continuing the paragraph via reflection)

MICHAEL: For now, yes. I am sure other options will come about. You know, the more I talk about this the more motivated I am to quit. I mean I must quit using. I have a family to worry about, a job, I can't be messin' around like I used to.

CLINICIAN: Drug use is not, in your mind, taking responsibility for your life, and it's not consistent with your purpose. (simple reflection that reinforces taking responsibility for not using drugs and introducing the ultimate concern of purpose)

Exploring Other Ultimate Concerns

Guiding clients from immediate concerns to ultimate concerns is one task of the existential clinician. Using basic counseling skills, while remaining attuned to the existential nature of client problems, can help provide a format as clinicians introduce existential themes. As can be drawn from the following exchange between Michael and the clinician, Michael's immediate concern about drug use segues into the ultimate concerns of death and meaning.

> **MICHAEL:** Look, jail might be just the tip of the iceberg. Using hasn't been that good for my health—palpitations, high blood pressure—my wife is pissed at me but also worried. She's afraid if I keep drinkin' and druggin' I won't be around much longer. It's starting to scare me.

> **CLINICIAN:** Your drug use has her scared, and you think her fear is justified. How do you experience what she is concerned about? I mean, how do you experience your own death? (reflection and highlighting ultimate concern of death)

> **MICHAEL:** You are getting to the heart of it now, doc. When she is scared, I get angry, but now I know that my anger and druggin' was a cover-up for the fact that she is right. I will lose my life early if I keep this up. I can't hide it anymore. It's not worth it. I mean there's still so much that I want to do … school, a decent job, my family, and a legacy they can be proud of.

> **CLINICIAN:** It is common for humans to cover up our anxiety about death through substance use or other anxieties. It is almost as if this confrontation with death has thrust you in a mode of wanting to change, to live more genuinely and authentically. (providing information and pointing out how the idea of death can save us)

> **MICHAEL:** Yes, yes, living genuinely and authentically—being the man I know I can be instead of running away from it all.

> **CLINICIAN:** It seems you know what you want, almost as if school, a good job, and family legacy gives you some meaning. Meaning to you is being a good person and drug free. (reflection emphasizing ultimate concern of meaning)

> **MICHAEL:** Exactly. Substance use is so lonely, so empty. I mean, don't get me wrong. I had some good times. But those are in the past. What gives me passion and, as you say, meaning now is attending to recovery, job, school, and family. I am a good person.

> **CLINICIAN:** Substance use is void of meaning and leading your life in a way consistent with your values could restore meaning. So, what does all this mean right now? (reflection that that supports meaning and question that moves closer to action)

Moving From Meaning Into the Will to Act

According to existential theory, awareness must be followed by action (Fernando, 2007; Yalom, 1980). From the previous excerpts, it appears that Michael has accepted greater responsibility for his behavior and has begun to forge a more meaningful life. He also lived through a boundary experience (what he described as "rock-bottom" moment) that confronted him directly with his own mortality. As such, a foundation of existential awareness has been established; at this point, the clinician gently directs the client toward will and action. The following excerpt with Michael illustrates how this would appear in practice.

> **CLINICIAN:** Michael, you have really confronted some deep issues that have made you think more seriously about your life. Clearly, staying drug free is important to you, as is your family. These two elements seem to be the foundation for a sense of purpose and meaning in your life. You know change needs to happen, but you're just not exactly sure what needs to change or how to go about changing. What ideas do you have about what could change? (brief summary, reflecting existential themes and talk, open-ended question exploring possibilities)

MICHAEL: Well, as I said, I could be more consistent with AA, that used to really help, and I know I need to get back on track with them. I've always wanted to take some courses, too. Our company is offering some management courses that interest me and could help get in better with my boss. I know if I keep busy, then using won't be an issue.

CLINICIAN: These are good ideas. You want to attend AA more consistently, and possibly take some courses. You believe these activities will create a positive vibe in your life, so you won't even think about using. If your experience right now is to give these activities a shot, what would be the first step you need to take? (summary, reinforcing his experience of wanting to try these activities, assessing will to act by open-ended question)

MICHAEL: AA is easy. I am familiar with the program and could do that tonight. For the courses, I just need to talk to our college connection representative. She is really nice and would not have a problem signing me up.

CLINICIAN: Doing these soon gives you a real sense of control in your life. (reflection that emphasizes the client's choice and responsibility)

MICHAEL: Yeah. If I'm honest with myself, I have neglected myself and family. And, you are right, going to AA and taking a class is my idea and nobody else's. I own it.

CLINICIAN: How does owning something like this relate to your acting? (connecting to action)

MICHAEL: I feel like it hasn't come down from somebody, like my probation officer. It's my decision, and I feel good about that. I'll give it try by the time we meet again.

Strengths, Limitations, and Ethical Issues Related to Existential Therapy

Existential therapy is quite a contrast to traditional forms of substance use counseling based on the disease concept. Whereas the disease concept is based on progressive deterioration and addiction as incurable, existential therapy places much greater emphasis on choice, meaning, responsibility, and will. It can be used as a standalone approach or infused throughout the counseling process. The "givens" of existence, or ultimate concerns, can be seen in all forms of severe substance use behavior: confrontations with death, lack of meaning, shirking responsibility, and feeling isolated and alone. The deeper issues of existence apply to all human beings as psychological and behavioral problems usually trace back to some core existential issue. Existential therapy adds depth to the counseling process and, for substance use clients who are open to such explorations, can shed light and awareness on how individuals live inauthentic, meaningless lives through their substance use.

Existential therapy may frustrate clinicians who need more structure and technique in the therapy hour. Although confrontation and exploration of the givens of existence is a main approach to existential therapy, one might wonder how talking about death and meaningless can help clients who already live in a problem-saturated world. As Yalom (1980) pointed out, why stir up the hornet's nest (by talking about death)? For a complete review of the strengths, limitations, and ethical issues related to existential therapy as applied to substance use treatment, see Table 14.1.

TABLE 14.1   Summary of Strengths, Limitations, and Ethical Concerns
of Existential Therapy in the Treatment of Substance Use Problems

Strengths	<ul><li>Existential therapy can be used effectively in individual and group therapy formats, making it applicable to substance use counseling.</li><li>Existential therapy focuses on the "givens" of existence, which seem particularly relevant to clients who abuse substances. "Rock-bottom" moments, like almost dying from an overdose, can thrust one into an existential crisis, leading to a more genuine, authentic existence. Meaning is another ultimate concern that resonates strongly with individuals with substance use disorders.</li><li>Existential therapy gets to the core of the issue and thus provides depth to the therapy hour.</li><li>The focus on here-and-now existence avoids nonproductive discussions about the past or worry about the future. In existential therapy, individuals learn to accept, instead of avoiding, the givens of life, enhance awareness of these issues, and subsequently make better choices per increased responsibility.</li><li>Existential clinicians are technical eclectics; they utilize whatever works for the client. However, underlying these techniques is the existential theoretical foundation that provides a backdrop for their work.</li></ul>
Limitations	<ul><li>Existential therapy may not be suitable for all clients. Some clients simply want more concrete help, and some may not wish to talk about the meaning of life.</li><li>Clinicians may struggle with existential therapy because of the limited techniques of the approach.</li><li>Existentialism may be criticized because of its sole focus on individualism, and that social factors to human problems are overlooked. This may be problematic in substance use treatment because of the influences of racism, oppression, and discrimination in substance use behavior.</li><li>It is difficult to argue against the notion that some clients struggling with substance use disorders need to examine their thought processes and learn life skills. Focusing on meaning and the philosophy of life is important, but it may not coincide with what the client needs now.</li><li>As with Gestalt therapy, existential therapy does not have a well-developed empirical base with clients using substances. This is mostly a feature of the approach; existential therapy operates in the here and now of the therapy session, making operationalization and measurement of concepts difficult.</li></ul>
Ethical Issues	<ul><li>The topic of death and death awareness may not be appropriate for some clients, especially those who are suicidal or having difficulty facing their own mortality. Pushing clients to talk about death before they are ready may be grounds for ethical concern.</li><li>Existential therapy rejects many of the traditional addiction concepts and applications, some of which have empirical support. Using existential methods to the full exclusion of evidenced-based substance use treatment practice may be grounds for ethical concern. Therefore, clinicians wishing to practice from an existential perspective may need to consider integrating evidence-based practices in their therapy work.</li></ul>

References

Archer, J., & McCarthy, C. J. (2007). *Theories of counseling and psychotherapy: Contemporary applications*. Pearson.

Bugental, J. F. T. (1981). *The search for authenticity: An existential-analytic approach to psychotherapy* (rev. ed.). Holt, Rinehart, & Winston.

Bugental, J. F. (1987). *The art of the psychotherapist*. Norton.

Ciarrocchi, J. W., & Brelsford, G. M. (2009). Spirituality, religion, and substance coping as regulators of emotions and meaning making: Different effects on pain and joy. *Journal of Addictions and Offender Counseling, 30*, 24–36.

Copeland, A., Jones, A., & Field, M. (2020). The association between meaning in life and harmful drinking is mediated by individual differences in self-control and alcohol value. *Addictive Behavior Reports, 11*, 1000258.

Corey, G. (2009). *The theory and practice of counseling and psychotherapy* (8th ed.). Brooks/Cole.

Corey, G. (2017). *The theory and practice of counseling and psychotherapy* (10th ed.). Cengage.

Fernando, D. M. (2007). Existential theory and solution-focused strategies: Integration and application. *Journal of Mental Health Counseling, 29*, 226–241.

Ford, G. G. (1996). An existential model for promoting life change: Confronting the disease concept. *Journal of Substance Abuse Treatment, 13*, 151–158.

Frankl, V. E. (1978). *The unheard cry for meaning*. Washington Square.

Frankl, V. E. (1988). *The will to meaning: Foundations and applications in logotherapy*. Meridian.

Frankl, V. E. (1992). *Man's search for meaning: An introduction to logotherapy* (4th ed.). Beacon Press.

Hart, K. E., & Singh, T. (2009). An existential model of flourishing subsequent to treatment for addiction: The importance of living a meaningful and spiritual life. *Illness, Crisis, and Loss, 17*, 125–147.

Johnson, R. A., Griffin-Shelley, E., & Sandler, K. (1987). Existential issues in psychotherapy with alcoholics. *Alcoholism Treatment Quarterly, 4*, 15–25.

Junior, V. (2006). Purpose and meaning in life relative to time in recovery from alcoholism. *International Forum for Logotherapy, 29*, 99–102.

Kellogg, S., & Triffleman, E. (1998). Treating substance-abuse patients with histories of violence: Reactions, perspectives, and interventions. *Psychotherapy, 35*, 405–414.

Kim, E. S., Ryff, C., Hassett, A., Brummett, C., Yeh, C., & Stretcher, V. (2020). Sense of purpose in life and likelihood of future illicit drug use or prescription medication misuse. *Psychosomatic Medicine, 82*, 715–721.

Krentzman, A. R., Farkas, K. J., & Townsend, A. L. (2010). Spirituality, religiousness, and alcoholism treatment outcomes: A comparison between Black and White participants. *Alcoholism Treatment Quarterly, 28*, 128–150.

Laudet, A. B., Morgen, K., & White, W. L. (2006). The role of social supports, spirituality, religiousness, life meaning, and affiliation with 12-step fellowships in quality-of-life satisfaction among individuals in recovery from alcohol and drug problems. *Alcoholism Treatment Quarterly, 24*, 33–73.

Logogroup. (2010, June 22). *Logotherapeutic techniques and their spiritual source*. http://meaningtherapy.wordpress.com/2010/06/22/logotherapeutic-techniques-and-their-spiritual-source/

Martin, R. A., MacKinnon, S., Johnson, J., & Rohsenow, D. J. (2011). Purpose in life predicts treatment outcome among adult cocaine abusers in treatment. *Journal of Substance Abuse Treatment, 40*, 183–188.

May, R. (1977). *The meaning of anxiety* (Revised ed.). Norton.

McInerney, K., Garip, G., & Benson, T. (2022). "We all need a purpose and reason to be here.": A qualitative investigation of how members of Alcoholics Anonymous with long-term recovery experience aging. *Alcoholism Treatment Quarterly, 40*, 100–115.

Miller, W. R. (1998). *Motivational interviewing: Professional training* [DVD]. University of New Mexico.

Nam, J. S., Heritage, J. G., & Kim, J. K. (1994). *Predictors of drug/alcohol abuse and sexual promiscuity of college students.* Paper presented at the meeting of Tennessee Counseling Association, Chattanooga, TN, November 20–22, 1994.

Norcross, J. C. (2010). The therapeutic relationship. In B. L. Duncan, S. D. Miller, B. E. Wampold, & M. A. Hubble (Eds.), *The heart and soul of change: Delivering what works in therapy* (2nd ed., pp. 113–141). American Psychological Association.

Olive, K. W. (1990). Meaning in drug treatment. *The International Forum for Logotherapy, 13*, 131–132.

Paul, N. C., & Lucas, M. N. (2005). Reconceptualizing treatment for tobacco abuse: Exploring subjectivity and intentionality. *The Humanistic Psychologist, 33*, 45–57.

Robinson, E. A. R., Cranford, J. A., Webb, J. R., & Brower, K. J. (2007). Six-month changes in spirituality, religiosity, and heavy drinking in a treatment-seeking sample. *Journal of Studies on Alcohol and Drugs, 68*, 282–290.

Seligman, L., & Reichenberg, L. W. (2014). *Theories of counseling and psychotherapy: Systems, strategies, and skills* (4th ed.). Pearson.

Sharf, R. S. (2004). *Theories of psychotherapy and counseling: Concepts and cases* (3rd ed.). Brooks/Cole.

vonDeurzen-Smith, E. (2000). *Existential counseling in practice.* SAGE.

VonDras, D. D., Schmitt, R. R., & Marx, D. (2007). Associations between aspects of spiritual well-being, alcohol use, and related social cognitions in female college students. *Journal of Religious Health, 46*, 500–515.

Yalom, I. D. (1980). *Existential psychotherapy*: Basic Books.

Yalom, I. D. (1998). *The Yalom reader.* Basic Books.

Yalom, I. D. (2008). *Staring at the sun: Overcoming the terror of death.* Jossey-Bass.

Yalom, I. D. (2009). *The gift of therapy: An open letter to a new generation of therapists and their patients.* Harper Perennial.

CHAPTER 15

Key Considerations and Theory Integration

We have covered a vast amount of information for you to consider when counseling clients struggling with substance-related problems. The field of substance use counseling continues to expand and grow, with both time-honored approaches/interventions and newer perspectives, interpretations, and techniques as additional research accumulates. One thing is for sure: Substance use counseling is a dynamic field that is everchanging. The work we do as mental health and substance use counselors can be lifesaving!

This book was written on the premise that counseling theory can serve as an effective foundation from which to help those struggling with substance use disorders. The underlying philosophies of change, various techniques and strategies, and their focus on building the counseling relationship are all powerful strategies to help clients stop using and build a life of recovery. However, certain theories may apply better with some clients as opposed to others. I have had clients respond well to CBT, but not to Gestalt. The astute clinician is aware that there is not a one-size-fits-all strategy to heal substance use disorders. Cultural variables always need to be considered. I suggest the flexible use of theory depending on client culture, needs, and extent of the problem. Each client is unique and requires a distinctive approach depending on the presenting problems.

In this chapter, and based on information in this book, I propose six key considerations when counseling clients struggling with substance disorders. These considerations highlight major points in this text; think of this as a "checklist" of considerations and answering the question "What does substance use counseling look like in session?" Of course, there are *many* considerations, and I will no doubt miss some that other professionals may deem important. However, in my experience, these elements are critical for successful outcomes.

Consideration 1: Evaluation—Screening, Assessment, and Diagnosis

When a substance use disorder is suspected, the evaluation process begins with screening (red flags, observations, instruments, etc.), even if the clinician is not a substance use counselor. Screening "casts a wide net" to determine if a substance use problem is likely present.

Should screening procedures indicate the possibility of a substance use problem, the clinician then moves on to assessment. Assessment entails a lengthier, more thorough investigation of the substance use issue. If done correctly, the clinician should have a firm foundation from which to make clinical interpretations and decisions. Following the assessment process, the clinician then makes diagnosis. Key questions here include these:

- Does the client meet criteria for a substance use disorder? If so, is there more than one SUD?
- Does the client experience co-occurring mental health issues?
- If so, what is the severity level of use (mild, moderate, severe)?
- What is the client's general functioning overall?

As clinicians gain more experience, it can be helpful to have go-to instruments and procedures when conducting a substance use assessment. There is a bevy of instruments in the public and private domains that can assist in the evaluation process. Establishing flexible assessment protocols can also help clinicians stay on track and follow through with their evaluation plans.

Consideration 2: Determine Proper Needs/Placement and Treatment Format

After the evaluation process, the clinician and client need to consider the best placement and treatment option for the client. The goal should be to place the client in *the least restrictive and yet most effective* environment. Based on the American Society of Addiction Medicine criteria (ASAM, 2022), there are several dimensions to consider when determining a placement. These dimensions include (a) acute intoxication/withdrawal potential, (b) biomedical conditions or complications, (c) emotional/behavioral conditions or complications, (d) treatment acceptance and resistance, (e) relapse potential, and (f) recovery environment. Where a client falls on each dimension can help with the placement process. For example, a client experiencing severe withdrawal, who has several medical complications, and is in a poor recovery environment may be best suited for an inpatient/more restrictive setting. General options for treatment placement, from most restrictive to least restrictive, include medical/detoxification facilities (e.g., hospital), residential or inpatient treatment centers, partial hospitalization or intensive outpatient treatment centers, and outpatient treatment agencies. Aligned with the ASAM placement criteria, the clinician can ask several questions in determining if inpatient or outpatient programs are the best option:

1. Is the client's condition associated with significant medical or psychiatric conditions or complications? *If so, lean toward inpatient. If not, outpatient.*

2. What is the severity of actual or anticipated withdrawal from drug(s) being used? *If severe, lean toward inpatient. If mild or moderate, lean outpatient.*

3. Has the client had multiple failed attempts at outpatient treatment? *If the client has, lean toward inpatient. If not, outpatient.*

4. What is the strength of the client's support systems? *If strong, lean toward outpatient. If no support system, inpatient.*

5. What is the severity of client's substance use and possibility of polysubstance use? *If severe, lean more inpatient. If only one substance, outpatient.*

Once a client is in a treatment setting, clinicians and clients can determine the best treatment format. In substance use counseling, these usually include individual, group, family, or some combination. In some cases, the clinician and client may not have much wiggle room with the treatment format: Treatment facilities, agencies, and hospitals may have their own programs to follow. However, it is my contention that involving clients collaboratively in the treatment process, including decisions on the type of treatment they receive, can lower discord, increase ownership of their care, and increase intrinsic motivation to change. Twelve-step mutual support groups are usually concomitant with counseling.

Consideration 3: Motivation and Stages of Change

After completing the evaluation process and determining the best treatment setting, we are ready for interventions. In Chapter 6, the philosophy, skills, and processes of MI were described in detail. MI was born out of the substance use treatment field and has become an important, evidence-based treatment for deleterious substance use behavior. As such, it should be part of any substance use counseling protocol. Closely aligned with MI are the stages of change (precontemplative, contemplative, determination, action, maintenance), and both can be utilized in the following manner.

For clients who are initially in the "early" stages of change (e.g., precontemplation, contemplation), consider using a heavy dose of MI to lower discord, increase motivation, and resolve ambivalence. For clients who present in the "later" stages of change (e.g., determination, action), MI can still be used, but the clinician may find that motivation is high, ambivalence is resolved, and discord is low; in essence, the client may not need MI, and other theoretical models may be more useful.

Recall the different ways to utilize MI: (a) as an approach in and of itself, where MI is the main intervention throughout treatment; (b) to begin counseling designed to increase motivation to change followed by use of other interventions and theories; and (c) on an as-needed basis; that is, use MI as the client's motivation tends to ebb. In my clinical practice, I start every new treatment with MI, as it can be a very effective approach to build rapport. From there, I either continue to use MI or move on to other approaches depending on the client's presenting substance use issues, stage of change, and so forth.

Consideration 4: To What Model of Addiction Do You Adhere?

Another important consideration is the model of addiction from which you base your substance use interventions and treatment. In Chapter 2, several models of addiction were presented, each emphasizing biological, psychological, sociological, and/or some combination thereof.

If you subscribe to the disease model, continuous evaluation, goal setting, and development of the treatment plan will most likely be completed by a comprehensive treatment team, including you as the counselor, client, medical specialist, social worker, and/or case manager. Recall that from the disease model perspective, either one is using/drinking or not; there is no gray area or "in between." In addition, because of the loss-of-control hypothesis, *any* ingestion of the substance will result in a full-blown relapse. Therefore, abstinence must be the only treatment goal (although other goals can be explored related to lifestyle changes). The use of MI can be combined with the disease model perspective; however, keep in mind that because the treatment goal (abstinence) is preestablished, the common practice of collaborating on goals in MI would be less emphasized. Treatment from a disease model perspective also would emphasize social support with strong encouragement (and in some cases requirement) to attend 12-step mutual help groups.

If you subscribe to the psychological model, consider again starting things off with a heavy dose of MI to build motivation. From there, you can choose from any theoretical approach discussed in this text (or additional approaches). Theoretical models discussed in this text are excellent for treating the psychological aspects of substance use disorders. For some agencies or treatment centers, however, there may be some restrictions in what can be applied within treatment plans. For example, some substance use treatment centers will focus on one primary approach, such as CBT or DBT, and all clinicians would be expected to follow the general tenets of these theories. Although treating substance use disorders from a single approach can be effective, the preference is for clinicians to have flexibility in their use of the full range of theoretical interventions as client factors, levels of motivation, severity of substance use, and steps in the recovery process may dictate the best overall approach.

Theoretical Integration

As with any psychological/counseling theory, there is a danger for clinicians to tout their own approach to the exclusion of others. In the history of psychotherapy, this was a common occurrence: Each theory had a cadre of followers who had the best approach and would not dream of using other approaches, or even elements of other approaches, that were seen as inferior or, at worse, ineffective. Thankfully, the concept of theoretical integration has garnered significant professional interest in the past few decades (Norcross, 2005). There are numerous reasons for this, although two critical ones include the rise of new therapies and the shortcomings of single theoretical approaches (Norcross, 2005).

Norcross (2005) proposed four paths to integration: technical eclecticism, theoretical integration, common factors, and assimilative integration.[1] In technical eclecticism, clinicians

---

1   In this chapter, I will only discuss technical eclecticism, theoretical integration, and assimilative integration.

use techniques from different theories, without worrying about staying committed to the theories from which they came. For example, I might use the empty chair technique (Gestalt therapy) to help a client process their substance use experience and then use a downward arrow technique (CBT) related to an irrational thought that came up during the exercise. In this case, the clinician used two techniques from two different psychotherapies because the techniques worked in the moment, not because they were theoretically consistent.

In theoretical integration, the clinician is interested in melding two or more psychotherapies so that the integrated version is superior to either one individually. Theoretical integration is not about simply combining two approaches or blending techniques. Here, clinicians want to synthesize the best from each theory to create a unified framework (Norcross, 2005). Theoretical integration can be difficult as all theories have their unique underlying assumptions, beliefs about the causes of distress, and philosophical influences that can be difficult to reconcile with other approaches. Indeed, within the psychotherapy integration world, most clinicians practice eclectically and see integration as something from which to aspire (Norcross, 2005)

Assimilative integration is where a clinician has a primary school of psychotherapy but incorporates strategies and assumptions from other schools (Messer, 1992). A strict Adlerian therapist, for example, might use several SFC techniques but stay grounded in the overall Adlerian treatment protocol.

The differences between these forms of integration are probably less discerning in clinical practice. That is, their distinctions may be more didactic, and for the practicing substance use clinician, not noticeable at all (Norcross, 2005). Nonetheless, substance use clinicians may find great value in psychotherapy integration related to their substance use counseling.

The theories presented in this book, although standalone approaches, can be thoughtfully combined with other approaches to best help the client. Although theoretical integration may be difficult to implement, technical eclecticism and assimilative integration could be viable options for substance use counselors who are looking to best utilize approaches and techniques to help their clients. In my clinical work, I tend to use MI and Gestalt theory but find the techniques of CBT, Adlerian, and existential theory quite useful in helping clients struggling with substance use disorders. The decision to use eclecticism or assimilation comes at the practice level; it is the practitioner who is sitting in front of their client making decisions on the best course of action. The thoughtful incorporation of techniques from one or more schools of thought can help address limitations or weaknesses in each one individually.

Consideration 5: Blending of Models May Be Appropriate and Useful

As with theoretical integration, clinicians can be flexible with models of addiction as well. For example, cognitive behavioral counseling may work for clients who manifest irrational beliefs related to remaining abstinent. In this instance, the goal of abstinence suggests operating from the disease model, yet the CBT intervention suggests the psychological model is utilized to help the client remain alcohol free.

As another example, existential therapy is used to help create meaning in one's life, a meaning involving living substance free or abstinence. Again, the goal of abstinence is consistent with the disease model, yet the application of existential theory suggests utilization of the psychological model of addiction. The new meaning narrative can include activities such as commitment to AA, which is consistent with disease model thinking.

Consideration 6: Consider an Appropriate Aftercare Program

Given the chronic nature of substance use disorders, it is imperative that clients have an aftercare program to solidify treatment gains, continue to make progress, and put measures in place to avoid backsliding. Treatment for substance use disorders, like any other mental or behavior problem, is rarely effective if the client attends a treatment program and then goes directly back into the same environment with no follow-up care. As discussed in Chapter 3, the brains of those with substance use disorders needs significant time without substances to heal. Given brain-related changes that occur because of substance use, clients need continual support as they strengthen themselves in the recovery process.

An aftercare program usually entails intensive outpatient or outpatient counseling, one to several times a week. Less frequent sessions occur as the client makes gains in recovery. Aftercare also may include elements of family counseling as many close relationships have been harmed by the client's substance use. Within the outpatient setting, clinicians and clients should work on relapse prevention/management plans in the event the client finds themself in high-risk situations. Once again, 12-step mutual help groups are strongly encouraged to maintaining progress and growth in recovery.

There are several issues, however, that can negatively impact the success of an aftercare program (or any treatment program). For example, a significant aftercare concern for many clients is transitional living issues. We know that if clients do secure safe and reliable housing, they are in much better shape, and their recovery tends fall into place (McCauley, 2020). Unfortunately, after living in a halfway house for several months, many clients can't simply pick up where they left off, resume their job and relationships, and return to a home life like nothing happened.

Additional hurdles may include finances to support intensive treatment, not having insurance, daycare concerns, long work hours, or health care issues. Even among those who are well intentioned about abstaining from chemicals and have energy to commit to the treatment process, many hurdles may still get in the way. In my work as a mental health and substance use counselor, I saw firsthand the impact of hurdles on client care. The most common example was where a client needed more intensive care than what I could provide in an outpatient clinic, but which their insurance did not cover or for which they could not afford. In these instances, after sharing my concerns with the client, we agreed that they could at least get *some* care in an outpatient setting, that we would make the best out of what we could, and that we would continue to look for more intensive care opportunities. Clinicians need to be strong advocates for clients by providing referrals to community resources that can help basic needs and care. As such, building a treatment, recovery, and aftercare plan takes collaboration, teamwork, use of adjunct services, and a committed staff to help clients succeed.

Summary

These considerations represent key prompts for mental health and substance use clinicians to keep in mind as they work with clients struggling with substance use disorders. In my professional experiences, substance use issues will inevitably come up in your clinical practice. The issues can relate to your client, your client's loved one(s), or your client's family history. As I tell my students, even if they are not going to specifically work with clients struggling with substance use issues, it is extremely beneficial to have some background in what substance use counseling looks like should it show up unexpectedly in their practice.

References

American Society of Addiction Medicine. (2022, February 21). *ASAM criteria: What is the ASAM criteria.* https://www.asam.org/asam-criteria/about-the-asam-criteria

McCauley, K. T. (2020). *Addiction & recovery update: 2020: The latest clinical takeaways from neuroscience research.* Trauma & Addiction Online Conference. PESI. https://catalog.pesi.com/item/addiction-recovery-update-2020-latest-clinical-takeaways-neuroscience-research-67066

Messer, S. B. (1992). A critical examination of belief structures in integrative and eclectic psychotherapy. In J. C. Norcross & M. R. Goldfried (Eds.), *Handbook of psychotherapy integration* (pp. 130–165). Basic Books.

Norcross, J. C. (2005). A primer on psychotherapy integration. In J. C. Norcross & M. R. Goldfried (Eds.), *Handbook of psychotherapy integration* (2nd ed., pp. 3–23. Oxford University Press.

Index

About the Author

Todd F. Lewis, PhD, LPC, NCC is a professor of counseling and counselor education at North Dakota State University. He is a Licensed Professional Counselor and a National Certified Counselor. Dr. Lewis is past treasurer and president of the International Association of Addictions and Offender Counselors (IAAOC), a subdivision of the American Counseling Association. Throughout his career, Dr. Lewis has taught graduate-level students in motivational interviewing, substance use counseling, assessment, diagnosis, treatment planning, and quantitative research methods. He has presented on these topics at numerous local, state, national, and international venues. Dr. Lewis has published numerous research articles related to substance use, collegiate drinking, and theoretical approaches to addictions treatment. He has twice received the Exemplary Research Award from IAAOC for his research. Dr. Lewis is currently a member of the Motivational Interviewing Network of Trainers (MINT). He has secured internal and external funding for his work in motivational interviewing, primarily using the approach to address health disparities within surrounding communities. In private clinical work, Dr. Lewis was past coordinator for substance use clinical research and treatment services with clients struggling with a range of substance use and mental health issues. In addition to his faculty work, Dr. Lewis currently maintains a small private practice where he trains and consults with other mental health professionals in the area of motivational interviewing and counsels those struggling with mental, emotional, and substance use issues.

Printed in the USA
CPSIA information can be obtained
at www.ICGtesting.com
LVHW070716050124
768188LV00002B/3